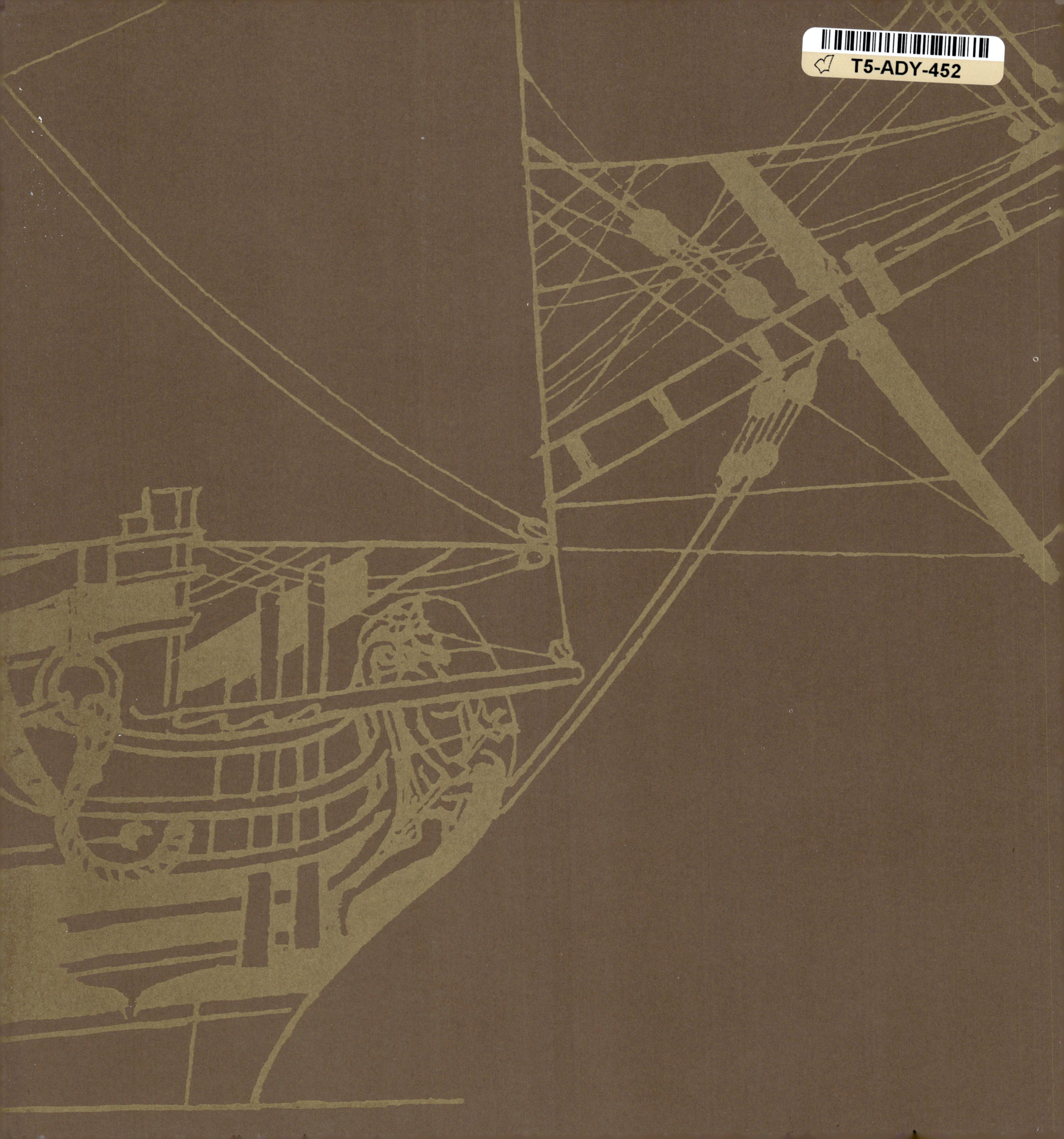

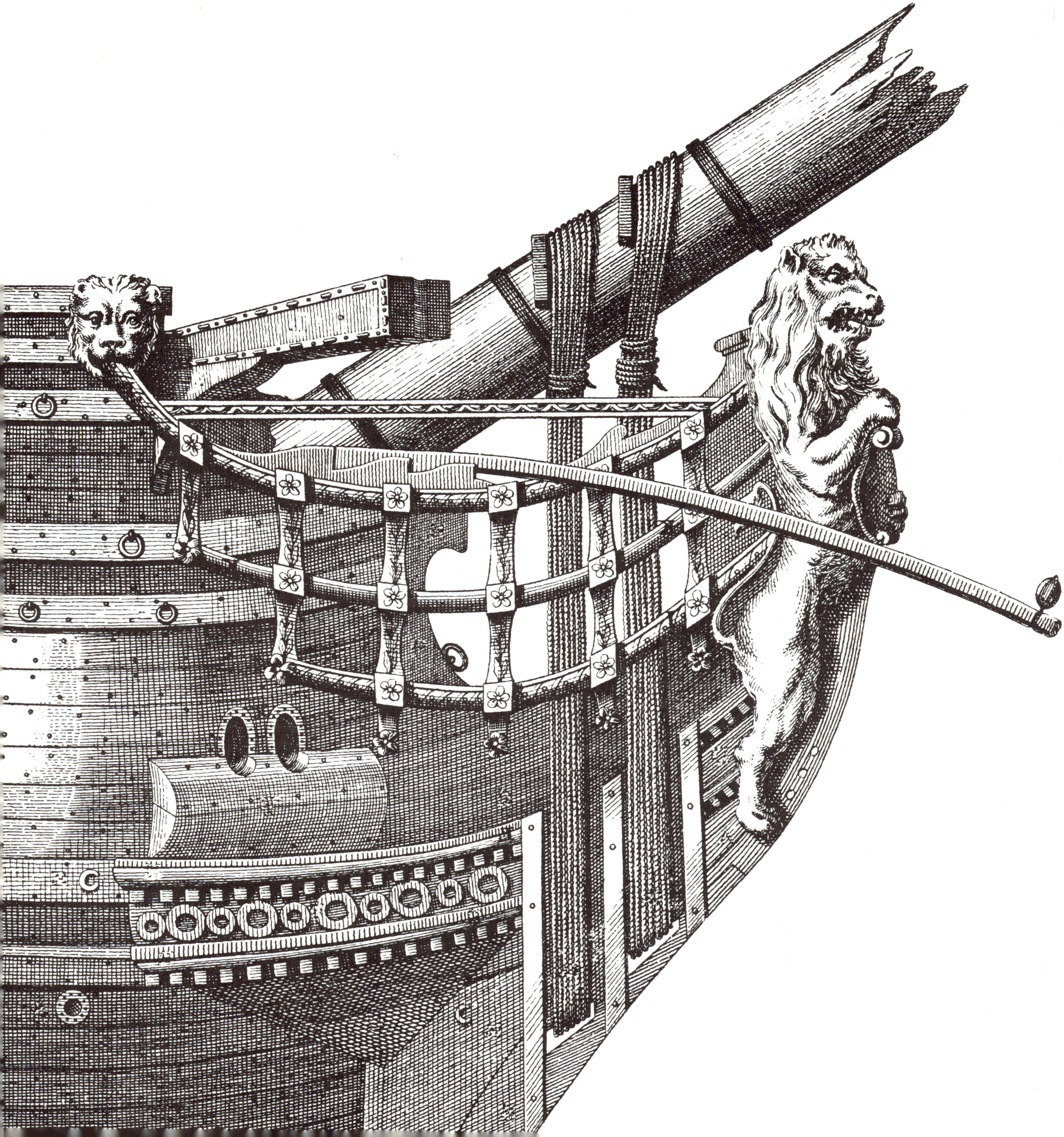

THE LORE OF SHIPS

NORDBOK

CRESCENT BOOKS   NEW YORK

*Copyright © 1975
by AB Nordbok, Gothenburg*

*All rights reserved including
the right to reproduce this book
or portions thereof in any form.*

*This edition published by
CRESCENT BOOKS
a division of Crown Publishers, Inc.
by arrangement with
AB NORDBOK.
a b c d e f g h*

*Library of Congress Catalog
Card Number:
63-18428*

B7US10754
Printed in Great Britain, 1975.

Acknowledgments

The Lore of Ships was designed by Tre Tryckare.
The Tre Tryckare team was led by Bengt Kihlberg (editorial), Curt Sture Görman (art), and Per Nielsen (hand lithography). This new and revised edition was planned and produced by AB Nordbok, Gothenburg, Sweden, under the direction of Einar Engelbrektson. Text and illustration research was handled by Janne Lundbladh, marine editor.

World rights for this book belong to AB Nordbok.

Experts from a number of countries have co-operated in the production of this book

The late SAM SVENSSON, sea captain and internationally known maritime expert, was the chief adviser of the original edition. He participated in the production of the book, from planning to finished product, consulting with the many experts concerned, checking the illustrations and texts, and writing the Introduction and commentaries to the sections, *Spars and Rigging* and *The Sail*. A former curator of the Maritime Museum in Stockholm, Captain Svensson helped to salvage and restore the Swedish warship *Wasa,* which sank in Stockholm harbor in 1628.

WILLIAM A. BAKER, American naval architect, assisted in checking the texts and illustrations, and wrote the commentary for *The Hull*. He is a well-known expert on historical and modern shipbuilding, and was closely involved in the reconstruction of the *Mayflower*. In this new and revised edition, Mr. Baker has acted as chief adviser, recommending the necessary changes, and re-writing his commentary on *The Hull,* up-dating it completely.

JANNE LUNDBLADH, marine editor and chief editor for this new and revised edition, has written the commentary *Modern Pleasure-Boating*.

The late TAGE BLUM, an engineer and shipbuilding teacher at the Polytechnic Institute, Copenhagen, Denmark, wrote the commentary for *Propulsion*.

GEORG TIMMERMANN, an engineer as well as head of the Maritime and Fishing Section at the Altonaer Museum in Hamburg, Germany, wrote the commentary for the chapter on *Fishing*.

GEORGE P. B. NAISH, Lieutenant Commander and Assistant Keeper at the National Maritime Museum in London, England, did the commentary, *Yachting*.

ALAN W. H. PEARSALL, M.A. and Assistant Keeper at the National Maritime Museum in London, England, is responsible for the commentary on *Gunnery*.

ROLF SCHEEN, Naval Captain in the Norwegian Marines, is the author of the commentary introducing *Navigation and Ship-Handling*.

The following writers and experts have also contributed to the book:
P. Å. BERG, Engineer, Chalmer's College of Technology; S. CARLSSON, Editor; Captain H. FORSHELL; Commander O. R. LILJEQVIST; Å. LINDHOLM, Engineer, Chalmer's College of Technology; Commander S. NOTINI, former chief of the Maritime Museum of Göteborg; and Captain K. WOLLTER.
Extensive work, such as preparatory studies, sketches, and drawings – serving as basic material for most of the illustrations – has been carried out by the late GORDON MACFIE, artist, Stockholm; and ÅKE GUSTAVSSON, artist, and others in the Art department of Tre Tryckare. Some sketches have also been done by WOLFGANG SELL of Hamburg, Germany.
Original drawings were made by BENGT BERGLUND, RUNE BÅGMARK, BIRGIT DAHLSTRAND, SIV ENGLUND, VERA FAHLSTRÖM, JOHAN LINDSTRÖM, JOSÉ LLOBETT JUAN, FRITZ ROHDE, LARS-ERIK STRÖM, RUNE SVENSSON, among others.
For checking design, illustrations, and texts in the course of the preparation of the book, Tre Tryckare and AB Nordbok wish to thank the following individuals and institutions:
JOHN MUNDAY and other experts at the National Maritime Museum in London, England; HOWARD CHAPELLE, Curator for the Division of Transportation at the Smithsonian Institute, Washington, D.C.; Keeper SVEIN MOLAUG and Curator ERIK VEA at the Norwegian Maritime Museum in Oslo, Norway; Captain HELMUT GRUBBE, Lübeck-Travemünde; the late W. STEPHENS, yacht designer, London, England; B. BOTHEN, engineer, yacht designer, SYŘ, Göteborg, Sweden; Curator GÖSTA WEBE at the Maritime Museum in Stockholm, Sweden; BENGT MICHAEL JOHANSSON, Helsinki, Finland; HERRICK SUNDMAN, Åbo, Finland; Marine Director CURT BORGENSTAM, Stockholm, Sweden; Marine Director MALTE JÖNSSON, Stockholm, Sweden.

Gratitude is also due to the following for advice and material:
The Royal British Navy; The Royal Danish Navy; The Royal Swedish Navy; The United States Navy; Arkeologiska Museet (The Archaeological Museum), Göteborg, Sweden; Chalmers Tekniska Högskolas Bibliotek (Library of Chalmer's College of Technology), Göteborg, Sweden; Göteborgs Universitetsbibliotek (Library of the University of Göteborg), Sweden; National Maritime Museum, London, England; Norsk Sjöfartsmusem (Norwegian Maritime Museum), Oslo, Norway; Göteborgs Sjöfartsmuseum (The Maritime Museum of Göteborg), Göteborg, Sweden; Statens Sjöhistoriska Museum (Maritime-Historical Museum), Stockholm, Sweden; ASEA, Västerås, Sweden; AB. Bofors, Sweden; C.A. Clase AB., Göteborg, Sweden; De Danske Statsbaner (The State Railways of Denmark); Decca Navigator and Radar AB., Göteborg, Sweden; Deutsche Bundesbahn (The State Railways of West Germany), Hamburg, Germany; AB. Electrolux, Stockholm, Sweden; Japanese Embassy, Stockholm, Sweden; Eriksbergs Mek. Verkstads AB., Göteborg, Sweden; AB. Götaverken, Göteborg, Sweden; Kockums Mek. Verkstads AB., Malmö, Sweden; AB. Lindholmens Varv, Göteborg, Sweden; Merriman Bros., Inc., Massachusetts; Motor Boating, New York, New York; Philips Teleindustri AB, Järfälla, Sweden; Sasebo Heavy Industries Co. Ltd., Tokyo, Japan; Sparkman & Stephens, Inc., New York, New York; Statens Järnvägar (The State Railways of Sweden), Stockholm and Göteborg; Svenska Seglarförbundet, Stockholm, Sweden; Oy Wärtsilä Helsingforsvarvet AB., Helsinki, Finland; AB. Volvo Penta, Göteborg, Sweden; Vikinglinjen AB, Mariehamn, Finland; Yachting Publishing Corporation, New York, New York.

THE LORE OF SHIPS

PREFACE

Water has lured the heart of man all of his days — whether it was the silvery line of a river, the gilded sparkle of a lake, or the phosphorescing green glint in an ocean. Angry or calm, fresh or salt, helpful — in giving man his food — or cruel — in bringing him an enemy — the sea makes its presence always known to humans.
Man has depended on it for food, for sport, for transportation. From the moment an ancient man first used the water — perhaps floating down a river holding to a log — when he developed primitive dugout canoes, rafts, barges and sailing ships, liners and tankers, and atomic submarines and surface ships, man has needed the sea. And during this slow, and often painful, evolution, man has tried to conquer the vastness of the oceans. The Lore of Ships illustrates man's fascination with the sea and gives him a chance to satisfy — at least partly — his love of ships and shipping. It is an illustrated book which shows, by means of simplified illustration and detailed drawing, the most important parts of the construction, equipment, and development of all kinds of ships. An explanatory, numbered text allows the reader to follow the diagrams of rigging, sail, engines, spars, fishing, flags — even the weapons used aboard ships through the ages. Each of the chapters begins with a short introduction to the developments that took place in the various subdivisions of nautical history. For example, the first chapter, called "The Hull," explains each part of the evolution of this structure, from its initial appearance covered with animal skin or tree bark to the refined and sophisticated hulls of today's sleek atomic ships. Illustrated details — the basic structure, rudders, steering gears, anchors, and many others — make it easy for the reader to ground himself thoroughly in the lore of the hull.
The technical editors of The Lore of Ships include a curator of a maritime museum, a naval architect, engineers, sea captains, and many more. The book was produced under the expert guidance of captain Sam Svensson, internationally known maritime expert. Dictionary, survey, illustrated book — The Lore of Ships is most of all for the enjoyment of those who would go down to the sea in ships.

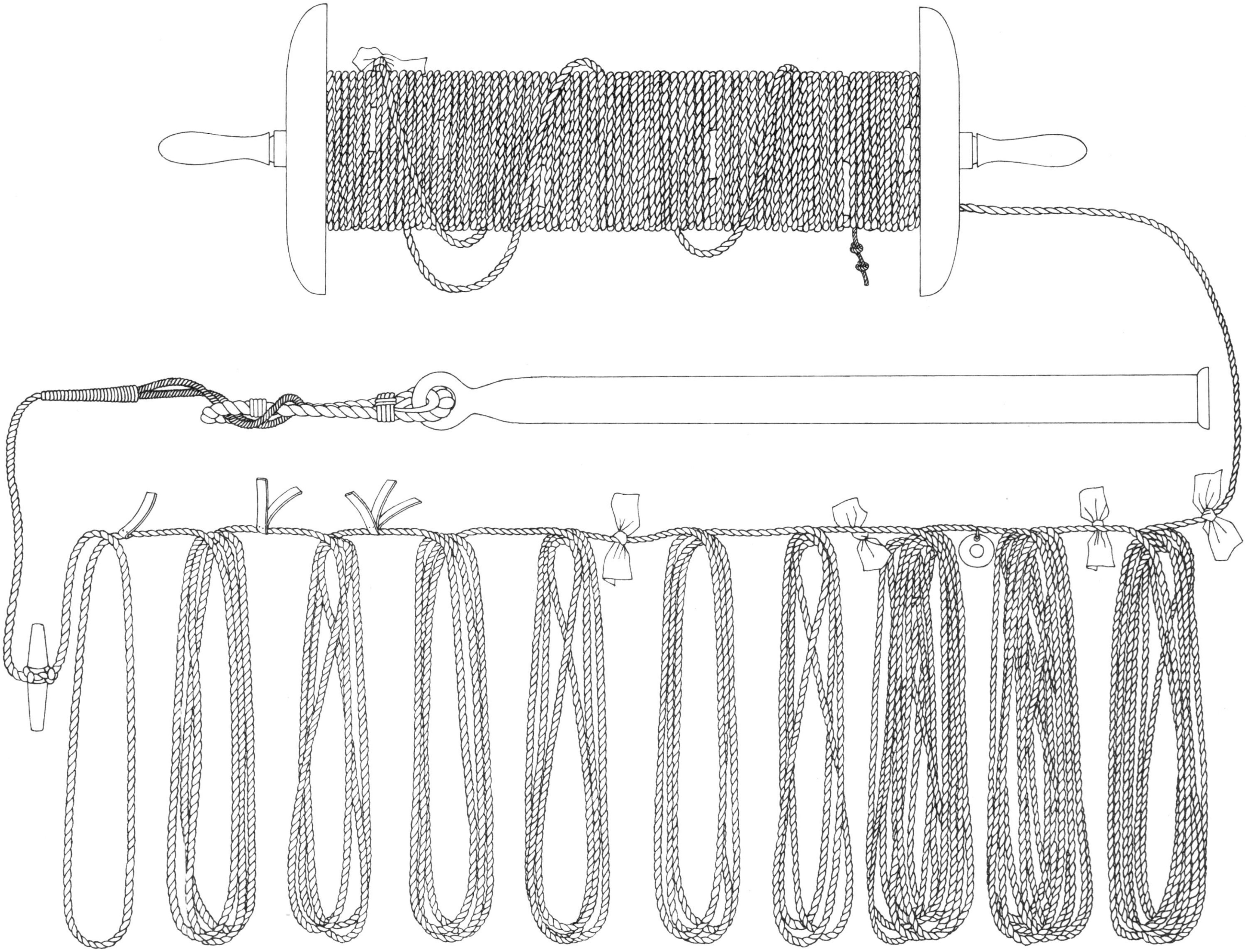

Contents

PICTORIAL CONTENTS 12

The illustrations serve as a pictorial guide for the reader who wants to identify details and objects which he cannot name.

INTRODUCTION BY CAPTAIN SAM SVENSSON 14

THE HULL 17

COMMENTARY BY WILLIAM A. BAKER, *18*

Plans, *22, 24;* midship sections, *26, 30;* forebodies, *32, 36;* tools, *34;* details of hulls, *28, 38;* afterbodies, *40, 44;* rudders, *42;* steering gears, *46;* stabilizers, *48;* funnel marks, *49;* decoration, *50;* draft marks, *52;* type of hulls, *53;* anchors, *54;* windlasses, *56;* winches, *58;* bells and whistles, *59;* accommodations, *60;* galley, *61;* pumps, *62;* hatches, *63;* lanterns, *64;* lifeboats and davits, *66*.

SPARS AND RIGGING 68

COMMENTARY BY CAPTAIN SAM SVENSSON, *69*

Masts and spars, *72;* tops and crosstrees, *78;* stays and shrouds, *80;* bowsprits, *86;* details of mainmast and main yard, *90;* rigging of older steamers, *92;* rigging of modern ships, *93*.

THE SAIL 95

COMMENTARY BY CAPTAIN SAM SVENSSON, *96*

Different sails, *99;* names of sails in various ships, *100;* the square sail, *104;* the studding sail, *110;* patent reefing, *112;* different rig of lower square sails, *113;* the gaff sail, *114;* the gaff topsail, *117;* the staysail, *118;* bonnets and reefs, *120;* bowlines and beatas, *121;* different blocks, *122;* halliards, sheets, and blocks, *124;* tools for sail-making and rigging, *125;* types of sailing ships, *126;* merchant flags, *134;* house flags, *136;* signal flags, *137;* cordage, *140;* wires, *141;* knots and whippings, *142*.

PROPULSION 145

COMMENTARY BY TAGE BLUM, *146*

Oars, *148;* old steam engines, paddle wheels, and propellers, *150;* old boilers, *152;* modern boiler and engine, *156;* steam turbine, *157;* engine-room telegraph, *158;* gas turbine, *159;* nuclear power, *159;* old and modern engine-powered ships, *160;* the diesel engine, *166*.

FISHING 169

COMMENTARY BY GEORG TIMMERMANN, *170*

Old fishing implements, *172;* types of fishing boats, *173;* fishing with seine net, 177; fishing with drift nets and long lines, *178;* trawls, *179;* fish and marine creatures, *180*.

YACHTING 183

COMMENTARY BY GEORGE P.B. NAISH, *184*

The Dragon, *186;* old yachts, *188*.

MODERN PLEASURE-BOATING 190

COMMENTARY BY JANNE LUNDBLADH, *190*

Olympic classes, *191;* modern sailing yachts, *192;* racing, *194;* yacht details, *196;* cruising yacht, *191, 198;* motorboat types, *200;* motorboat details, *201*.

WARSHIPS AND GUNNERY 203

COMMENTARY BY ALAN W.H. PEARSALL, *204*

Old guns, *206;* automatic gun, *209;* coast defence ship, *210;* anti-aircraft gun, *212;* mines, *213;* minesweeping, *214;* torpedoes, *215;* anti-submarine weapons, *216;* weapon control systems, *217;* old and modern warships, *218*.

NAVIGATION AND SHIP-HANDLING 223

COMMENTARY BY ROLF SCHEEN, *224*

The lead, *226;* the log, *228;* the compass, *230;* old navigational instruments, *232;* bearings, *234;* wireless direction finder, *235;* Decca and Loran, *236;* radar, *237;* lighthouses, *238;* charts, *242;* theory of sailing, *244;* sailing on different courses, *246;* small boat handling, *247;* sailing ship handling, *248;* maneuver: to heave to, *251;* maneuvering of engine-powered ships, *252;* mooring and belaying, *254;* auxiliary vessels, *255;* sailor's outfit, *258;* provisions, *259;* sailor's hobbies, *261*.

INDEX 263

and here on the jib-boom I could look at the ship as at a separate vessel — and there rose up from the water, supported only by the small black hull, a pyramid of canvas, spreading out far beyond the hull, and towering up almost, as it seemed in the indistinct night-air, to the clouds. The sea was as still as an inland lake; the light trade-wind was gently and steadily breathing from astern; the dark blue sky was studded with the tropical stars: there was no sound but the rippling of the water under the stem: and the sails were spread out, wide and high; — the two lower studding-sails stretching, on each side, far beyond the deck; the top-mast studding-sails, like wings to the topsails; the top-gallant studding-sails spreading fearlessly out above them; still higher, the two royal studding-sails, looking like two kites flying from the same string; and, highest of all, the little skysail, the apex of the pyramid, seeming actually to touch the stars, and to be out of reach of human hand. So quiet too, was the sea, and so steady the breeze, that if these sails had been sculptured marble, they could not have been more motionless. Not a ripple upon the surface of the canvas; not a quivering of the extreme edges of the sail — so perfectly were they distended by the breeze

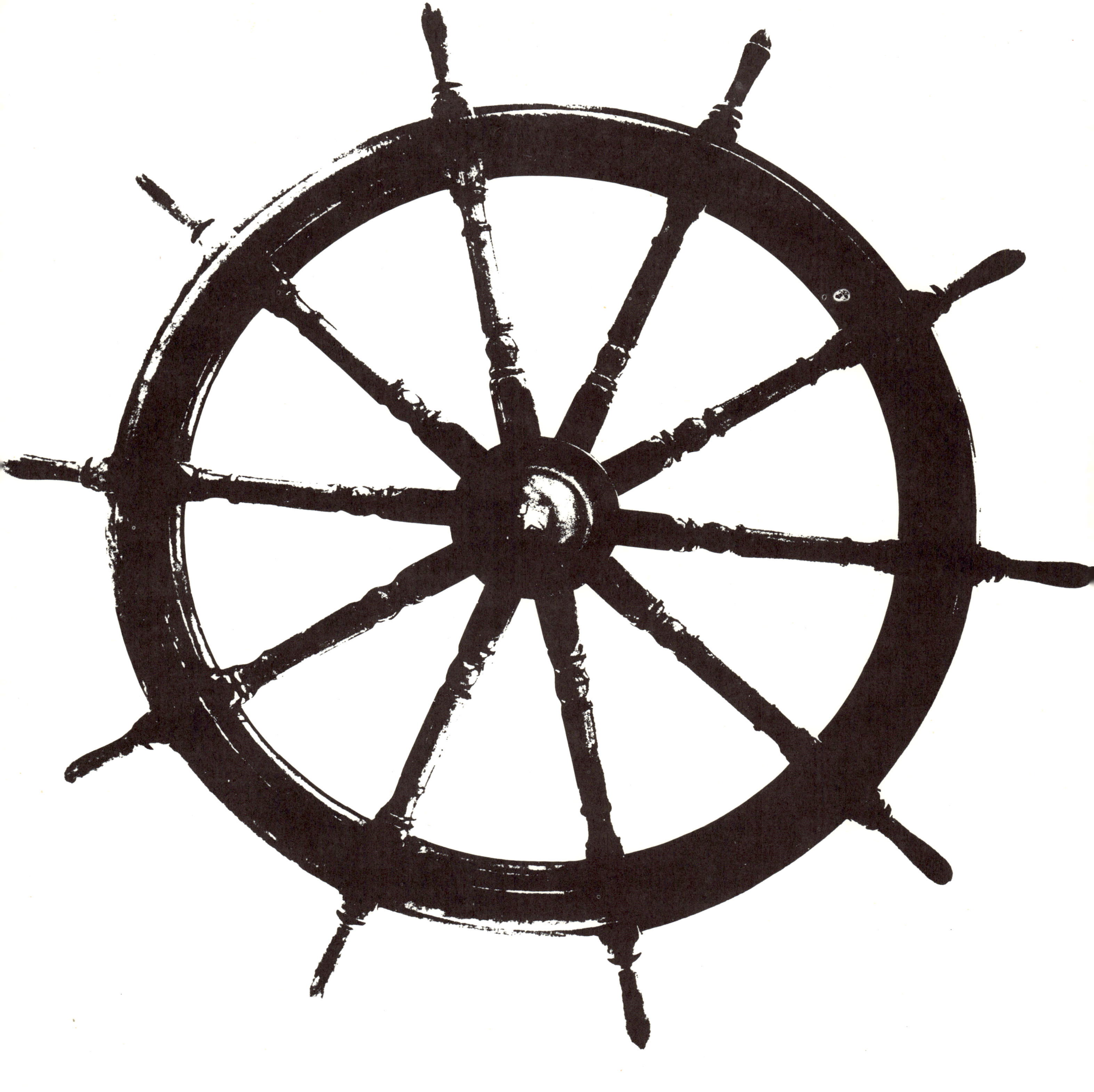

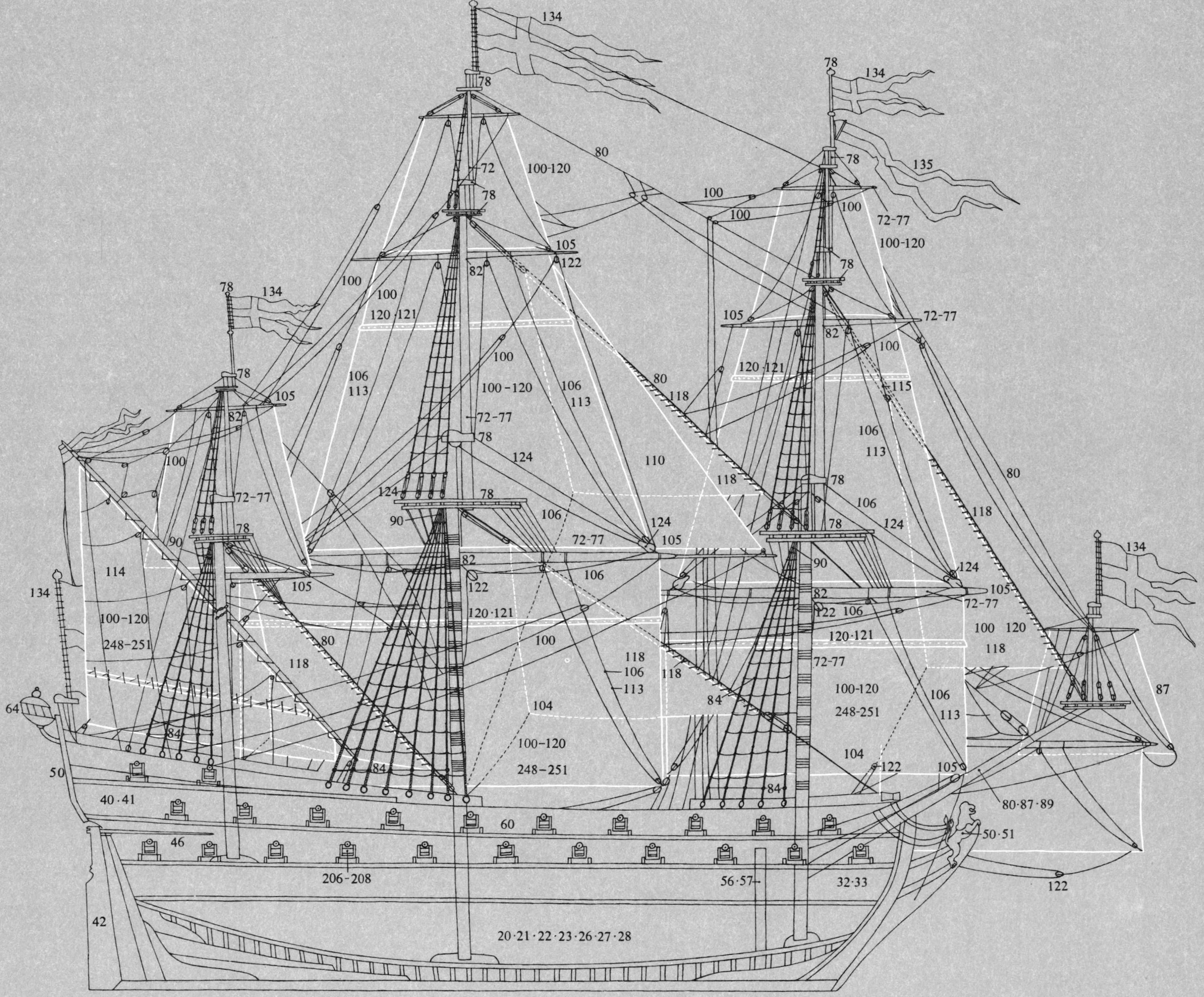

78
134
78
134
80
72
100-120
78
100
100
135
100
72-77
100-120
105
122
82
78
100
100
120·121
72-77
105
82
100
120·121
100
100-120
106
113
106
113
80
115
118
78
105
82
72-77
106
113
124
78
110
118
80
100
114
90
78
72-77
124
90
78
106
124
106
124
105
72-77
105
134
82
122
106
124
105
90
82
122
106
72-77
134
100-120
248-251
120·121
120·121
100
120
80
118
100
118
118
106
113
118
72-77
100-120
248-251
106
113
87
64
84
104
84
100-120
248-251
104
122
105
50
84
80·87·89
40·41
60
50·51
46
206-208
56·57
32·33
122
42
20·21·22·23·26·27·28

PICTORIAL CONTENTS

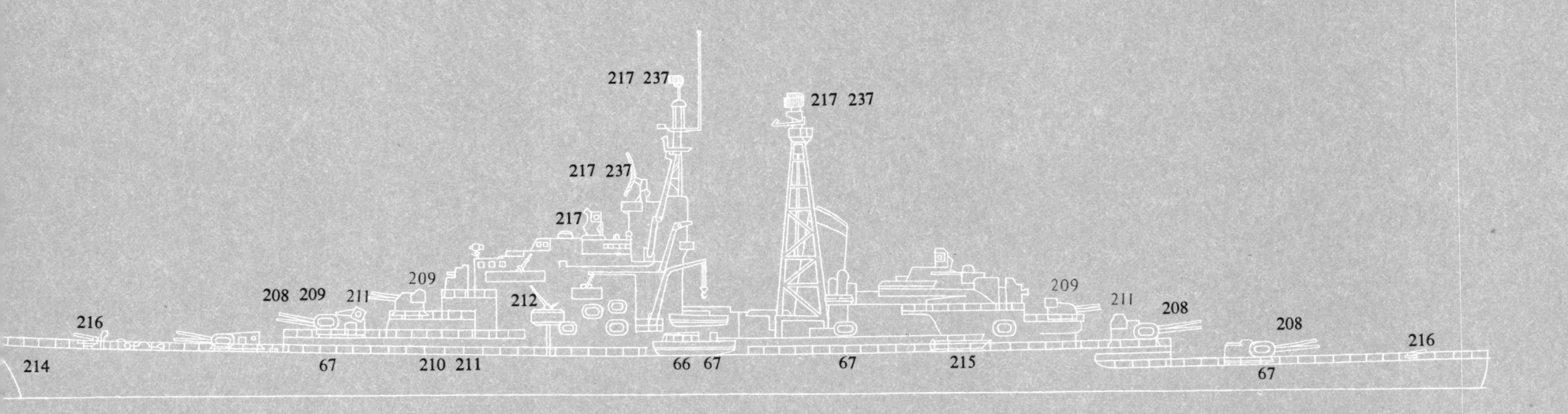

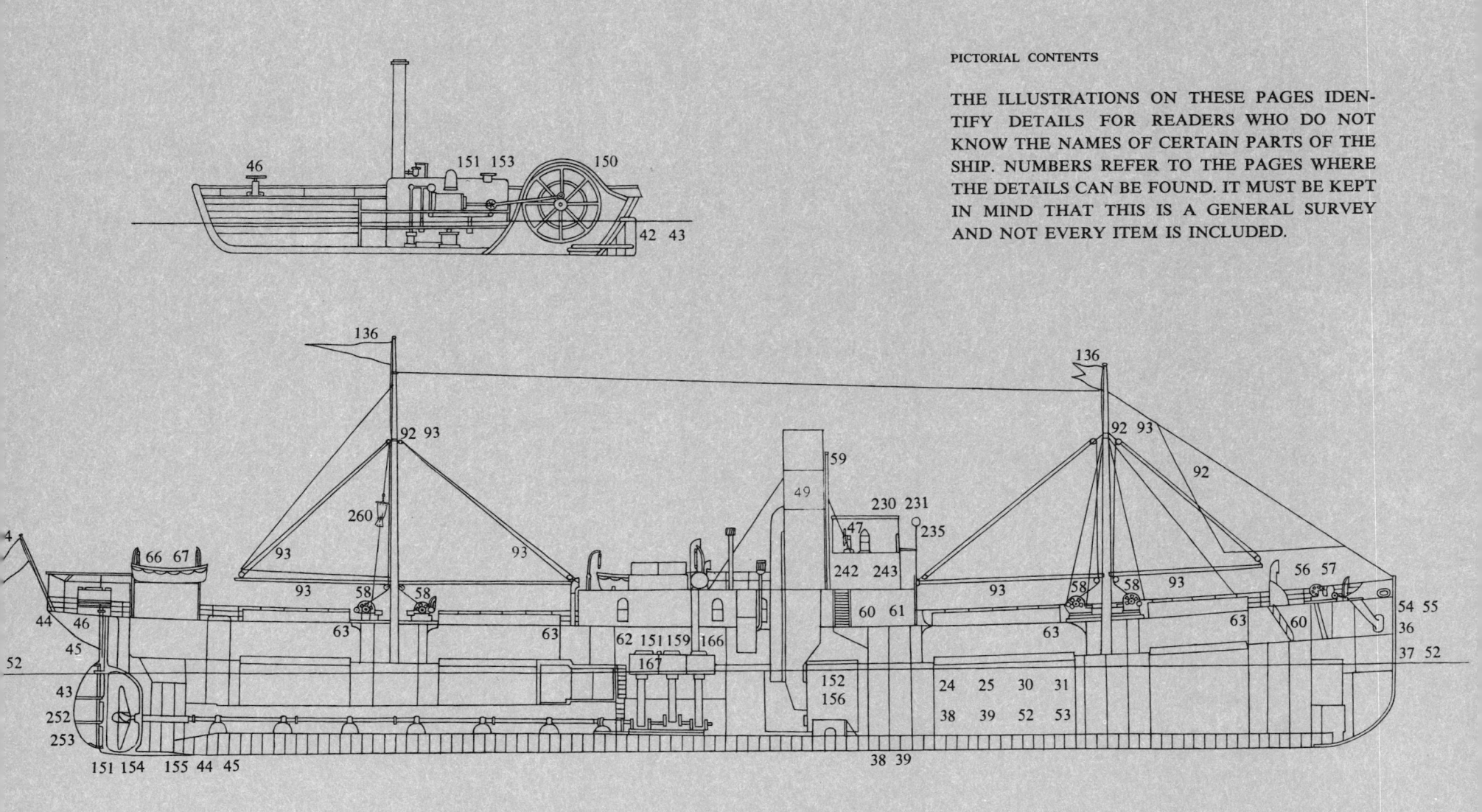

THE ILLUSTRATIONS ON THESE PAGES IDENTIFY DETAILS FOR READERS WHO DO NOT KNOW THE NAMES OF CERTAIN PARTS OF THE SHIP. NUMBERS REFER TO THE PAGES WHERE THE DETAILS CAN BE FOUND. IT MUST BE KEPT IN MIND THAT THIS IS A GENERAL SURVEY AND NOT EVERY ITEM IS INCLUDED.

The text on page 10 is a quotation from one of the classics of nautical literature, Two Years Before The Mast by Richard Henry Dana, who went to sea because his poor health had compelled him to interrupt his law studies. His description of his experience at sea is contained in one of the finest and most authentic books ever written about life on shipboard. The book was first published in 1834.

INTRODUCTION

BY SAM SVENSSON

From ancient times sailing the seas has been a unique profession, with techniques and methods which have always puzzled the landlubber. One thousand years before Christ, Solomon said that the way of a ship in the midst of the sea was too wonderful for him to understand.

In our time there have been radical technical developments. On the seas, ships as well as the life of the sailor has been changed to such a degree that no similarity whatsoever with the olden days exists. This may be why general interest in old nautical things and in the sailing ship in particular has grown to such an extent. People all over the world now want accurate data about the construction, equipment, and handling of old ships.

Long ago, ships were always built of wood, except in the case of even more primitive materials such as reed, skin, and bark; but these materials were only used for the most primitive sailing in narrow seas. Since ancient times ships have been built according to two methods: carvel and clinker. The first method was developed in the eastern Mediterranean countries, where Egyptians, Phoenicians, and others built ships with outside planking ingeniously joined by being placed edge to edge. This art came into general use in Southern Europe, and during the Middle Ages it spread along the coast of Western Europe, reaching the Baltic during the latter part of the 15th century. It then became the dominant way of shipbuilding, and after the middle of the 16th century all large vessels were carvel-built.

During the latter half of the 17th century, however, when shipbuilding had become a science and ships could, theoretically, be constructed in advance, larger and sturdier ships were being built. The pictures on pages 32 and 40 show constructional details of a large 18th-century ship. During the second half of the 19th century, when iron and steel were being used more generally for shipbuilding, fewer wooden ships were being constructed. Yet, these wooden ships were still used chiefly in the United States, where large wooden merchant sailing vessels were built up to the time of the First World War. The four-masted bark *Roanoke*—3,439 gross tons, built in 1892—and the six-masted schooner, *Wyoming*—3,730 tons, built in 1909—indicate the size limits of wood used in constructing ships. In many other places, perhaps mostly in the Eastern Mediterranean and in the Near East, but also in the Baltic, small sailing vessels were built of wood as late as the early years of the 20th century. In addition to carvel-built wooden ships, clinker-built vessels were also being constructed. This method originated in the Baltic where, even during the Viking Age, large clinker-built ships sailed to Iceland and Greenland. In the Middle Ages the clinker-building method was predominant in Northern Europe, and many large ships were constructed. Perhaps one of the largest was Henry IV's ship *Grace Dieu*, built in 1418; she was almost fifty meters long and about twelve meters wide. She had a complicated treble-clinker planking. According to the clinker method, the planking was built first and the frames were inserted afterward. We know this because the wreck of the *Grace Dieu* was discovered near Southampton, and showed that the rivets of the skin were clinched underneath the frames.

Experimental ships of iron were built during the first half of the 19th century, until, gradually, iron came into more general use. After 1850, England had several shipyards which built only iron vessels. The introduction of the steam engine for propulsion also encouraged the use of iron as a shipbuilding material. The first iron ships were built according to the same principles as those used for wooden vessels, but as builders grew more experienced, special methods were adopted for the structure of iron ships. One early change was to provide the iron steamship with a double bottom and internal keel, instead of the former bar keel used in sailing vessels. The keelson was now placed on top of the floors. Longitudinal framing, which slowly came into use around 1900, also deviated from the kind of standard shipbuilding that had been used for a thousand years.

Electric welding, which was used experimentally on a large scale for German pocket battleships built between the two World Wars, has now completely revolutionized all shipbuilding techniques. Many large ships are now built in sections according to highly specialized methods on the principle of the assembly line. As yet we cannot determine the extent of this development. The most up-to-date shipyards have the facilities to build and equip a ship from the first steps to the point where it is ready for the sea.

The steam engine and later the diesel engine have only been in existence for a very short time in the whole history of navigation. During most of this time, masts and sails were the only means of propulsion on long voyages. For ages, rigging consisted of one mast and one sail only, and it was not until the end of the Middle Ages that mechanical progress made it possible to construct better and more functional rigging. These developments continued for several centuries and reached their high point after the middle of the 19th century, when, due to competition from the steamship, shipyards turned out perfectly sparred and rigged sailing ships.

There have been many important phases in the history of rigging: such as setting a topsail above the original single square sail, using fidded topmasts that could be sent down, the footrope and the jackstay, which together revolutionized the work of handling sails, the introduction of wire, first for the standing rigging and then for the running gear, and, finally, mechanical aids for handling sails in large ships, such as patent sheaves and brace-and-halliard winches. The introduction of the auxiliary engine with a propeller has, on the other hand, nothing to do with the improvement in sailing vessels.

Flags are not only decorative but also useful. Originally, flags come from field banners carried in ancient battles. In comparison with the flags of ancient kings and military commanders, our national flags are of very recent date. The oldest national flag now in use is the Danish flag, according to a legend of 1219, and was probably followed by the Swedish and Dutch flags. Among the flags of world powers, America has the oldest, dating in its present general form of stars and stripes from 1777. The French tricolor is dated 1794; the English flag in its present form is from 1801.

Page 136 shows the flags used by some of the old sailing ship companies. Perhaps Hansan's red-and-white flag of the Middle Ages should come as number one on this list. On page 137 there are flags that are still in use by shipping companies known all over the world today.

Once the oar had been invented, there were very early attempts to find some mechanical aid which could move ships in a calm or drive them against a head wind. There was no mechanical power. Thus, it was not until the steam engine was invented and perfected to some degree that steam navigation got under way. The first ships of this type were used for river traffic in the United States, and also for coastal traffic around the British Isles.

Steady improvements in the design of the steam engine contributed to the more widespread use of steam navigation. The engine was given several cylinders and was fitted with a condenser. The boilers had forced draft, superheaters, and oil fueling. Finally, the reciprocal steam engine was replaced by a steam turbine, which is frequently used today in very large ships.

In the years just preceding the First World War, attempts were made to use diesel motors as marine engines. Right from the start they appeared to have certain advantages: they had less weight and required less space both for the engine and the bunker. As the reliability of the diesel increased, more motor-driven ships were used throughout the world. In this respect the Scandinavian countries have been in the lead, for example, Sweden's merchant navy consists almost exclusively of motor-driven ships.

Deep-sea fishing is fun, but it is also an important means of getting food. Of old, deep-sea fishing was always carried out in fishing craft fitted with sails. Well-known examples of such craft are the English fishing smacks on the North Sea banks and the American schooners on the Newfoundland coast. Today, both large and small fishing boats are motor-driven, the catch is well taken care of, and there are some factory ships where the catch is cleaned and prepared and then canned or deep-frozen right on board. The most important methods of fishing are line fishing and fishing where a large net is dragged along the sea bed. Now, floating trawls are also used to catch fish on the surface. These trawls are towed by two boats, and the method is more effective than the ordinary drift net. Modern fishing vessels are equipped with echo sounders for locating shoals of fish.

Sailing as a sport has an old heritage. Caligula had pleasure boats in Lake Nemi, and the Doge of Venice had a luxurious galley which he used every year in the ceremony of marrying himself to the sea. In ancient times pleasure sailing was a sport reserved for kings and men of rank only. During the 19th century, it began to occupy more industrialists and businessmen, and, gradually, sailing as a sport has reached the widespread popularity of our own time. Today, there are yacht clubs in all countries where there is access to navigable waters. In order to standardize rules for yachting competitions a great many so-called one-design boats have been constructed, boats which are built according to accurate measurements and regulations so that they will be exactly alike; thus it will be mostly the skill of the helmsman that decides the race. Pages 192 and 193 show many such internationally registered one-design boats. Yacht-racing courses are also decided according to an international standard. Figure C on page 194 shows the fixed track used for all Olympic sailing contests.

As long as man has sailed the ocean, he has struggled for supremacy on the sea. Even in ancient times, a variety of ships were built specifically for war or trade; nevertheless, merchant ships have been used in war and warships in commerce down through the years. As the nations were industrialized, diversity according to function became more noticeable. While today's merchant ships and warships differ in design, there are also various differences in a single category. Warships for both offensive and defensive combat are steadily being altered and improved. Mines, torpedoes, pom-pom guns, and tracer projectiles are standard equipment. Radar and data-processing machines are employed by naval forces; and submarines are fitted with underwater missiles.

It might be said that navigation is the sailor's theory and seamanship his practice. The sounding lead is the sailor's oldest instrument; recognition of the coastline his only way of piloting. In deep waters and when land was out of sight this simple method of navigation was useless. Before the compass was invented, the sailor had to find his way by observations that would indicate a definite direction: the movement of the sun and stars, the direction of the wind and how the clouds were drifting, changes in ocean swell, the flight of birds and how the fish swam. On a long voyage not even the compass was a sufficient guide, so that such trips could not be undertaken until astronomic navigation had been discovered. Even then, for hundreds of years the only means by which a sailor could measure the sun's meridian height was with a simple instrument which determined latitude. The ability to make longitudinal calculations came at a much later date. For that purpose the navigator required Hadley's octant or a sextant, as well as a chronometer and complete nautical tables, or if there were no chronometer, he had to be able to calculate the longitude by means of lunar distances. As in other fields, electronics now does most of the work formerly done by astronomic navigation.

Previously, seamanship could be defined as the care and handling of sailing ships. Page 250 illustrates a portion of this almost forgotten art: how a brig can be put to sea against the wind by backing and filling downriver. Today, a vessel is guided by means of the rudder and the screw. To maneuver a large power-driven vessel properly differs vastly from the skillful handling of a large sailing ship. The art of guiding a power-driven vessel has been mastered by many of today's seamen, but skill in sailing is rarely to be found. *The Lore of Ships* has tried to recover some small part of this forgotten art.

The first chapter of The Lore of Ships deals with the hull and some of its more important details. The next page shows a sketch of Columbus' ship, the SANTA MARIA.

THE HULL

THE HULL

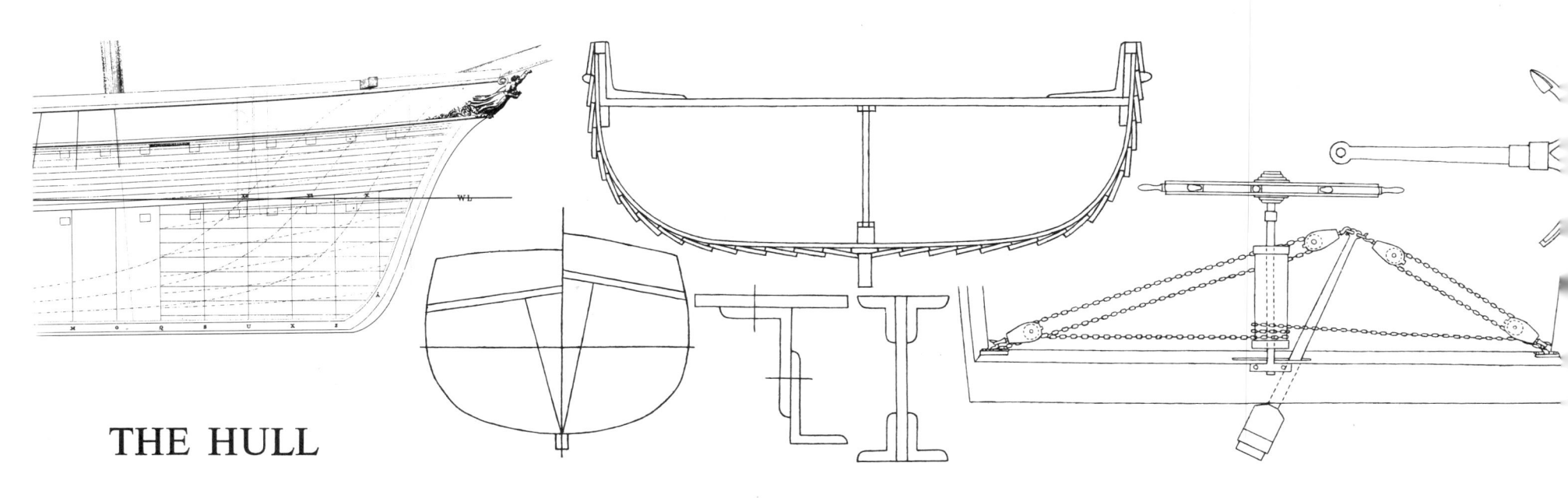

BY W.A. BAKER

Throughout history the shape of ships' hulls has been determined by the materials and methods of construction, means of propulsion, use, fashion, and whim. Primitive craft still range in form from the round (woven baskets, skin-covered frameworks, and even pottery) to the long and narrow (bundles of reeds and shaped logs). Quite early the Egyptians sewed wooden planks together to produce flat-bottomed boats having the proportions of their reed craft. Other ancient peoples learned to improve the hollowed-out log canoe by spreading it open and adding one or more planks on each side. For centuries built-up hulls followed the general shape of such canoes.

The continued existence of primitive craft in various parts of the world serves to emphasize the regions where major sea-going types of vessels developed – the Mediterranean basin, northern Europe, and China. Through most of recorded history there was a parallel development of the two basic hull forms noted above, the "round" ship or bulky cargo carrier and the "long" ship built for speed. Shipbuilding history is concerned mainly with wooden oar-propelled and sailing vessels; metal ships and mechanical propulsion are relatively recent developments.

Two basic techniques have been employed in the construction of wooden vessels, the "shell" and the "skeleton", and combinations of them can be found as early as the 7th century. In the first, the planking is secured together and supporting frames added; in the second, as the term implies, a framework is erected to which the planking is fastened. The frames of a vessel built by the shell method take their shapes from the assembled planking while the planking of a skeleton-built ship must follow the predetermined shape of the frames. A possible explanation of the transition from the older shell technique to the skeleton is the retention in the hull of moulds erected to guide the shaping of the planking. Perhaps the earliest evidence of the skeleton method of construction is an early 14th-century painting showing Italian shipbuilders at work.

The features of early built-up vessels were the result of materials and tools employed. Early Scandinavian shipbuilders, for example, used the axe and adze to shape one long plank from each half of a split log. The planks so fashioned were lapped at the edges and secured together by withes or animal sinews (later by metal rivets); this is basically the present day clinker planking. When a suitable number of planks had been fastened to each other and to the stem and sternpost, supporting frames were added which were held in place by lashings to lugs that had been left on the planks during the original shaping. Experts do not fully agree on the origin of the Viking ship. Some believe it developed from the skin boat when thin planks replaced sewn skins on a flexible framework but others favor the descent from the distended log canoe to which planks were added. The midsection of the famous Gokstad ship, *circa* 900 A.D., page 26, shows a late example of lashed-on planking; the lower eight planks were lashed to the frames while the upper planks were nailed.

Shipbuilders in ancient Egypt employed the saw to produce several planks from each log. The usual native woods, acacia and sycamore, were obtainable only in relatively short lengths which led Herodotus to liken the construction of an Egyptian ship to the building of a brick wall. In preserved vessels the planks were fastened edge to edge by various combinations of dowels or tenons, recessed dovetail pieces, and lashings which produced the smooth outside finish now called carvel planking. Being primarily river craft, Egyptian ships often had only a thick plank instead of a structural keel. Some types, built without frames, had arc-shaped midsections and were kept from spreading by deck beams that protruded through the planking. Large versions of Egyptian flat-bottomed boats had widely-spaced supporting frames and it is now believed that the larger round-bottomed vessels also had them. A prominent feature on many Egyptian vessels was a heavy rope truss, fitted from bow to stern, to keep the ends from drooping.

Available information indicates that Phoenician, Greek, and Roman ships were basically double-enders and that their builders, who employed the shell technique, had a sound knowledge of the structure needed in seagoing vessels. Records of numbers of Roman warships constructed in short periods of time, 220 ships in three months in 254 A.D., imply the use of some sort of moulds to achieve duplication of these shell-built vessels. The Romans had three basic types of vessels – chubby sailing merchantmen, stout warships propelled by oars and used for ramming in sea battles, and light speedy galleys for carrying messages and important persons.

From Roman times to about 1200 A.D. there was little change in the shapes of Mediterranean ships. The merchant sailing vessels remained double-enders with rather full sterns and they were still steered by heavy side oars. Following the earlier practice deck beam ends protruded through the carvel planking and were secured to heavy fore-and-aft wales. "Castles", not part of the hull, were fixed prominently on bow and stern, the light square work of house carpenters contrasting with the sturdy curved work of the shipwrights. One important change was the shift from the Roman square rig to a two- or three-masted lateen rig for the majority of the merchant vessels, although the older rig continued to exist.

From the time of the first Crusade in 1095, when northern European vessels in large numbers entered the Mediterranean, the features of Northern and Southern "round" ships slowly mingled. By then, in the north, the typical Viking ships had been superseded by double-ended sailing vessels in which the clinker planking, high stem and sternpost, and side rudder persisted. These vessels became wider in proportion to length and deeper; they were fitted with a single deck supported inside the hull but a few heavy tie beams protruded through the planking. Small castles appeared on the bow and stern which became more substantial as time passed. Stern rudders were first used during the second half of the 12th century. Southern builders also adopted the stern rudder and returned to the square rig for their larger ships.

The more or less standard merchant ship type that resulted from the mingling of features, commonly called the cog, was employed from the Mediterranean to the Baltic into the early 15th century. The cog was basically a double-ender whose after body seems to have been fuller than her forebody. Her straight sternpost that carried the rudder had little rake; her stem, which had considerable rake forward, was usually straight in the north and curved in the south. The forecastle, triangular in plan, projected over the stem but its after end was partially faired into the hull. The stern castle was an angular house whose after corners overhung the sharp stern. The standard rig was one mast with a single square sail; the first addition to this rig seems to have been a lateen mizzen to improve steering balance. Still there were readily apparent differences between the Northern and Southern cogs. The former had clinker planking, a few projecting tie beams, and decks supported inside the hull, while cogs of the Mediterranean region had carvel planking with all deck beams protruding and secured to wales. Pictorial evidence for details of Northern cogs was substantiated in 1962 when a nearly complete 14th-century cog was found in the River Weser at Bremen.

Western historians, in concentrating their studies on the nations of the Mediterranean basin, tend to overlook the activities of Chinese seamen who from about 700 to 1500 A.D. probably were the world leaders in ocean shipping. There were well-documented voyages to Africa's east coast in the 14th and 15th centuries in ships that were about 200 feet long, had four or more masts, and carried complements of several hundred persons. There is a strong probability that Chinese ships sailed westward around the Cape of Good Hope and into the South Atlantic before 1459, nearly twenty years before the Portuguese rounded the Cape eastbound.

The origins of Chinese vessels are lost in time but it is thought that knowledge of shipbuilding was brought by colonists who came into China from the West. Some 20th-century types on the upper Yangtze River are practically identical with Egyptian craft of 1600 B.C. A Chinese treatise of 1119 A.D. likened the hull shape of the biggest ships to a rectangular grain measure that had sloping sides and ends and described a matting sail that moved around its mast like a door on a hinge. Marco Polo's descriptions of Chinese vessels at the end of the 13th century are well known; some information about Chinese ships may have reached Europe earlier through Arab traders. Far in advance of western technology, Chinese shipbuilders produced vessels with numerous transverse watertight bulkheads which are thought to have been inspired by the bamboo, centerline balanced rudders by the 1st century of our era, and leeboards by the mid-8th century. After the 15th-century African voyages official Chinese maritime activities were reduced to the minimum necessary to protect coastal shipping. Some types of vessels developed by that time probably have changed little since; other types are known to have been influenced by foreign contacts. The variations of proportions and details are almost impossible to catalog but all are well-suited to local conditions.

During the 15th century European seagoing ships grew larger until Northern shipbuilders eventually realized that there was a limit to the size of successful clinker-built ships. The largest known, the *Grace Dieu* built in England in 1418, was a failure and sailed only from Southampton to the Hamble estuary near Bursledon where she was struck by lightning and burned in 1439. Projecting deck and tie beams, difficult to make watertight, were abandoned and the larger European ships became a combination of Northern and Southern features – smooth planking generally hung on pre-erected framing with inside supported decks. Today it is difficult to describe accurately some of the ship types that followed the cog, such as the galleon, galleass, and galiot derived from the proportions of oar-propelled vessels, and the hulk, carrack, and caravel, the bulky cargo ships.

During the 15th and 16th centuries the above-water appearance of European ships' hulls changed considerably. Castles remained large but lost their angular look and were merged into the main hull. Around 1550 large ships were given a square stern that provided better support to the superstructure than the medieval round stern. About the same time the forecastle lost its triangular form; its projection was dropped to form a beakhead below the bowsprit in imitation of the galley's ram. The major ship type for the next 75 to 100 years was the galleon, which had less sheer and lower superstructure than earlier types and was narrower in proportion to length.

During the 17th century there was considerable change in framing details. Up to the late 16th century the single frame of several naturally curved pieces with scarfed joints was standard for almost all sizes of vessels. Such joints were weak and one improvement was to shift the pieces so that they overlapped each other side by side for several feet. The lowest pieces, the floor timbers, were nearly square in section and were spaced along the keel about their own thickness apart. In way of the overlapping there was nearly solid timber for the length of the ship; the pieces of framing were not fastened together but were held in place by the outside planking and inside sheathing. By the early 18th century the pieces had been extended to butt against each other and were fastened together to form complete frames that could be erected as units. This is essentially the pattern of framing still employed in the building of large wooden ships. Space does not permit descriptions of the various combinations of double full and single filling frames used in the intervening years.

The rough semicircular shape of the log canoe was poor for stability but builders soon learned that it could be improved by flattening the bottom of the log. In general, a flattened semicircle would be a simple description of the underwater midsection shape of nearly all vessels until the early part of the 18th century. The unusual V-shape of the Viking ships remained a local Scandinavian feature. Radical changes in the underwater forms of ships came in the 18th and 19th centuries.

The earliest preserved ship plans and treatises on shipbuilding date from the early 1400s. Written in Italian, they describe Mediterranean practices and indicate a long tradition of ship design using arcs of circles and their derivatives to shape hulls and their parts. Succeeding works from other countries amplify the details and show that hull proportions and parts were defined in terms of breadth or keel length, usually the former. Vessels built for fast sailing differed from bulky carriers more in relation of length to breadth than in the shape of the sections. In 1750, and perhaps even later, it was still possible to design a satisfactory ship with no tools but a pair of compasses and a straight-edge.

About 1670 the results of what perhaps were the first systematic ship resistance experiments were recorded in England. Other scientific studies followed, particularly in France, where the first treatise on stability was published in 1746.

In the 18th century many legal and extra-legal operations required the use of small fast-sailing vessels. Those built first on Jamaica and later on Bermuda and the shores of Chesapeake Bay became world famous. The terms Virginia-built or Virginia-model became almost synonymous with speed; by the early 19th century the type was known as the Baltimore clipper. A major feature of the type was a return to the V-shaped bottom of the Viking ship, the so-called rising floor, which for a time was adopted for large ships whenever speed was more important than cargo capacity.

Baltimore clippers were tried in the East India and China trades but their speed could not overcome their limited cargo capacity, a result of their V-shaped underbodies. The best ships in the China trade had a modified packet ship form. The clipper ship era, which began in the mid-1840s, ended in the United States in 1857 and in England about 1870. The large, extreme clippers developed out of a rising fashion for speed and publicity that was exaggerated by the discovery of gold in California and Australia. Speed at any cost prevailed over cargo capacity. Successful clippers were built with both rising and flat floors although the faster ships tended toward the latter as the era progressed. Few had the hollow water-lines popularly associated with the type, the average being more like those shown on pages 22 and 23. Clipper ship speeds were very largely the result of hard driving made possible by their larger size. Economic pressures finally forced a return to the best of the packet ship forms, ships nearly as fast but capable of carrying more cargo.

The presence of figures of animals, gods, and goddesses on ships can be traced into antiquity; the latter two probably were used more to ensure divine protection than as decoration. The Vikings fitted fierce dragon heads on their ships to frighten their enemies. About 1600 there began a period of over a century of elaborate ship decoration on both merchant and warships in the form of stern and quarter galleries embellished with carvings, carved panels along the sides, large figureheads, and complicated head structures. By 1800 these had been reduced to some stern windows with a few carvings around them on the transom, small quarter galleries, and relatively simple head structures.

The introduction of successful commercial steam propulsion in the early 19th century brought new problems to shipbuilders – the concentrated weight of the machinery and the stresses induced by the paddle-wheels or the screw propeller. Until the end of their days paddle-wheel steamers from European shipyards had their paddle-boxes constructed as appendages to the hull. Except on ocean-going vessels builders in the United States carried the superstructures out to a line that enclosed the paddle-boxes.

Until about 1870 ocean-going steamships had the general form and construction of the sailing ship and, because of the unreliability of steam machinery, carried large sailing rigs. Sails for emergency use did not entirely disappear until nearly World War I.

By the middle of the 19th century further resistance experiments and practical experience with steam propulsion had shown that fine lines were necessary for speed. A sailing ship could add sail to overcome poor lines, but early steam machinery was limited in power and breakdowns were frequent, occasionally with disastrous results.

Although a few iron parts had been used on wooden ships as far back as 1675, commercial iron shipbuilding did not start until the 1830s. Early practice was to have an iron structural member similar to every wooden part, which can be seen by comparing the sections shown on pages 27 and 30. Many shipowners were prejudiced against iron and before it was fully adopted there was the interim phase of the composite ship in which iron framing and tie plates were used with wood planking and decking, as shown on page 27.

As shipbuilders gained experience with iron vessels they learned that the longitudinal material could be distributed to better advantage than in wooden ships in which the keel was considered the backbone that provided most of the strength. It was soon realized that a metal ship should be built as a girder with as much strength in the deck as in the bottom. This, of course, is modern shipbuilding practice. Steel, which is now practically the universal material in all large ships, began to replace iron about 1870. Special nickel steel alloys are being used for the construction of ships' tanks for the transportation of cold liquefied gases. Lightweight metals, particularly aluminum, are finding wide employment in the construction of superstructures on large ships and the entire hulls of yachts and other small vessels.

The use of iron, steel, and light metals in shipbuilding has provided designers and builders with almost limitless possibilities. Nearly any conceivable shape can be obtained and, while riveted joints offered certain problems, the general introduction of electric welding, beginning in the 1930s, eliminated many difficult connections. Large sections of ships can now be assembled in convenient locations and placed in position on the building ways by cranes.

Modern ship forms are the result of countless towing-tank and full-scale experiments. Today a model is usually tested for each new design. While not as readily apparent as formerly there still are differences between ship shapes according to the service performed. One need only compare an oil tanker with a fast passenger ship to see the modern versions of the "round" and "long" ships. As bulk cargo carriers for both oil and ore have increased in size their speeds relative to their lengths put them for all practical purposes in the class of self-propelled barges and this allows even fuller forms. On some new bulk cargo ships the bows are no longer sharp but are vertical cylinders whose diameters are about half the breadths of the ships.

The shift in ship's cargo from separate bales, barrels, crates, and the like to large pre-stowed containers that can be mounted on wheels for land transportation has materially affected the design of cargo ships. Shipboard cargo booms and winches have been replaced by large shoreside cranes. Variations of this development are the roll-on/roll-off ships and those that carry pre-stowed lighters thus eliminating the need of a wharf at which to load or unload.

In the category of special ship types semi-submerged and fully submerged vessels offer interesting possibilities for the future. Twin-hulled craft – catamarans – have found employment in projects requiring stable platforms or some other advantage of their configuration. Vessels that fly on water-borne wings – hydrofoil craft – are used in many parts of the world for high-speed passenger services. Those supported on air cushions – hover craft – are employed for both passenger and light cargo carrying.

Chemical resins and glass fibers are now standard materials for the construction of yachts, small commercial craft, and even some naval vessels up to about 150 feet in length. Ferro-cement or steel reinforced concrete is a low-cost material that can be used by semi-skilled labor to produce yachts and small commercial vessels.

The worldwide energy crisis of the early 1970s has turned the thoughts of some seafarers to a renewed use of the winds for propulsion in some cargo-carrying services. This does not imply a return to the old-time sailing ship but rather a development of new hulls and rigs. Although the day of the wooden commercial ship is past and in some parts of the world wood is in limited supply even for the construction of pleasure boats there is a growing interest by young and old in learning and preserving the traditional handcrafts associated with the art of wooden shipbuilding.

WOODEN SHIP

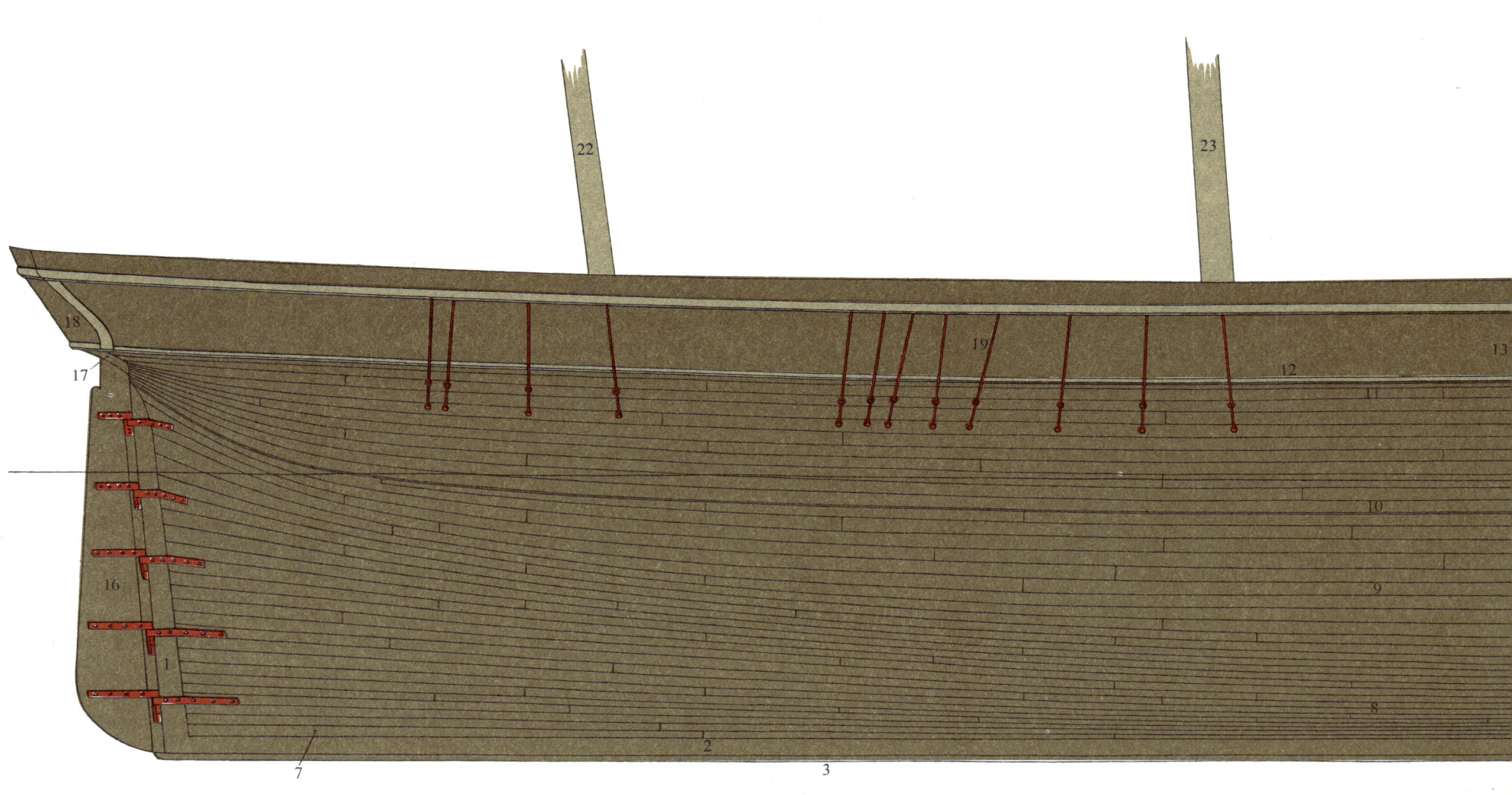

PROFILE OF A WOODEN SAILING SHIP, 1864.

This semi-clipper ship was constructed in 1862 by Niels Kierkegaard, naval architect and Master Shipwright at the Old Shipyard in Gothenburg. In 1864 he published a handbook on naval architecture which contained drawings of eighteen different ships, including this one. His example was followed by shipbuilders all over Scandinavia. The ship shown here has concave bows with narrow waterlines and a lean run under the transom counter and surmounting square stern. She was rigged as a bark, as indicated by the three shrouds and single backstay in the mizzen rigging and shown by the chain plates. All the chain plates are bolted flat to the side of the ship without any channels. They go through the main rail, so the deadeyes will be located inside the topgallant bulwark. The fore and main rigging has four lower shrouds, two topmast backstays, one topgallant backstay, and one royal backstay, as indicated by the chain plates. This same ship is shown on the next two pages.

WOODEN SHIP

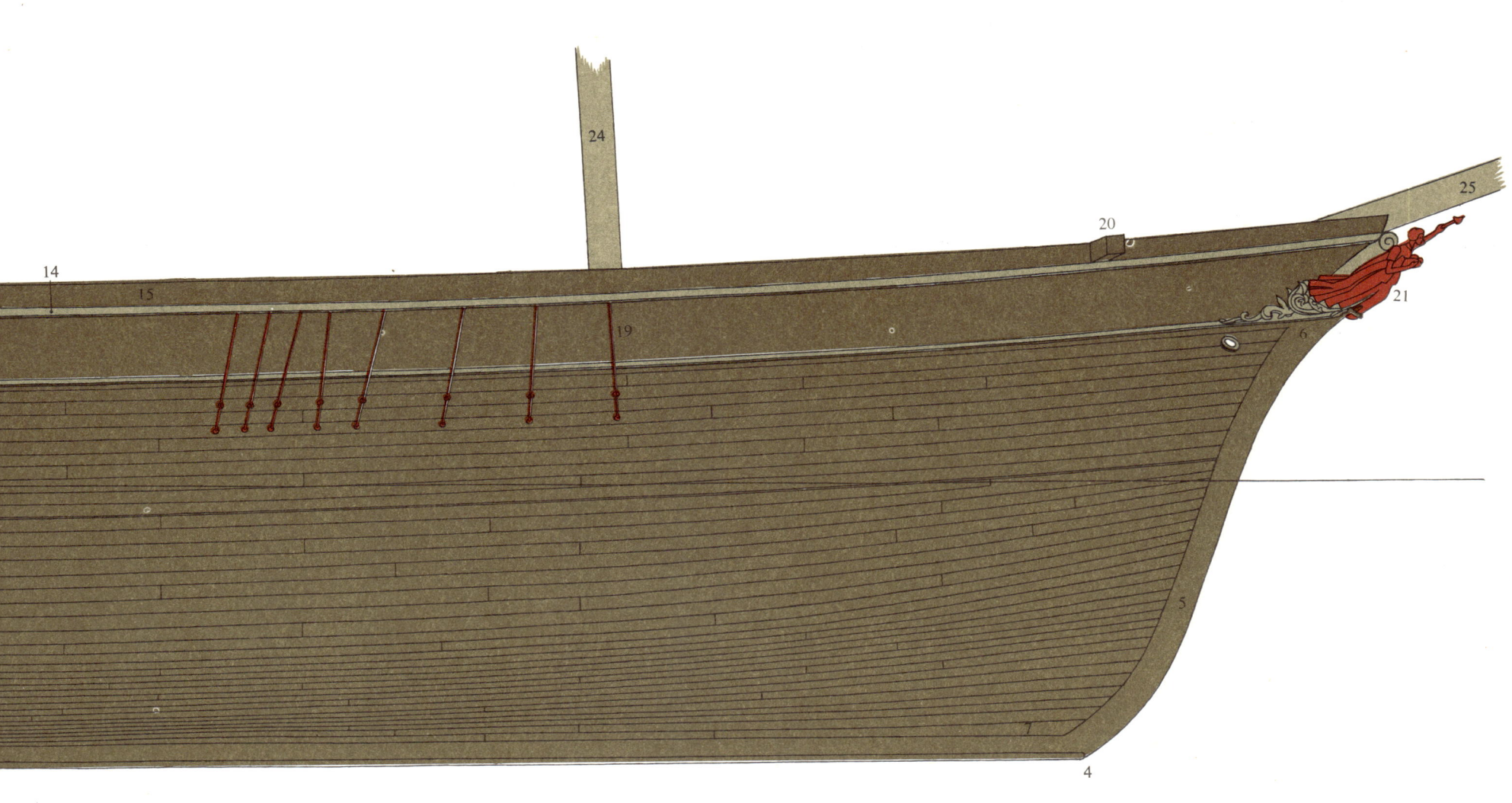

PROFILE OF A WOODEN SAILING SHIP, 1864

1 Sternpost	6 Headpiece	11 Sheer strake	16 Rudder	21 Figurehead
2 Keel	7 Garboard strake	12 Covering board	17 Counter	22 Mizzenmast
3 False keel or shoe	8 Bottom planking	13 Bulwark	18 Stern	23 Mainmast
4 Fore foot, gripe	9 Side planking	14 Rough-tree rail	19 Chain plates	24 Foremast
5 Stem	10 Wale	15 Topgallant bulwark	20 Cathead	25 Bowsprit

WOODEN SHIP

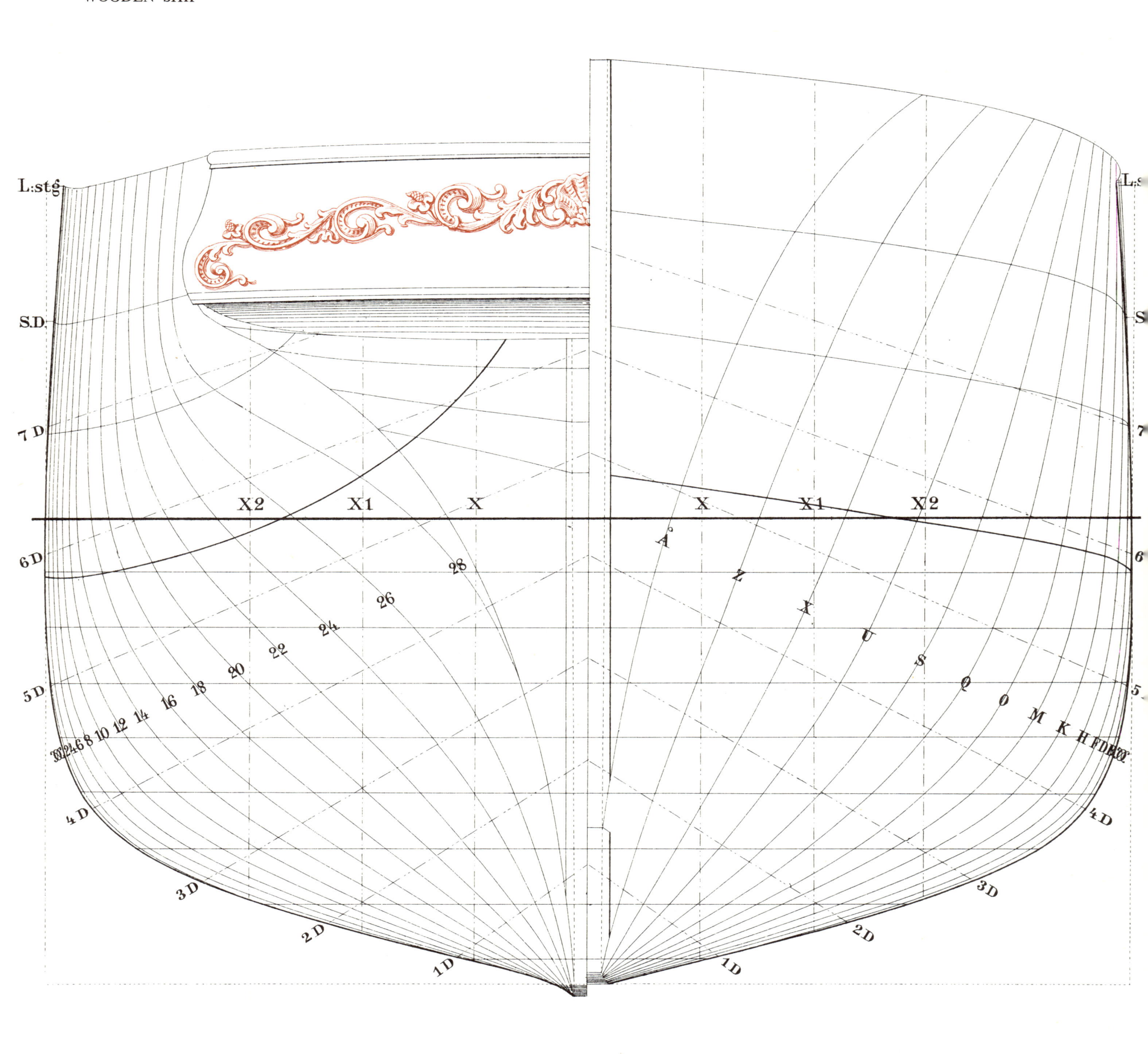

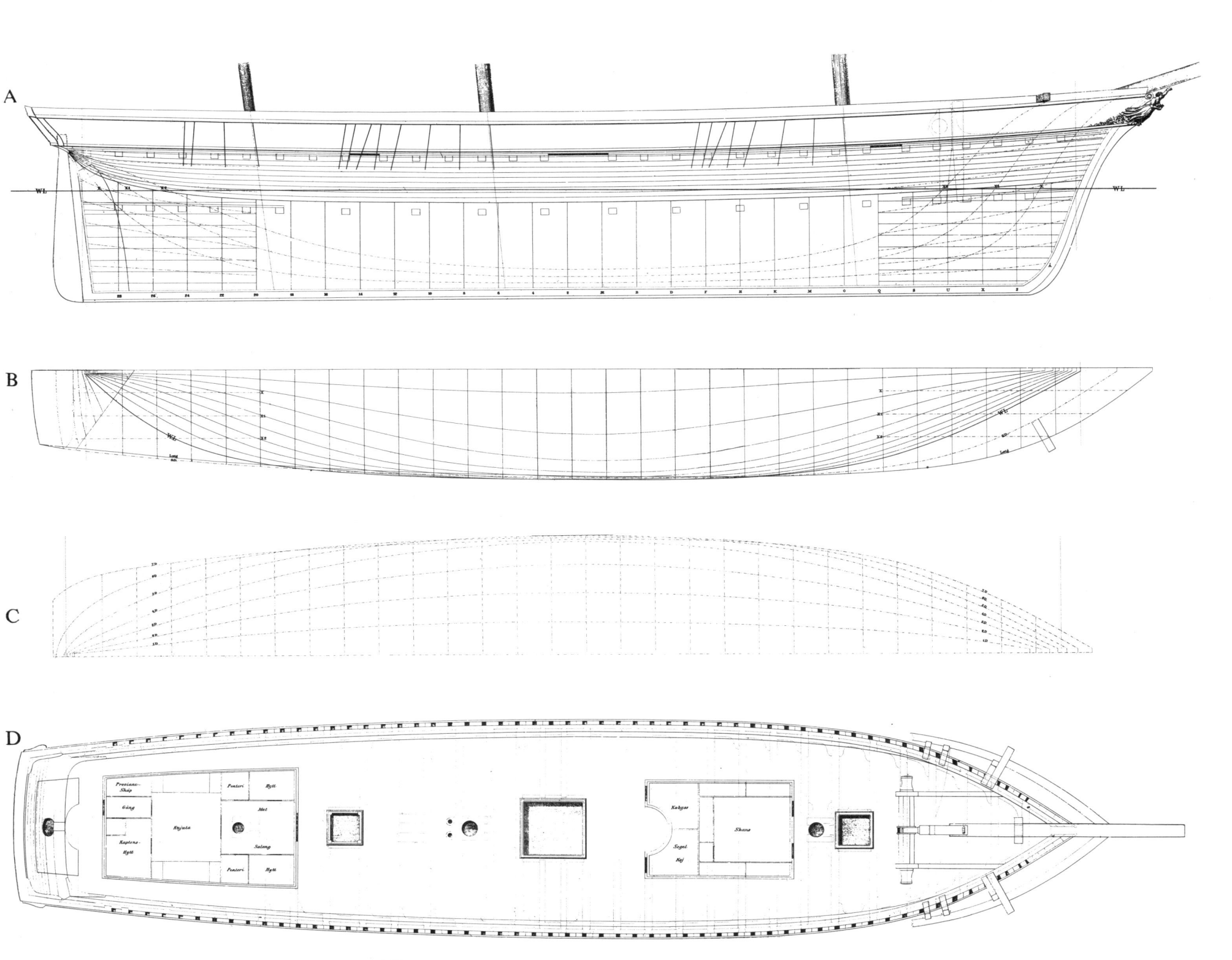

LINES OF A WOODEN SAILING SHIP OF 500 TONS DWT, 1864

The shape of the hull is determined by three sets of planes drawn at right angles to each other. Horizontal planes are called water lines, where they intersect the hull. They are shown as straight lines in A and as curves in B. WL indicates the load water line. Vertical planes going fore and aft and parallel to the longitudinal middle-line plane are called buttocks. Their intersections with the ship's hull are shown in A as curved lines, marked X, XI, and X2. Vertical planes going across the hull show the curves of the sides of the ship's transverse frame lines. Their shape is given in the body plan on page 22, which shows an end view of the hull. The frame lines are numbered in the afterbody and lettered in the forebody. The body plan also gives the diagonal lines extending from the middle-line plane. The diagonal intersections with the surface of the hull are drawn on page 23 in C. 23. D above gives the deck plan: three hatches, a fo'c'sle for 10 sailors, galley, and sail locker in the deckhouse, while the cabinhouse holds the captain's cabin, the mates' rooms, saloon, messroom, and pantries. The little house furthest aft holds the lamp locker and the officers' lavatory.

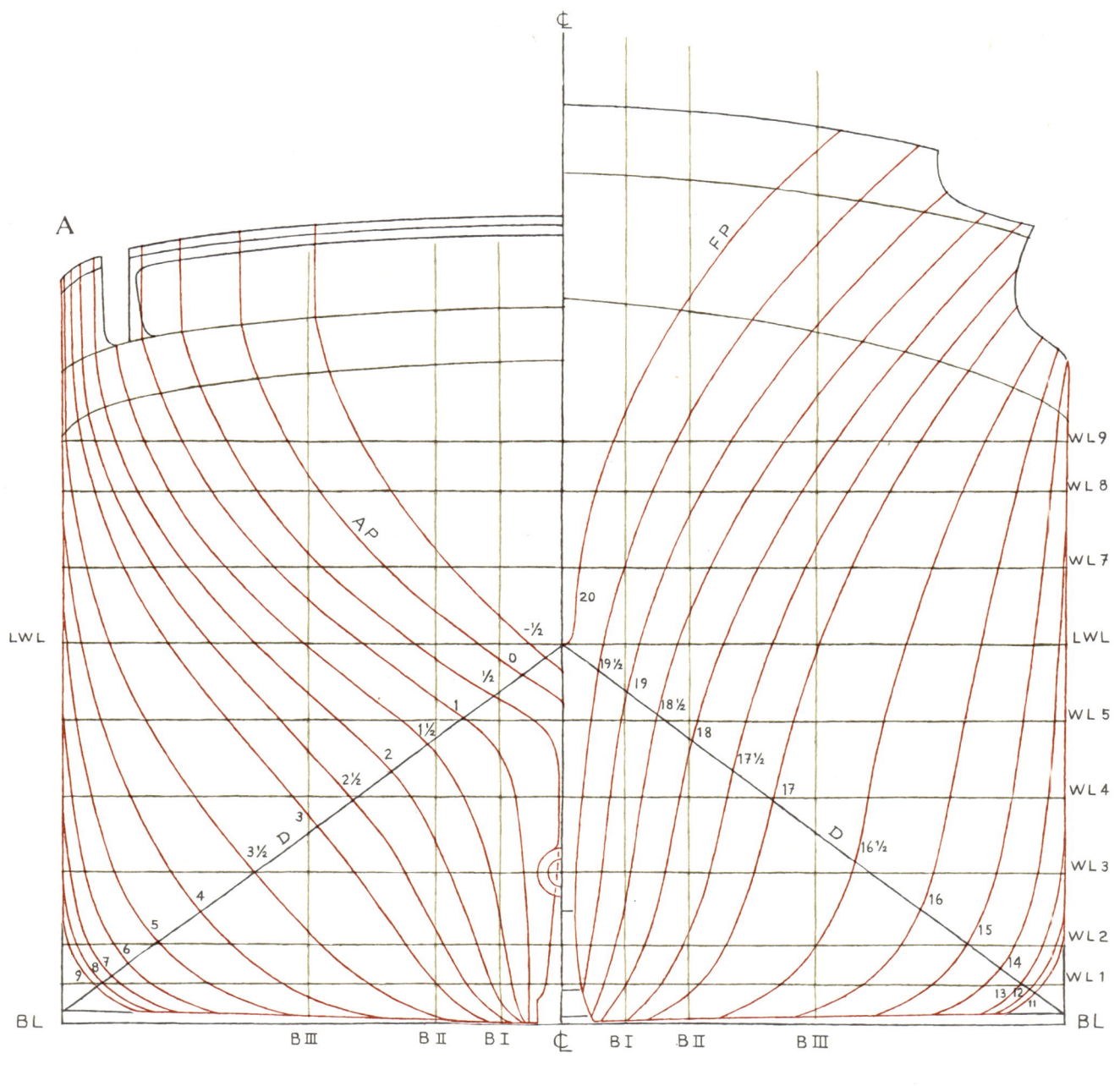

MEDIUM-SIZED CARGO SHIP

THE LINES OF A SHIP

A *Body Plan*
B *Sheer Plan*
C *Half Breadth Plan*

The shape of a ship is fully determined by three different systems of planes intersecting the molded surface of a ship's hull and drawn at right angles to each other.

Vertical sections going athwartship give the shape of the frames, as shown in red on the body plan. They are numbered from the sternpost forward. The distance between the first and last gives the length of the ship on her load water line, which equals the length between perpendiculars.

Sections drawn horizontally are called water lines, and are seen in brown on the half breadth plan, C. They are numbered from the bottom of the ship, which is the Base Line. One water line corresponds with the calculated Load Water Line, which is water line number six in this drawing. Vertical sections going fore and aft parallel with the middle line are called buttocks. They are shown in their true form as light brown lines on the sheer plan. They are marked in Roman numerals.

Besides all these lines, the shape of the hull is controlled by diagonal sections; only one is shown on the body plan. Such diagonal planes intersect the shell plating nearly at right angles, and, thus indicate any unfairness that may exist in the molded shape of the hull. The laid off diagonals are shown below the base line in the sheer plan.

The drawing gives one more curve, marked S, using the load water line in the sheer plan as a datum. This curve represents the displacement of the ship. The area of each section below the load water line is represented by a proportional vertical line set off at the corresponding station. Thus the area within the curved line represents the volume of the submerged part of the ship's hull, i.e., her displacement. On the drawings are:

AP	After perpendicular
BL	Base line
CL	Center line
FP	Forward perpendicular
LWL	Load water line
D	Diagonal
S	Curve of areas (displacement curve)
0—20	Numbers of sections
WL 1—WL 9	Water lines
B I—B III	Buttock lines

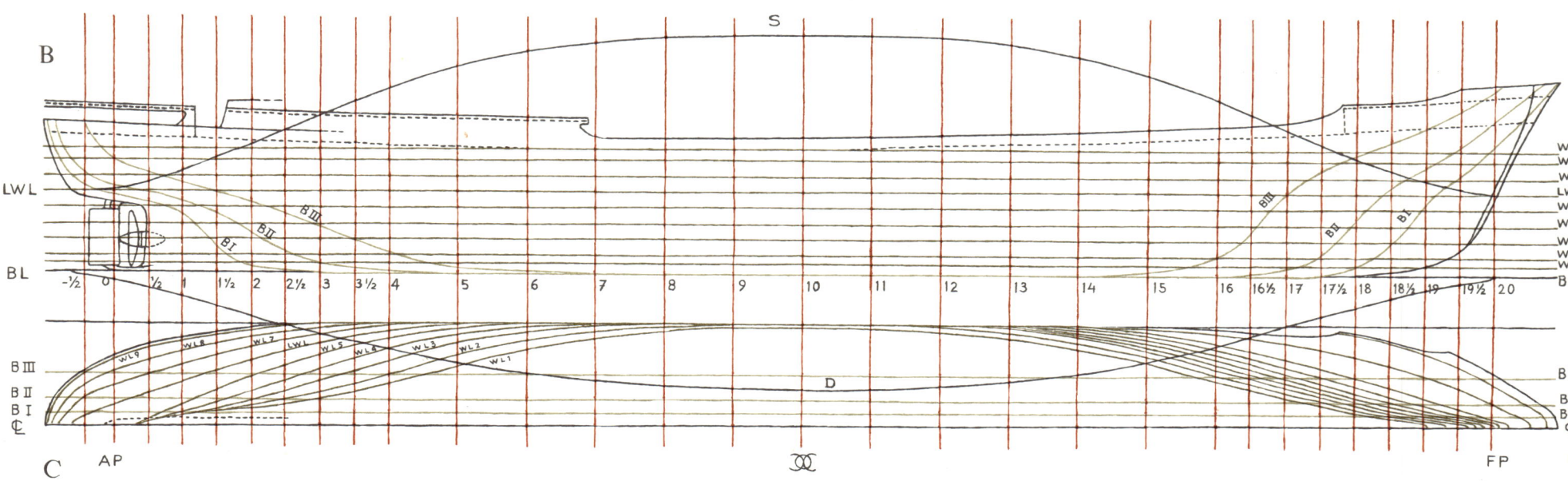

MEDIUM-SIZED CARGO SHIP

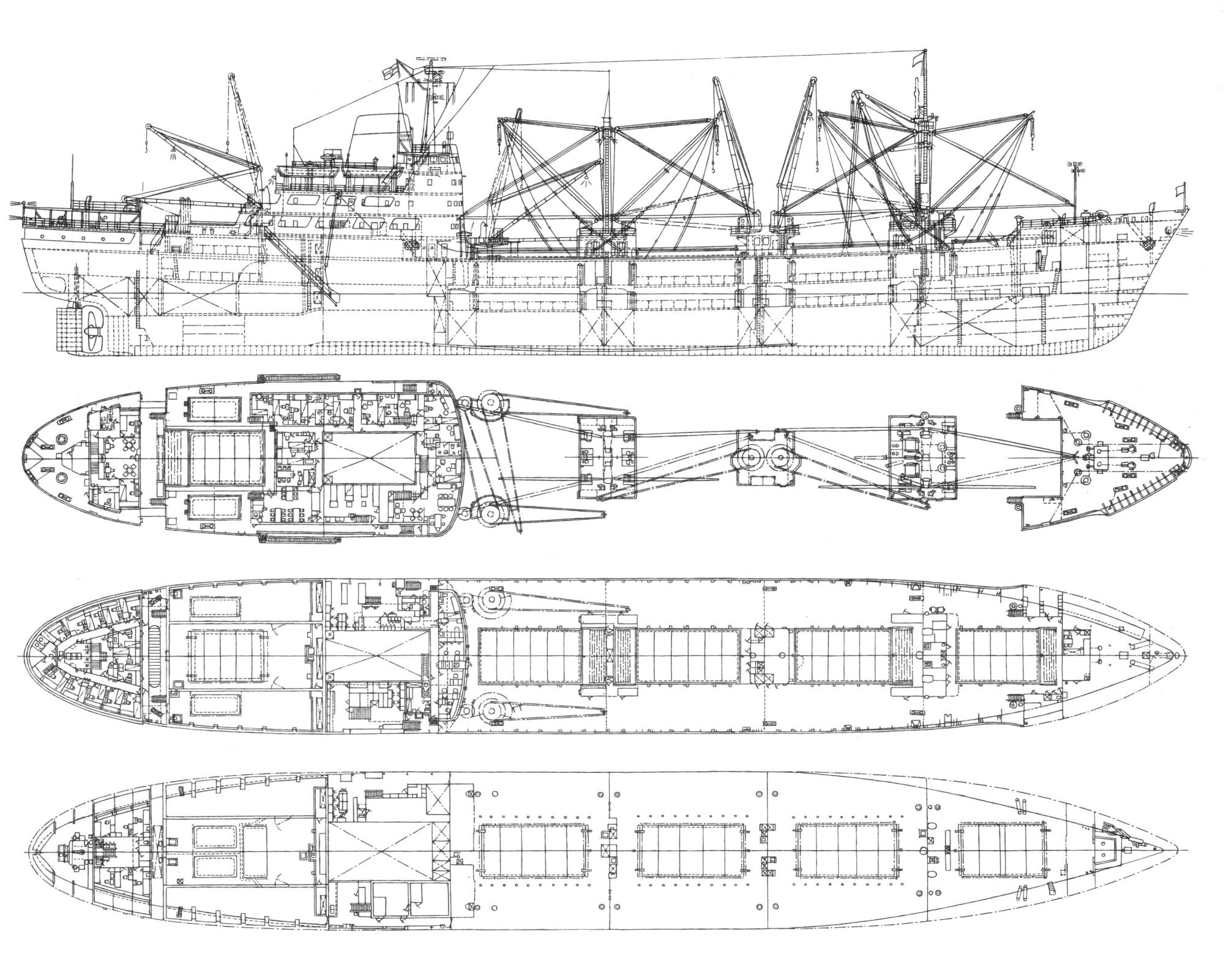

GENERAL ARRANGEMENT OF A MEDIUM-SIZED CARGO SHIP

Shelter-decked ship of 8,200 tons dwt, built by Götaverken, 1961. Class: Lloyd's Register + 100 A 1. Ice class: 3

Dimensions
Length over all: 471'—7⅝"
Length between p.p. as per class: 430'—3"
Breadth molded: 65'—0"
Depth molded to shelter deck, 39'—0"
Depth molded to main deck, 29'—0"
Draft on summer freeboard: 26'—1½"

Machinery:
One six-cylinder, supercharged diesel engine
Two cycle single-acting: 8,950 IHP
Diameter of cylinder: 29.92"
Length of stroke: 59.06"
Revolutions per minute: 112
Diameter of propeller: 16'—10¾"
Pitch of propeller variable: 17'—2½"

The top drawing gives the general appearance of the ship, with principal layout details of the hull. The ship is of the shelter-deck type with fo'c'sle, bridge, and poop. The bridge is separated from the poop by only a narrow well, where the tonnage opening is placed. The ship has five cargo holds, and the number 5 hold is divided into several rooms for chilled cargo. For handling cargo there are four booms and a heavy lift boom at the foremast, two deck cranes between hatches 2 and 3, two samson posts with four booms between hatches 3 and 4, two deck cranes in front of the bridge, and another two cranes for number 5 hold.

Below the profile are three plans of the different decks. The first gives the fo'c'sle head, top of deckhouses, bridge deck, and poop deck. The middle plan shows the shelter deck with the space below the fo'c'sle head, bridge deck, and poop deck. The third plan is the main deck.

VIKING SHIP

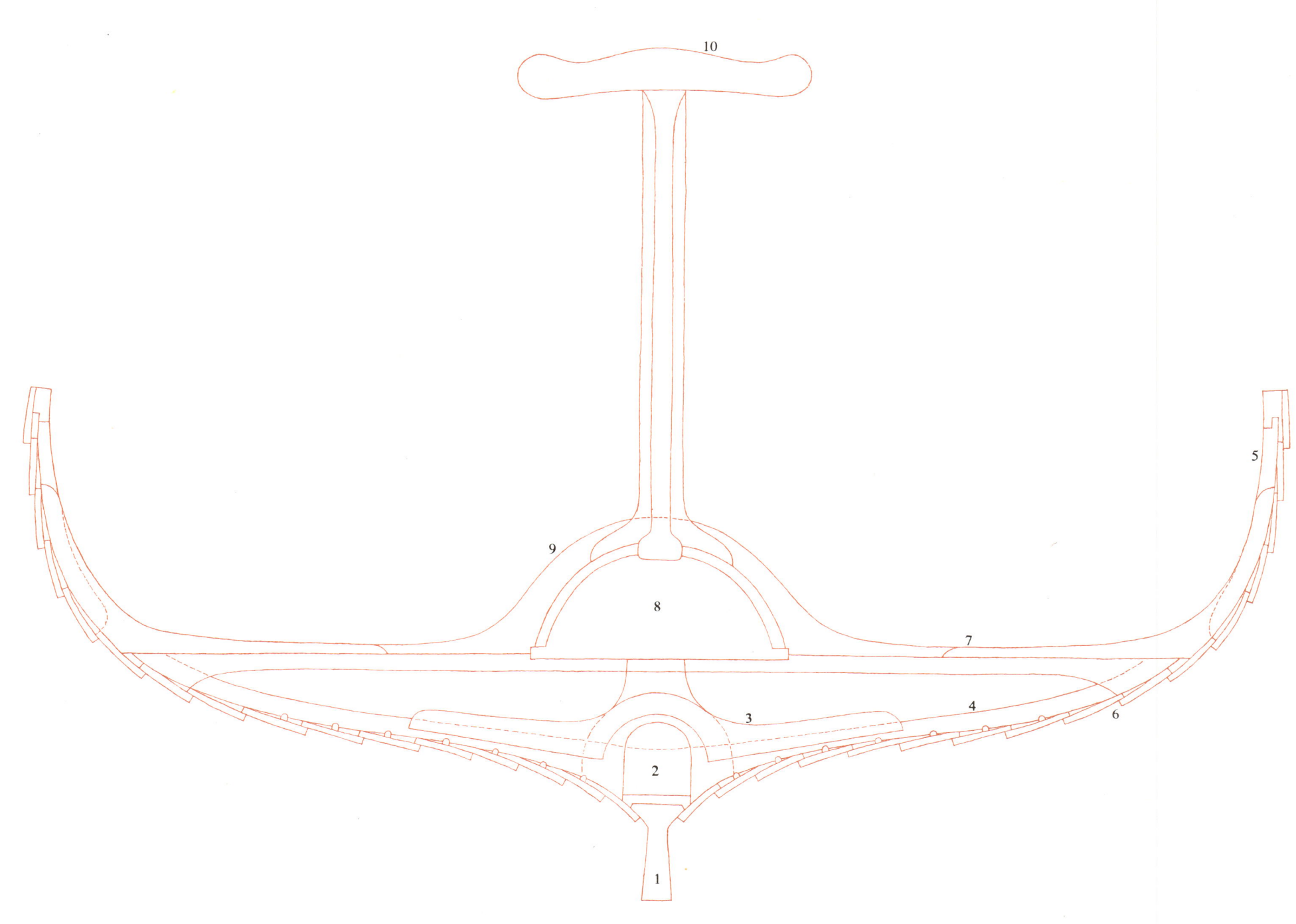

MIDSHIP SECTION OF A VIKING SHIP, MIDDLE OF 9TH CENTURY

(After the Gokstad ship). The ship is clinker-built from oak, with 16 boards on each side, and has a large keelson, and a deep keel for sailing. The lower eight boards are tied to the ribs through cleats that are left on each board-plank. The rest of the boards are nailed. The ship is undecked, but has a flat floor, on top of which a very heavy mast partner runs over six of the beams. The high gallows make it possible to erect a large tent on board. There are no rowing-benches. The oarsmen probably sat on loose benches or sea-chests.

1 Keel
2 Keelson
3 Floors
4 Futtocks
5 Toptimber
6 Clinker-built skin
7 Flooring
8 Mast partners
9 Riders to keep mast partners in place
10 Gallows

Page 27: MIDSHIP SECTION OF TWO DIFFERENT SHIPS, SECOND HALF OF THE 19TH CENTURY

A *Wooden ship*
1 Keel
2 Garboard strake
3 Bottom planking
4 Bends or wales
5 Topside planking
6 Sheer strake
7 Floor
8 2nd futtock
9 4th futtock
10 Long toptimber
11 Limbers, water course
12 Keelson
13 Limber board
14 Limber strake
15 Floor ceiling
16 Thick strakes of ceiling
17 Air courses
18 Lower deck hanging knee
19 Lower deck shelf
20 Lower deck clamp
21 Hold stanchion
22 Lower deck beam
23 Lower deck, lower deck planking
24 Lower deck waterway
25 Lower deck spirketing
26 Tween deck ceiling
27 Upper deck hanging knee
28 Upper deck shelf
29 Upper deck clamp
30 Tween deck stanchion

26

WOODEN AND WOOD AND IRON VESSEL

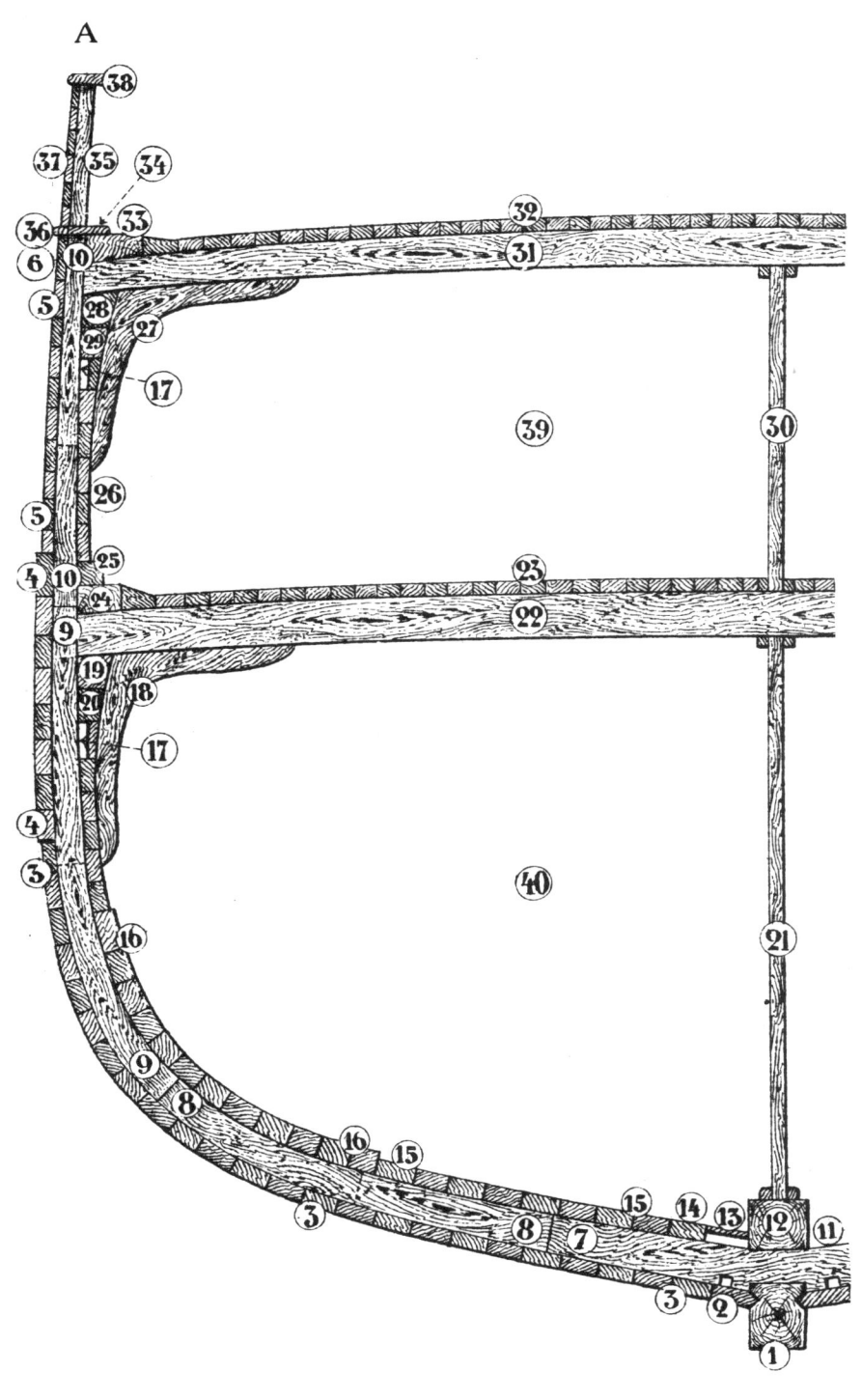

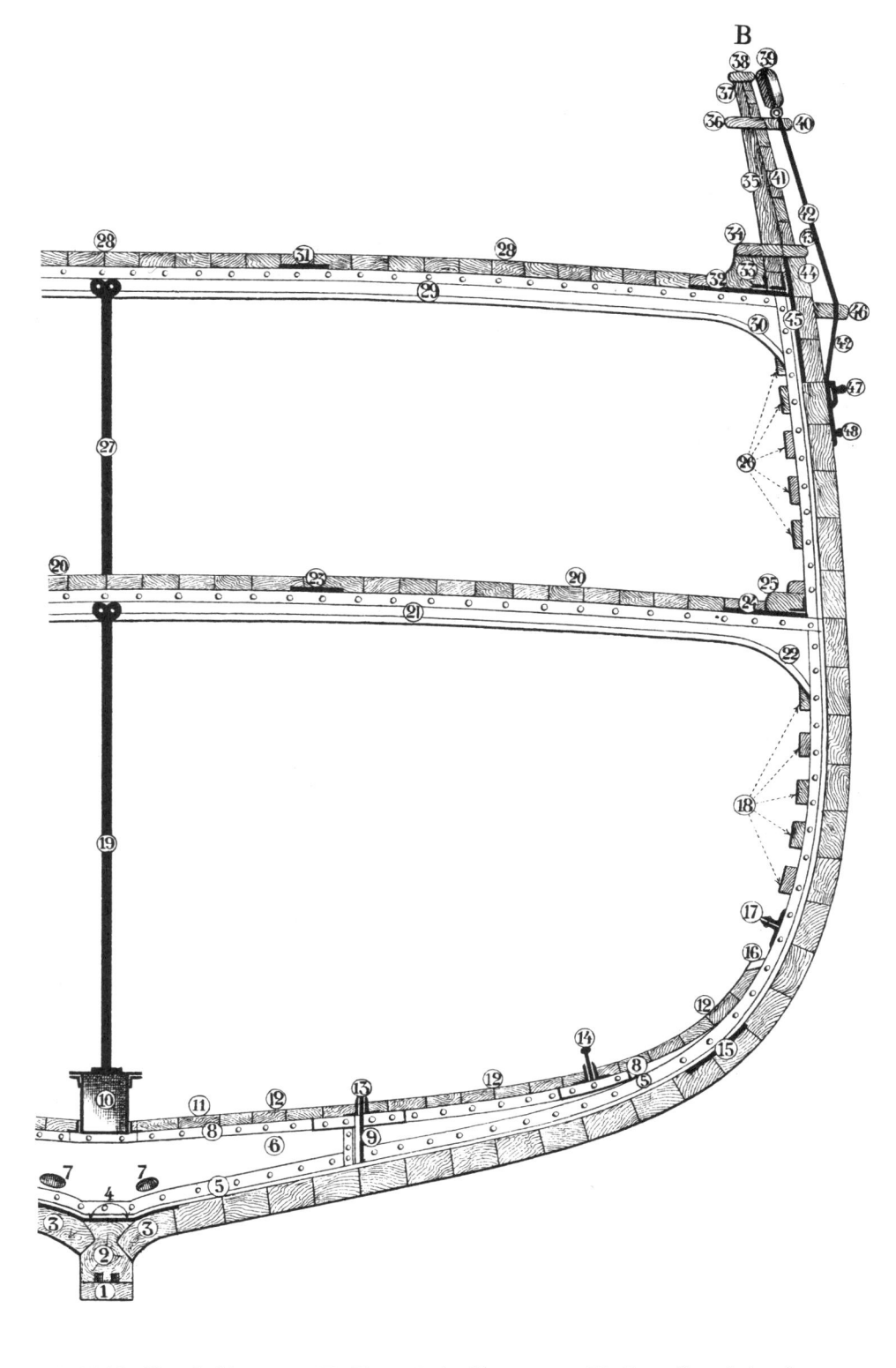

Continued

31 Upper deck beam
32 Upper deck, upper deck planking
33 Upper deck waterway
34 Covering board
35 Bulwark stanchions
36 Planksheer
37 Bulwark planking
38 Main rail
39 Tween decks
40 Hold

B *Composite ship (wooden vessel with iron frames)*
1 False keel or shoe
2 Keel
3 Garboard strake
4 Keel plate
5 Frame
6 Floor
7 Limbers
8 Reverse frame
9 Side intercostal keelson
10 Center line keelson
11 Limber boards
12 Ceiling
13 Side keelson
14 Bilge keelson
15 Bilge plate
16 Covering board
17 Bilge stringer
18 Cargo battens (in hold)
19 Hold pillar; hold stanchion
20 Lower deck
21 Lower deck beam
22 Bracket end (of lower deck beam)
23 Lower deck tie plate
24 Lower deck stringer
25 Lower deck waterway
26 Cargo battens (between decks)
27 Upper deck pillar, upper deck stanchion
28 Upper deck
29 Upper deck beam
30 Bracket end (of upper deck beam)
31 Upper deck tie plate
32 Upper deck stringer plate
33 Upper deck waterway
34 Covering board
35 Bulwark stanchion
36 Main rail
37 Topgallant bulwark stanchion
38 Topgallant rail
39 Deadeye
40 Upper channel
41 Bulwark planking
42 Chainplate
43 Planksheer
44 Sheer strake
45 Iron sheer strake
46 Lower channel
47 Chain bolt
48 Preventer bolt

WOODEN SHIP DETAILS

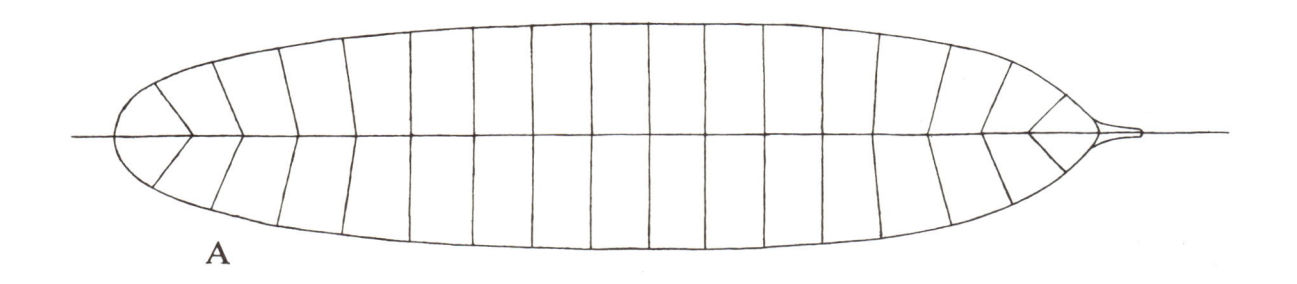

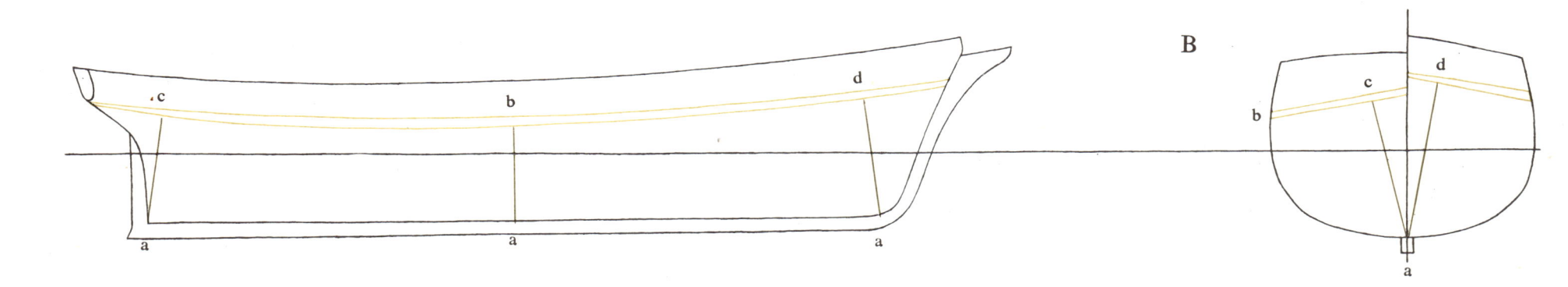

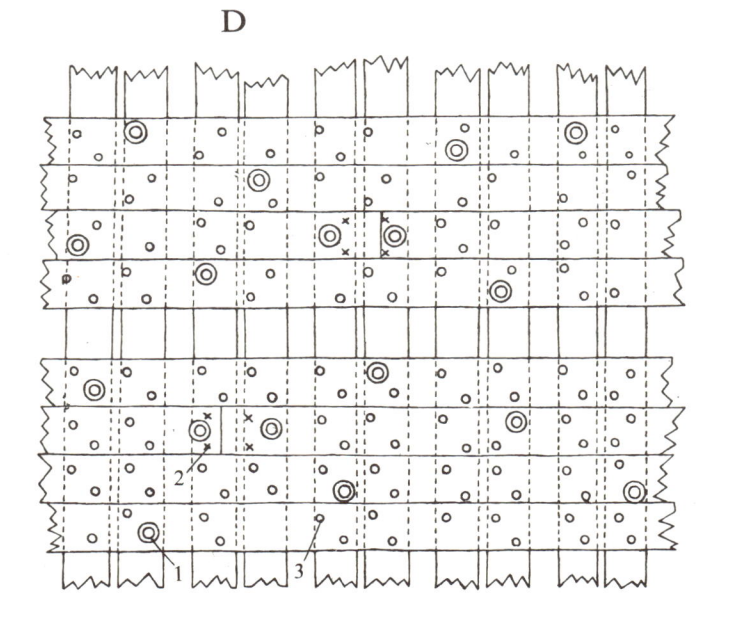

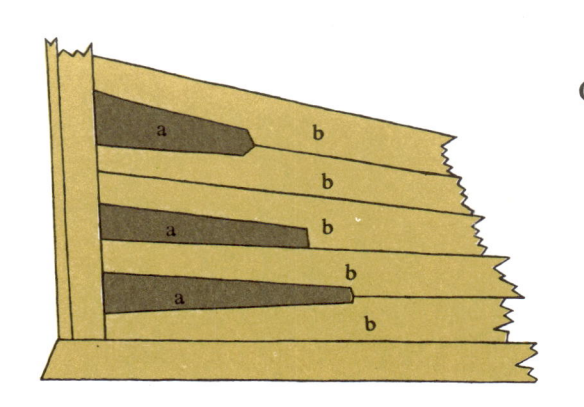

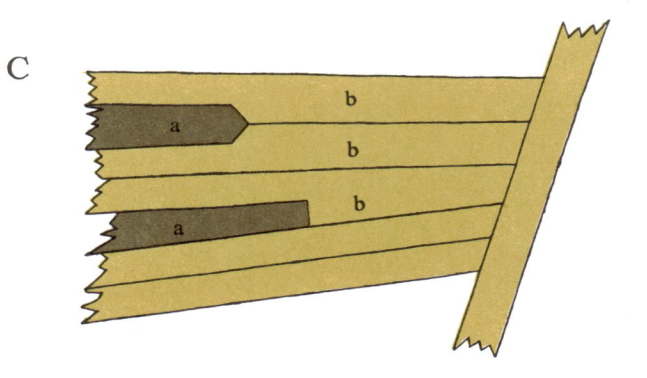

SOME CONSTRUCTION DETAILS OF WOODEN SHIPS, 19TH CENTURY

A The timbers were placed at right angles to the keel, except at the ends, both fore and aft, where they were placed at right angles to the ship's side. These frames were called cant timbers.

B To make the plank strakes run fair, fore and aft, the midship bend (ab) was divided into the same number of planks as the frames (ac) and as at the ends of the ship (ad)

C At the ends of the ship, if the planks were too wide, stealers (a) were put in between them; if too narrow, they were formed as joggle planks (b)

D Below the water line tree nails (trunnels) and bolts were used to fasten the planking to the frames in addition to *two bolts and one tree nail in each plank butt*

1 Tree nail
2 Bolt
3 Nail

WOODEN SHIP DETAILS

DETAILS OF A WOODEN VESSEL (FROM PAASCH)

A, B *Horizontal section of bow*
1. Stem
2. Stem rabbet
3. Apron
4. Eking
5. Deck hook
6. Deck hook bolts
7. Stem piece
8. Knight head
9. Hawse timbers
10. Fore cant timbers
11. Outside plank
12. Ceiling plank
13. Breast hook
14. Breast hook bolts
15. Deck beam

C *Deck and hatchway*
1. Hatch cover
2. Hatchway
3. Hatchway coamings
4. Hatchway carling
5. Head ledges
6. Fore and after
7. Hatch end beams
8. Half beams
9. Lodging knees
10. Deck stanchions
11. Mast hole
12. Mast carlings
13. Chocks
    (12 and 13 forming mast partners)
14. Mast beams
15. Deck planking

IRON SHIP WITH SINGLE BOTTOM

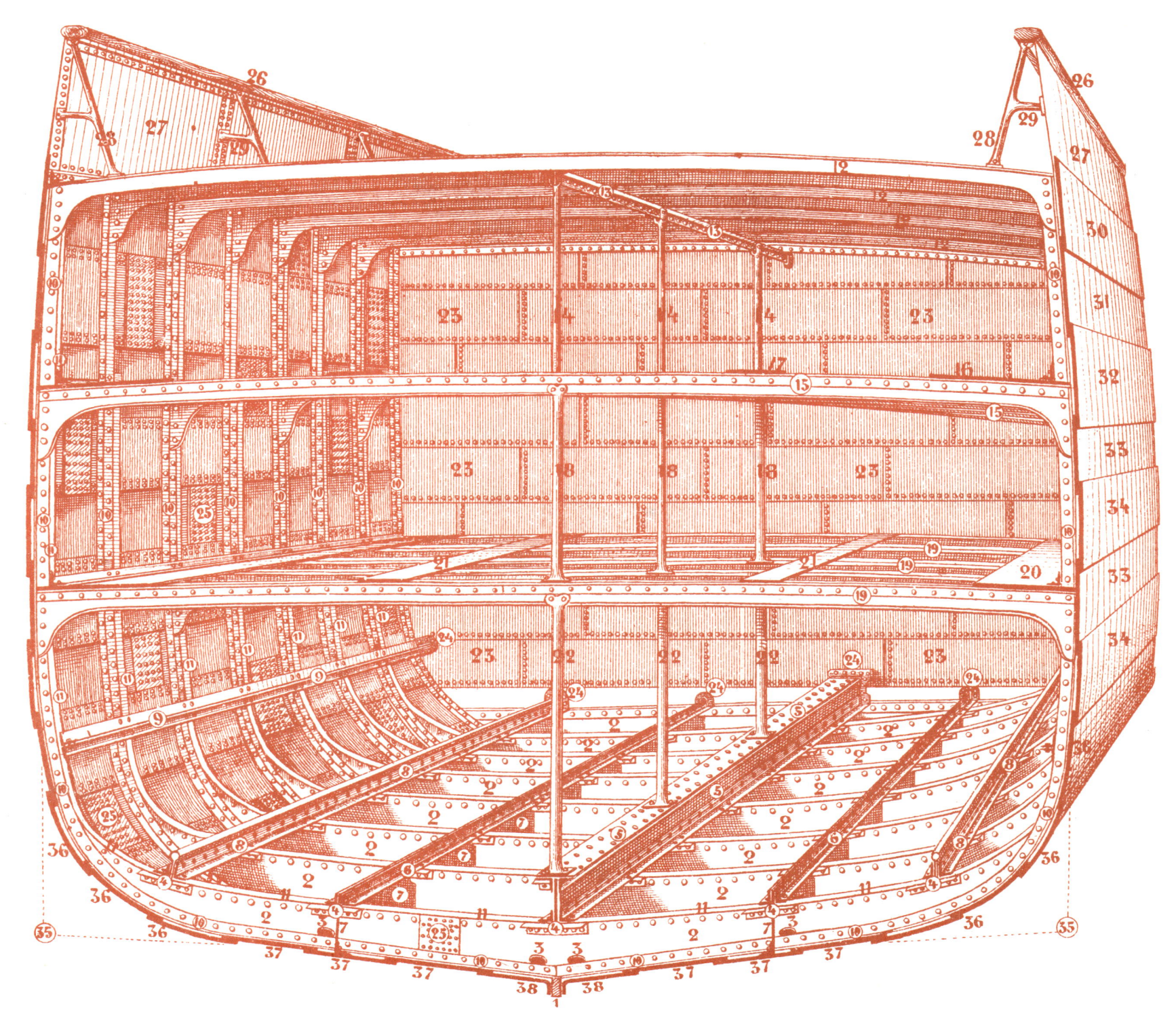

INSIDE VIEW OF A RIVETED IRON OR STEEL SHIP WITH SINGLE BOTTOM

1 Keel
2 Floors
3 Limber holes
4 Clips
5 Center line keelson
6 Side keelson
7 Intercostal keelson, side intercostal keelson
8 Bilge keelson
9 Bilge stringer
10 Frames
11 Reverse frames
12 Upper deck beams
13 Center line deck stringer or girder
14 Upper deck pillars or stanchions
15 Main deck beams
16 Main deck stringer plate
17 Main deck tie plate
18 Main deck pillars or stanchions
19 Lower deck beams
20 Lower deck stringer plate
21 Lower deck tie plate
22 Hold pillars or stanchions
23 Bulkhead
24 Collars
25 Butt straps
26 Main rail cap or bulwark cap
27 Bulwark plating
28 Bulwark stays
29 Spurs (of bulwark stays)
30 Upper sheer strake
31 Topside strake
32 Main sheer strake
33 Side plating (inside strakes)
34 Side plating (outside strakes)
35 Bilge
36 Bilge strakes
37 Bottom plating
38 Garboard strakes

PRE-FABRICATED UNITS

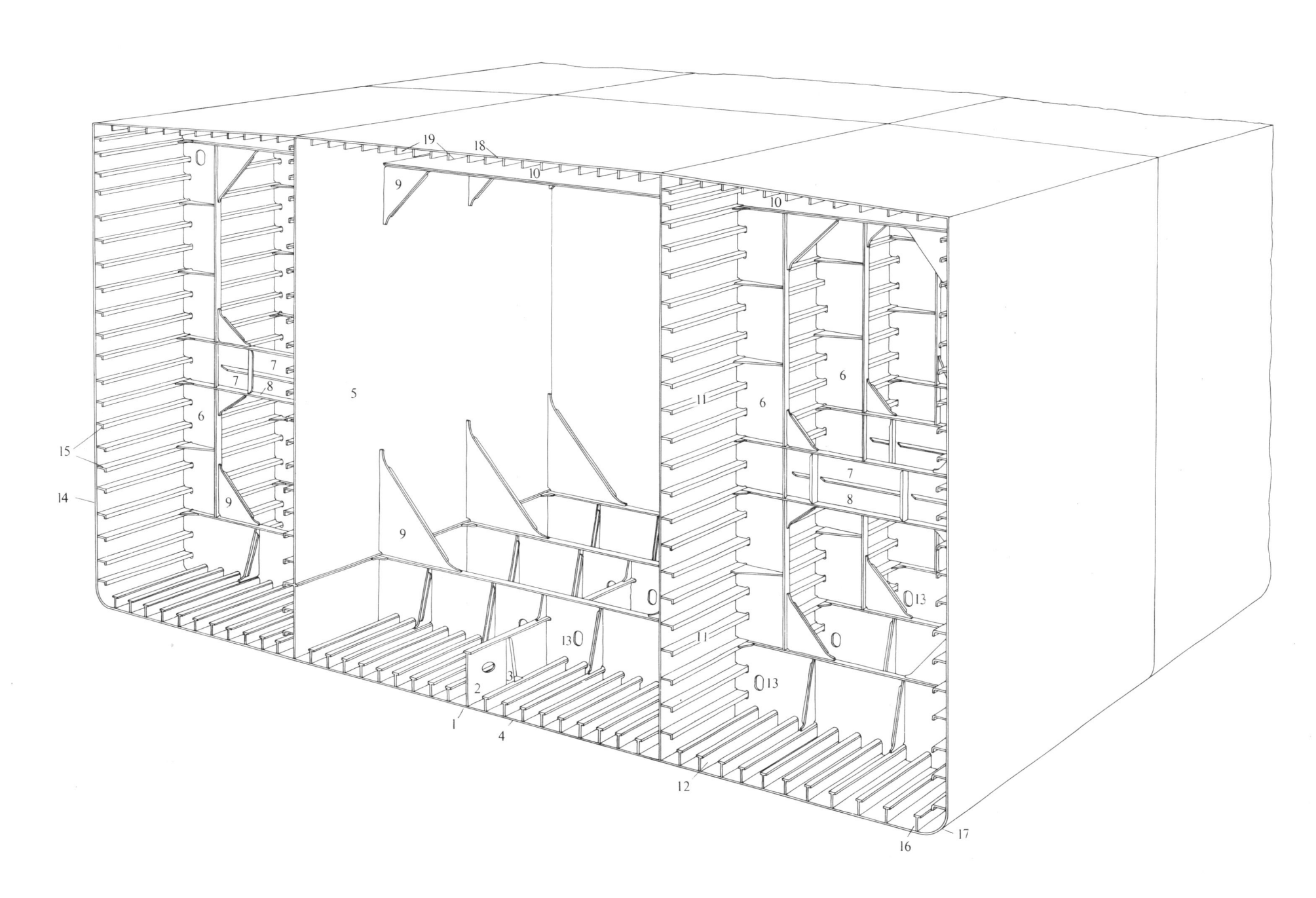

MIDSHIP SECTION (BOX SECTION) OF MODERN TANKER OF 102,000 TONS, BUILT FROM PRE-FABRICATED UNITS

1. Keel strake
2. Center girder
3. Tripping bracket
4. Bottom shell
5. Longitudinal bulkhead
6. Transverse web
7. Cross tie
8. Stiffener
9. Bracket
10. Deck transverse
11. Bulkhead longitudinal
12. Bottom longitudinal
13. Passage opening
14. Side shell
15. Side longitudinal
16. Bilge strake
17. Bilge keel
18. Upper deck
19. Deck longitudinal

FRIGATE OF 1768

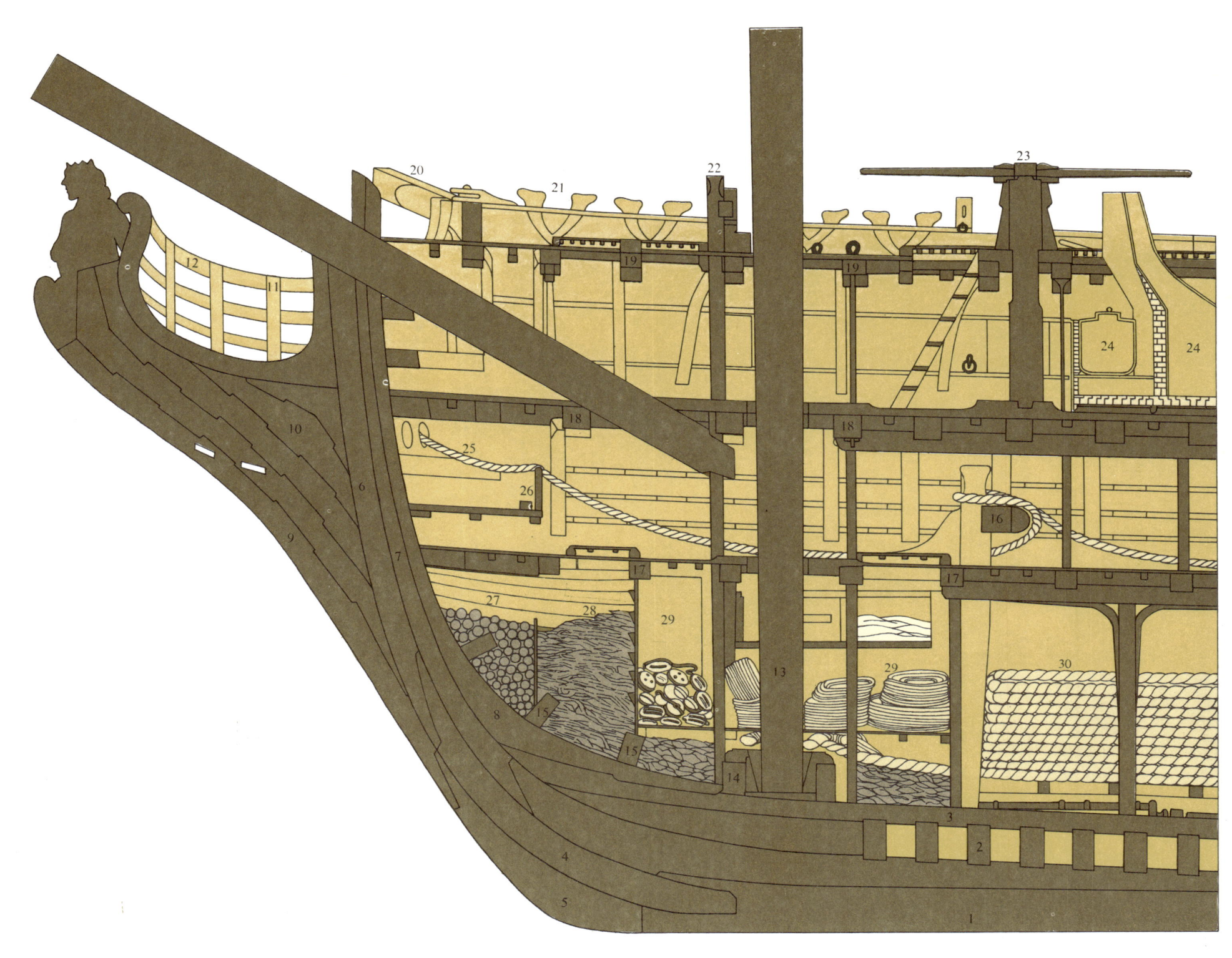

LONGITUDINAL SECTION OF THE FOREBODY OF A 40-GUN FRIGATE, 1768

1 Keel	6 Stem	11 Head timbers	16 Bitts	21 Kevels	26 Mangerboard
2 Floors	7 Apron	12 Head rails	17 Orlop deck beams	22 Topsail sheet bitt	27 Shotlocker
3 Keelson	8 Stemson	13 Foremast	18 Gun deck beams	23 Jeer capstan	28 Galley wood
4 Forefoot	9 Bobstay piece	14 Mast step	19 Upper deck beams	24 Galley	29 Bosun's stores
5 Gripe	10 Filling chocks	15 Breast hooks	20 Cathead	25 Cable	30 Cable tier

WOODEN SHIP

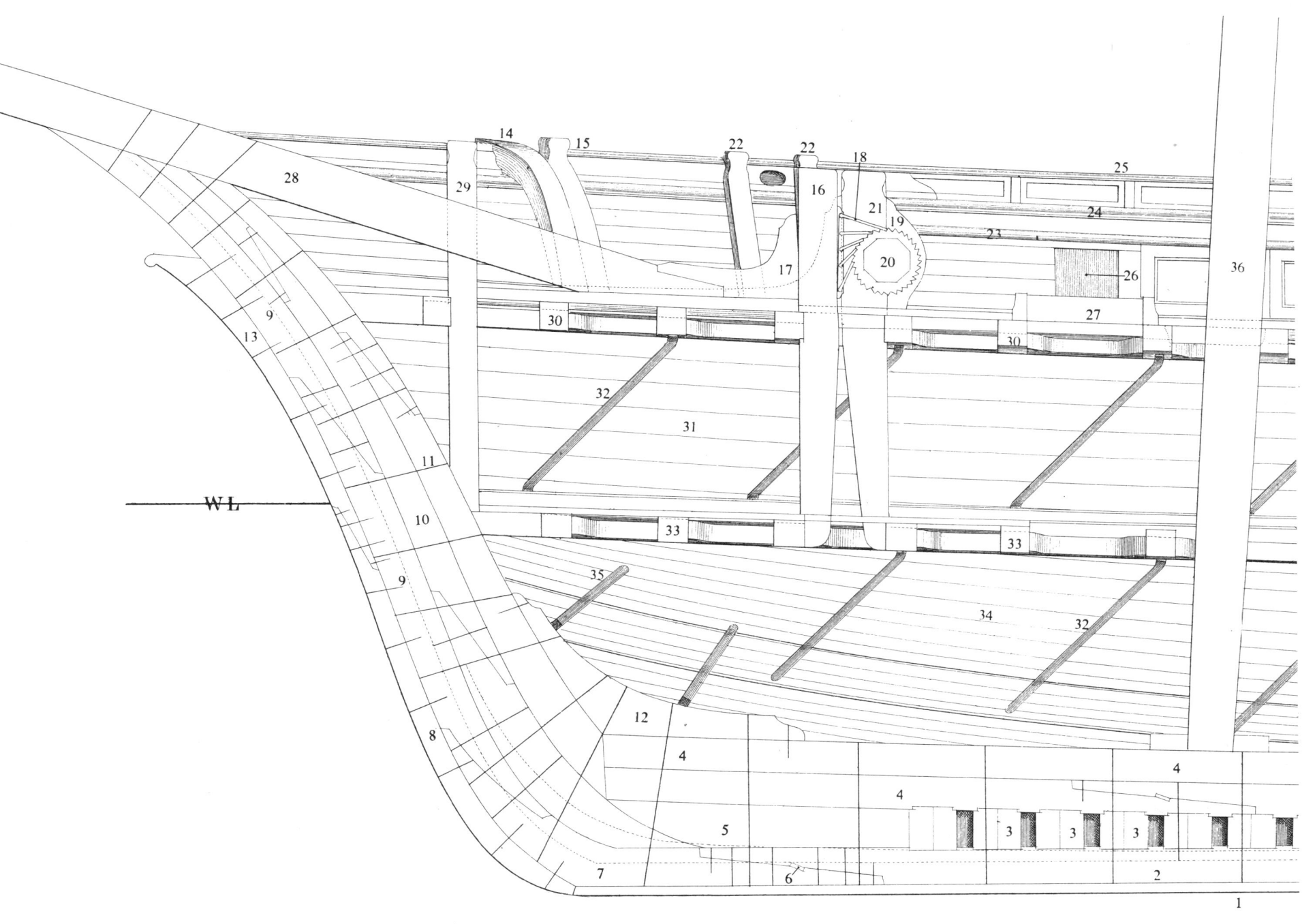

THREE-MASTED WOODEN SHIP, 500 TONS DWT, LONGITUDINAL SECTION OF THE FOREBODY

1 False keel or shoe	7 Fore foot	14 Cathead	21 Carrick bitt or windlass bitt	27 Fore hatch coaming	32 Main and 'tween deck diagonal hanging knees
2 Keel	8 Cutwater piece, gripe	15 Kevel head	22 Mooring bollards	28 Bowsprit	
3 Floors	9 Stem	16 Pawl bitt	23 Pinrail	29 Foreward bitt	
4 Keelson	10 Apron	17 Standard knee	24 Main rail	30 Main deck beams	33 'Tween deck beams
5 Fore deadwood	11 Stemson	18 Pawls	25 Topgallant rail	31 Tween deck ceiling	34 Lower hold ceiling
6 Keel scarf	12 Stem knee	19 Pawl rim	26 Port		35 Breast hooks
	13 Lace piece	20 Windlass barrel			36 Foremast

CARPENTER'S TOOLS

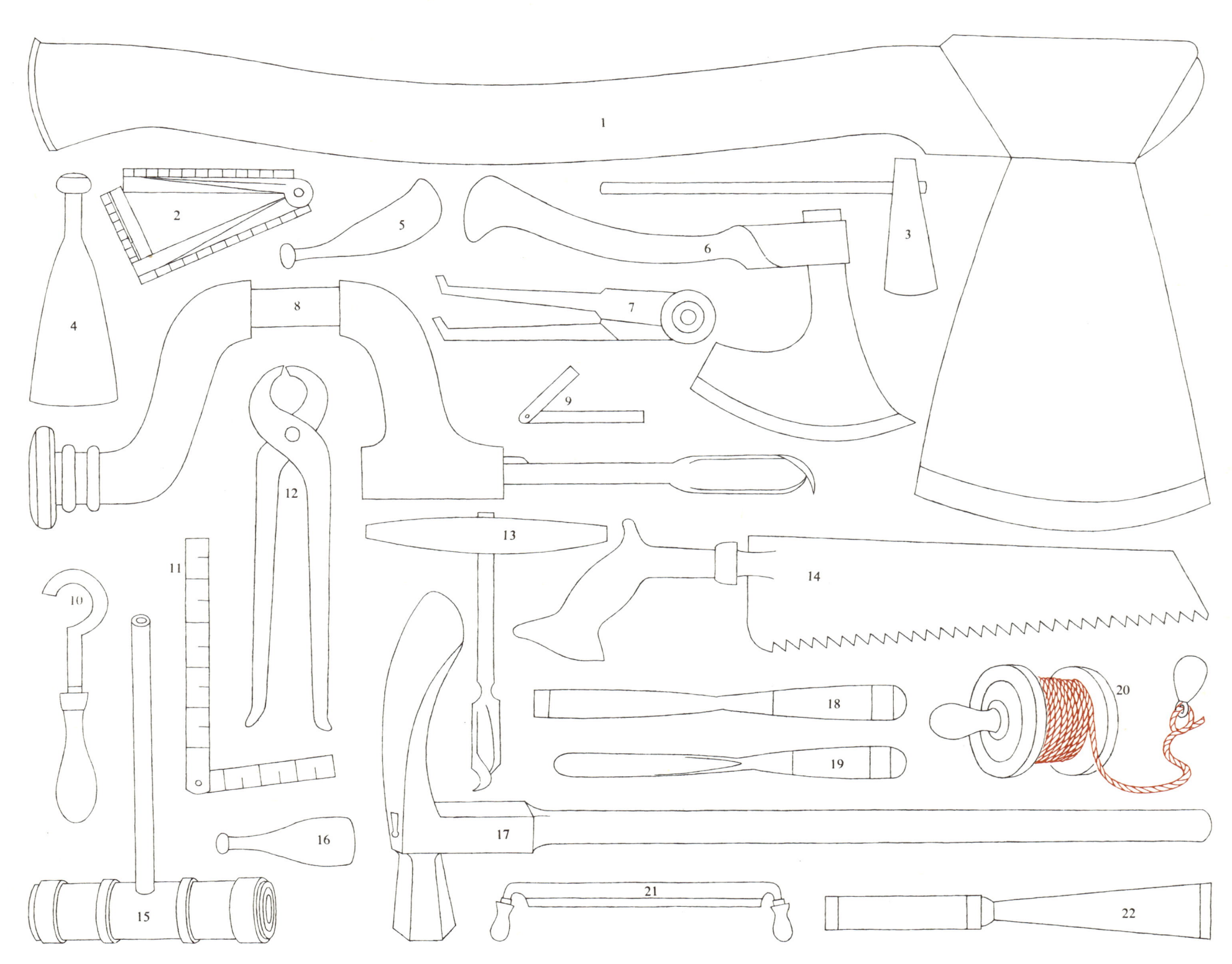

OLD CARPENTER'S TOOLS

From a book on shipbuilding, 1691

1. English broad axe
2. Folding rule, a foot and a half long
3. Horse iron with an iron handle
4. Reeming iron
5. Curved caulking iron
6. Carpenter's hatchet
7. Inside calipers
8. Dutch brace and bit
9. Small bevel
10. Crab iron
11. Dutch rule
12. Pair of pincers
13. English auger with a screw
14. Dutch handsaw
15. Big mallet with iron hoops
16. Caulking iron
17. English adze
18. English chisel
19. Gouge
20. Chalk line and reel
21. Draw knife
22. Chisel with a handle

CARPENTER'S TOOLS

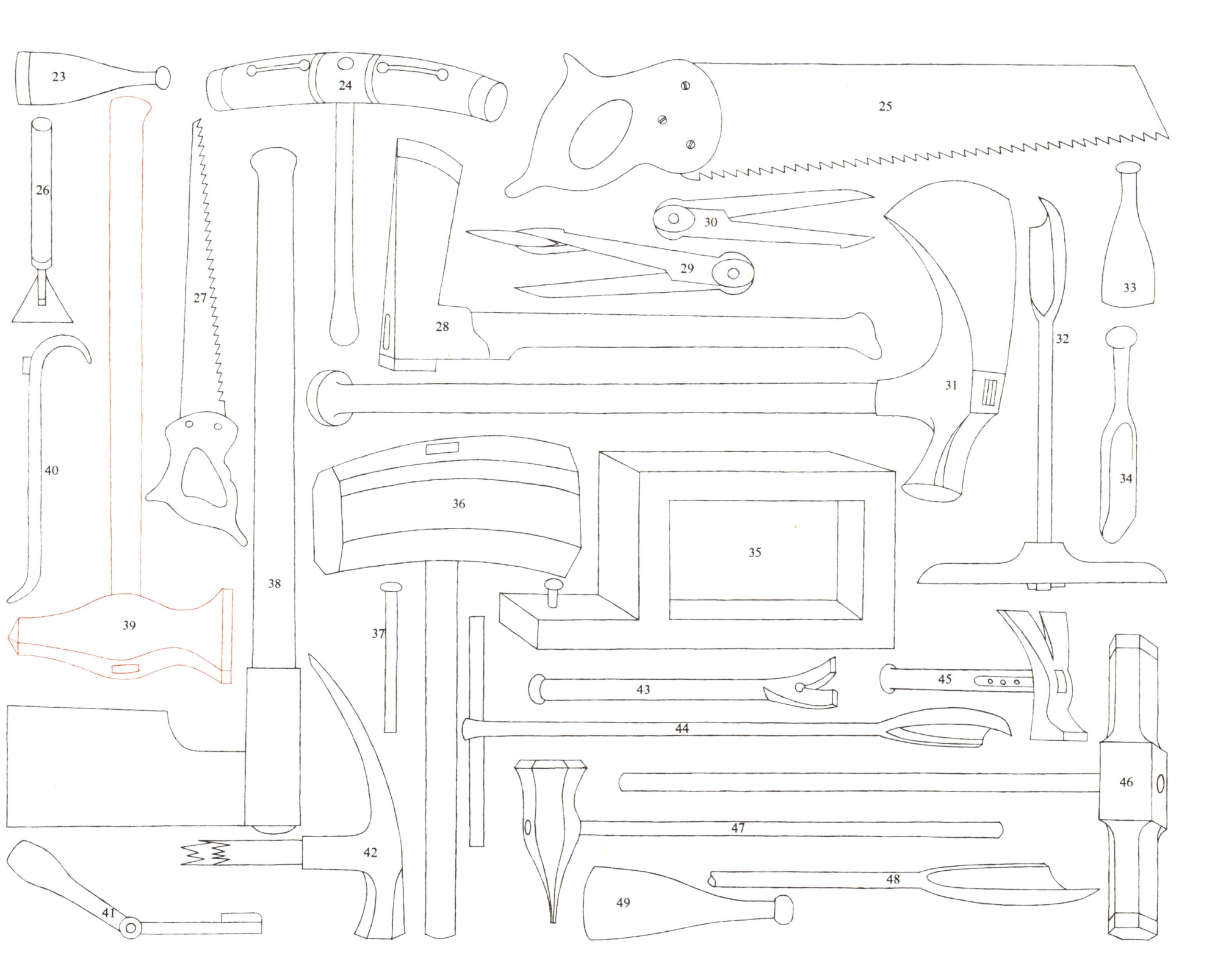

23 Making iron	28 Swedish chopping axe	34 Small gouge to start auger holes	38 Dutch axe	42 Adze, as seen from the side	46 English caulking mallet
24 Swedish caulking mallet	29 Compasses with crayon	35 Grease well to use when caulking	39 Sledge hammer	43 Crowbar	47 Common hammer
25 English handsaw	30 Dividers	36 English maul	40 Rave hook or ripping iron for cleaning caulking from seams	44 English auger with a wooden handle	48 Swedish gouge for pinewood
26 Deck scraper	31 Swedish adze	37 Spike iron	41 Crab iron, made like a clasp knife	45 English claw hammer	49 Reeming iron
27 Compass saw	32 Swedish auger				
	33 Caulking iron				

THREE-DECKED STEAMER

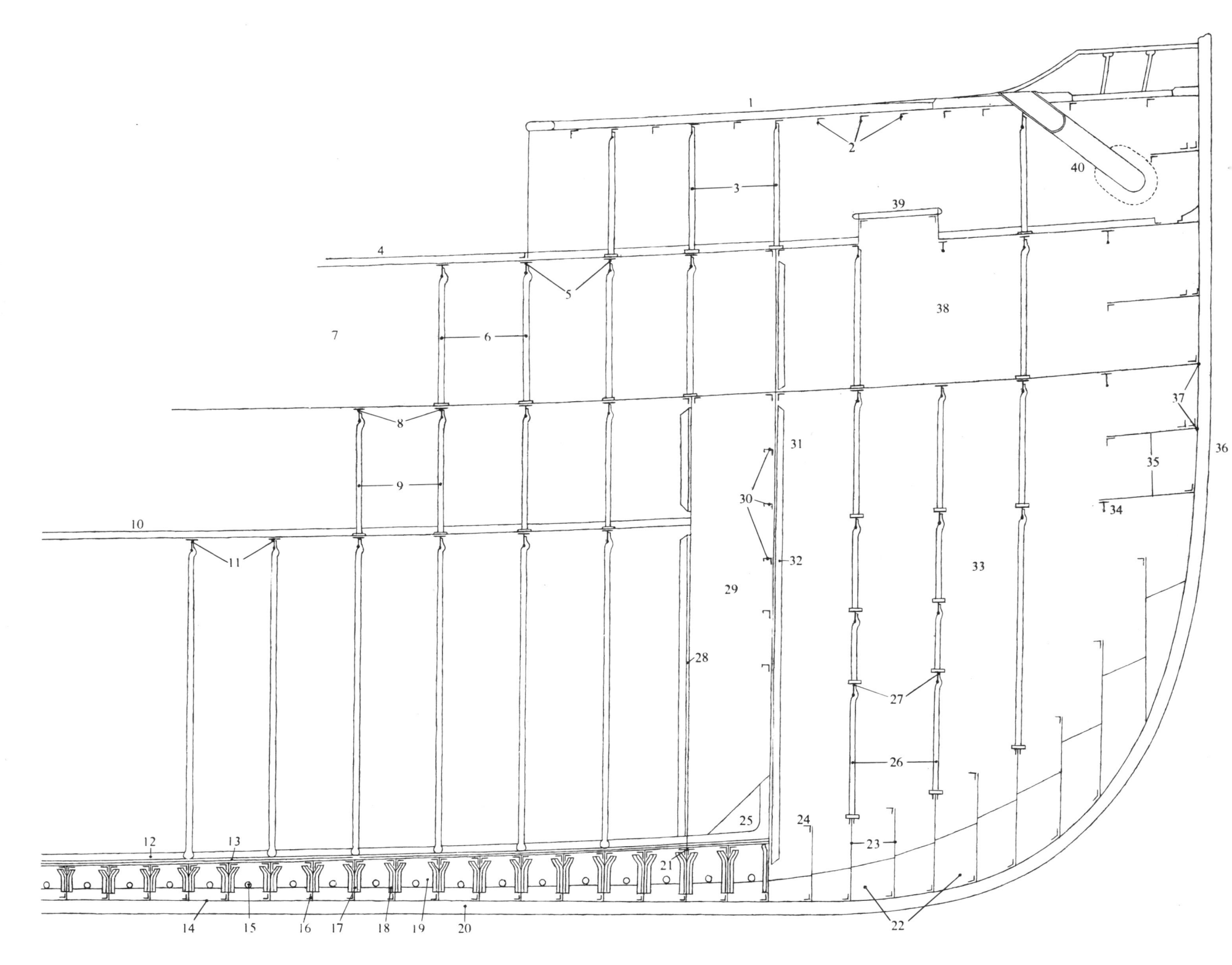

FORWARD ELEVATION OF A THREE-DECKED STEAMER, 1900

1. Fo'c'sle deck
2. Deck beams
3. Deck pillars
4. Main deck
5. Deck beams
6. Deck pillars
7. Tween deck
8. Deck beams
9. Deck pillars
10. Lower deck
11. Deck beams
12. Center keelson
13. Tank top plating
14. Bottom plating
15. Limber hole
16. Bottom frame
17. Floor
18. Angle clips
19. Center girder
20. Bar keel
21. Reverse frame
22. Cement filling
23. Deep floors
24. Reverse frame
25. Bracket
26. Pillars
27. Beams
28. Chain locker bulkhead
29. Chain locker
30. Horizontal bulkhead stiffeners
31. Forepeak bulkhead, collision bulkhead
32. Vertical bulkhead stiffeners
33. Forepeak tank
34. Beam
35. Breast hooks
36. Stem
37. Angle clips
38. Storeroom above forepeak tank
39. Hatch to storeroom above forepeak tank
40. Hawse pipe

36

OBO-SHIP

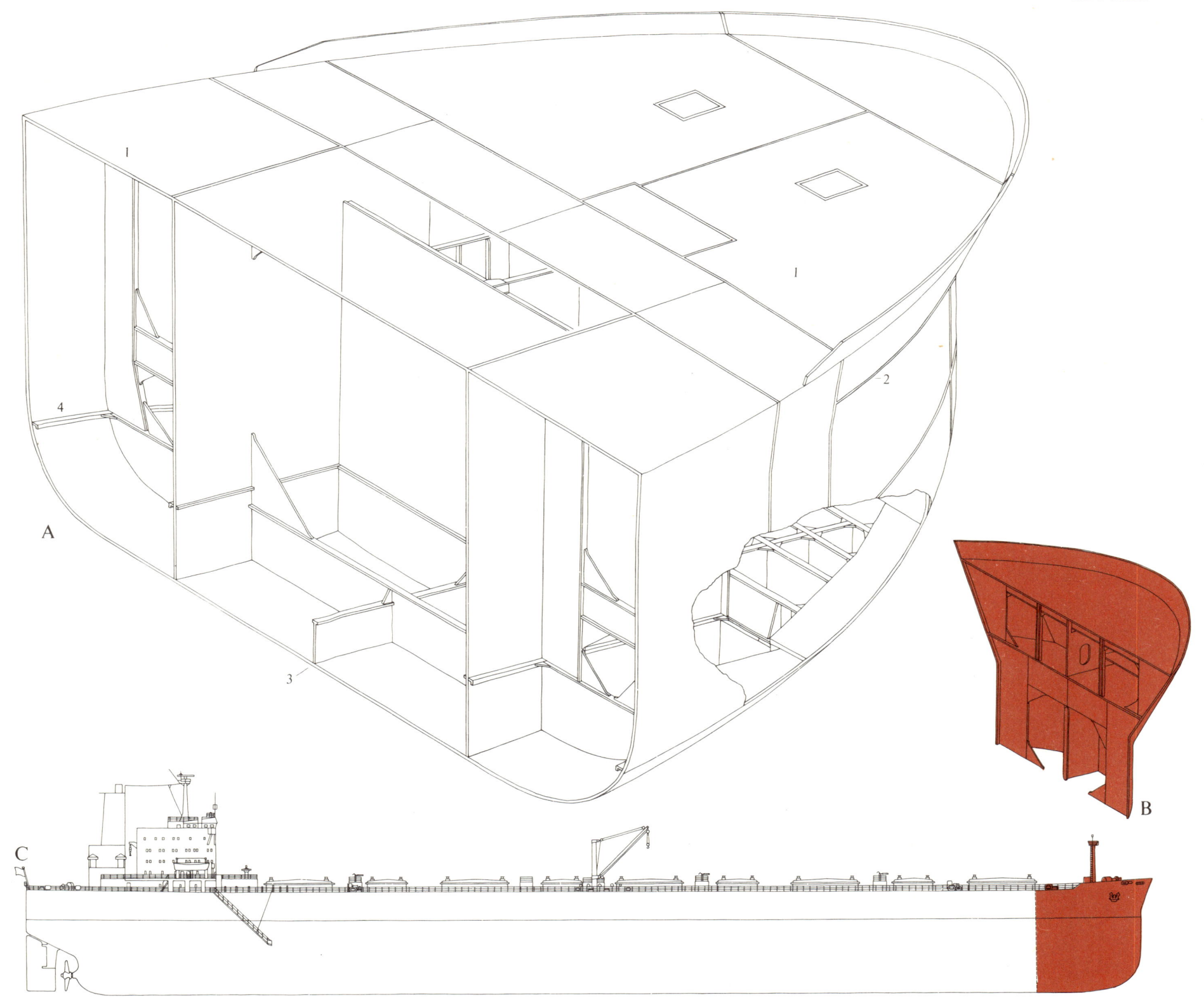

FOREBODY OF A STANDARDIZED OBO-SHIP, BUILT OF PRE-FABRICATED SECTIONS

Construction of forebody of a standardized OBO-ship of 124,000 dwt, 256.5 m (841.5 foot) long and 39 m (128 foot) in beam, built from pre-fabricated sections. The ship has a cylinder bow, which gives a slightly inferior hydrodynamic performance compared to the bulb bow, but which is easier and cheaper to build.

The forebody consists of 11 ready-made sections that are lifted into place and welded together in the construction dock. The sections range in weight from 74 to 453 tons.

A Assembled forebody with main-sections marked
1 Upper deck
2 Fore-peak roof
3 Centre line
4 Side stringer

B Foremost section with cylinder bow. Weight 96 tons

C Forebody seen from the side

IRON AND STEEL SHIPS

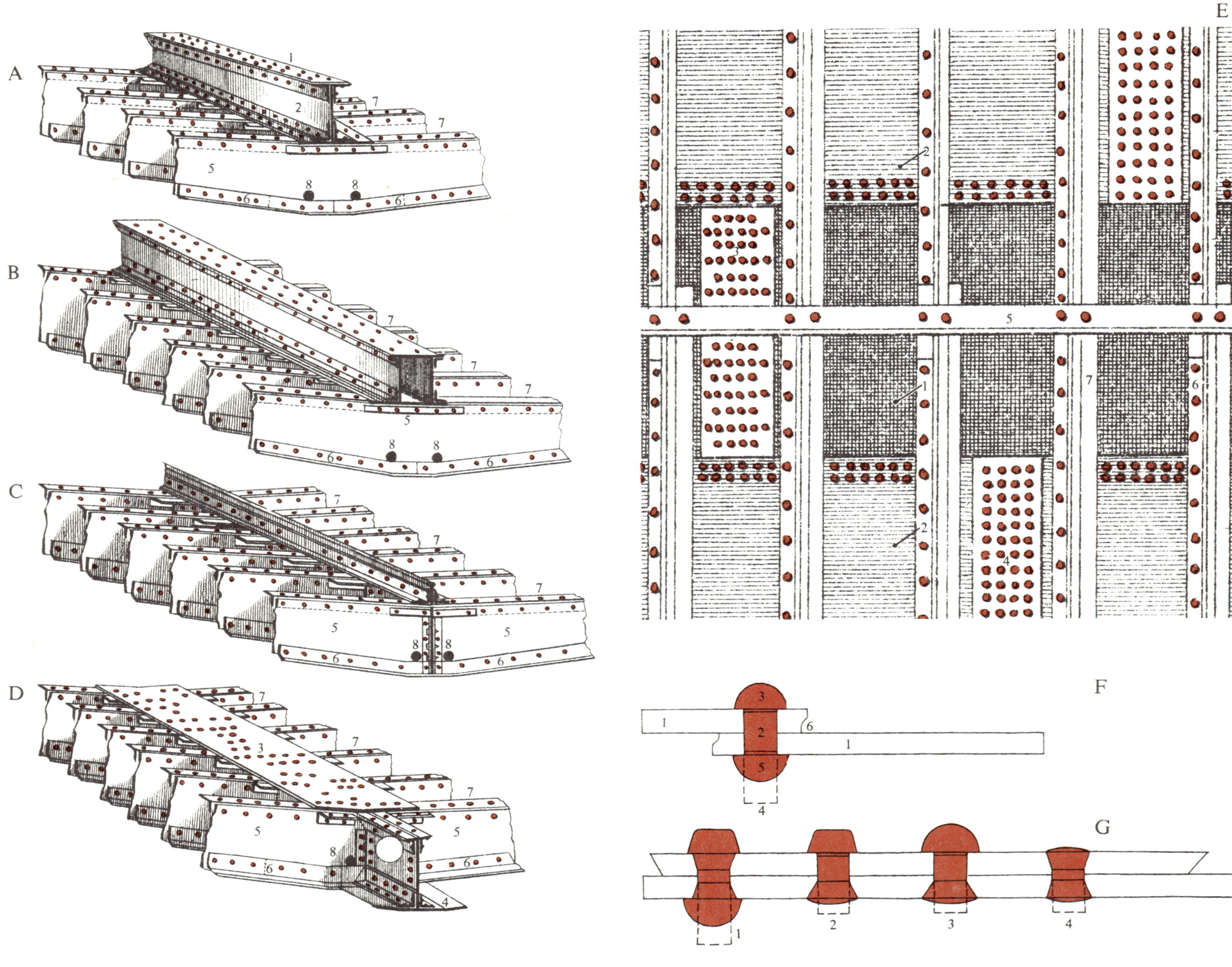

DETAILS FROM IRON AND STEEL SHIPS

- A *Single plate keelson*
- B *Box keelson*
- C *Intercostal vertical keel*
- D *Continuous vertical keel*

A—D
1. Rider plate
2. Vertical plate
3. Inner bottom center line strake
4. Flat plate keel
5. Floors
6. Frames
7. Reverse frames
8. Limber holes

E *Inside view of plating, frames, etc., of an older riveted steel ship*
1. Outside strakes
2. Inside strakes
3. Treble-riveted butt strap
4. Double-riveted butt strap
5. Angle bar stringer on top of reverse frames
6. Frames
7. Reverse frames

F *Single-riveted end lap*
1. Plate
2. Rivet
3. Snap head or button head
4. Rivet shank
5. Driven button head
6. Caulking seam

G *Various kinds of riveting*
1. Pan head, tapered rivet, button point
2. Pan head rivet, countersunk point
3. Button-headed rivet, countersunk point
4. Countersunk head and point

IRON AND STEEL SHIPS

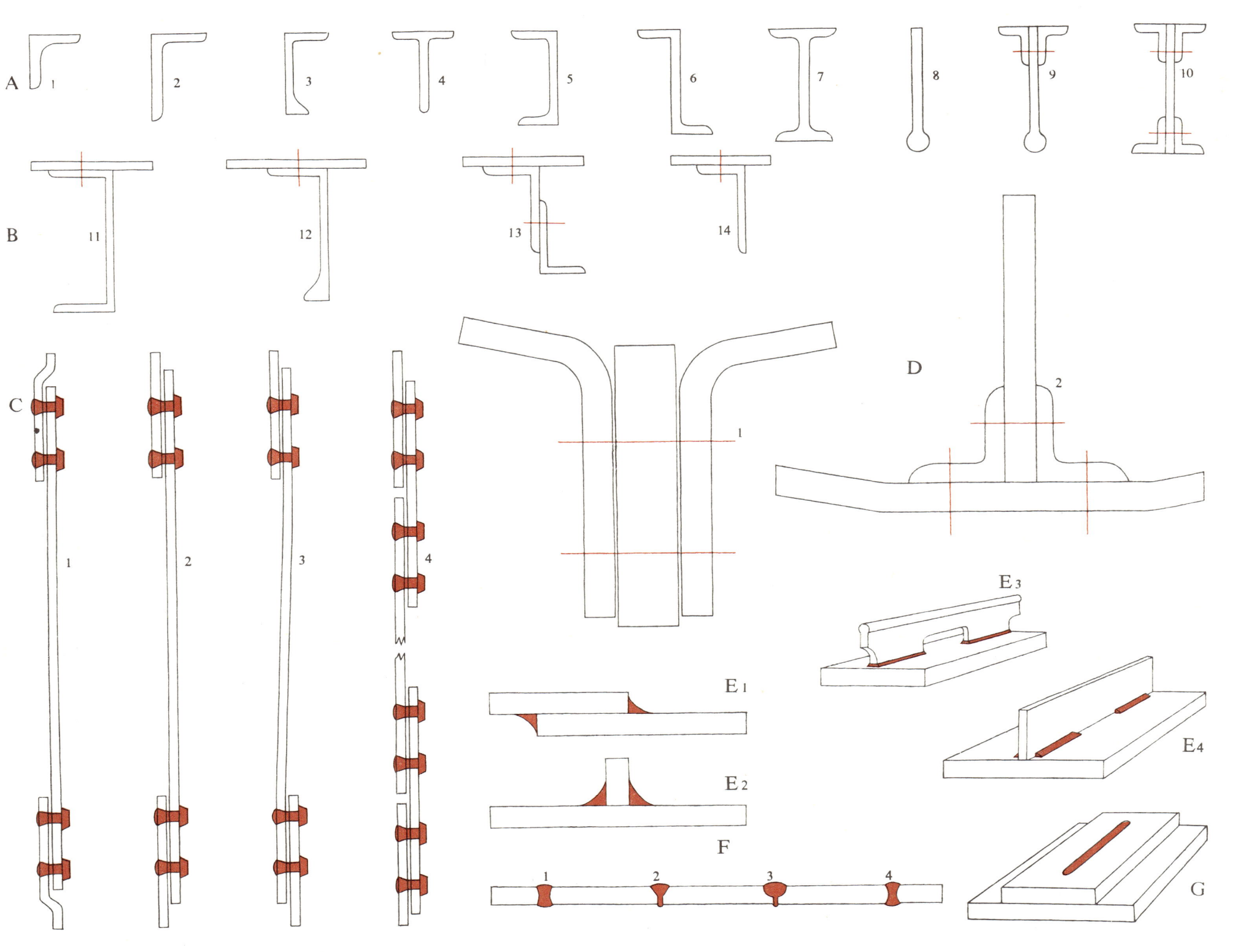

DETAILS FROM IRON AND STEEL SHIPS

- **A** *Various kinds of steel sections*
  1. Equal angle bar
  2. Unequal angle bar
  3. Bulb angle bar
  4. Tee bar
  5. Channel bar
  6. Z-bar
  7. I-beam
  8. Bulb plate
  9. Riveted section formed by two angles and a bulb plate
  10. Riveted section formed by four angles and a flat plate
- **B** *Various kinds of riveted frames*
  11. Channel
  12. Bulb angle
  13. Two angles
  14. Angle
- **C** *Various kinds of riveting in plating*
  1. Joggled outside strakes and flat inside strakes
  2. Inside and outside strakes without joggling
  3. Clinker built
  4. Carvel built
- **D** *Various kinds of keels*
  1. Bar keel
  2. Flat plate keel
- **E** *Fillet welds*
  1. Lap joint
  2. T-connection
  3. Double continuous weld with scalloped frame
  4. Intermittent fillet weld
- **F** *Butt welds*
  1. Square weld with gap
  2. V-weld without gap
  3. U-weld
  4. X-weld
- **G** *Slot weld*

FRIGATE OF 1768

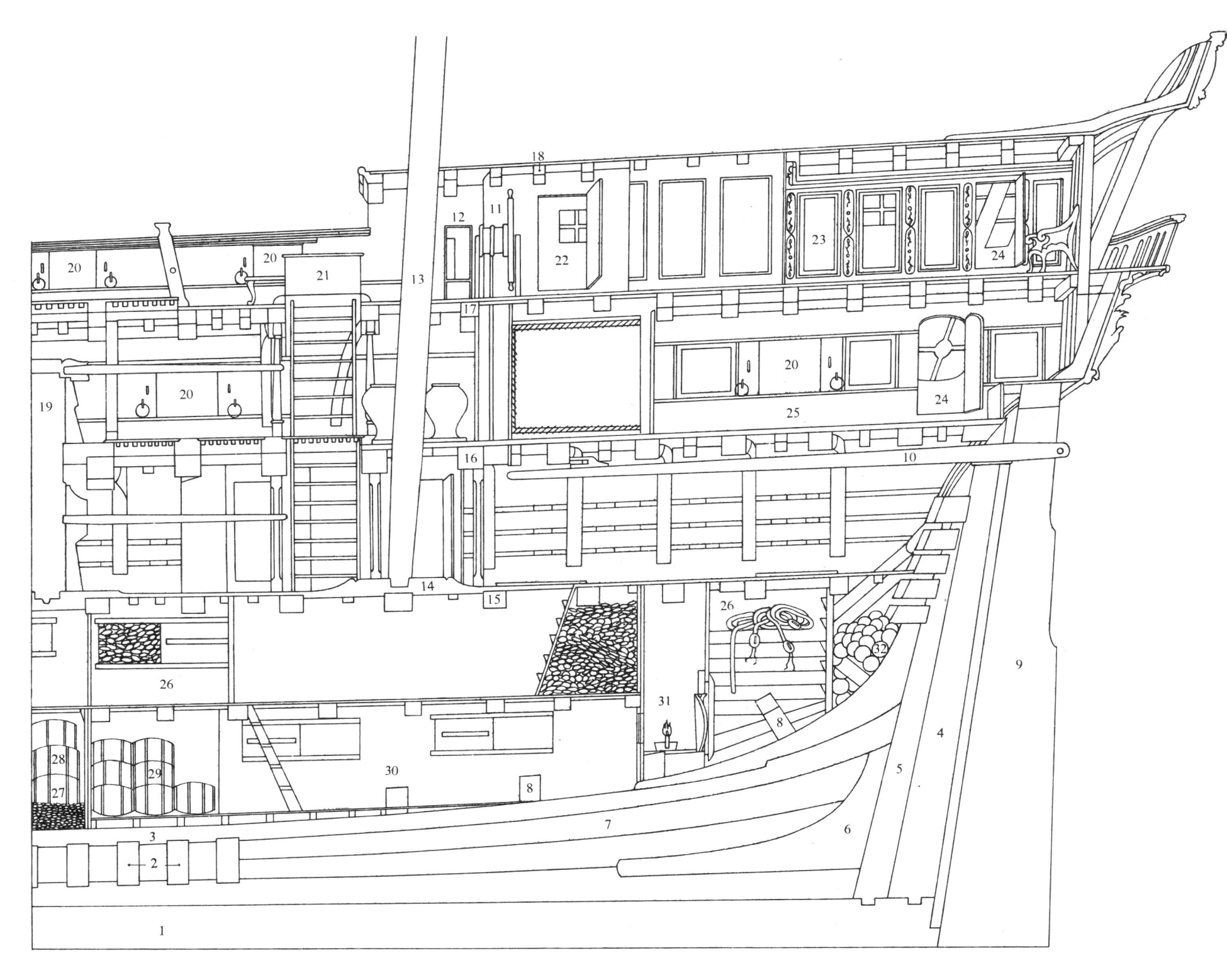

LONGITUDINAL SECTION OF THE AFTERBODY OF A 40-GUN FRIGATE, 1768

1 Keel	7 Deadwood	12 Binnacle	18 Poop deck beams	24 Doorway to quarter gallery	29 Salt meat
2 Floors	8 Crutches	13 Mizzenmast	19 Main capstan	25 Wardroom	30 Powder room
3 Keelson	9 Rudder	14 Mast step	20 Gunports	26 Storerooms	31 Lantern for powder room
4 Sternpost	10 Tiller	15 Orlop deck beams	21 Companion hood	27 Ballast	32 Shot locker
5 Inner post	11 Wheel	16 Gun deck beams	22 Officer's room	28 Water, beer casks	
6 Stern knee		17 Upper deck beams	23 Great cabin		

THREE-MASTED BARK

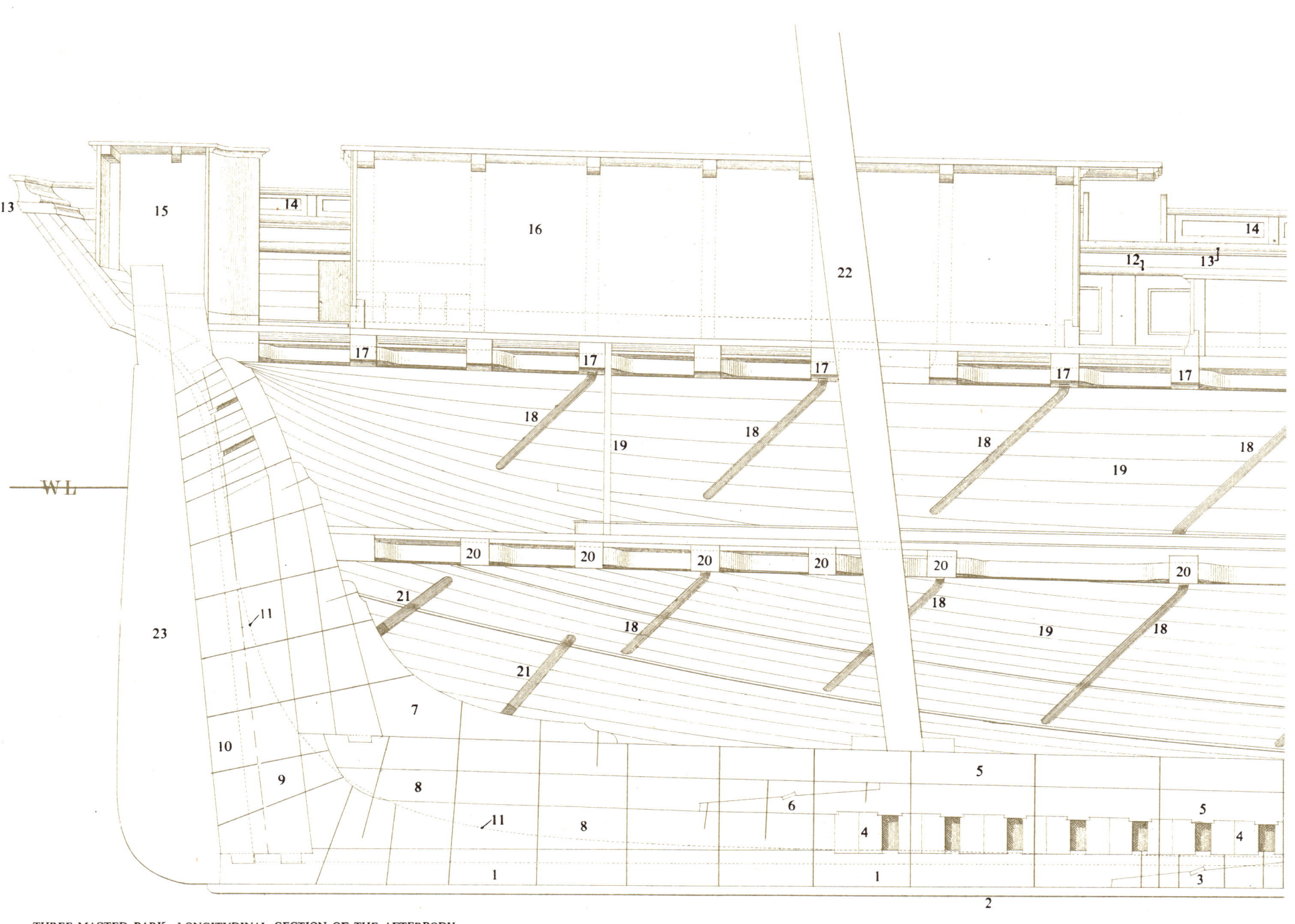

THREE-MASTED BARK, LONGITUDINAL SECTION OF THE AFTERBODY

1. Keel
2. False keel or shoe
3. Keel scarf
4. Floor
5. Keelson
6. Keelson scarf
7. Stern knee
8. After deadwood
9. Inner post
10. Sternpost
11. Bearding line
12. Pinrail
13. Main rail
14. Topgallant bulwark
15. Lamp locker, round-house
16. Cabin house
17. Main deck beams
18. Diagonal deck beam hanging knees
19. Ceiling
20. Tween deck beams
21. Crutches
22. Mizzenmast
23. Rudder

41

RUDDERS

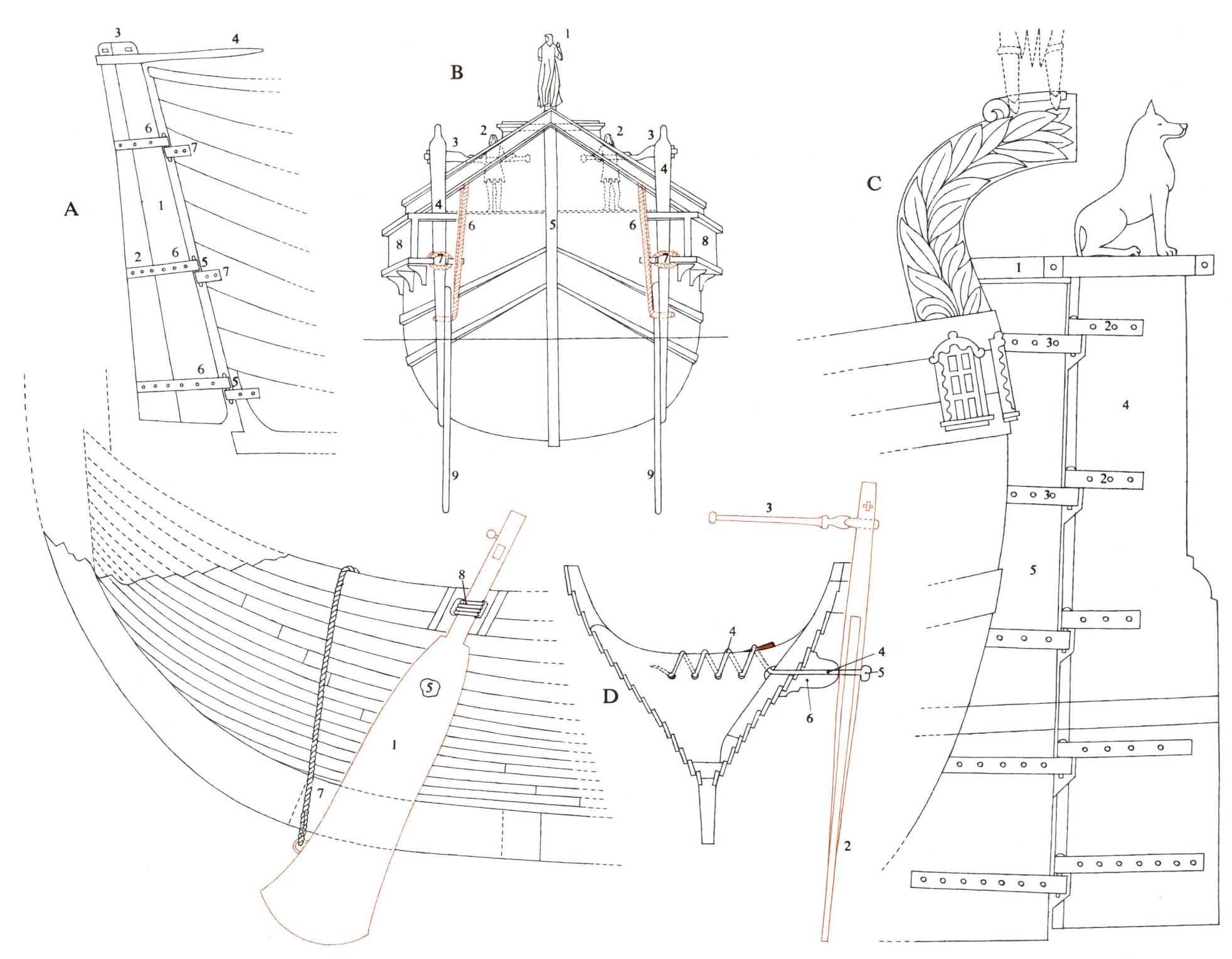

ANCIENT RUDDERS

A *Rudder of small medieval ship*
1. Main piece of rudder
2. Back piece
3. Head
4. Tiller
5. Pintles
6. Pintle straps
7. Gudgeon straps

B *Rudder arrangement in a Roman merchant ship about A.D. 200*
1. Stern ornament
2. Helmsmen
3. Tillers
4. Rudder stock
5. Sternpost
6. Carrying ropes
7. Lashing
8. Balcony
9. Rudder blade

C *Rudder of a Dutch fleut, middle of 17th century*
1. Tiller
2. Pintle straps
3. Rudder braces or gudgeon straps
4. Rudder blade
5. Sternpost

D *Rudder arrangement in the Viking era about A.D. 850 (Gokstad ship)*
1. Broadside view of steering oar
2. Stern view of steering oar
3. Tiller
4. Rudder rope
5. Knot
6. "Wart"
7. Tilting rope
8. Collar

42

RUDDERS

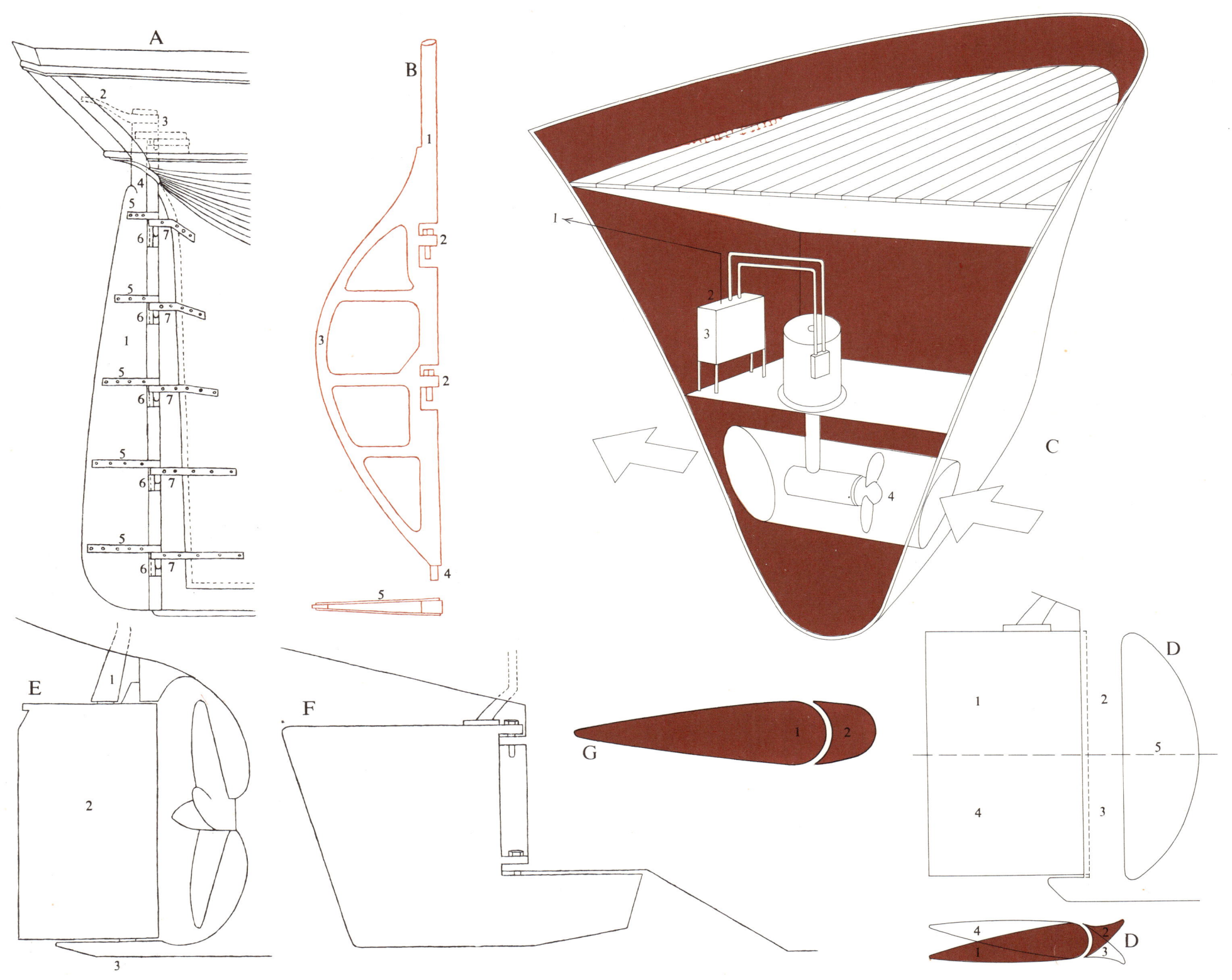

RUDDERS

A *Rudder in a wooden sailing ship*
1. Rudder blade
2. Tiller
3. Rudder head
4. Rudder stock
5. Pintle straps
6. Pintles
7. Gudgeon straps

B *Iron rudder*
1. Stock of rudder
2. Pintles
3. Rudder frame
4. Heel pintle
5. Rudder plate

C *The principle behind the steering screw in the bow-tunnel (bow-thruster)*
1. Bridge instrument and controls
2. Power-maintenance (current)
3. Junction-box
4. Propeller

D *Contra-guide rudder*
1. Rudder above shaft line
2. Sternpost above shaft line
3. Sternpost below shaft line
4. Rudder below shaft line
5. Shaft line

E *Balanced rudder*
1. Stock
2. Rudder
3. Heel of keel

F *Balanced rudder in a twin-screw ship*

G *Oertz rudder*
1. Rudder
2. Sternpost

43

OLD IRON STEAMER

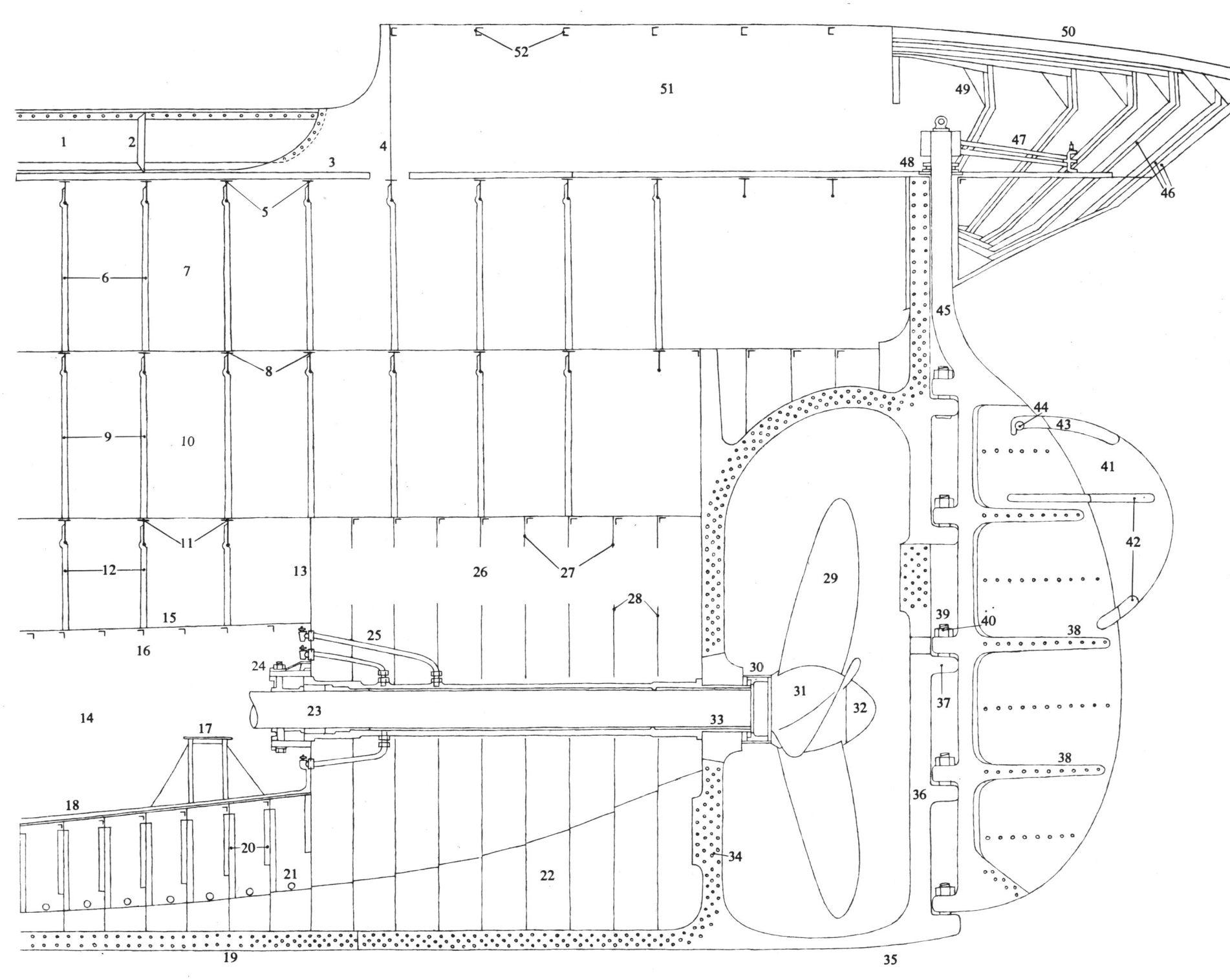

LONGITUDINAL SECTION OF STERN OF AN OLD IRON STEAMER

1. Bulwark
2. Bulwark stanchion
3. Main deck
4. Poop bulkhead
5. Deck beams
6. Deck pillars
7. Tween deck
8. Deck beams
9. Deck pillars
10. Lower deck
11. Deck beams
12. Deck pillars
13. Afterpeak bulkhead
14. Shaft tunnel or shaft alley
15. Top of shaft tunnel
16. Stiffeners on shaft alley top
17. Pedestal of shaft bearing
18. Tank top
19. Bar keel
20. Floors
21. Limber hole
22. Cement filling
23. Propeller shaft
24. Stuffing box
25. Water outlet pipe
26. Afterpeak tank
27. Beams
28. Deep floors
29. Propeller blade
30. Rope guard
31. Propeller boss
32. Propeller nut cap
33. Stern bearing
34. Sternpost
35. Sole piece
36. Rudder post
37. Gudgeon
38. Rudder arms
39. Pintle
40. Nut
41. Portable section for better steering in restricted waters
42. Stiffeners
43. Connecting strap
44. Bolt
45. Rudder stock
46. Cant frames at stern
47. Rudder quadrant
48. Rudder stock stuffing box
49. Brackets
50. Deck beams of whaleback
51. Poop
52. Deck beams

ALL-WELDED SHIP

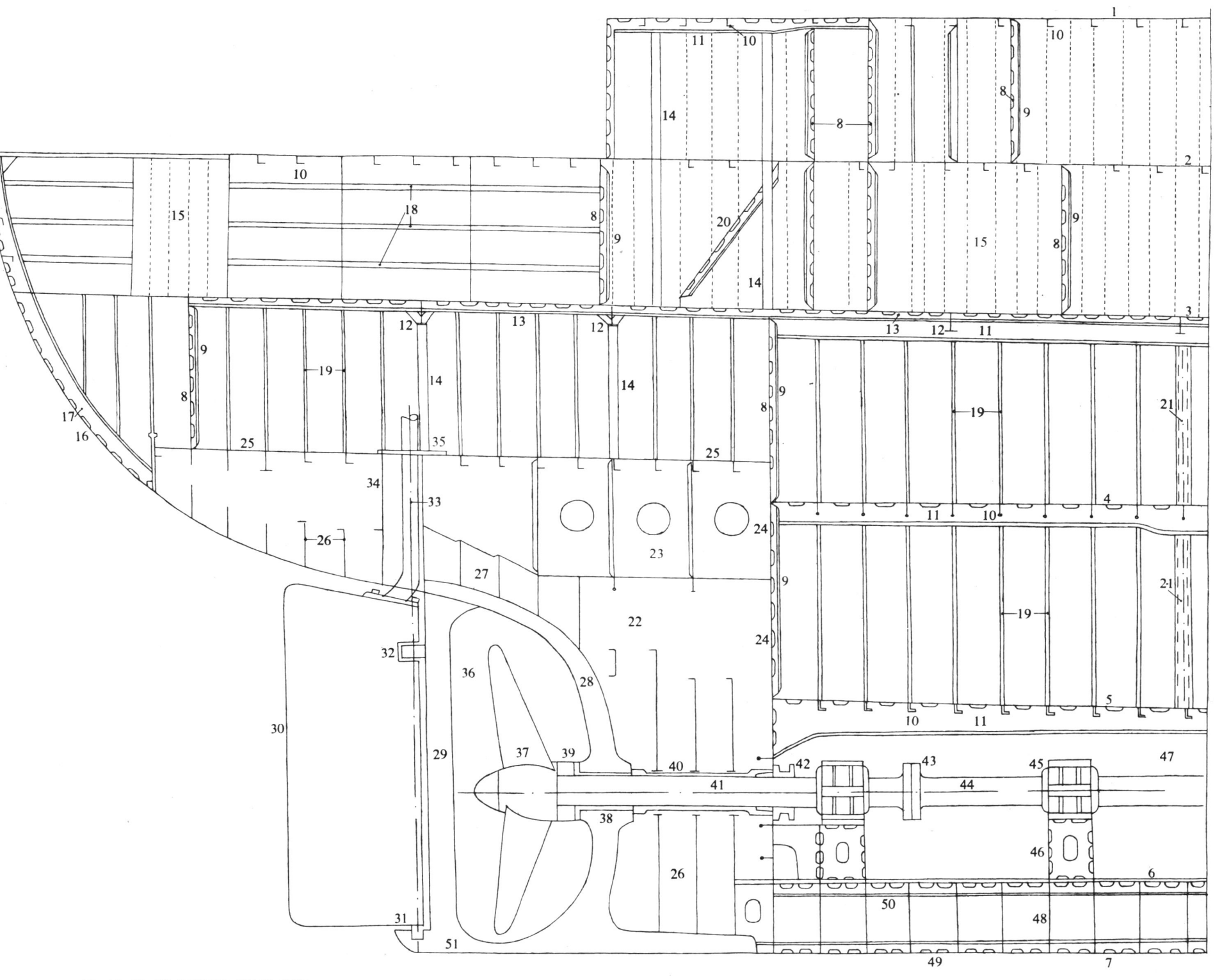

AFTER END OF AN ALL-WELDED CARGO SHIP

1. Boat deck
2. Poop deck
3. Shelter deck
4. Main deck
5. Top of shaft alley
6. Tank top
7. Bottom plating
8. Bulkhead
9. Bulkhead stiffener
10. Transverse deck beams
11. Longitudinal deck girder
12. Transverse deck web
13. Deck longitudinal
14. Pillars or stanchions
15. Longitudinal bulkhead
16. Cruiser stern
17. Vertical frame
18. Shell longitudinals
19. Main framing
20. Stairway
21. Hatch end pillar
22. After peak tank
23. Swash plate
24. Watertight bulkhead
25. Top of after peak tank
26. Deep floor
27. Cement filling
28. Stern post
29. Rudder post
30. Rudder
31. Pintle
32. Gudgeon
33. Rudder stock
34. Rudder stock trunk
35. Stuffing box
36. Propeller aperture
37. Propeller
38. Stern bearing
39. Stern tube nut
40. Stern tube
41. Tail shaft
42. Shaft stuffing box
43. Coupling flanges
44. Line shaft section
45. Line shaft bearing (plummer block)
46. Bearing foundation
47. Shaft alley
48. Bottom floor
49. Bottom longitudinal
50. Tank top longitudinal
51. Heel of rudder post

45

STEERING GEARS

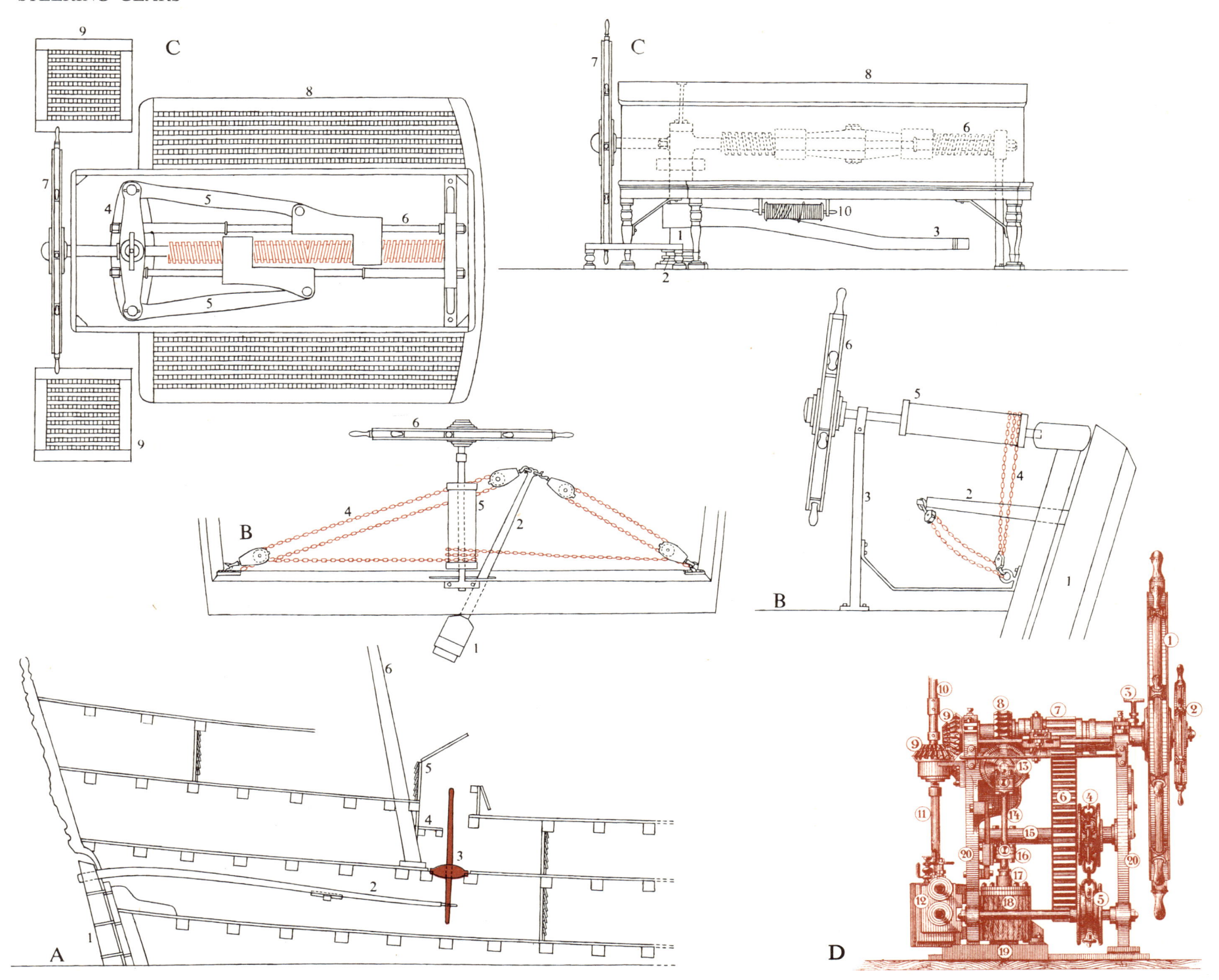

SOME STEERING GEARS

A *Steering arrangement in a big ship of the 17th century, when the rudder was controlled by a vertical lever called the whipstaff*
1. Rudder
2. Tiller
3. Whipstaff
4. Platform for the quartermaster
5. Hood for the quartermaster
6. Mizzenmast

B *Common steering gear in elevation and plan of small wooden sailing ship, 19th century*
1. Rudder
2. Tiller
3. Wheel stand
4. Tiller chain
5. Barrel or drum
6. Wheel

C *Mechanical screw steering gear in plan and elevation of big steel sailing ship, latter part of 19th century*
1. Rudder stock
2. Stuffing box on deck
3. Emergency tiller
4. Cross head
5. Coupling rods
6. Screw spindle-threaded right and left
7. Wheel
8. Wheel box with side seats
9. Wheel gratings
10. Log reel slung underneath wheel box

D *Vertical steering engine, end of last century*
1. Hand-steering wheel
2. Steam-steering wheel
3. Set-screw
4. Messenger wheel and steering chain
5. Guide pulleys
6. Spur wheel
7. Pinion
8. Scroll wheel
9. Miter wheels
10. Valve rod (to pilot bridge)
11. Valve rod
12. Valve casing
13. Crank disc
14. Connecting rod
15. Main shaft
16. Piston rod crosshead
17. Stuffing box
18. Cylinder
19. Bedplate
20. Standards

STEERING GEARS

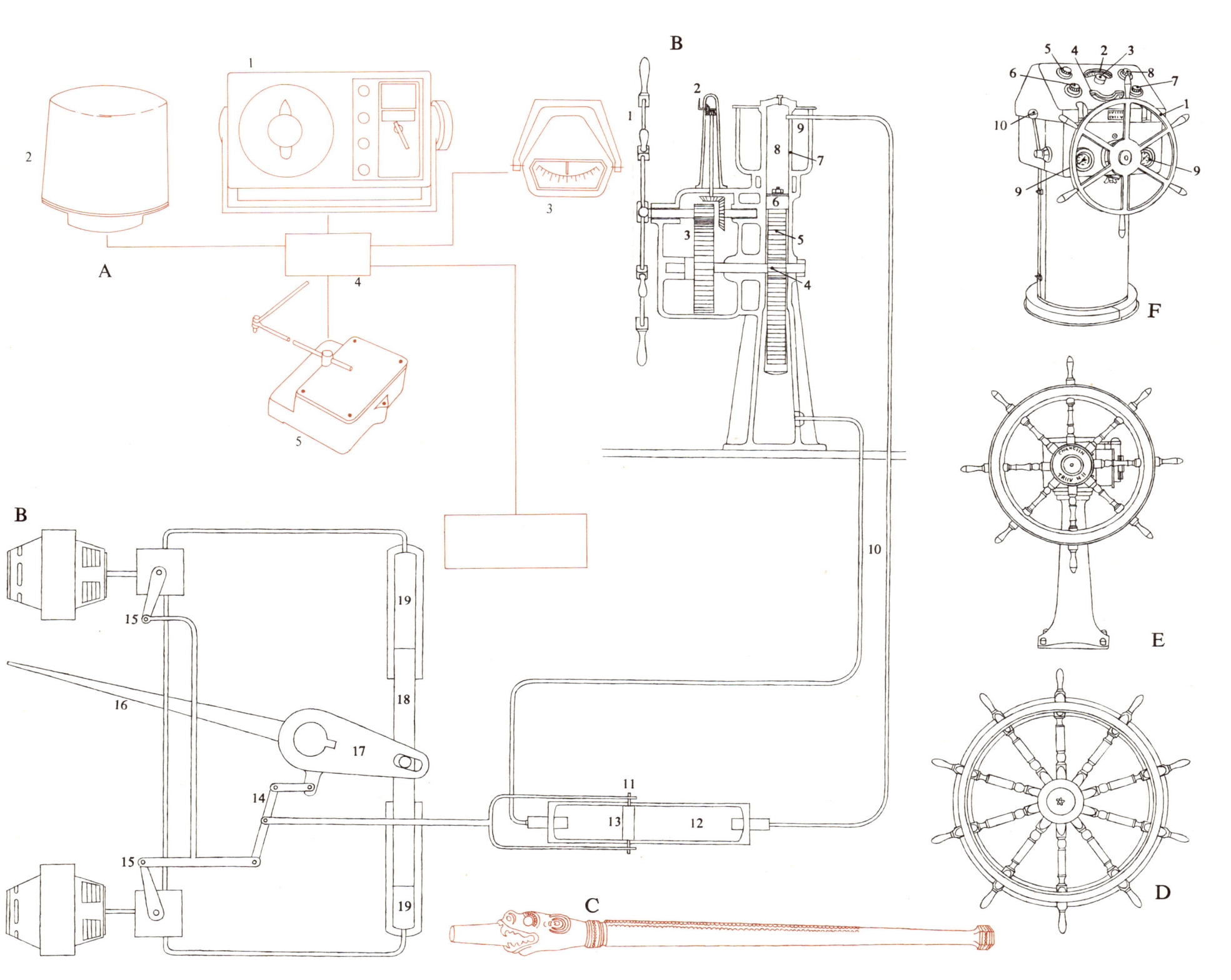

STEERING GEARS

A *Auto-pilot for coasters, tugs and larger pleasure-boats*
1 Course Setting Unit with controls for correction of course-errors, over-sheering and weather-sensibility. The latter control allows the ship to move more freely in heavy weather, before the auto-pilot corrects the course
2 Sensor
3 Helm indicator
4 Junction-box
5 Helm-follow-up linked to the rudder-stock

B *Telemotor system*
1 Steering wheel
2 Rudder position indicator
3 Gear pinion
4 Pinion
5 Rack
6 Piston
7 Cylinder
8 Fluid
9 Replenishing tank
10 Pipes to receiver
11 Receiver
12 Cylinder
13 Piston
14 Floating link
15 Pumps
16 Rudder
17 Tiller
18 Piston
19 Cylinder

C *Tiller of the Viking ship from Gokstad, ca. A.D. 900*

D *Steering wheel from sailing ship, middle of the 19th century*

E *Steering gear of steamer, beginning of the 20th century*

F *Modern gyro-hydraulic steering control*
1 Steering wheel
2 Gyrocompass repeater
3 Synchronizing knob for the repeater
4 Rudder order indicator
5 Automatic steering control weather adjustment
6 Adjustment of the angle of rudder desired, among other things dependent on the load of the ship
7 Panel lighting dimmer control
8 Course changing control
9 Hydraulic telemotor pressure gauges
10 Automatic steering off/on

STABILIZERS

STABILIZERS

A In the days of sail, ships were stabilized by the pressure of the wind on the sails

B Some very broad ships were built to reduce the rolling; this Russian royal yacht had a circular water line

C Today, many ships are equipped with stabilizers

D The stabilizers work as hydroplanes and can be turned through an arc of 50°

E The stabilizers work hydraulically on impulses from a gyroscope. In harbor, or when they are not in use, they can be housed in slots in the hull

F Automatic stabilizer-tank system operated by compressed air, controlled by a fluidistor unit. A normal 30° heeling can be reduced to 8° by this system
1. U-shaped tank with counter-weight water
2. Fluidistor unit
3. Measure vessel
4. Pendulum
5. Blowing nozzles
6. Cylinder with valve
7. Main valve for cylinder

G How the counter-weight functions when the ship heels. To the far left the ship has reached its maximum roll. The counter-weight water rushes to the lower half of the tank. As the ship rights itself, the water is locked in its last position in the tank, thus stopping the roll to the other side. The arrows on top of the picture show the heeling-direction, those at the bottom show the direction of the counter-weight's movement

FUNNELS

SOME COMMON FUNNELS

1. Furness Lines, London
2. Ellerman Lines, Ltd., London
3. Cie Générale Transatlantique, Paris
4. Blue Funnel Line, Liverpool
5. Swedish Orient Line, Gothenburg
6. A. P. Möller, Copenhagen
7. Union Castle Mail S. S. Co., Ltd., London
8. Nederland N. V. Stoomvaart Maatschappij, Amsterdam
9. Lloyd Brasileiro, Rio de Janeiro
10. Nederlandsch-Amerikaansche Stoomvaart Maatschappij, Rotterdam
11. American Export Lines, Inc., New York
12. Moore-McCormack Lines, Inc., New York
13. Keystone Shipping Co., Philadelphia
14. Italia, Società Per Azioni di Navigazione, Genoa
15. East Asiatic Co. Ltd., Copenhagen
16. Canada Steam Ship Lines, Ltd., Montreal
17. Tor Line, Gothenburg
18. Rederi Transatlantic, Gothenburg
19. AS Westfal-Larsen & Co., Bergen
20. Scindia Steam Navigation Co., Ltd., Bombay
21. Osaka Shosen Kaisha, Osaka
22. Bangladesh Shipping Corp., Dacca
23. Arctic Steamship Line, Murmansk
24. Lloyd Triestino, Società Per Azioni di Navigazione, Trieste
25. Salén Lines, Stockholm
26. AS Knut Knutsen, Haugesund
27. Seatrain Lines, New York
28. Hansa, Deutsche Dampfschiffahrts-
29. H.F. Eimskipafélag Island, Reykjavik
30. Fred Olsen & Co., Oslo (motor ships)
31. Empresa Nacional, Madrid
32. Viking Line, Mariehamn
33. Stockholms Rederi AB Svea, Stockholm
34. Hamburg—South American Line, Hamburg
35. Zim Israel Navigation Co., Ltd., Haifa
36. Finska Ångfartygs AB, Helsingfors

DECORATION

DECORATION

With most people illiterate, the name of a ship was often depicted by painted carvings on the stern, (for example A and B)

A The flower of the English hawthorn on the *Mayflower*, 1620 (from replica built in 1957)

B Stern of the Dutch pinnace *Dromedarus*, middle of the 17th century (from a model)

C Stern of the French ship *Le Soleil Royal*, built at Brest in 1669

D Head ornament of the three-masted fore-and aft schooner *Ellen* of Skärhamn, built at Thurö in 1908

E Name board of the Finnish barkentine *Ida*, wrecked on the west coast of Sweden in 1875

F Stern ornament of the three-masted fore-and aft schooner *Meta-Jan* of Skive, Denmark

DECORATION

DECORATION

A Sculptured lion's head on gun-port lid, perhaps intended to put heart in the crew and to frighten the enemy, the Swedish ship *Wasa*, 1628

B Figurehead of unknown vessel, from the middle of the 19th century

C Figurehead, from the 18th century

D Chinese junk with a painted eye on her bow, known as oculus decoration. "Suppose no eye no can see," the Chinese seamen says in his pidgin English. Such painted eyes may also be seen on fishing craft in the Mediterranean.

E Brigantine from the middle of the 19th century, with painted ports on her sides. This painting was originally intended to make the ship look like a man-of-war, but later it remained as decoration only.

F Dutch pinnace from the middle of the 17th century, with a painted waveline for a water line, to give an impression of speed. (Sketch from a model.)

51

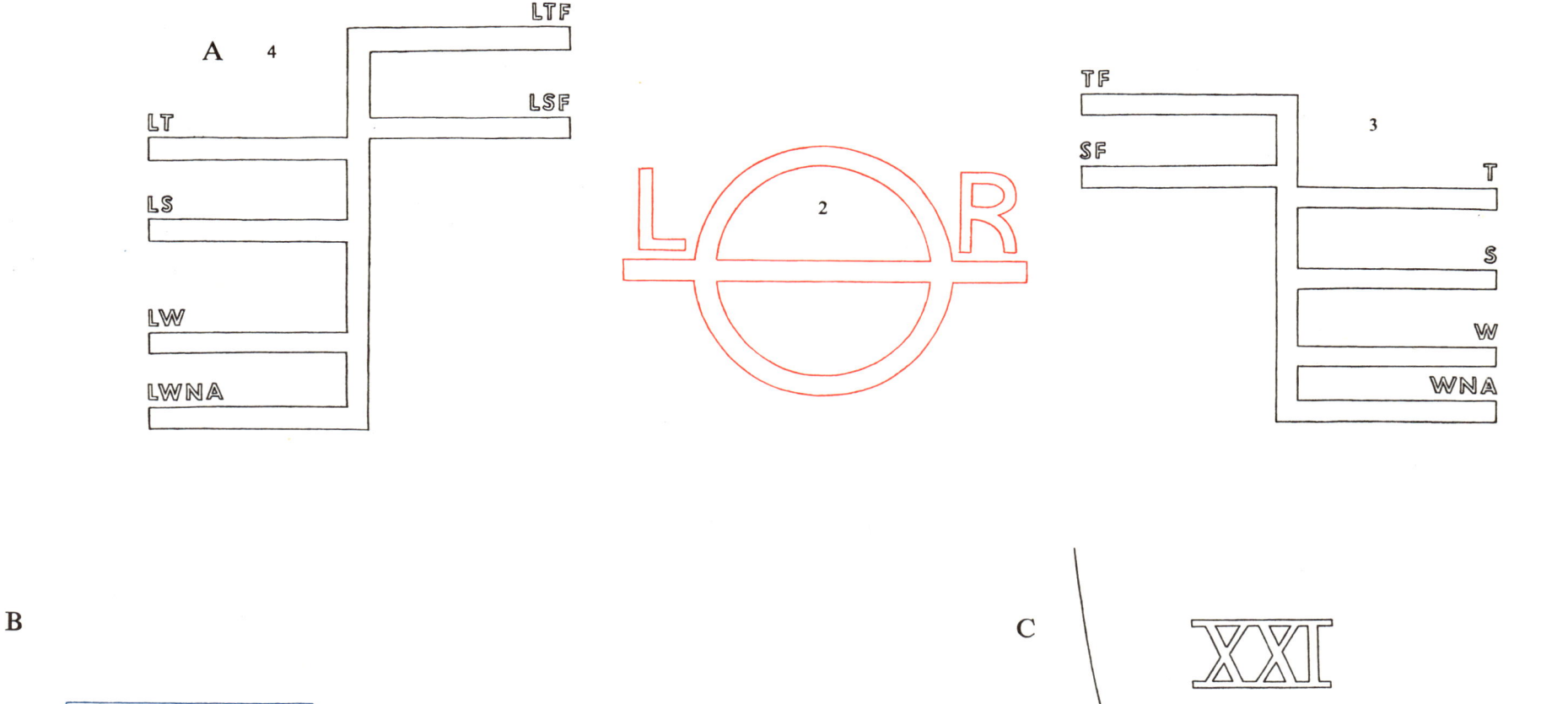

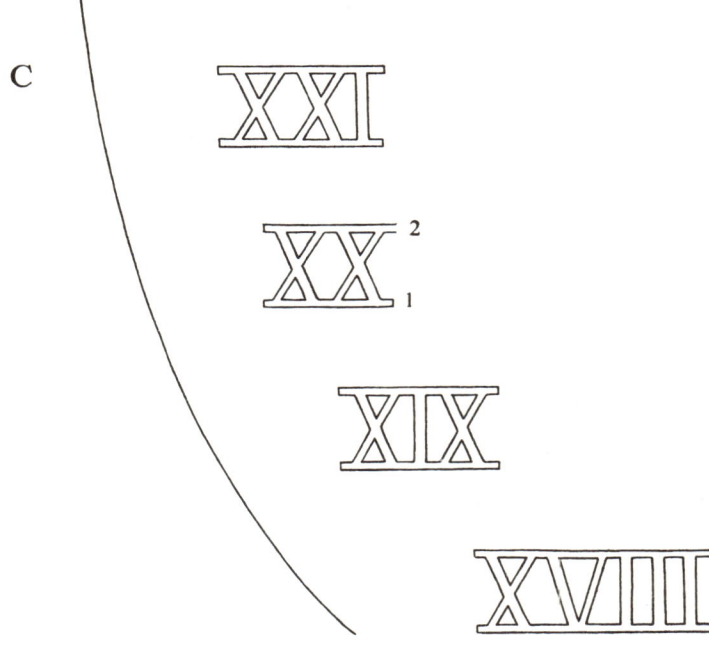

LOADLINES

LOAD LINES AND DRAFT MARKS

A *Ordinary and timber loadlines for steamships, starboard side shown*
1 Deck line
2 Loadline disc or Plimsoll mark. (The letters LR denote the classifying society, here Lloyd's Register. American ships have AB, the American Bureau of Shipping)
3 Ordinary loadlines
The letters indicate:
TF=fresh water tropical loadline
SF=fresh water summer loadline
T=salt water tropical loadline
S=salt water summer loadline
W=salt water winter loadline
WNA=winter North Atlantic loadline
4 When loaded with timber (lumber) and with a deck cargo, the ship may be loaded somewhat deeper, and the timber loadlines are shown abaft the disc
The letters indicate:
LTF=fresh water tropical timber loadline
LSF=fresh water summer timber loadline
LT=salt water tropical timber loadline
LS=salt water summer timber loadline
LW=salt water winter timber loadline
LWNA=winter North Atlantic timber loadline

B *Loadlines of a sailing vessel are not so complicated*
1 Deck line
2 Loadline disc or Plimsoll mark (The horizontal bar across the disc gives summer loadline in salt water)
The letters indicate:
F=fresh water loadline
WNA=winter North Atlantic loadline

C *Draft marks*
The draft of ships is measured in feet and marked in six-inch-high Roman figures in such a way that 1 in the diagram indicates 20 feet, 2 indicates 20 feet 6 inches, and so on

TYPES OF HULLS

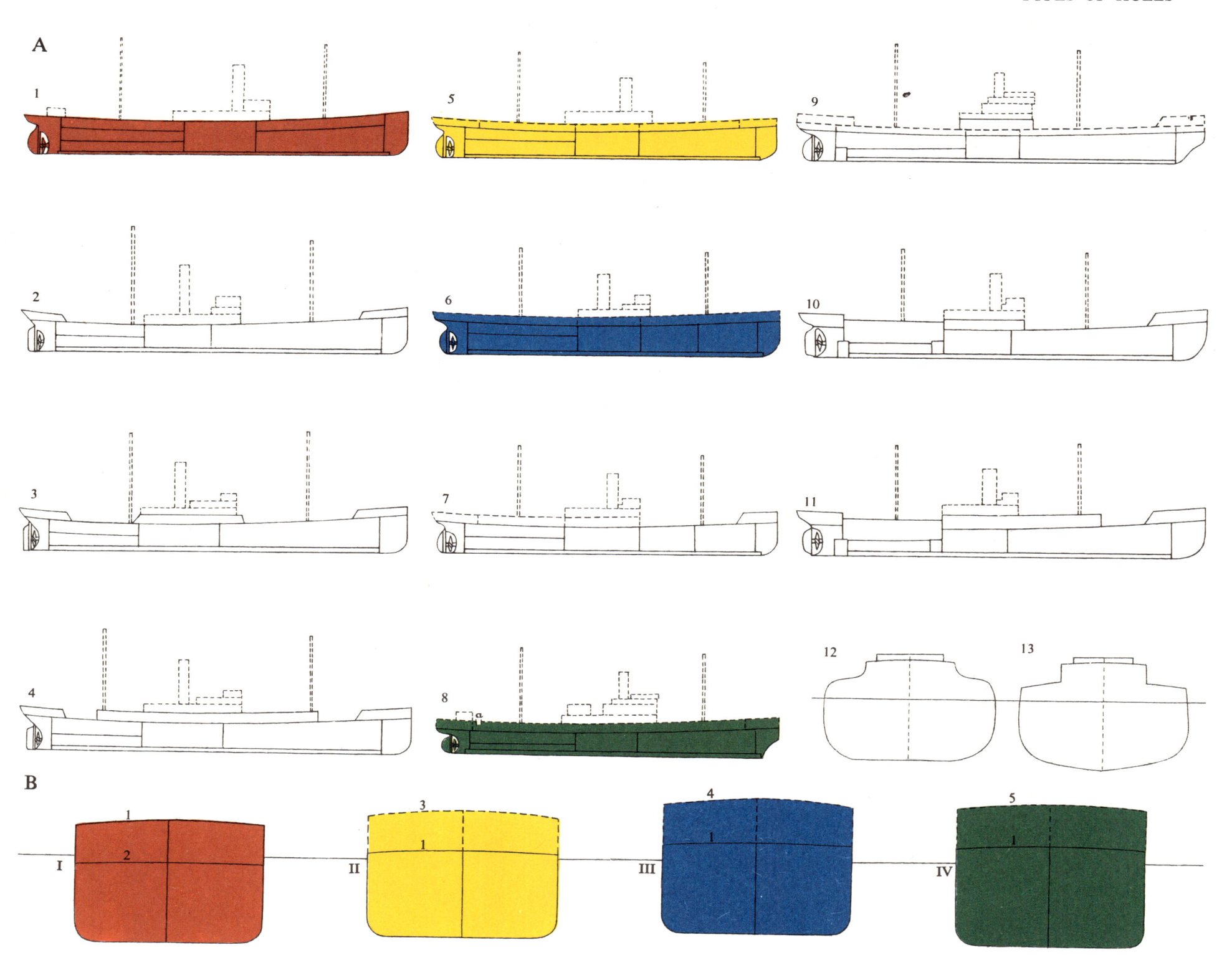

DIFFERENT TYPES OF HULLS (BROKEN LINES INDICATE LIGHTER MATERIAL)

A
1. Flush-decked ship with two decks
2. Vessel with fo'c'sle and poop
3. Three-Island vessel (The reason for this name is the appearance of the ship when she is hull down on the horizon)
4. Vessel with extended bridge, fo'c'sle head, and poop
5. Spar-decked vessel (This type had lighter material above the main deck and, consequently, had to be given a lighter draft when loaded. Only passengers and lighter cargo could be carried under the spar deck)
6. Awning-decked vessel (It has a very light superstructure above the main deck and, so, has a high free board)
7. Well-decked vessel has the upper deckline broken, forming a well down to the main deck
8. Open shelter-decked vessel (This type has a tonnage opening (a) in the shelter deck which must not be permanently closed; the space above the main deck is not included in the gross tonnage)
9. Closed shelter-decked vessel has no tonnage opening; by a slight increase of scantlings the vessel may be loaded deeper
10. Raised quarter-deck vessel (This type was constructed to compensate for the loss of space caused by the propeller shaft tunnel)
11. Raised quarter-deck vessel with extended bridge
12. Turret vessel, no longer built
13. Trunk vessel

B *Different free boards*
I. Full scantling ship
II. Spar-decked ship
III. Awning-decked ship
IV. Shelter-decked ship
1. Main deck
2. Tween deck
3. Spar deck
4. Awning deck
5. Shelter deck

53

ANCHORS

ANCHORS

A *Common anchor*
1 Anchor ring
2 Stock
3 Hoops of the anchor stock
4 Shank
5 Crown
6 Arm
7 Fluke
8 Pea or bill

B *Part of tree trunk with branches, used as an anchor*

C *Anchor, made from tree branches and stone*

D *Roman anchor of Caligula from Lake Nemi*

E *Viking anchor from the Oseberg ship*

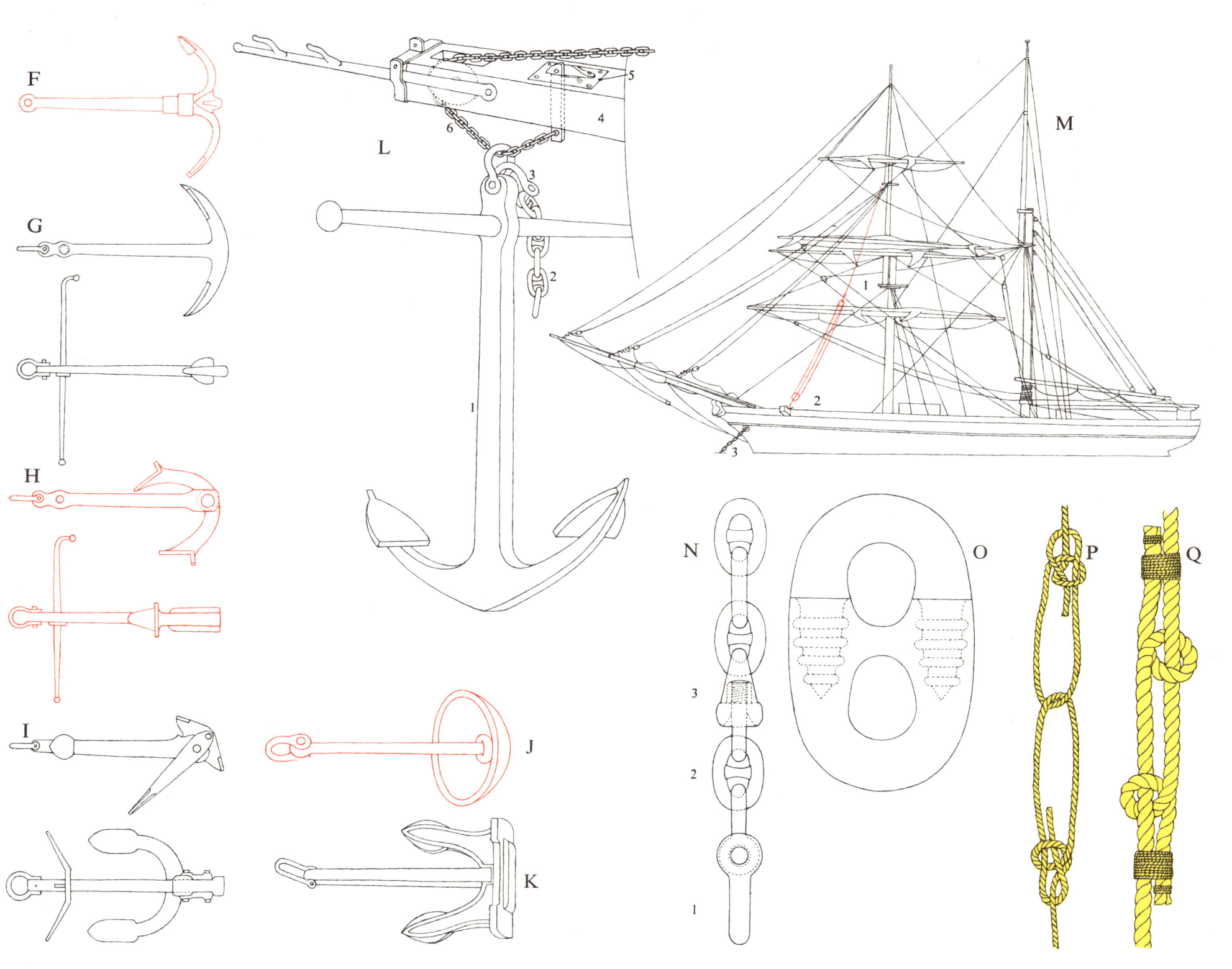

ANCHORS

ANCHORS AND ANCHOR GEAR

F Grapnel
G Iron-stocked anchor
H Trotman's anchor
I Inglefield's anchor
J Mushroom anchor
K Hall's anchor

L Cathead with anchor gear
  1 Anchor
  2 Cable
  3 Shackle
  4 Cathead
  5 Releasing gear
  6 Cathead stopper

M Arrangement for fishing an anchor
  1 Pendant with fish tackle
  2 Cathead
  3 Chain cable

N Chain cable
  1 Shackle
  2 Stud link
  3 Swivel

O Patent link
P, Q Hawser bends

55

WINDLASS AND CAPSTAN

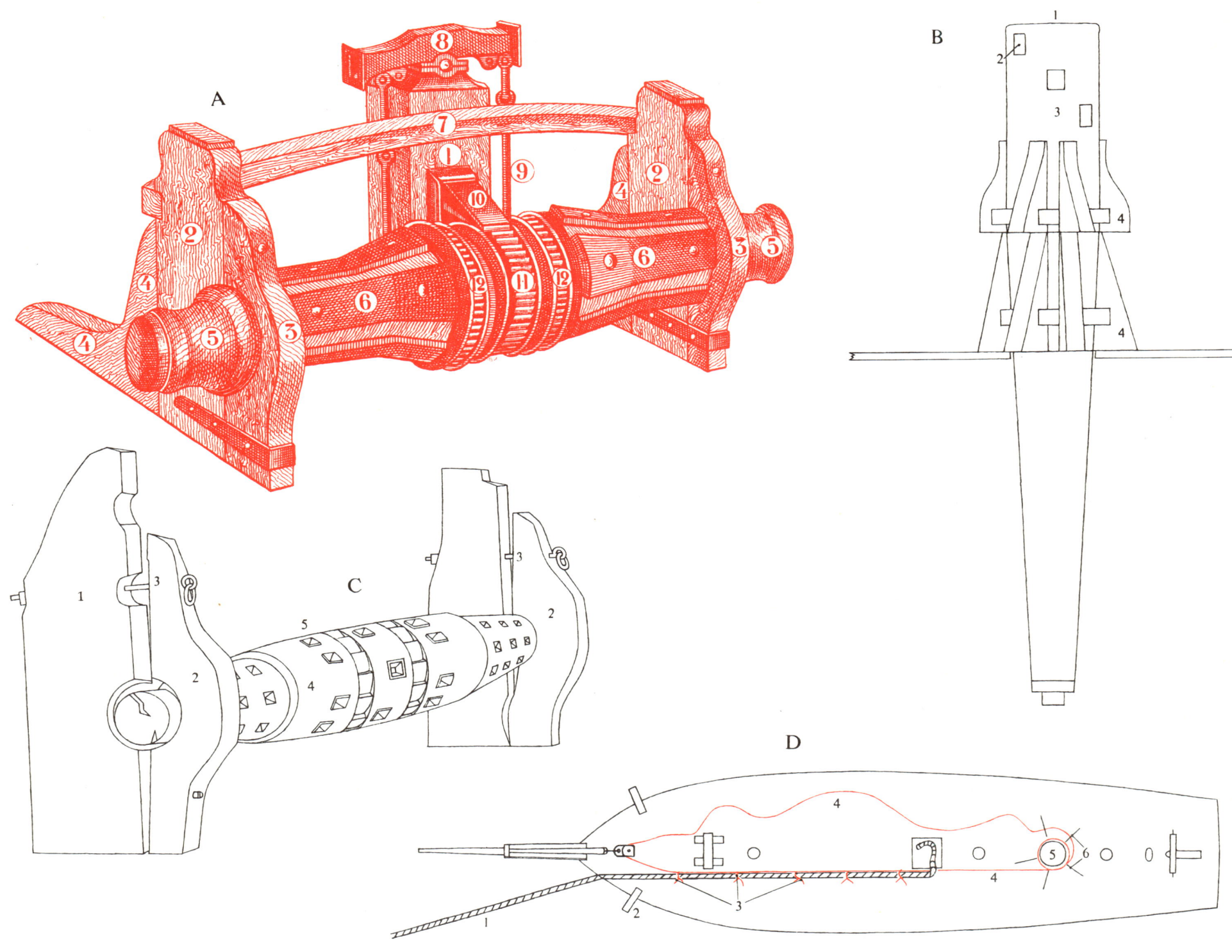

WINDLASS AND CAPSTAN

A *Windlass*
1 Pawl bitt
2 Windlass bitts
3 Cheeks of windlass bitts
4 Standard knees
5 Warping heads
6 Windlass barrel with whelps
7 Strongback
8 Crosshead
9 Purchase rod
10 Pawl
11 Pawl rim
12 Purchase rims

B *Capstan*
1 Head
2 Bar holes
3 Barrel
4 Whelps

C *Old windlass*
1 Windlass bitt
2 Cheek of windlass bitts
3 Bolts
4 Windlass barrel
5 Bar holes

D *Method of heaving anchor with a messenger*
1 Cable
2 Cathead
3 Nippers
4 Messenger (an endless rope)
5 Capstan
6 Capstan bars

WINDLASS AND CAPSTAN

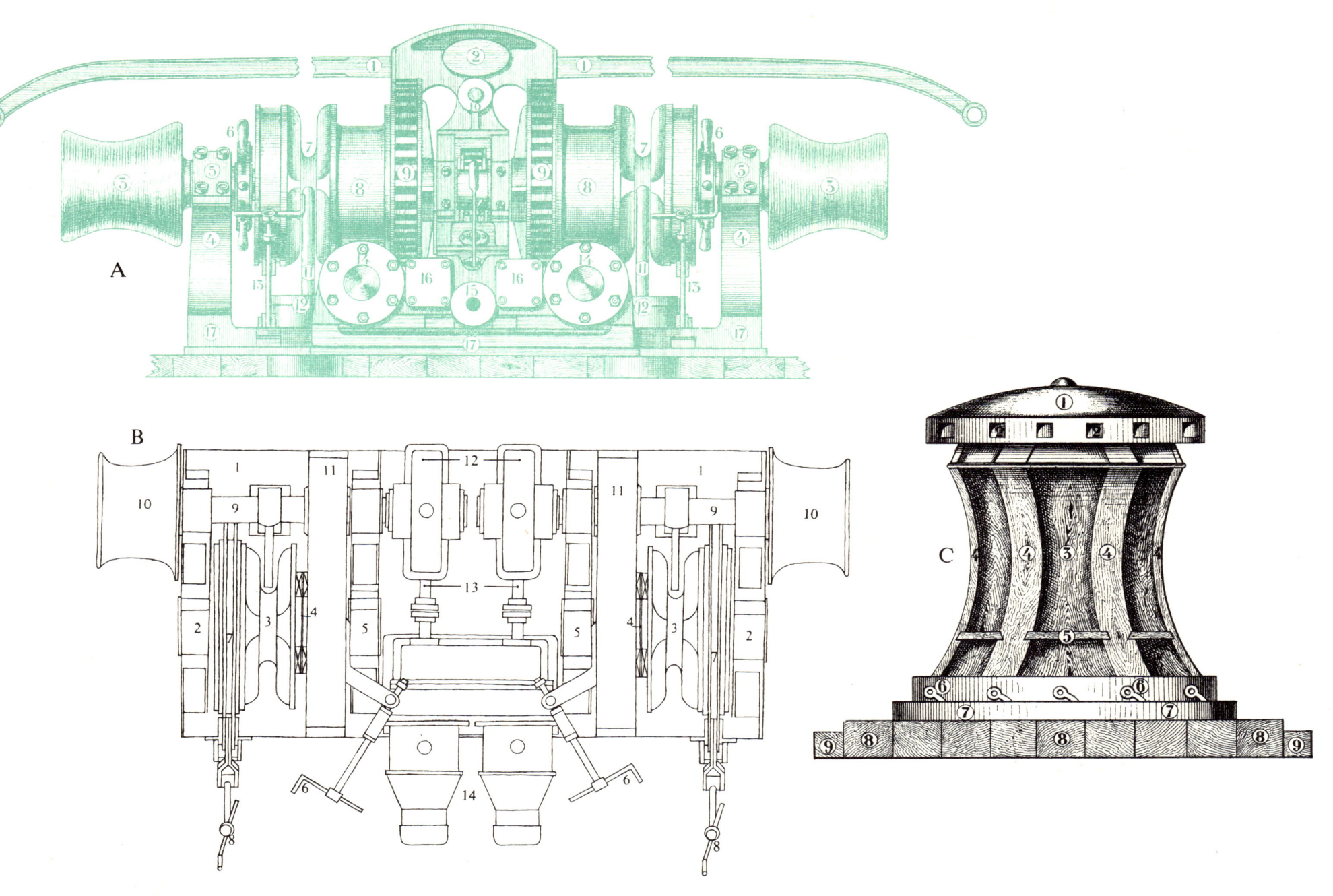

WINDLASSES AND CAPSTANS

A *Patent steam windlass*
1. Levers, hand-power levers
2. Crosshead
3. Warping heads
4. Side bitts
5. Bearing caps
6. Screwbrake nuts
7. Wildcats (Gypsies)
8. Windlass barrel or drum
9. Main cone driving wheels
10. Crosshead bracket
11. Cable relievers
12. Chain pipes
13. Bandbrakes
14. Cylinders
15. Steampipe flange
16. Valve casings
17. Bedplate

B *Electric windlass*
1. Bedplate
2. Side bitts
3. Wildcats (Gypsies)
4. Toothwheels
5. Operating clutches
6. Operating handles
7. Brakes
8. Brake handles
9. Pinion shafts
10. Warping heads
11. Gear coupling
12. Worm gears
13. Driving shafts
14. Electric motors

C *Capstan*
1. Drumhead
2. Capstan-bar holes
3. Barrel
4. Whelps
5. Whelp chocks
6. Pawls
7. Pawl rim
8. Capstan partners
9. Deck planking

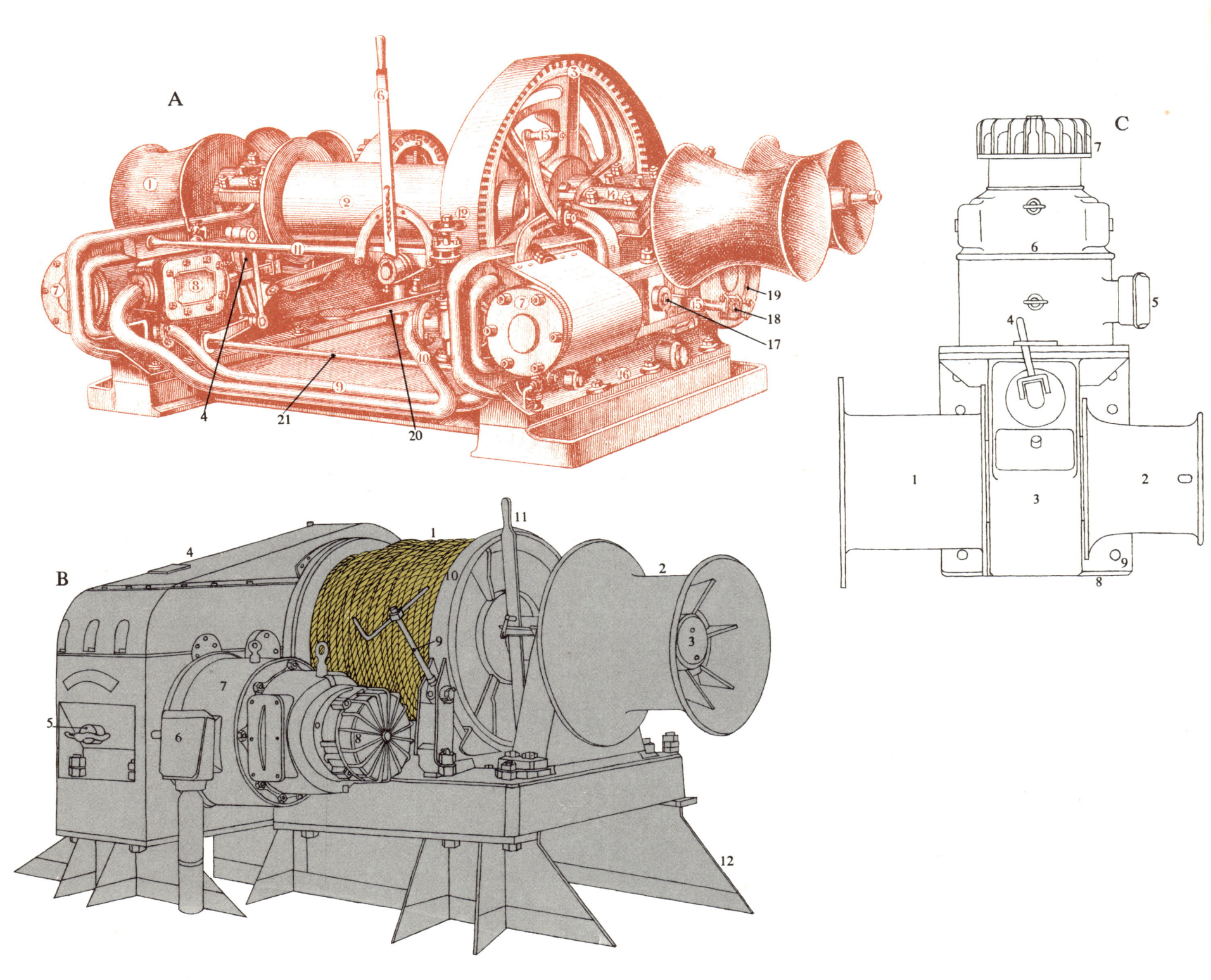

WINCHES

A *Steam winch*
1. Warping heads or gypsy heads
2. Winch drum
3. Main cogwheel
4. Reversing link
5. Pinion shaft cogwheel
6. Clutch lever
7. Cylinders
8. Slide-valve box
9. Steam exhaust pipe
10. Inlet steampipe
11. Tie rod, stay
12. Throttle valve
13. Reversing lever
14. Drum shaft bearing
15. Connecting rod
16. Bedplate
17. Piston rod and crosshead
18. Crank pin
19. Combined gear- and flywheel
20. Strap-brake pedal
21. Weigh shaft

B *15/5 ton automatic or constant-tension mooring winch*
1. Winch drum
2. Warping head
3. Drum shaft
4. Gear casing
5. Gear lever, 5 or 15 tons
6. Electric coupling box
7. Electric driving motor
8. Lamina brake
9. Strap-brake tightening screw
10. Strap-brake
11. Warping head coupling handle
12. Foundation

C *Worm-geared vertical cargo winch*
1. Winch drum
2. Warping head
3. Worm-gear house
4. Gear lever, 2 or 5 tons
5. Electric coupling box
6. Electric motor (vertical shaft)
7. Lamina brake
8. Bedplate
9. Foundation

BELLS AND WHISTLES

BELLS, HOURGLASS, AND WHISTLES

A A little bell placed aft, on which the helmsman struck the time, and which was repeated by the lookout at the main bell

B A bell hanging in a belfry, Nelson's *Victory*

C Hourglass, measuring half an hour. Each glass on board accounts for half an hour, and is sounded by one stroke of the bell; each watch of four hours is divided into eight glasses, corresponding to eight bells. The six watches are: the 1st watch 20—24, the 2nd watch (middle watch) 00—04, the day watch (morning watch) 04—08, the forenoon watch 08—12, the noon watch 12—16, and the afternoon watch 16—20. Three bells thus mean that the time is 01.30, 05.30, 09.30, 13.30, 17.30, or 21.30.
Eight bells mean that a watch is over. The number of glasses is struck on the bell as a series of double strokes. For instance, 15.30 (seven glasses):
+ + + + + + +
Eight bells mean a watch is over

D Boatswain's call

E Fog horn made from a bullock's horn

F Fog horn of copper

G Sirens and whistles

1 Siren
2 Bell whistle
3 Chime whistle
4 Organ pipe whistle

ACCOMMODATIONS

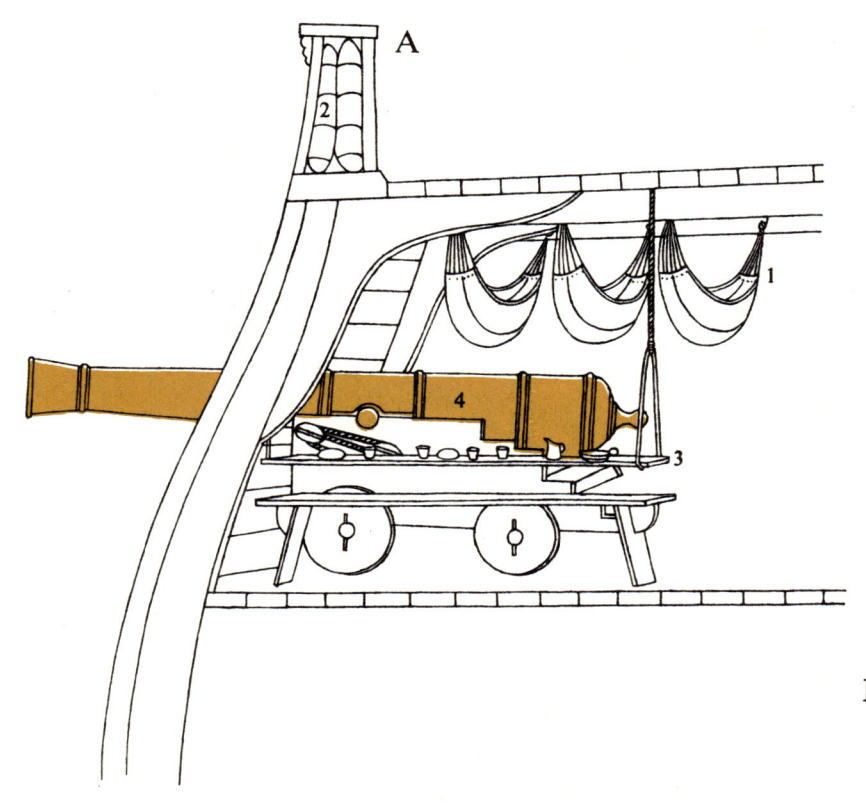

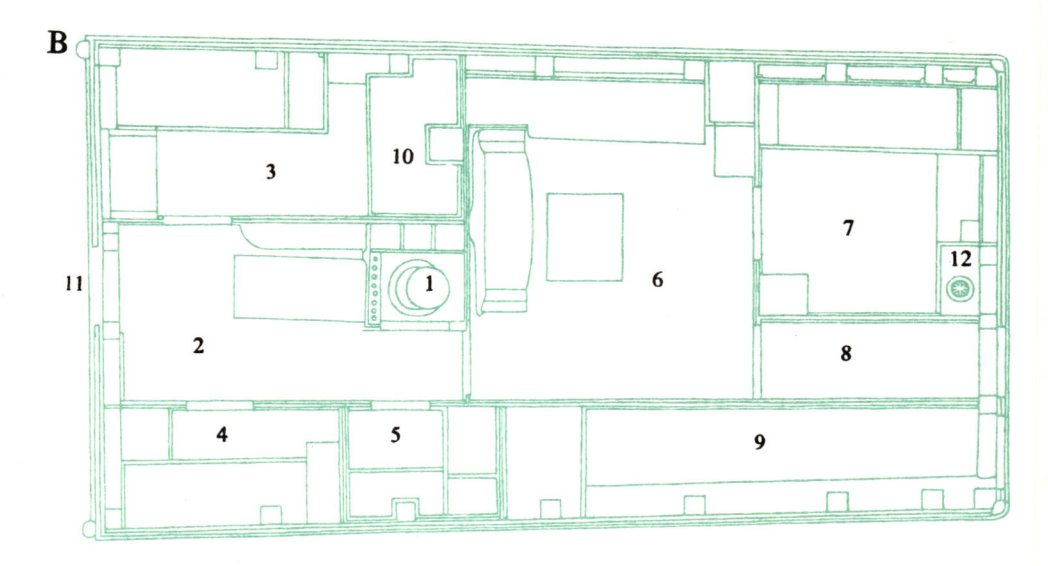

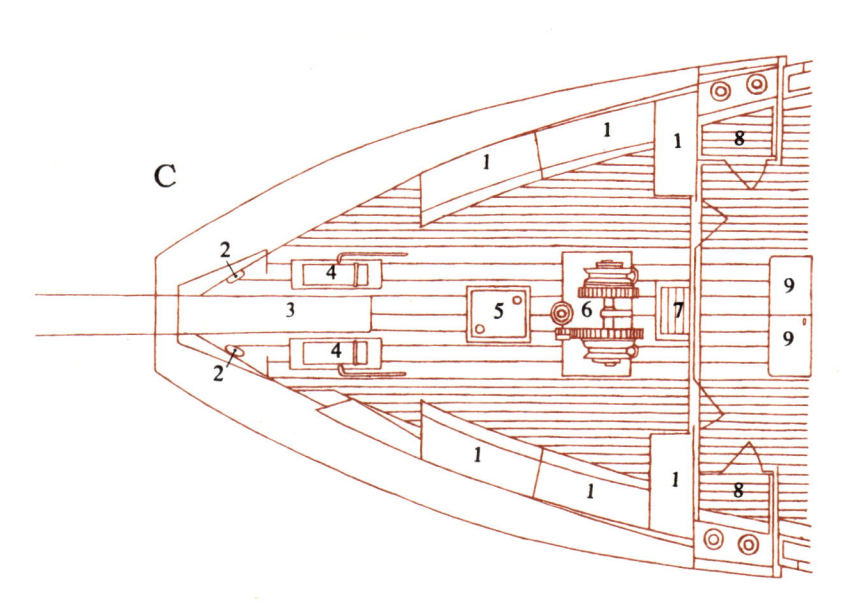

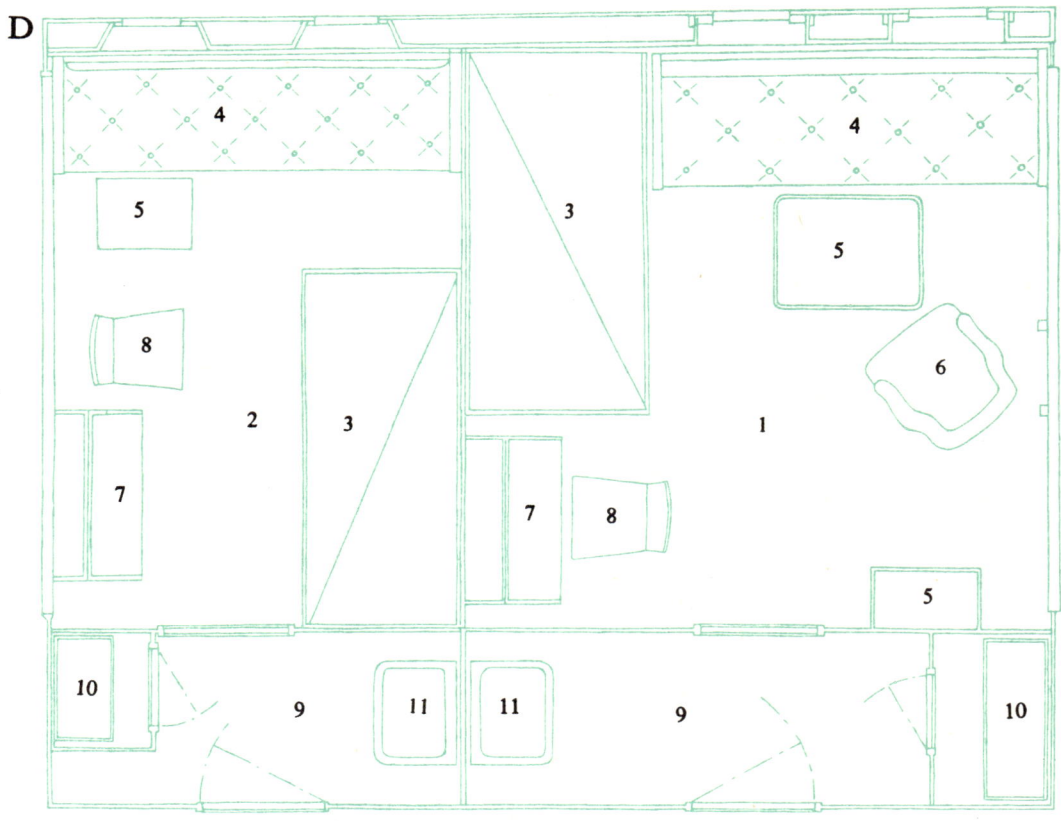

ACCOMMODATIONS

Up to the middle of the 17th century the crew had no special accommodations but had to sleep on the bare deck or find a place for themselves. Meals were eaten on deck without tables or chairs.

A *Early 19th century When hammocks were used in the navy they were slung from the deck-head beams; they were stowed in the topgallant bulwark for protection against musket fire when not in use*
1. Hammocks slung under deck beams
2. Hammocks stowed in bulwark
3. Mess table slung from overhead beam
4. Muzzle-loading gun with wooden carriage

B *Cabin accommodations on board a Swedish barkentine, built in Gävle, 1878*
1. Mizzenmast
2. Mess room
3. Mate's room
4. Second mate's and steward's room
5. Pantry
6. Cabin
7. Captain's bedroom
8. Alleyway
9. Sail locker and deck stores
10. Provisions
11. Entrance from deck
12. Steering compass

C *Accommodation for 12 seamen in fo'c'sle on board a British three-masted iron bark of 900 tons, built in Glasgow, 1879*
1. Upper and lower bunks
2. Hawse pipes
3. Bowsprit
4. Cable compressors
5. Fore peak hatch
6. Windlass
7. Hatch to chain locker
8. Crew's lavatory with light house above
9. Fore hatch

D *Modern staterooms*
1. Officer's room
2. Seaman's room
3. Berth
4. Sofa
5. Table
6. Armchair
7. Desk
8. Chair
9. Washroom
10. Wardrobe
11. Washstand

GALLEY

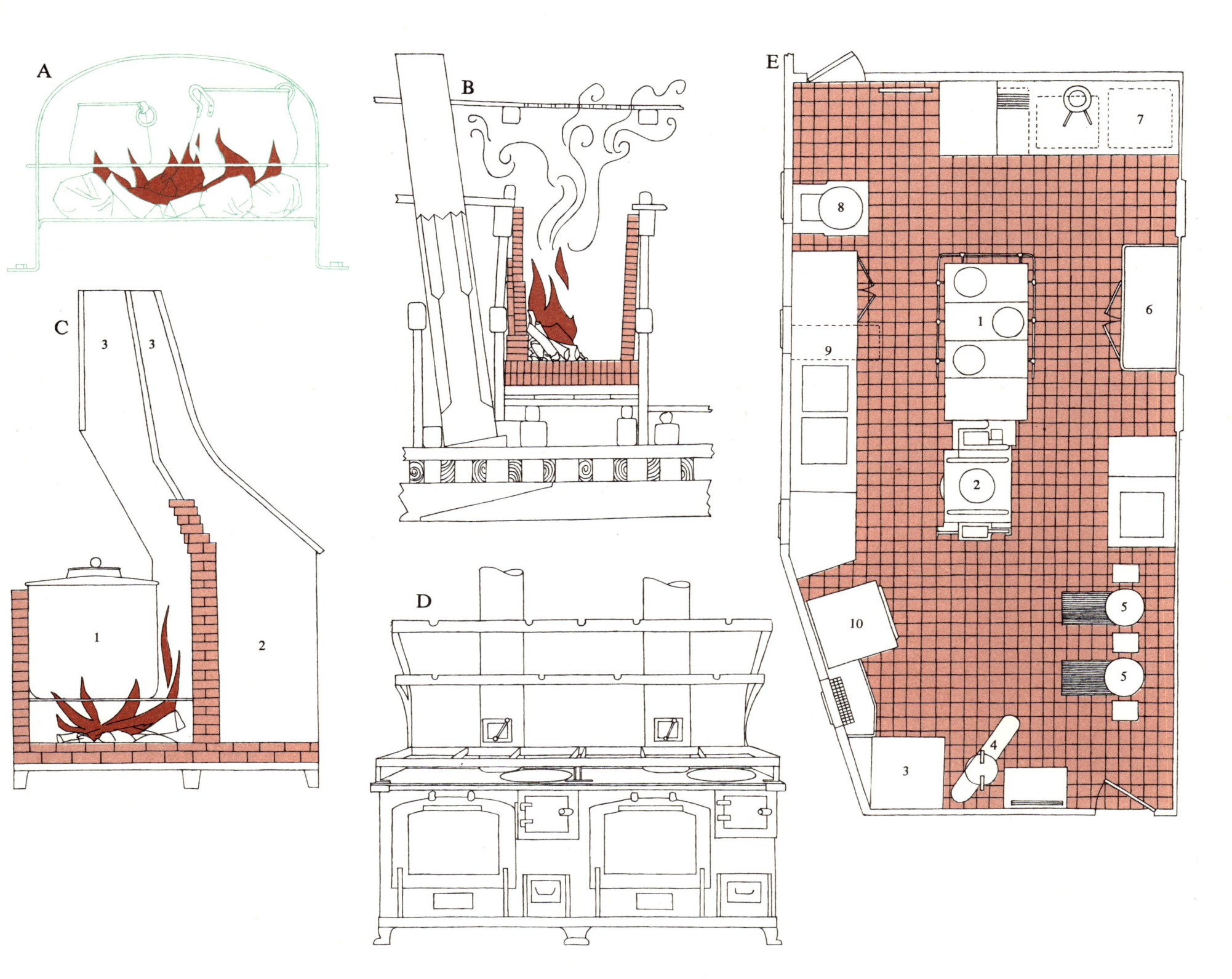

GALLEY

A Open sheet-iron fireplace, on the deck of a coaster in the Indian Ocean

B Brick fireplace on board the Swedish ship Wasa, 1628. There was no chimney and the smoke had to find its way out wherever it could.

C Ship's galley, according to Chapman, 1768
1 Pea-soup kettle
2 Brick fireplace
3 Galley stacks

D Big galley stove, from the beginning of the 20th century

E Modern ship's galley
1 Electric stove
2 Roaster
3 Dumbwaiter
4 Garbage chute
5 Steamer, steam kettles
6 Electric control panel
7 Refrigerator
8 Mixer
9 Sink
10 Oven

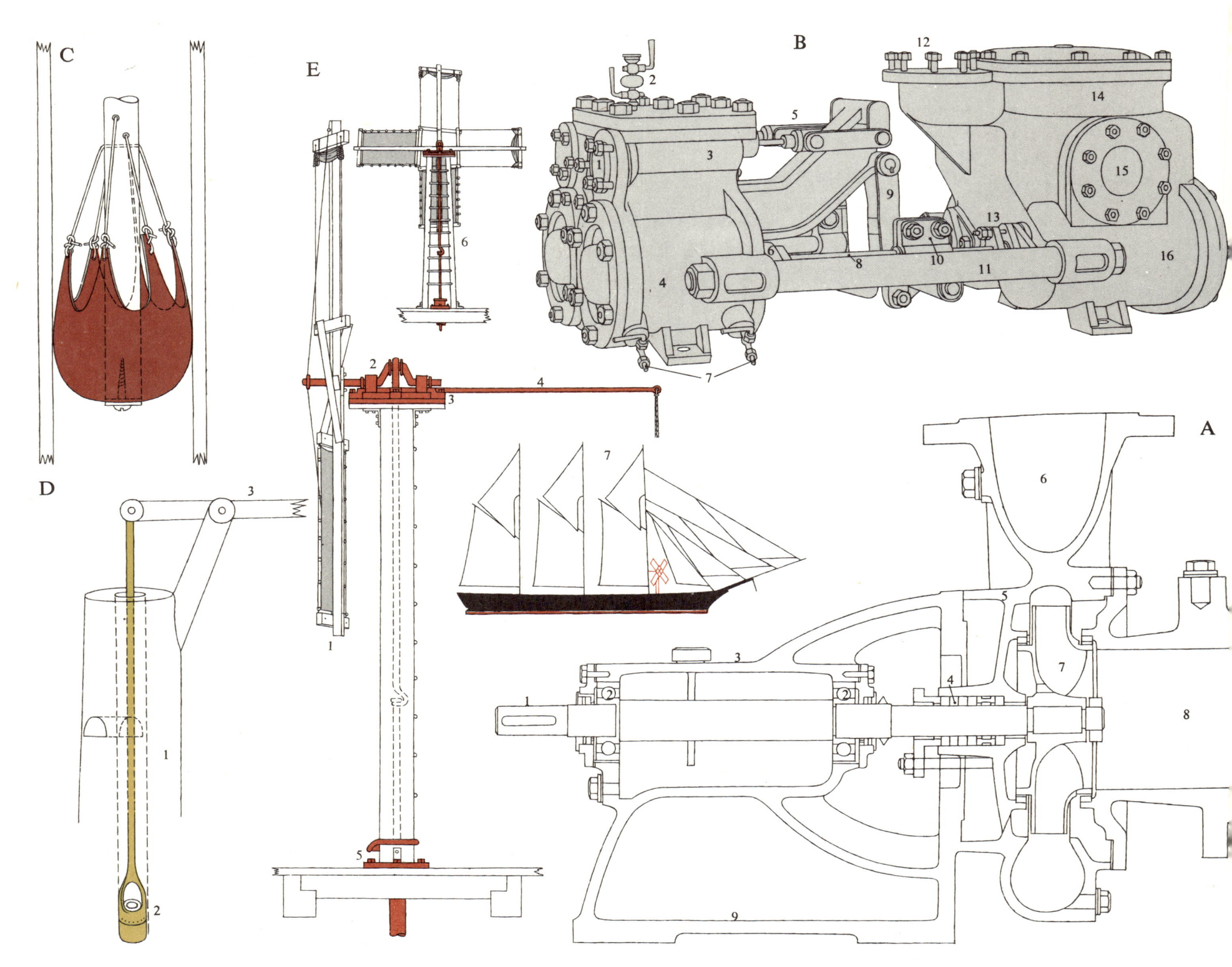

PUMPS

A Single-stage centrifugal pump
1. Pump shaft drive
2. Ball bearing
3. Oil-filled bearing box
4. Gland sealing
5. Pump casing
6. Discharge flange
7. Impeller
8. Suction flange
9. Mounting flange

B Duplex-type, direct-acting pump
1. Steam inlet
2. Cylinder lubricator
3. Slide-valve box
4. Steam cylinder
5. Slide-valve rod
6. Gland sealing
7. Drain and air cocks
8. Piston rod
9. Rocker arm
10. Crosshead connection
11. Column
12. Discharge flange
13. Gland sealing
14. Suction and discharge valve box
15. Suction flange
16. Pump cylinder

C Old-type bilge pump, once common in small craft in the Baltic area. It was constructed from a piece of leather, which formed a bag, and gave good service.

D The standard bilge pump in small wooden sailing vessels. It was made from a straight tree trunk, bored through the heart.
1. Trunk of pump
2. Pump bucket
3. Pump brake, handle

E Windmill pump with four sails, mounted on a turntable on top of a bipod erection. The windmill pump always had rigging. The three-masted fore-and-aft schooner, Eufrosine of Reval, had a windmill pump forward of the foremast.
1. Sails as seen from the side
2. Crankshaft
3. Turntable
4. Arm with braces, for setting the mill to the wind
5. The pump deck seating
6. Front view of windmill, showing two sails furled and two set
7. Three-masted fore-and-aft schooner with a windmill pump

HATCHES

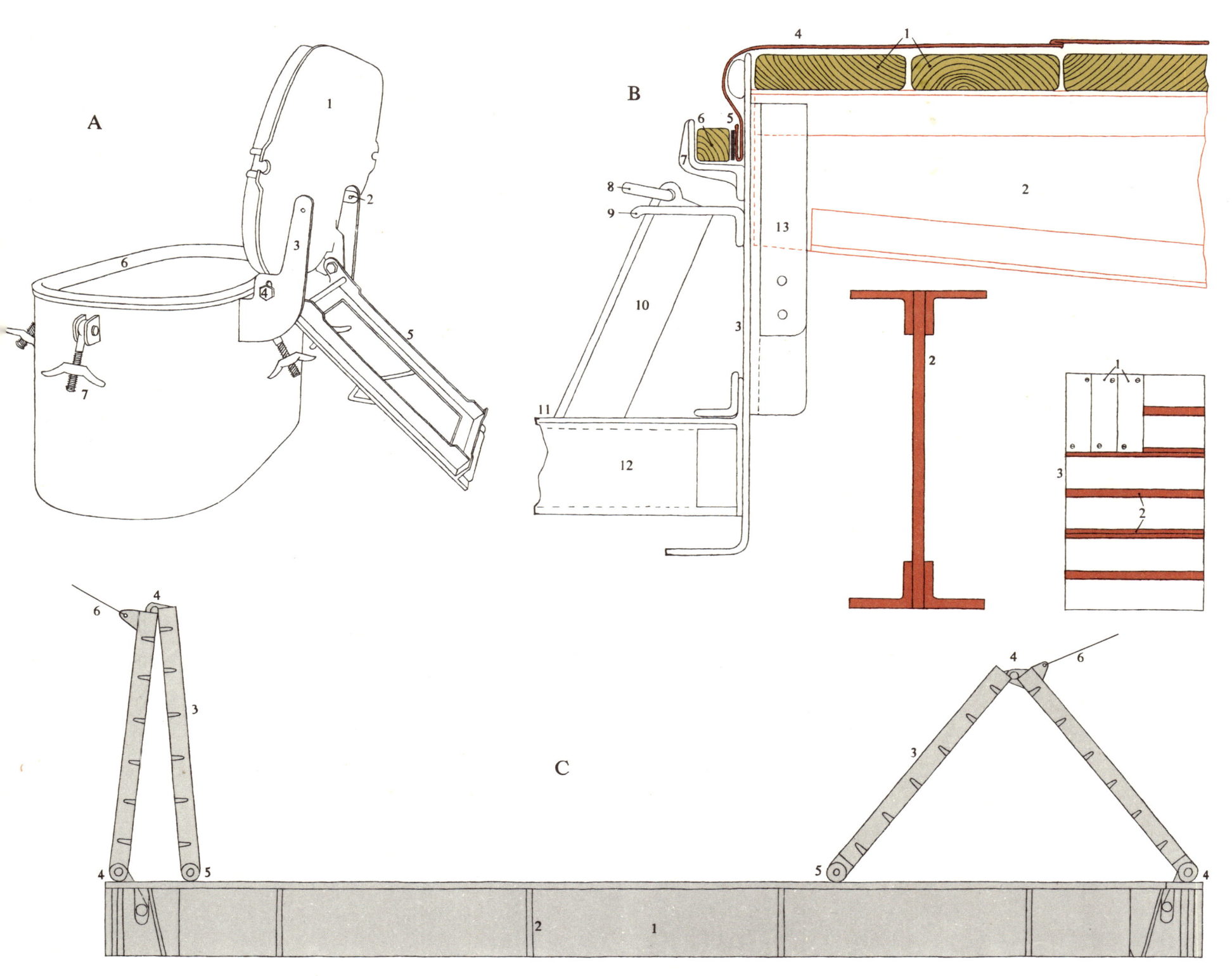

HATCHES

A *Oil tanker hatch cover*
1. Cover
2. Locking lug
3. Stop
4. Hinge pin
5. Strongback (opening lever)
6. Coaming
7. Locking screw with butterfly nut

B *Hatchway*
1. Wooden hatch covers
2. Hatch beams
3. Hatch coaming
4. Tarpaulin
5. Flat bar batten
6. Batten wedge
7. Batten cleat
8. Frapping ring
9. Bulb angle for stiffening
10. Coaming stanchion
11. Deck plating
12. Deck beam
13. Hatch beam support

C *Steel hatch cover*
1. Hatch coaming
2. Coaming stanchion
3. Folding steel hatch cover
4. Hinge
5. Rollers
6. Operating wire rope

63

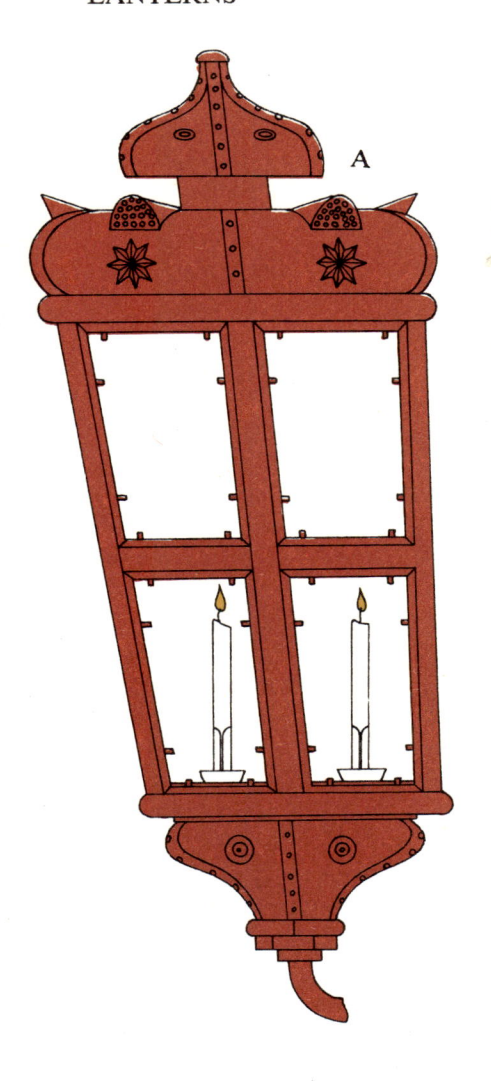

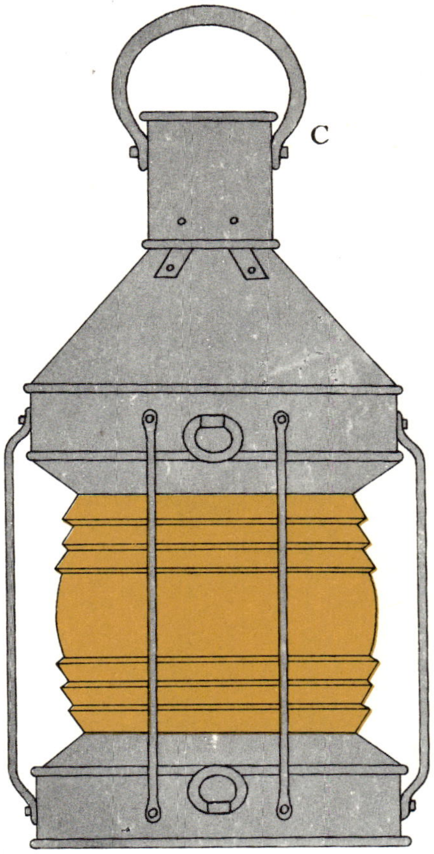

LANTERNS

LANTERNS

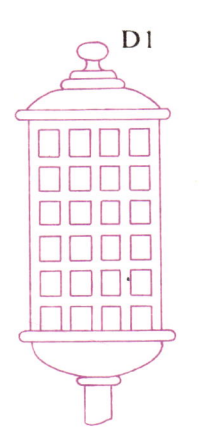

A *Swedish poop lantern from the 18th century*

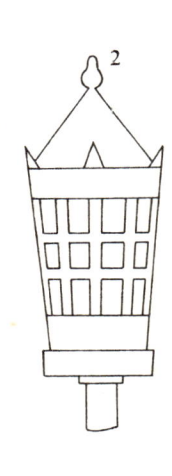

B *Lantern with horn windows from the 18th century*

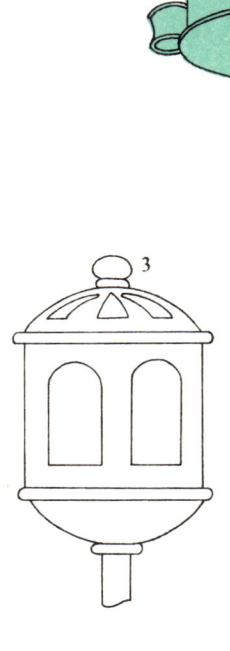

C *Riding light with a round wick lamp and Fresnel lens (A.J. Fresnel, French physicist, 1788-1827)*

D *Development of the poop lantern*
1. 1514, *Great Harry*
2. Middle of the 16th century, Sir Francis Drake's *Golden Hind*
3. The 17th century, Dutch poop lantern
4. The 17th century, English poop lantern, *Prince Royal*
5. The 18th century, poop lantern of a big French ship, built at Brest in 1756
6. The 18th century, Swedish poop lantern (same as A)

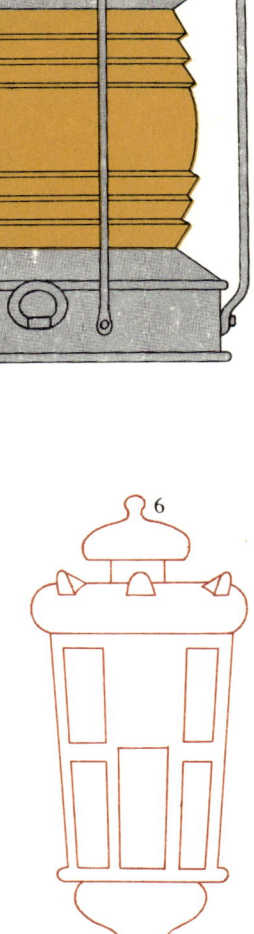

LANTERNS AND SIDELIGHTS

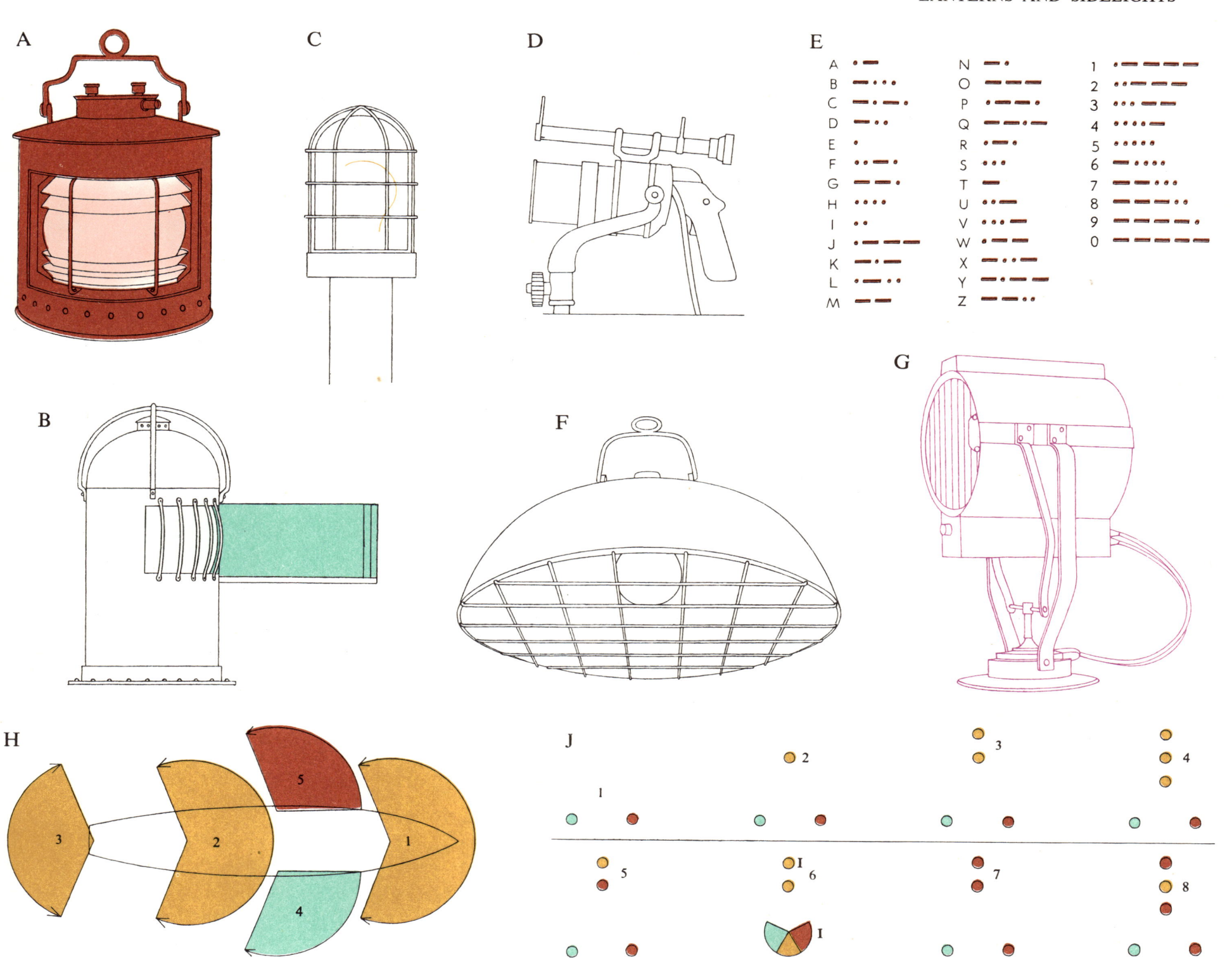

LANTERNS AND SIDELIGHTS

A *Sidelight for kerosene, paraffin oil, from the beginning of the 20th century*

B *Starboard side light house on board big sailing ship, the 19th and 20th centuries*

C *Morse lamp for merchant ship, all around illumination*

D *Day Morse lamp for a man-of-war*

E *Morse code (named after its inventor, S.F.B. Morse, 1791—1872)*

F *Electric light cluster for illumination of gangways, holds, etc.*

G *Searchlight*

H *Arcs of lights*
  1 Masthead light (fore steaming light), from right ahead over an arc of 112½° to each side (total arc 225°)
  2 Range light (after steaming light), from right ahead over an arc of 112½° to each side (total arc 225°)
  3 Stern light (overtaking light), from right astern over an arc of 67½° to each side (total arc 135°)
  4 Starboard side light, from right ahead over an arc of 112½° to starboard
  5 Port side light, from right ahead over an arc of 112½° to port

J *Lights of different ships, under way at night, seen from straight ahead*
  1 Sailing vessel
  2 Power-driven vessel with a length of less than 150 ft.
  3 Power-driven vessel with range light (after steaming light); this light is to be carried by vessels over 150 ft. in length. The figure may also indicate a tug with two masthead lights (fore steaming lights), that is, with a tow not exceeding 600 ft.
  4 A tug with three masthead lights (fore steaming lights), length of tow over 600 ft., may also indicate a tug with two masthead lights (fore steaming lights), one range light (after steaming light); the tow must then not exceed 600 ft.
  5 Power-driven pilot vessel; in addition, a white flare is burnt at intervals not exceeding 10 minutes
  6 Steam trawler at night. The upper masthead light (steaming light) (I) is showing green, white, and red lights See lower sketch
  7 Vessel not under command, but steaming
  8 Cable-laying vessel under way

65

LIFEBOATS DAVITS

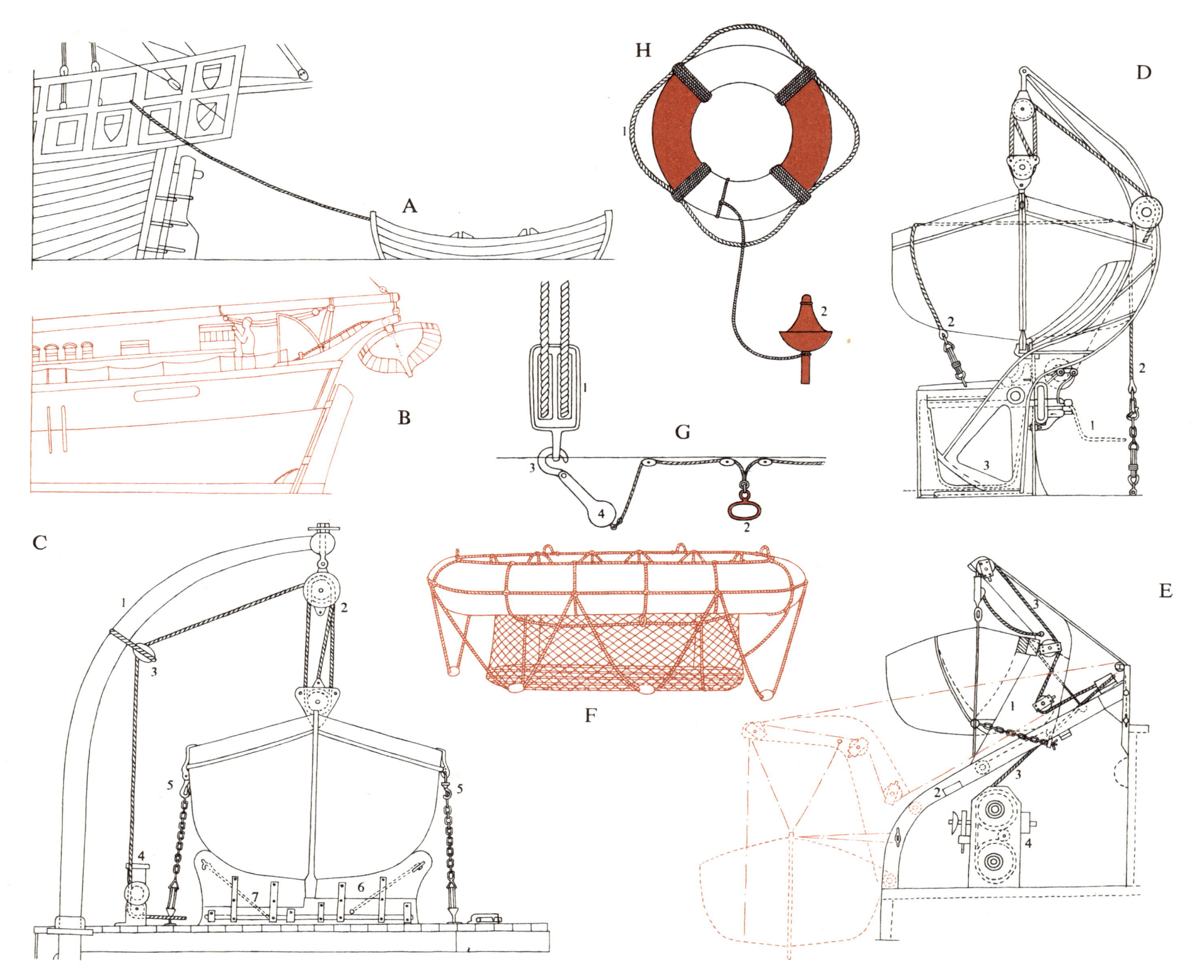

SOME TYPES OF LIFEBOAT DAVITS

- **A** *Medieval ship towing her barge*
- **B** *Auxiliary coaster with her boat slung from short davits across her transom stern*
- **C** *Radical davit*
  1. Davit
  2. Boat fall
  3. Leading block
  4. Staghorn bollard
  5. Gripes
  6. Boat chocks
  7. Hinged chocks on the outboard side
- **D** *Quadrant davit*
  1. Crank for turning out davit
  2. Gripes holding boat steady
  3. Toothed quadrant
- **E** *Gravity Davit*
  Davits with details shall, according to the 1960 Convention for Safety of Life at Sea, be constructed for quintuple safety, but wires must have sextuple safety. Further, gravity davits must fall into position even if the ship lists 25° to either side, and the trackway must have an angle of at least 30° to the horizontal plane.
  1. Cradle mounted on rollers
  2. Trackway
  3. Boat fall
  4. Winch
- **F** *Carley life float*
- **G** *Mills release apparatus*
  1. Block
  2. Releasing handle
  3. Hook holding the block until the handle is pulled
  4. Weight keeping the hook in place
- **H** *Life buoy*
  1. Life line
  2. Battery operated self-igniting buoyant light

LIFEBOATS

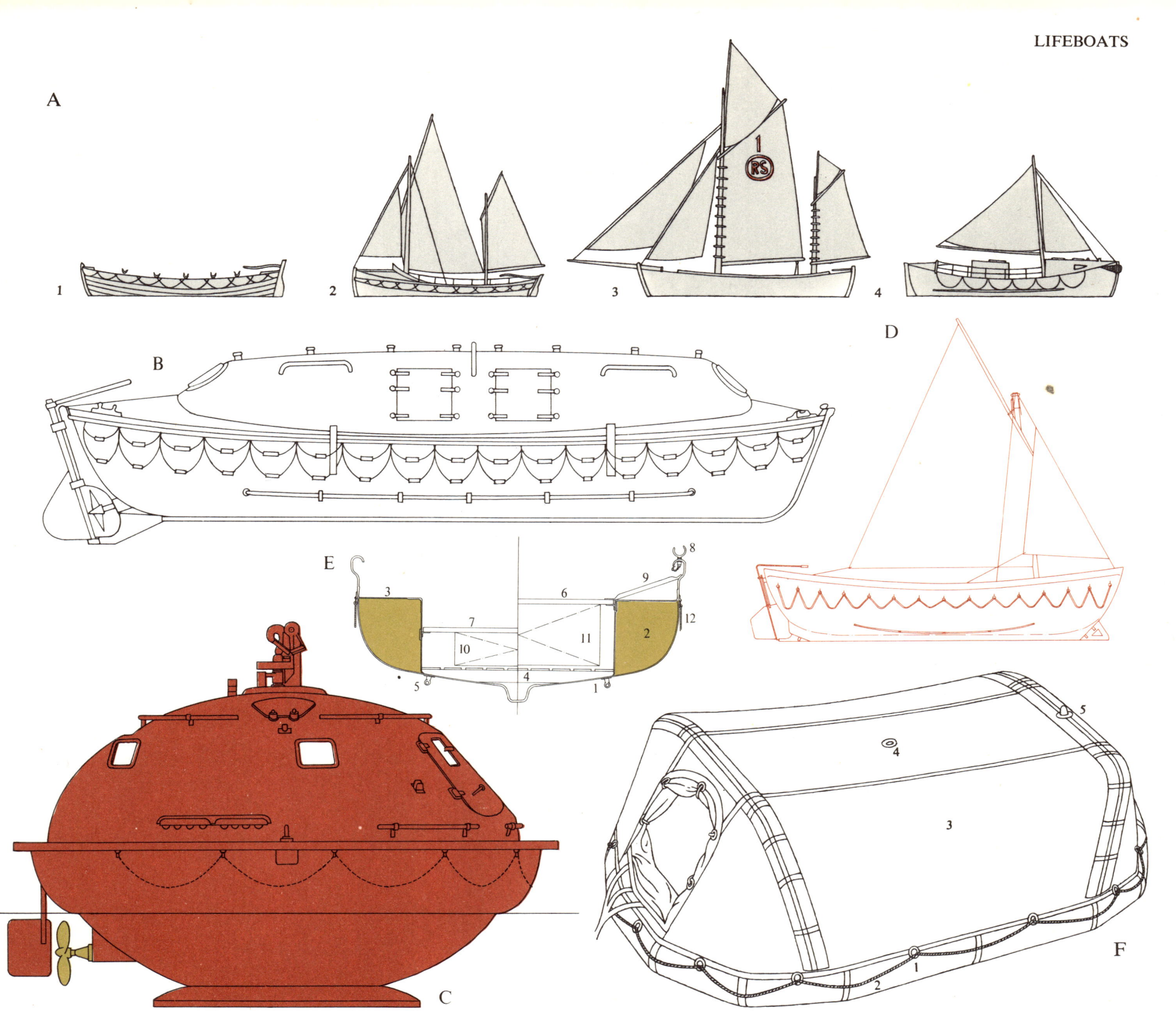

LIFEBOATS

The 1960 Convention for Safety of Life at Sea, with additions made in 1970, states that lifeboats must be made of aluminum or fiberglass-reinforced plastic, if they are to be approved. Furthermore, the Convention rules that the beam of the lifeboat, at half the length of the boat, must be not less than 95 percent of the boat's maximum beam at the same draught, and at one quarter of the length not less than 75 percent. The freeboard at maximum load must not go below 44 percent of the given draught for the boat. Buoyancy tanks must be mounted along the inner sides of the lifeboat and have a volume of at least one tenth of that of the boat, to which is added a volume-figure corresponding to the weight of the boat loaded, multiplied by 0.76 for aluminum boats and 0.5 for fiberglass boats. The lifeboat must be painted with an easily noticeable orange color both inside and outside. Tanker lifeboats must offer maximum security from fire.

A *Examples from the development of lifeboats*
 1 Old pulling lifeboat
 2 English sailing lifeboat about 1900
 3 Norwegian cruising lifeboat, Colin Archer, 1893
 4 British self-righting lifeboat from 1960

B *Fire-proofed tanker lifeboat*

C *Multi-person rescue and survival capsule for off-shore drilling-platforms*

D *Typical fiberglass lifeboat*

E *Midship section of lifeboat*
 1 G R P hull
 2 Polyurethane foam buoyancy tank
 3 G R P side benches
 4 Wood bottom boards and bearers
 5 A L alloy bilge rail
 6 Thwart
 7 Lower seat
 8 Malleable rowlocks and keep chain
 9 Gunwale stay
 10 Water tank
 11 Food tank
 12 Grab rope

F *Modern inflatable life raft; canopy attached, filled by CO_2 bottle*
 1 Buoyancy tube
 2 Life line
 3 Canopy
 4 Drain tube
 5 Light

The SANTA MARIA *is shown once again to introduce the chapter on spars and rigging. There is not much rigging left on modern ships, therefore most of this chapter will deal with times gone by.*

SPARS AND RIGGING

SPARS AND RIGGING

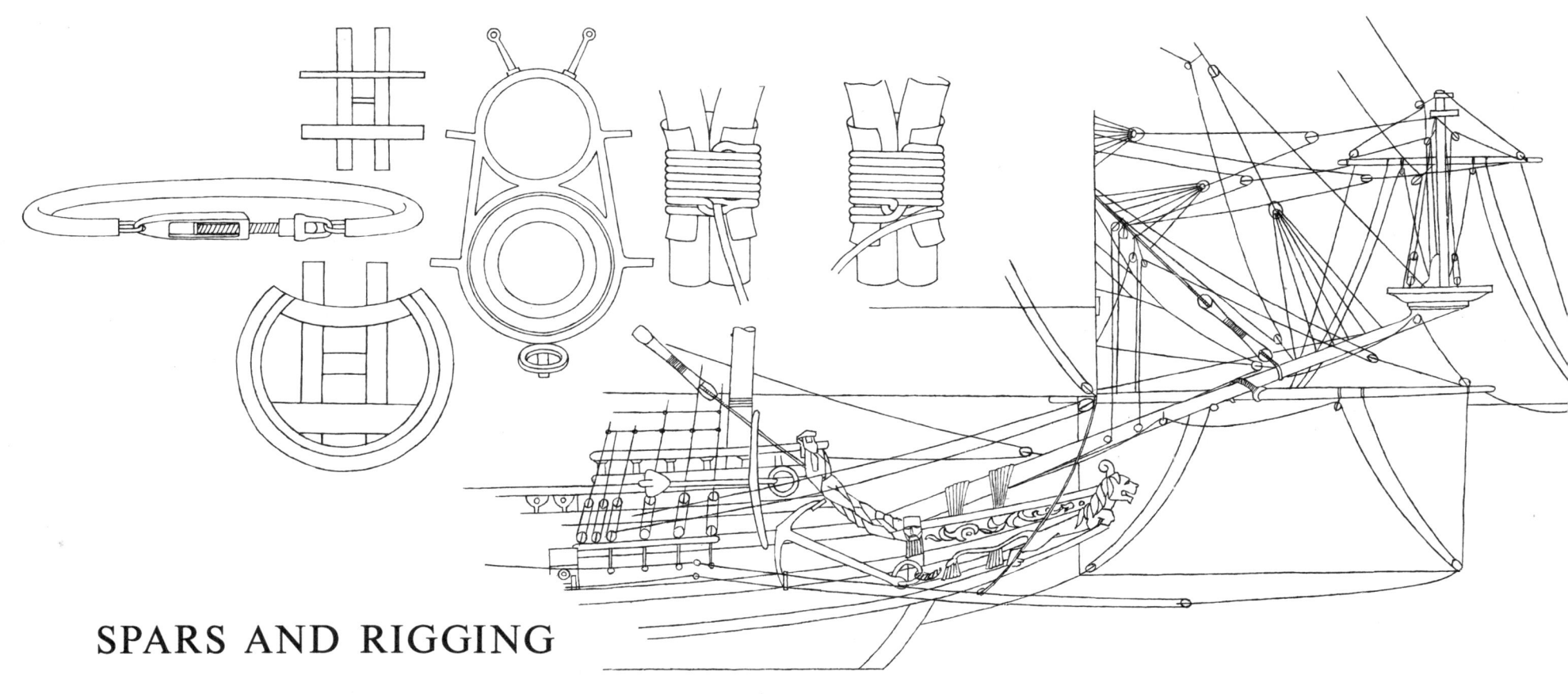

BY SAM SVENSSON

Exactly when and where primitive man first rigged a mast and sail to his simple boat remains a mystery. But quite early, he must have noticed that if he stood up in his craft, he would drift in the direction in which the wind was blowing. If he wanted to go in this direction, he might very well have speeded up his journey by holding up a cloak or animal hide to catch the wind. The time that elapsed between this first step and the introduction of the first real mast was certainly extremely long. And for many thousands of years a single mast and a simple square sail were the limit of the ancient sailor's ability to rig a boat.

Far along through the ages, from the Old Empire in Egypt and well into the European Middle Ages, the single mast remained the only rig. One break in the monotony comes in the Roman era, when the Roman sailing ship had a bowsprit, sometimes seen as a greatly inclined foremast.

In Mediterranean lands, where the rowing galley played an important role, the mast and sail evolved somewhat differently than in Western Europe, where the single mast and square sail were prevalent up to the beginning of the 15th century. The standing rigging was very simple. Smaller ships at times had none, as in the rudimentary sailing boats of the early Scandinavian fishermen.

The running gear also was very simple. The halliard hoisting the sail was led aft and acted as a backstay, thus also serving to strengthen the mast when sailing. In the early Middle Ages bowlines were added to the sail and led forward to a spar, called the bowsprit, which was rigged out over the stem.

The shrouds were set up with deadeyes and lanyards, and the rigging was rattled down, forming rope ladders to facilitate going aloft. The Northern ship was also given a fighting top at the masthead. This top is actually very old. In fact, our oldest reproduction of the fighting top is to be found on an Egyptian relief from about 1200 B.C. The oldest top mentioned in Scandinavia is in the saga of Haakon Hardabred, 1159, contained in *Snorres Konungasagor*.

Sometime during the first half of the 15th century larger ships were built with two or three masts. In northwest Europe evolution quickly culminated in three masts. The mainmast kept its location in the middle of the ship, and from the beginning the new masts were stepped in the fore- and aftercastles. As improvements were made, it was most likely that flags or banners were first flown there, a common practice during the Crusades, and that it was just as easy to hoist a small sail on this same flagpole. One could even go so far as to say that every square sail, except the first, of course, was preceded by a flag on a pole. Thus, big ships unfurled a banner aloft on a staff in the fighting top, and toward the end of the 15th century they appeared with a small sail on the same staff. From the beginning this small sail was handled by the men in the top, and it was from this that the name topsail was derived. The Dutch, Germans, and Scandinavians used a similar term; to them the sail was known as the "märssegel." The main topsail was soon followed by a second sail on the foremast. Both were small at first, but they continually increased in size as they came to be used more and more. The clews were sheeted to the yardarms below, and, with braces and clewlines leading down to the deck, the sail became more functional. As it could be set flatter, it could be used when sailing on the wind.

The triangular lateen sail, in general use in galleys and fishing boats of the Mediterranean, was eventually used as the mizzen in big ships all along the European coast. Its use had spread all the way to the Baltic Sea by the end of the Middle Ages. There, it gradually supplanted the older square sail as the mizzen. In the 250 years that followed, the lateen mizzen continued to be used in all larger ships.

The bowsprit had originally served only to lead the bowlines. By the end of the Middle Ages, however, a square sail had been rigged under the bowsprit. This sail was called a blind in Medieval English, as it wholly blocked the view ahead. It was, perhaps, the blind that prompted the need for a lookout aloft. Later, it became known as the spritsail.

By the last quarter of the 15th century larger ships began to have as many as four masts. The two aftermost masts generally had lateen sails only, but the main mizzenmast could carry a triangular topsail on a topmast as well. The smaller mizzen, known as the bonaventure mizzen, usually reached abaft the ship where it was sheeted to a spar rigged out over the stern.

The topsail continued to grow in size, and around the middle of the 16th century larger ships began to carry a third square sail, the topgallant sail, on the fore- and mainmasts. Until this time, however, the topmasts had been fixed extensions of the masts themselves and could not be rigged down. But around the 1570's, topmasts began to be stepped, to be fidded as the term was, so they could be rigged up or taken down depending on circumstances. This innovation, credited to the Dutch, was found to be very practical and was soon adopted for general use. Consequently, the fidded topmasts grew larger in relation to the lower masts; the topsail grew deeper, and the lower sail shallower.

Around 1620 it was common to equip the third mast with a square topsail. At the same time, the bonaventure mizzenmast was discarded. This marked the creation of the three-masted ship, with square sails on each mast. These early ships always had one yard less on the mizzenmast than on the fore- and mainmasts.

It was not until the latter half of the 18th century that rigging had evolved to the point where each mast had the same number of yards. This was the time when the term full-rigged ship became universal. The full-rigged ship usually referred to a merchant vessel, while sailing warships with such a rig were referred to by their rating: ship of the line, frigate, or sloop. The ships of the early 17th century were built with low heads and high sterns.

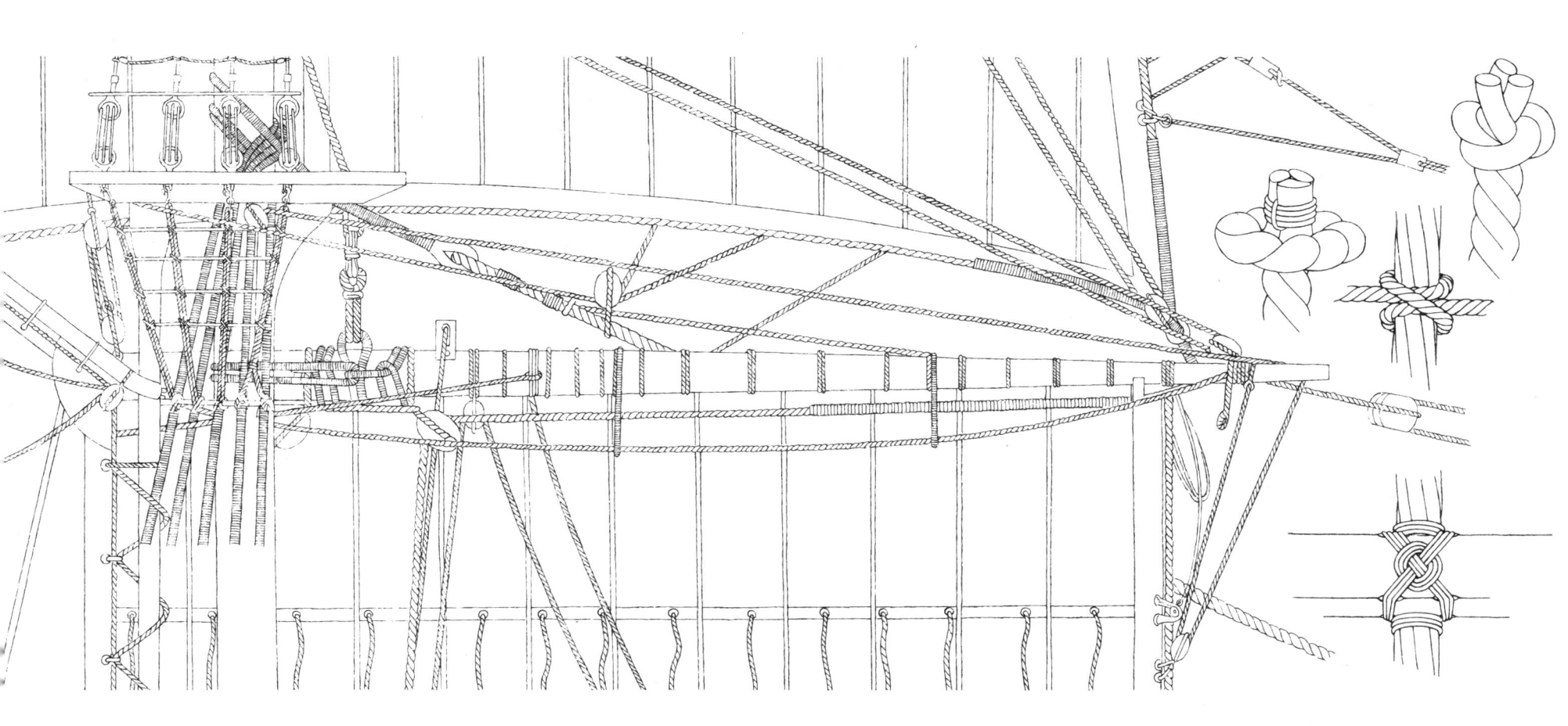

This design made them very hard to steer when the wind was abaft the beam, and the need for more headsail was keenly felt. To remedy the problem all larger ships of the 19th century were rigged with a spritsail topsail on a small mast at the end of the bowsprit. This sail was very impractical, though it was found to be very necessary, and it remained in use for over a hundred years before it was replaced with more practical and effective staysails.

Staysails had been used quite early in small craft, but not in the big ships. By the 1670's, however, the larger ships began carrying staysails, first between the masts and later over the bowsprit. This fore topmast staysail over the bowsprit was difficult to set because of the complicated rigging of the spritsail and sprit topsail. This was also the case with the staysails between the masts, because of the braces and bowlines leading to the stays. The staysails won out over the others, though, and in the beginning of the 18th century the spritsail topmast was discarded and the running gear was gradually changed to make more room for the staysails of the mainmast. This development continued through the entire 18th century, and by the end of the century larger ships carried a staysail on every possible stay.

When the spritsail topmast was discarded in the first decade of the 18th century, a new spar, the jib boom, was rigged out on the bowsprit. A new staysail, called the jib, was placed over it ahead of the fore topmast staysail. After the middle of the same century the lateen mizzen's long yard was exchanged for a gaff. This change occurred earlier in the smaller vessels than in the big ones.

During the Napoleonic wars, at the end of the century, other changes began to take place in the rigging. The mizzen was enlarged and sheeted to a boom extending over the stern. Under the bowsprit a new spar, called the martingale or dolphin striker, was inserted to improve the staying of the jib boom. This all developed into a new spar and staysail, the flying jib boom and flying jib, which were rigged outside the jib. A fourth yard above the topgallant yard, called the royal yard, now became more and more common on larger ships. Men-of-war always set it flying, while merchant ships set it as a standing sail carried on the upper part of the long topgallant mast. Only on hard winter trips was it rigged down. But this, of course, was true of all unnecessary rigging in prolonged bad weather.

The 19th century's mechanical revolution gradually began to influence the rigging of sailing ships. At first, it was merely a replacement on masts and yards of rope fittings, strops, and so on, with forged iron bands. Then the rope trusses of the lower yards were replaced with iron trusses, called patent trusses. Wherever possible, the heavier running rigging was replaced with chain, first the topsail ties and sheets and then the topgallant ties and sheets, and then just about anywhere chain could be used to advantage. By the middle of the 19th century British ships began to have the standing rigging replaced with wire. The rigging had previously been made of tarred hemp rope, but wire was cheaper and stronger and more durable. It had less surface exposed to the wind, and as the early attempts to build iron vessels were crowned with success, wire rigging was used more and more on larger ships, especially on steamships, which always had rigging and sails by the 19th century.

The huge topsails on larger sailing ships were extremely hard to handle during storms, when they had to be reefed. The American captain, Robert Forbes, devised a rig with double topsails in 1841. In 1854, another American sea captain, named Howes, improved this rig, and it became common in big ships. Twenty years later, in 1874, the largest ships were also rigged with double topgallant yards, as well as double topsail yards.

By this time the use of wire for standing rigging and of chain for sheets and halliards was entirely accepted. Standing rigging now featured turnbuckles instead of deadeyes and lanyards, the system used ever since the early Middle Ages. Strong but stiff tarred hemp was replaced with Manila rope for running gear. Manila rope was softer and easier to work and just as strong, though not as durable as the hemp used formerly. Block sheaves were furnished with roller bearings, which also served to lighten the work on board ship. In fact, so much was done to ease the work on deck and aloft that the vessels could now be sailed with fewer hands, and larger ships could be sailed with the same crew as had been required for a smaller ship twenty years earlier. Sail handling became more mechanized in the large ships. In the 1890's, the Scottish sea captain, J.C.B. Jarvis, devised a geared mechanical winch that allowed a couple of men to brace the yards in the largest ships in rough weather. This was, of course, a big help. In the last of the big ships the topsail and topgallant halliards of chain were replaced with wire regulated by a hand-operated drum winch. Equipped with a conical drum, the winch considerably eased the effort of raising the yard.

All these innovations were part of that universal sequence of events that provided labor-saving devices in many areas of trade. For the sailing ship, these innovations had to be adapted to the special needs of the sea. They were needed to enable the sailing ship, with only the wind for power, to face up to the competition now provided by the coal- and oil-burning ships of the new age. It was obviously not a successful struggle, and the new means of propulsion became a prime factor in the disappearance of the sailing ship from all the seas of the world.

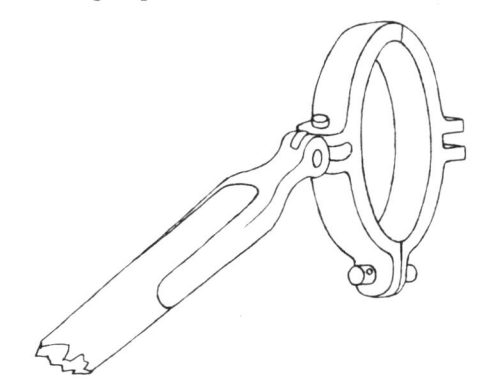

SPARS

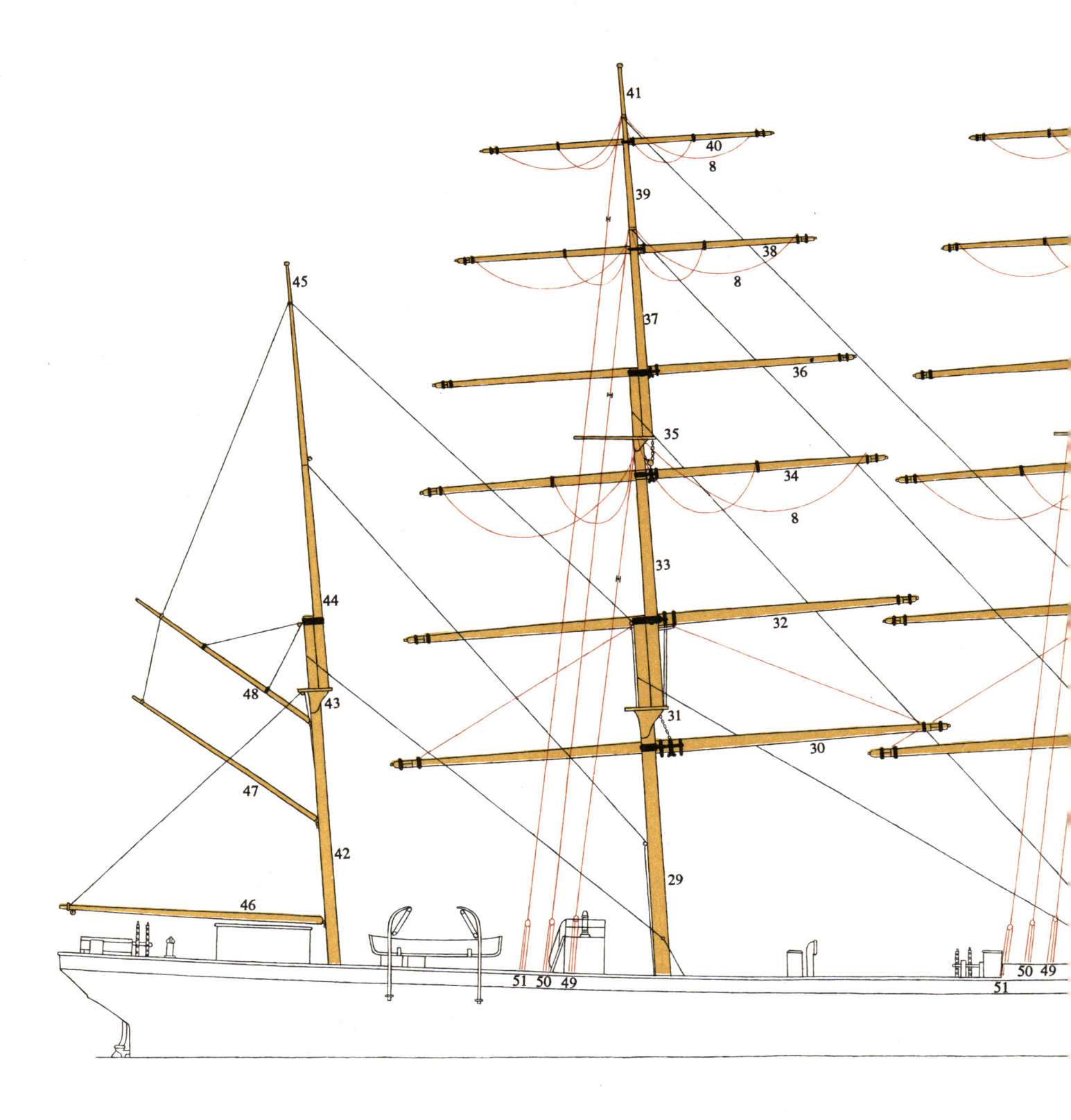

SPARS

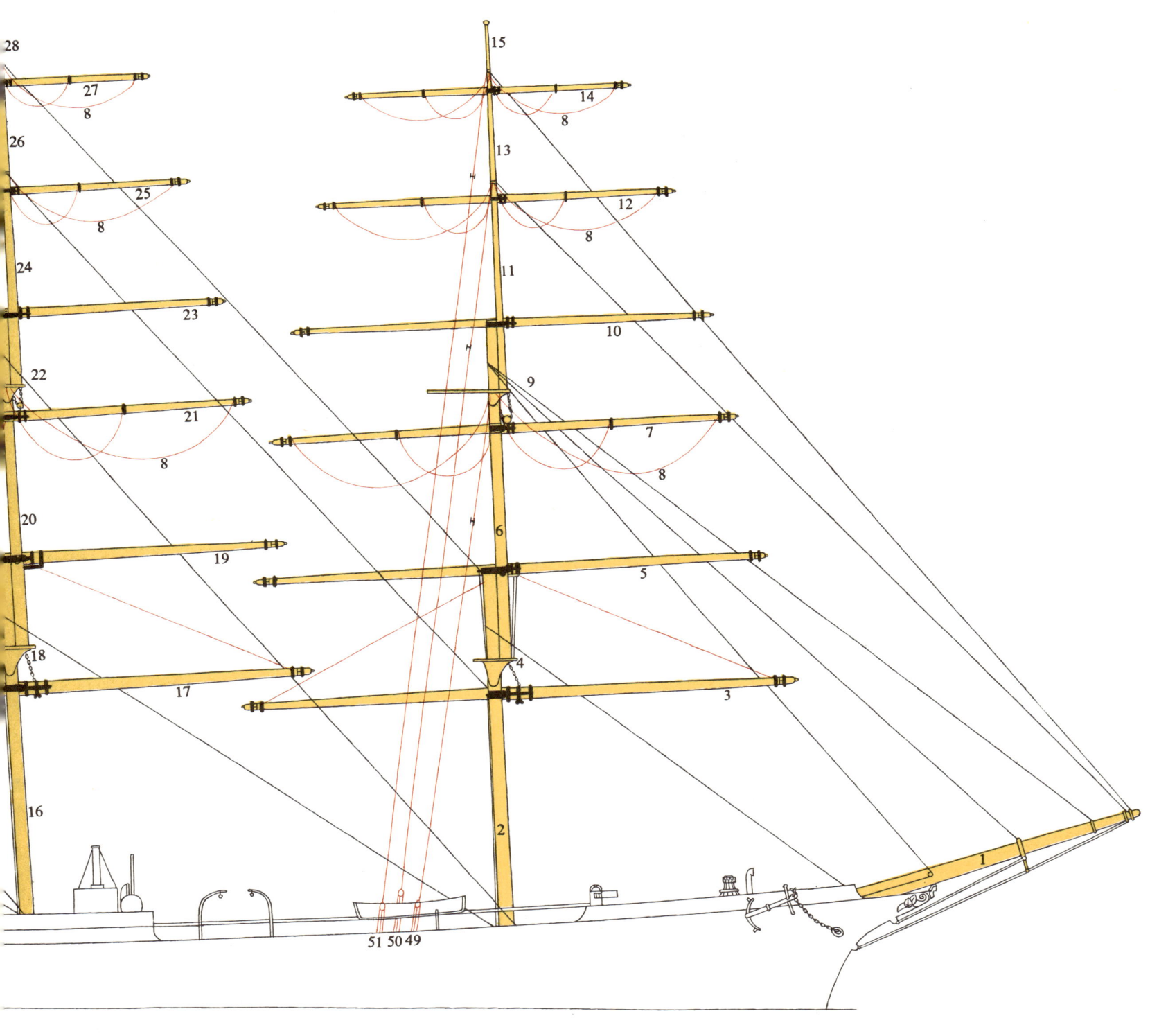

SPARS OF A FOUR-MASTED BARK

1. Spike bowsprit
2. Fore lower mast
3. Fore yard
4. Fore top
5. Fore lower topsail yard
6. Fore topmast
7. Fore upper topsail yard, hoisted
8. Lifts
9. Fore topmast crosstree
10. Fore lower topgallant yard
11. Fore topgallant mast
12. Fore upper topgallant yard, hoisted
13. Fore royal mast in one with topgallant mast
14. Fore royal yard, hoisted
15. Fore royal pole
16. Main lower mast
17. Mainyard
18. Main top
19. Main lower topsail yard
20. Main topmast
21. Main upper topsail yard, hoisted
22. Main topmast crosstree
23. Main lower topgallant yard
24. Main topgallant mast
25. Main upper topgallant yard, hoisted
26. Main royal mast
27. Main royal yard, hoisted
28. Main royal pole
29. Mizzen lower mast
30. Crossjack yard
31. Mizzen top
32. Mizzen lower topsail yard
33. Mizzen topmast
34. Mizzen upper topsail yard, hoisted
35. Mizzen topmast crosstree
36. Mizzen lower topgallant yard
37. Mizzen topgallant mast
38. Mizzen upper topgallant yard, hoisted
39. Mizzen royal mast
40. Mizzen royal yard, hoisted
41. Mizzen pole
42. Jigger lower mast
43. Jigger top
44. Jigger topmast
45. Jigger pole
46. Spanker boom
47. Lower spanker gaff
48. Upper spanker gaff
49. Upper topsail halliard
50. Upper topgallant halliard
51. Royal halliard

73

MASTS

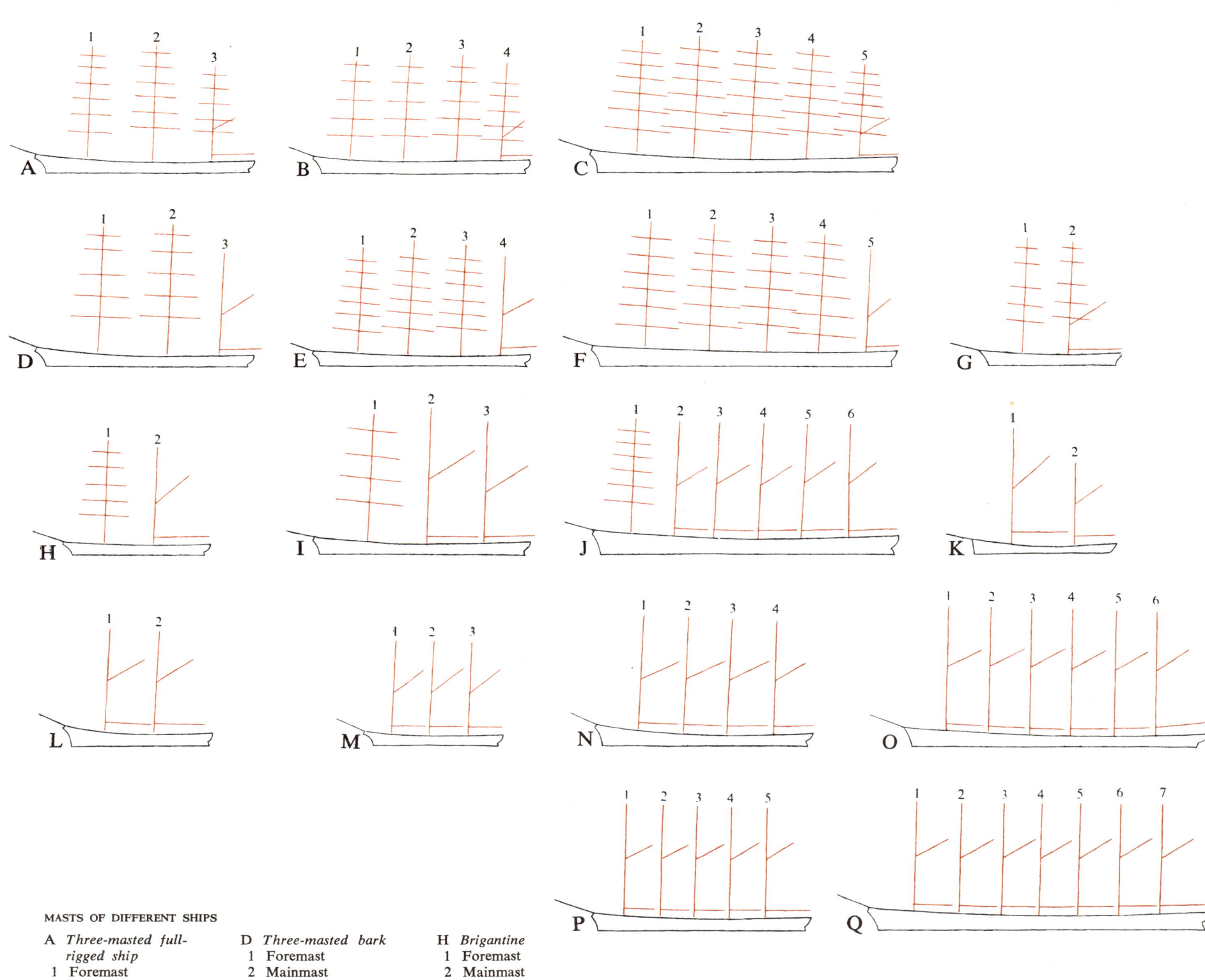

MASTS OF DIFFERENT SHIPS

A Three-masted full-rigged ship
1 Foremast
2 Mainmast
3 Mizzenmast
B Four-masted full-rigged ship
1 Foremast
2 Mainmast
3 Mizzenmast
4 Jiggermast
C Five-masted full-rigged ship
1 Foremast
2 Mainmast
3 Middlemast
4 Mizzenmast
5 Jiggermast
D Three-masted bark
1 Foremast
2 Mainmast
3 Mizzenmast
E Four-masted bark
1 Foremast
2 Mainmast
3 Mizzenmast
4 Jiggermast
F Five-masted bark
1 Foremast
2 Mainmast
3 Middlemast
4 Mizzenmast
5 Jiggermast
G Brig
1 Foremast
2 Mainmast
H Brigantine
1 Foremast
2 Mainmast
I Three-masted barkentine
1 Foremast
2 Mainmast
3 Mizzenmast
J Six-masted barkentine
1 Foremast
2 Mainmast
3 Mizzenmast
4 Jiggermast
5 Driver mast
6 Spanker mast
K Ketch
1 Mainmast
2 Mizzenmast
L Two-masted fore-and-aft schooner
1 Foremast
2 Mainmast
M Three-masted fore-and-aft schooner
1 Foremast
2 Mainmast
3 Mizzenmast
N Four-masted fore-and-aft schooner
1 Foremast
2 Mainmast
3 Mizzenmast
4 Spanker mast
O Six-masted fore-and-aft schooner
1 Foremast
2 Mainmast
3 Mizzenmast
4 Jiggermast
5 Driver mast
6 Spanker mast
P Five-masted fore-and-aft schooner
1 Foremast
2 Mainmast
3 Mizzenmast
4 Jiggermast
5 Spanker mast
Q Seven-masted fore-and-aft schooner
1 Foremast
2 Mainmast
3 Mizzenmast
4 Jiggermast
5 Driver mast
6 Pusher mast
7 Spanker mast

Regarding the names of masts of a seven-masted schooner, see also page 132

MASTS AND SPARS

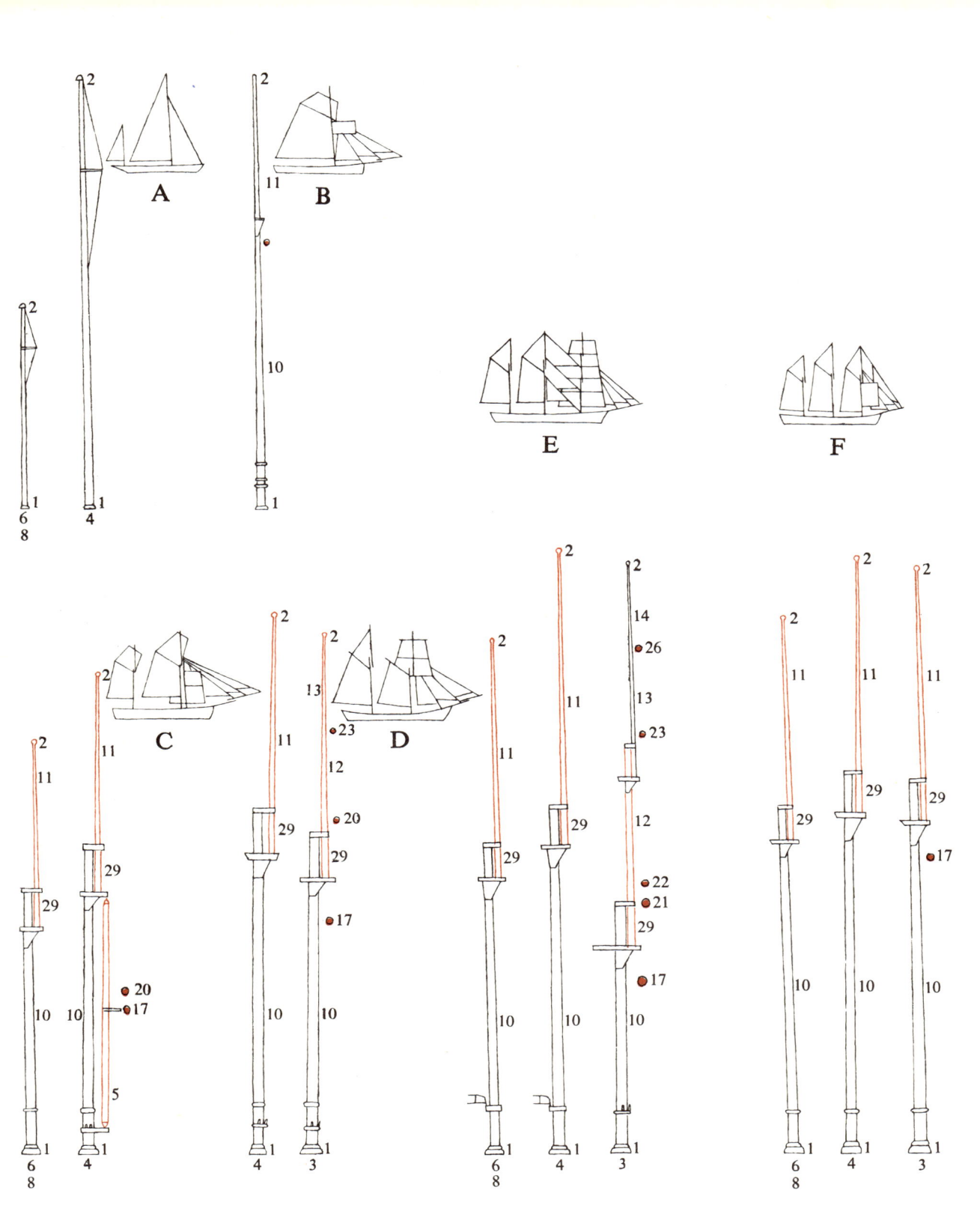

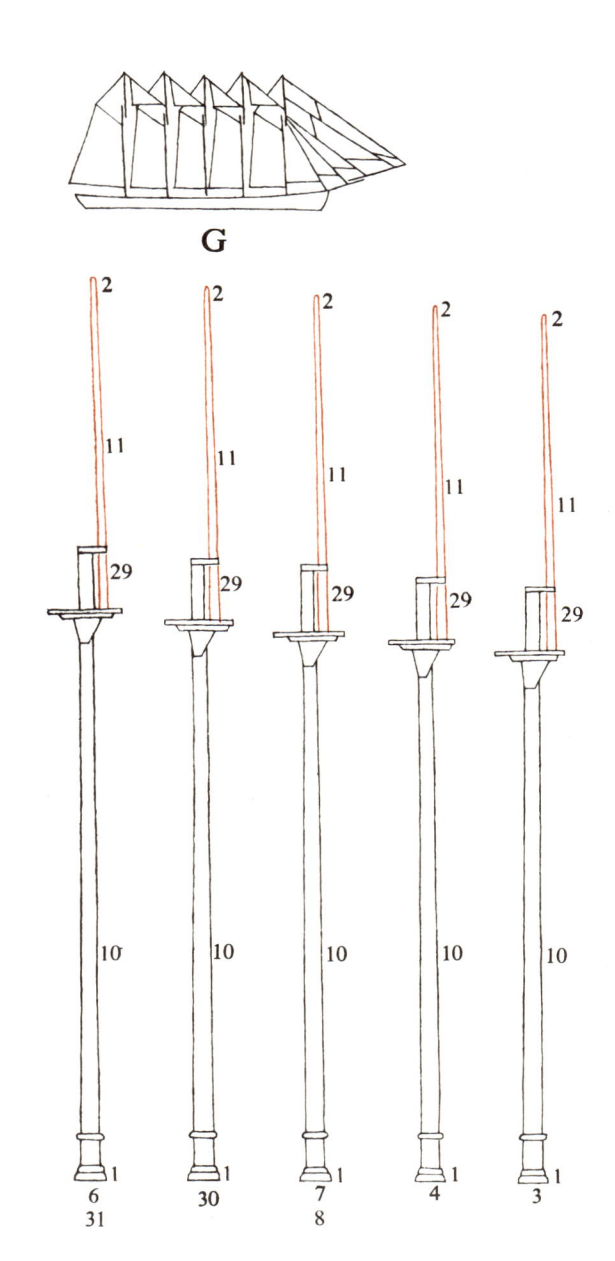

MASTS AND SPARS IN DIFFERENT SHIPS

- A *Yawl*
- B *Sloop, about 1900*
- C *Ketch, end of the 19th century*
- D *Topsail schooner*
- E *Barkentine*
- F *Three-masted fore-and-aft schooner*
- G *American five-masted fore-and-aft schooner*

1. Mast coat
2. Truck
3. Foremast
4. Mainmast
5. Snow mast
8. Mizzenmast
9. Laeisz mast
10. Lower mast
11. Fore-and-aft-rigged topmast
12. Square-rigged topmast
13. Topgallant mast
14. Royal mast
15. Skysail mast
16. Moonsail mast
17. Fore yard
18. Main yard
19. Crossjack yard
20. Topsail yard for single topsail
21. Lower topsail yard
22. Upper topsail yard
23. Topgallant yard for single topgallant sail
24. Lower topgallant yard
25. Upper topgallant yard
26. Royal yard
27. Skysail yard
28. Moonsail yard
29. Masthead and housing of topmast
30. Jiggermast
31. Spankermast
32. Flagpole
33. Laeisz yard
34. Jigger yard

The terminology for masts varies in different languages. Numbers 6 and 7, missing in list above, refer to Teutonic languages only.

MASTS AND SPARS

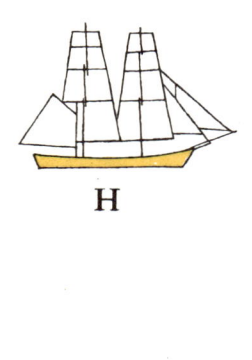

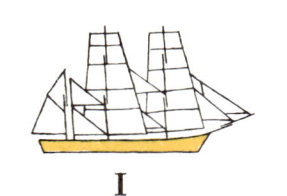

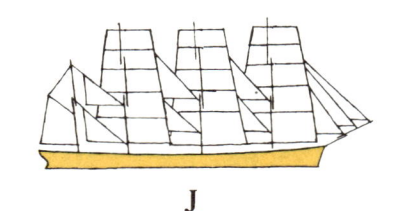

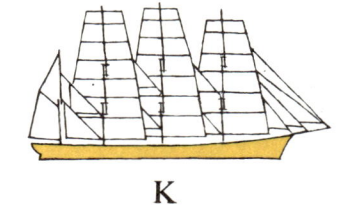

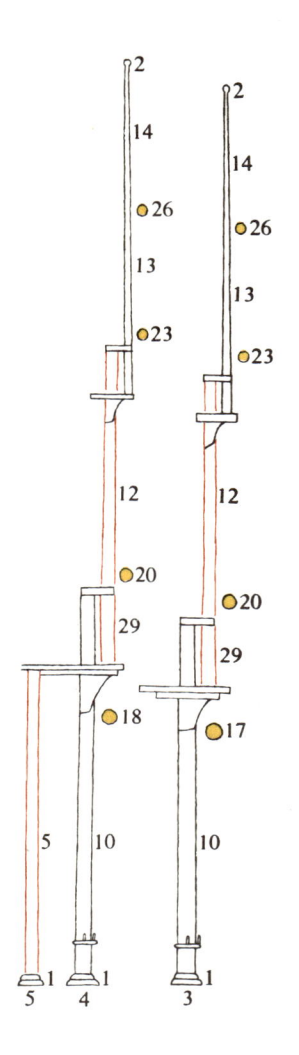

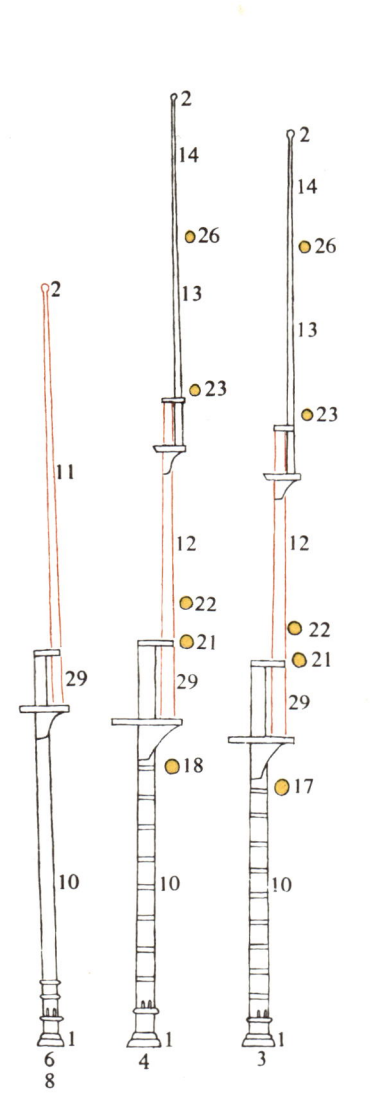

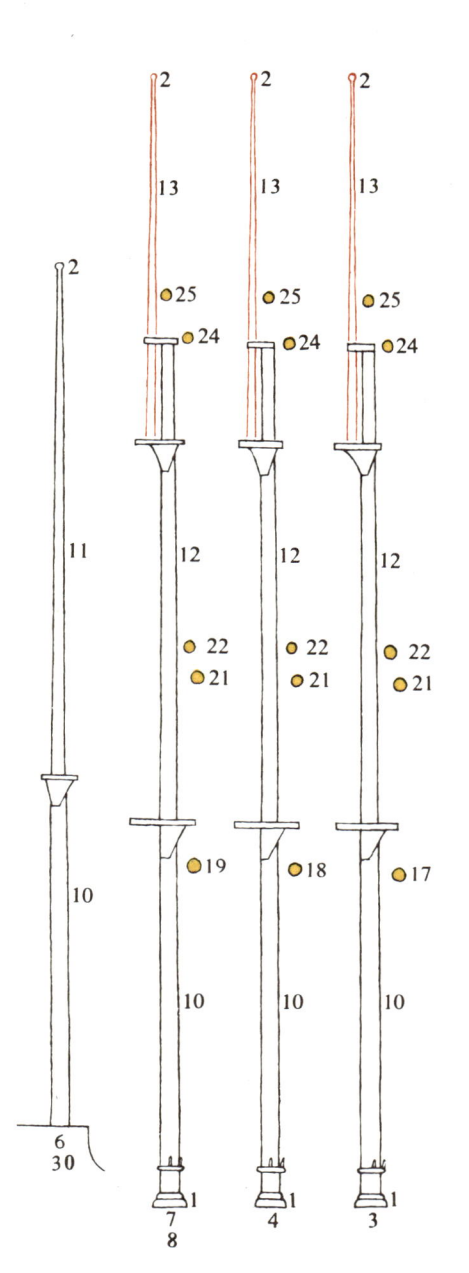

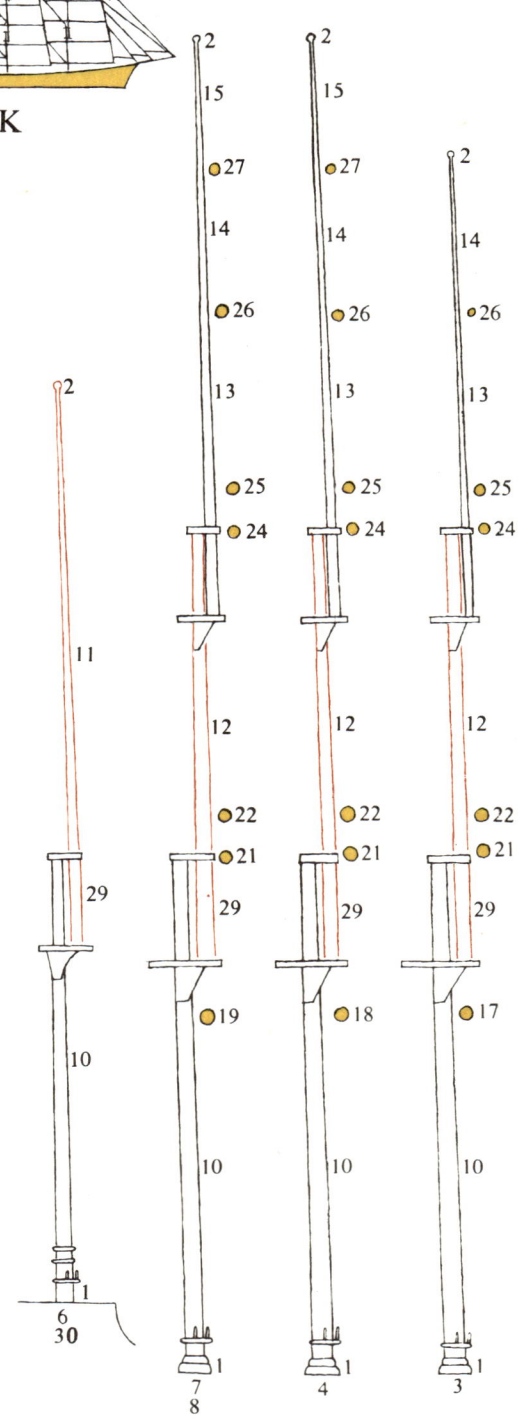

H Snow with single top-sails
I Three-masted bark with double topsails
J Four-masted bark with short topgallant masts abaft the top-masts
K Four-masted bark with royals and double topgallant sails, skysails on the main and the mizzen
L Three-masted, full-rigged ship, American clipper, about 1850, with skysails and a main moonsail
M Ship, about 1700
N Five-masted full-rigged ship (Preussen, the only ship of this rig ever built)

76

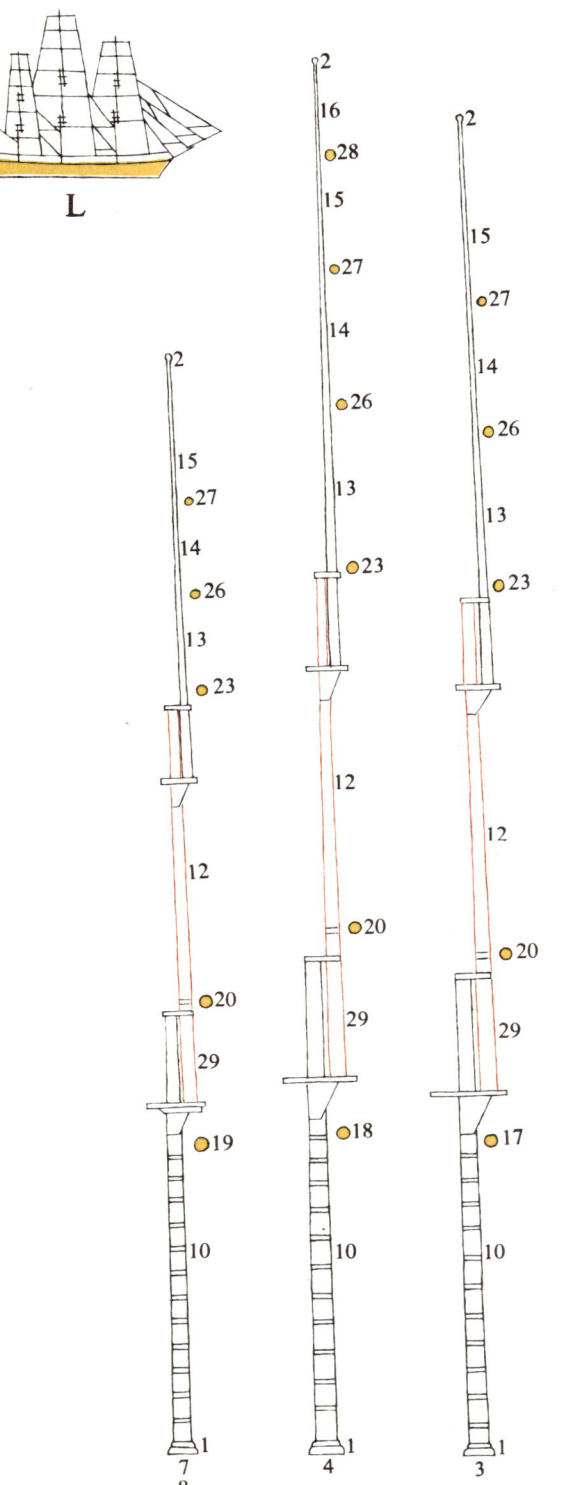

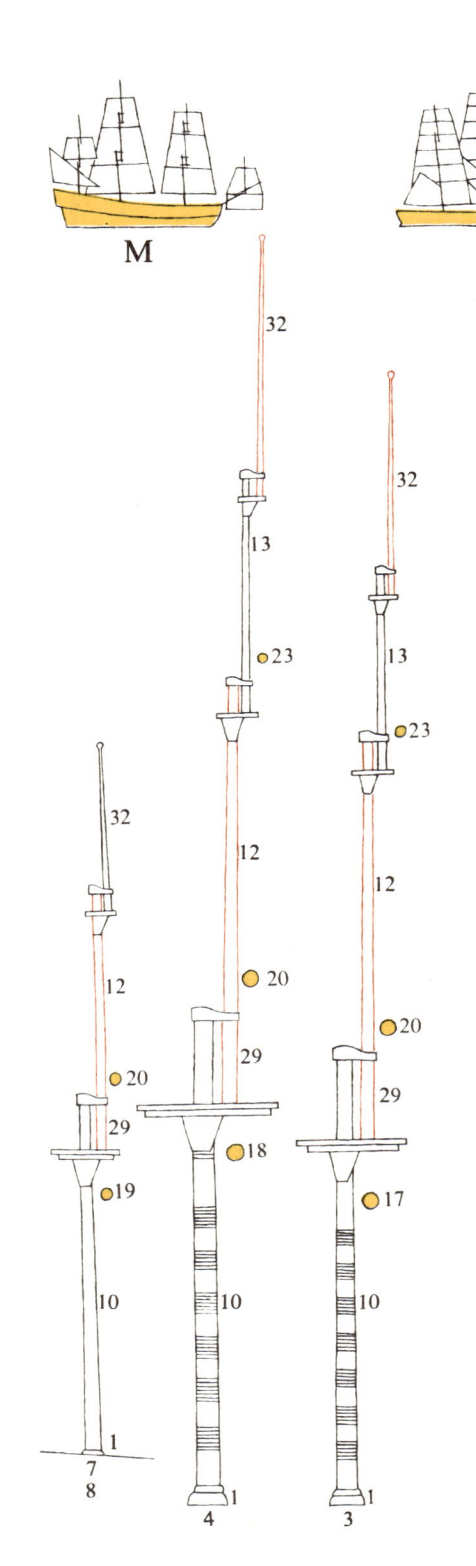

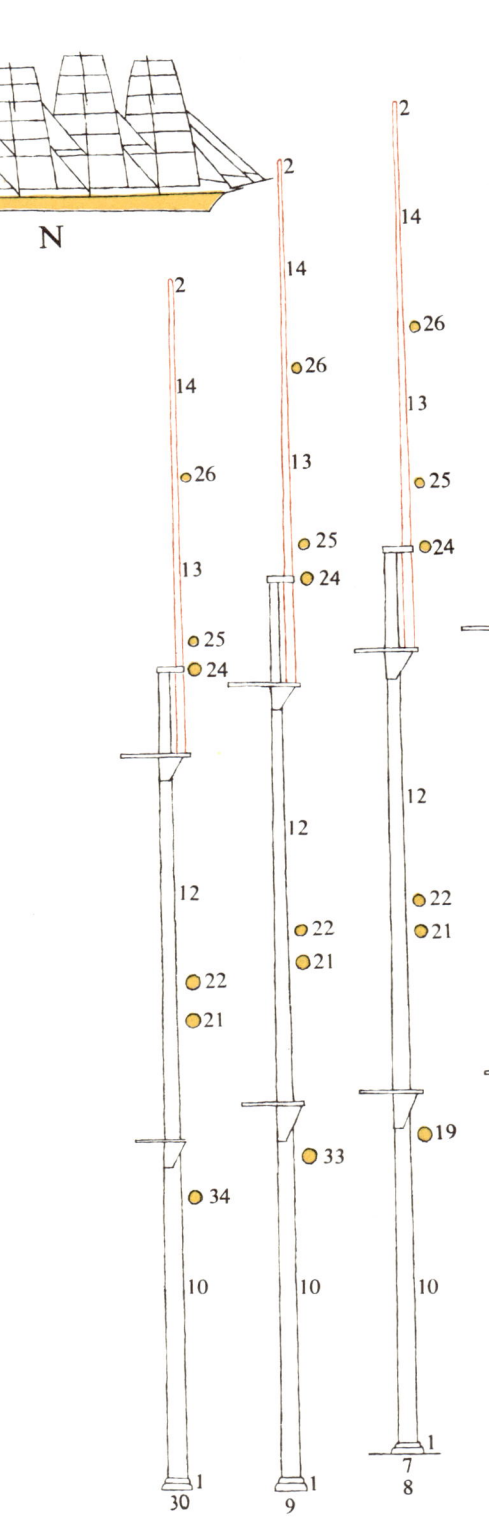

MASTS AND SPARS

1	Mast coat	12	Square-rigged topmast	21	Lower topsail yard	28 Moonsail yard
2	Truck	13	Topgallant mast	22	Upper topsail yard	29 Masthead and housing
3	Foremast	14	Royal mast	23	Topgallant yard for	of topmast
4	Mainmast	15	Skysail mast		single topgallant sail	30 Jiggermast
5	Snow mast	16	Moonsail mast	24	Lower topgallant yard	31 Spankermast
8	Mizzenmast	17	Fore yard	25	Upper topgallant yard	32 Flagpole
9	Laeisz mast	18	Main yard	26	Royal yard	33 Laeisz yard
10	Lower mast	19	Crossjack yard	27	Skysail yard	34 Jigger yard
11	Fore-and-aft-rigged topmast	20	Topsail yard for single topsail			

The terminology for masts varies in different languages. Numbers 6 and 7, missing in list above, refer to Teutonic languages only.

77

MASTS AND TOPS

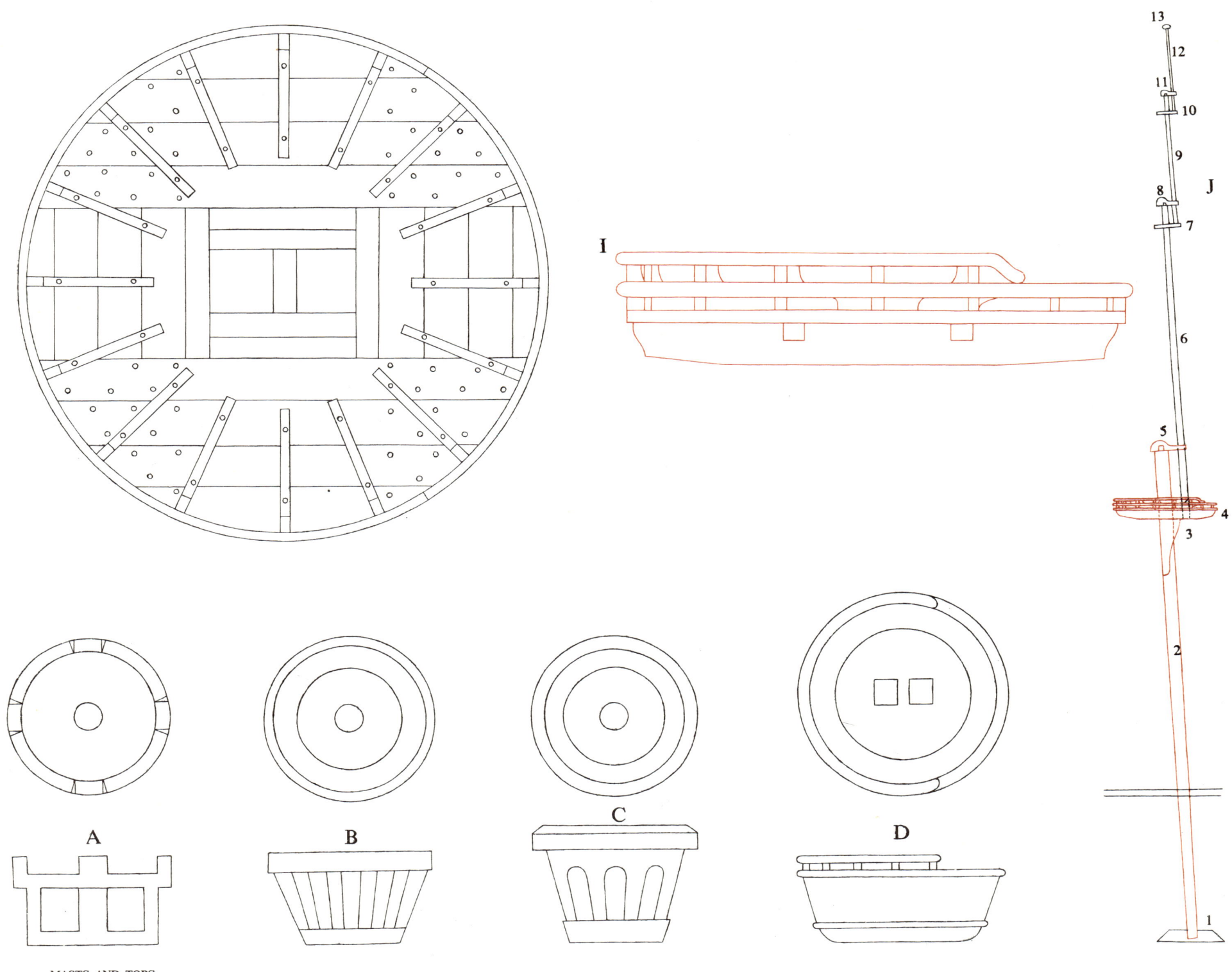

MASTS AND TOPS

A Early medieval top
B Medieval top
C Medieval top
D Top, about 1550
I Top from the end of the 17th century
J Mast from the end of the 17th century (from an old book on ship building)

1 Mast step in keelson
2 Lower mast
3 Cheeks
4 Trestletrees supporting rigging and topmast
5 Lower cap
6 Topmast
7 Topmast crosstree
8 Topmast cap
9 Topgallant mast
10 Topgallant crosstree
11 Topgallant cap
12 Flagpole
13 Truck

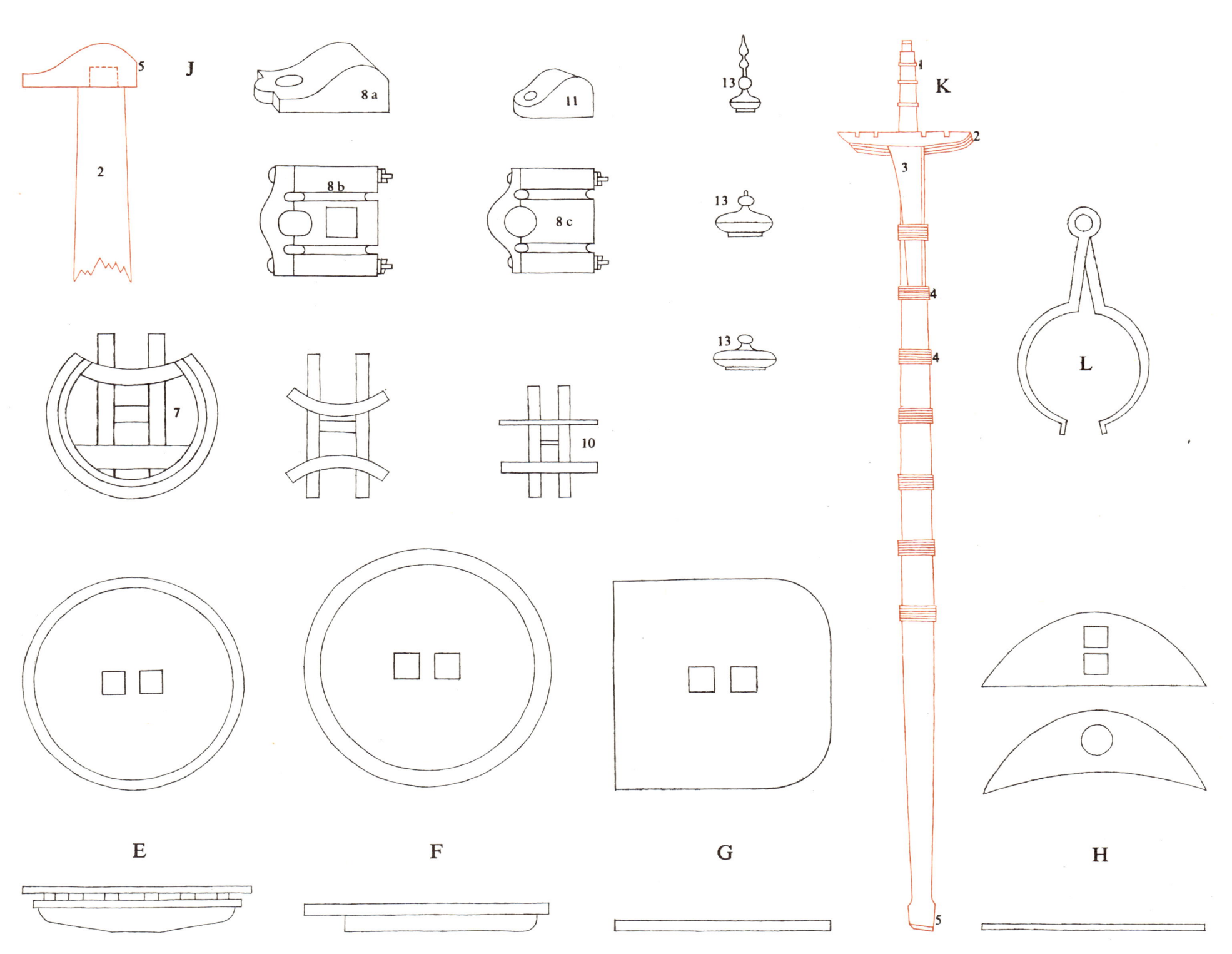

MASTS AND TOPS

MASTS AND TOPS

E *Top in the 17th century*
F *Top in the 18th century*
G *Top in the 19th century*
H *Tops, about 1900*

J *Mast from the end of the 17th century (continues from J on page 78)*
2 Lower masthead
5 Lower cap

7 Topmast crosstree
8 Dutch cap made in one piece, a: as seen from the side, b: another Cap made in two pieces as seen from below, c: the same as seen from above

10 Topgallant crosstree
11 Small Dutch cap
13 Trucks from the 17th century

K *Lower mast seen from port side*
1 Lower masthead
2 Trestletrees
3 Cheeks
4 Rope wooldings around the mast
5 Heel of mast

L *Mast calipers*

79

STANDING RIGGING

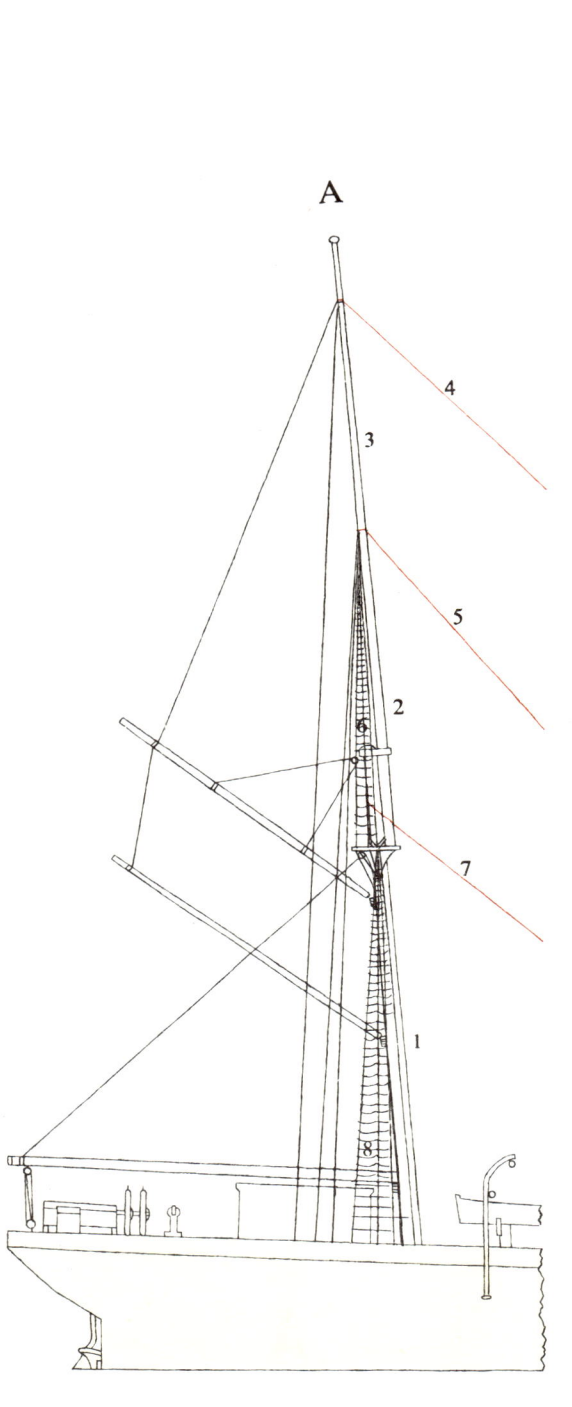

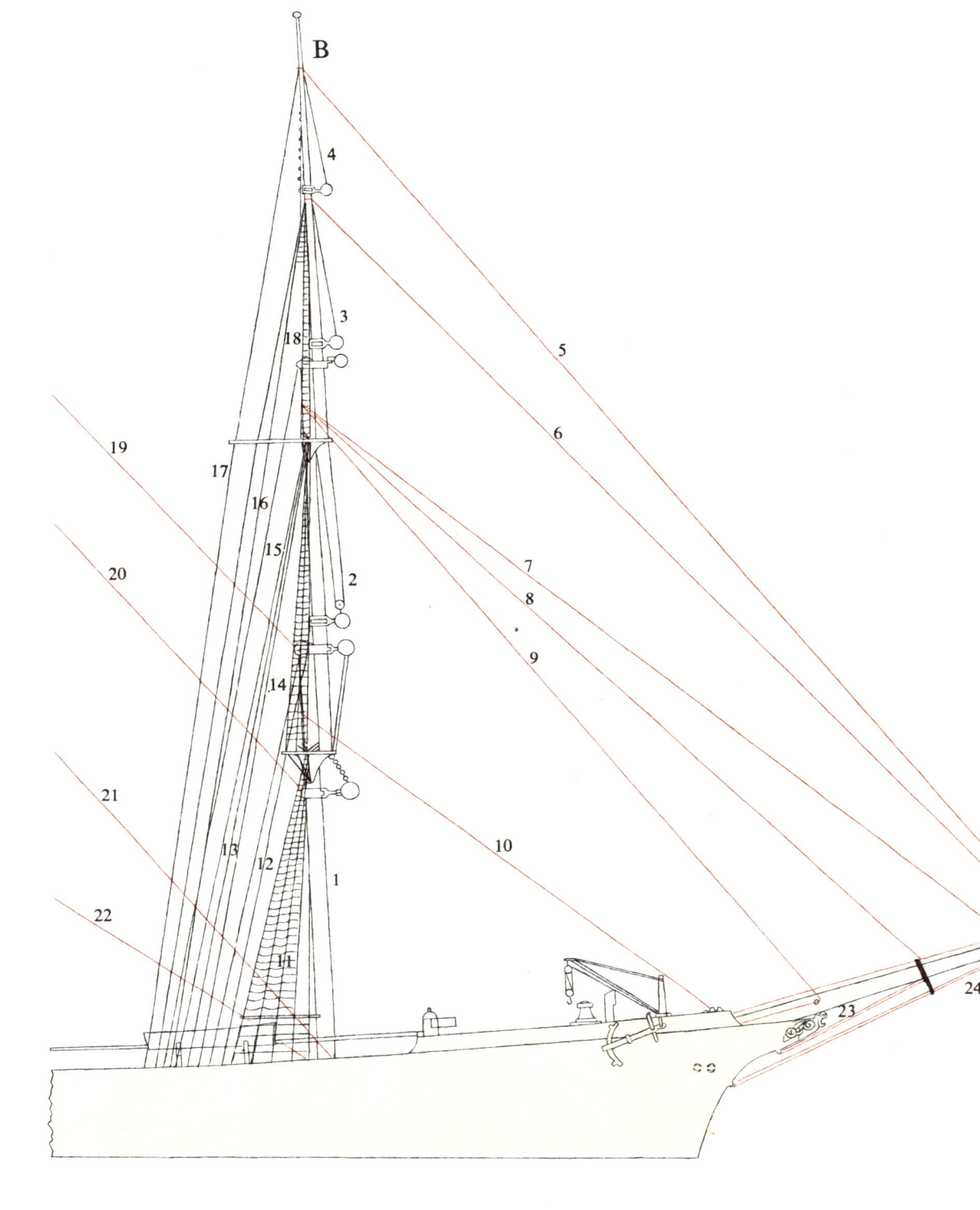

STANDING RIGGING OF A FOUR-MASTED BARK

A *Jigger mast* (identical with mizzenmast of a three-masted bark)
1. Jigger lower mast
2. Jigger topmast
3. Jigger topgallant mast
4. Jigger topgallant stay
5. Jigger topmast stay
6. Jigger topmast rigging or shrouds
7. Jigger stay
8. Jigger rigging or jigger shrouds

B *Foremast* (identical with mainmast and mizzenmast except in the lead of the stays)
1. Fore lower mast
2. Fore topmast
3. Fore topgallant mast
4. Fore royal mast
5. Fore royal stay
6. Fore topgallant stay
7. Outer jib stay
8. Inner jib stay
9. Fore topmast stay
10. Fore stay
11. Fore rigging or shrouds
12. Fore cap backstays
13. Fore topmast backstays
14. Fore topmast rigging or shrouds
15. Fore topmast cap backstay
16. Fore topgallant backstays
17. Fore royal backstay
18. Fore topgallant rigging or shrouds
19. Main royal stay
20. Main topgallant stay
21. Main topmast stay
22. Main stay
23. Bob stay
24. Outer bob stay

STAYS AND SHROUDS

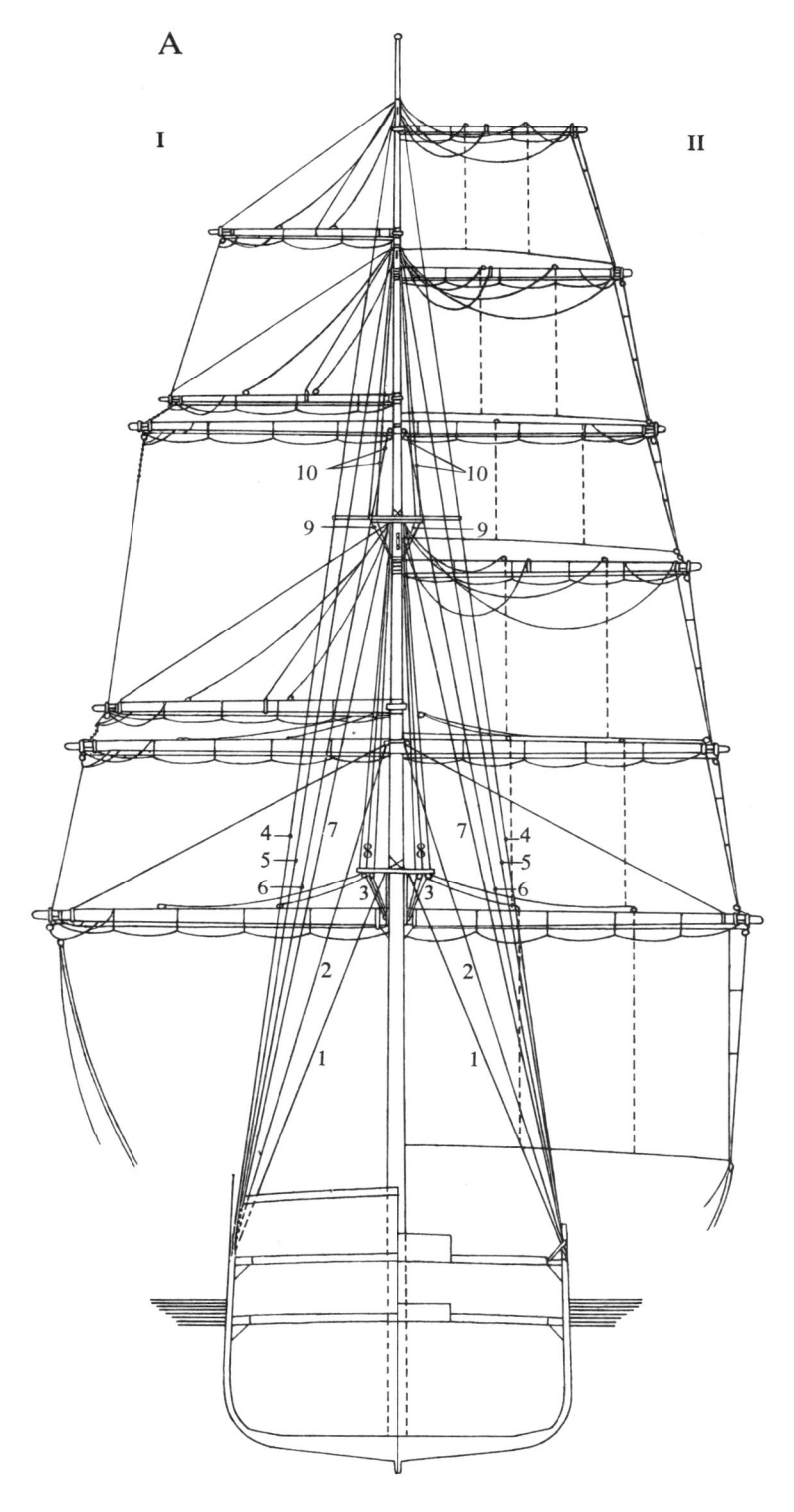

STAYS AND SHROUDS

A *Square-rigged foremast of a big modern sailing ship as seen from aft, with the sails furled on the port side (I) and set on the starboard side (II)*

1. Lower rigging or shrouds
2. Cap backstay
3. Futtock rigging, futtock shrouds
4. Royal back stay
5. Topgallant backstay(s)
6. Topmast cap backstay
7. Topmast backstay(s)
8. Topmast rigging, topmast shrouds
9. Topmast futtock rigging
10. Topgallant rigging, topgallant shrouds

B *This picture of a top, seen from the side, shows how shrouds and stays are fastened to the mast*

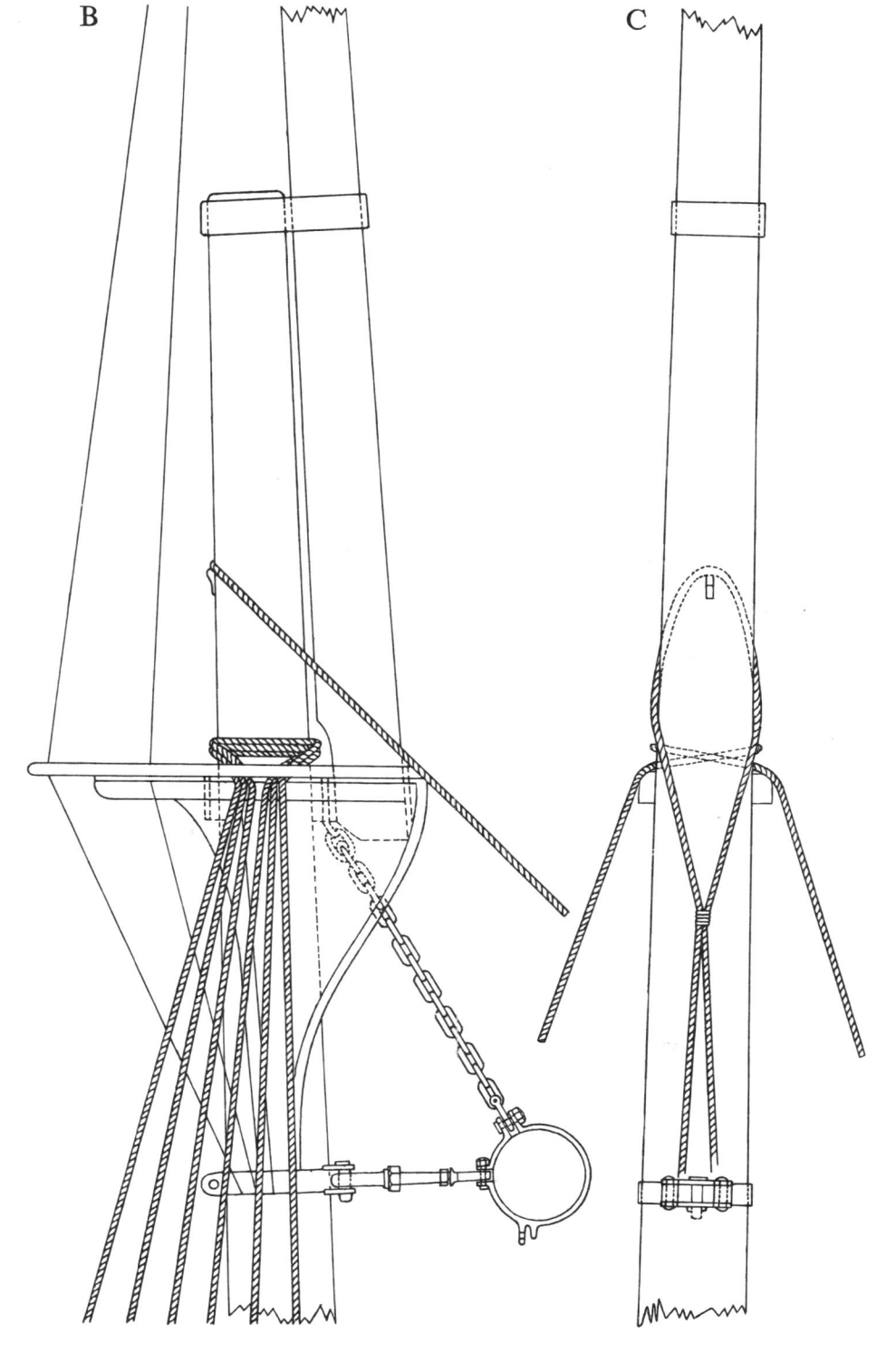

C *The same top as B, here seen from ahead*

PARRELS

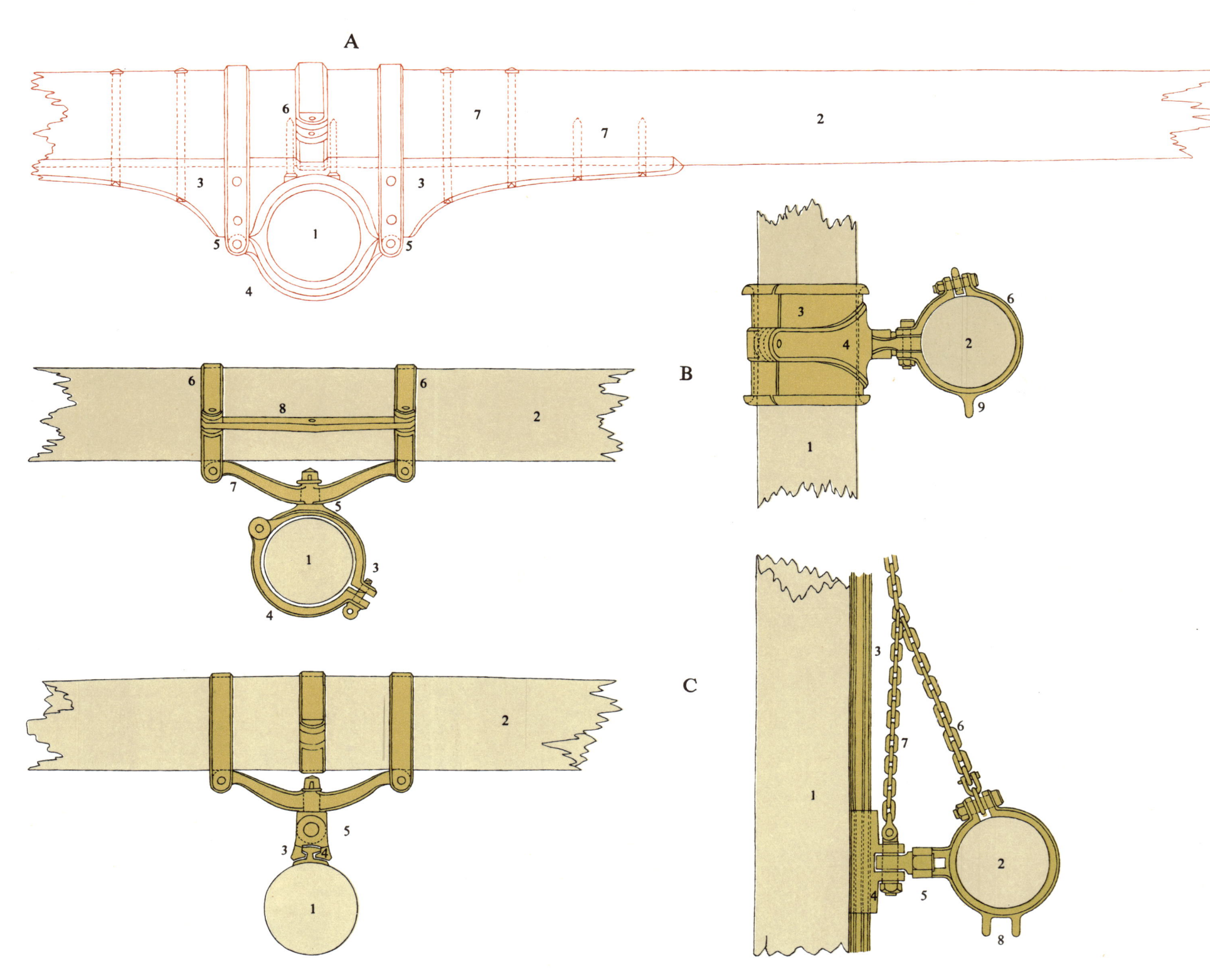

DIFFERENT PARRELS

A *Parrel with cleats on a wooden yard*
1 Topmast
2 Yard
3 Wooden cleats
4 Half-iron hoop served with leather
5 Pins forming hinges to open the parrel
6 Iron band to take the tie
7 Iron straps and bolts securing parrel to yard

B *Tub parrel for iron yard*
1 Topmast
2 Yard
3 Tub divided in halves
4 Iron binding for same
5 Gooseneck bolt
6 Iron bands to take parrel and tie
7 Yoke for the parrel
8 Yoke for the tie
9 Eye bolt for quarter-block

C *Parrel, sliding on T-bar in a big ship*
1 Topmast
2 Topsail yard
3 T-bar
4 Slide
5 Two-way coupling
6 Tie
7 Connecting chain keeping slide in place
8 Eye bolts for quarter-blocks

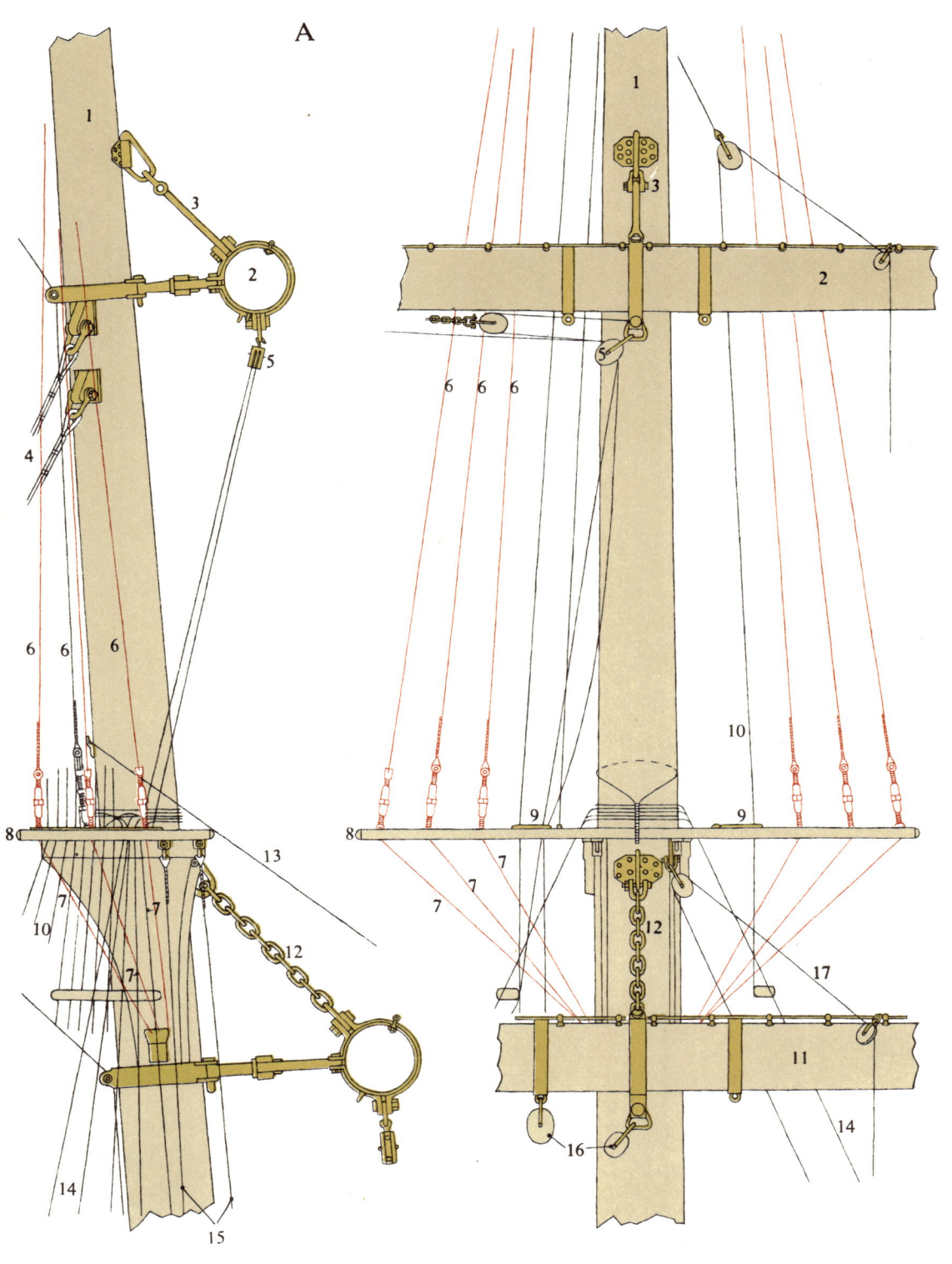

TOP AND CROSSTREE

TOP AND CROSSTREES IN A BIG MODERN SAILING SHIP

A *Details around the top*
1. Topmast, built in one with lower mast
2. Lower topsail yard with its truss
3. Lower topsail yard tie
4. Lower cap backstays
5. Quarter block for upper topsail sheet and topsail clewline
6. Topmast rigging, ratlines not shown
7. Futtock shrouds
8. Top
9. Fairleader
10. Running gear rove through fairleader
11. Lower yard with its truss
12. Lower yard tie
13. Lower stay, doubled
14. Lower rigging, ratlines not shown
15. Pendants for braces from mast ahead, leading to brace winch
16. Quarterblock for topsail sheet and the course clewgarnet
17. Buntline with its leading blocks

B *Details around the topgallant crosstrees*
1. Topmast
2. Topgallant mast
3. Topmast head
4. Topgallant crosstrees
5. Spreader of topgallant backstays
6. Topmast cap
7. Lower topgallant yard
8. Lower topgallant truss
9. Lower topgallant tie
10. Upper topsail yard
11. Upper topsail parrel, slide running on a T-bar
12. Topsail halliard, wire tackle leading to winch on deck
13. Leading block for topsail brace from mast ahead
14. Topmast backstays
15. Topmast cap backstay
16. Topgallant futtock shrouds
17. Topmast stay
18. Topgallant rigging
19. Spreader lift
20. Quarterblock for lower topgallant clewline and upper topgallant sheet
21. Quarterblock for topsail downhaul and lower topgallant sheet

RIGGING

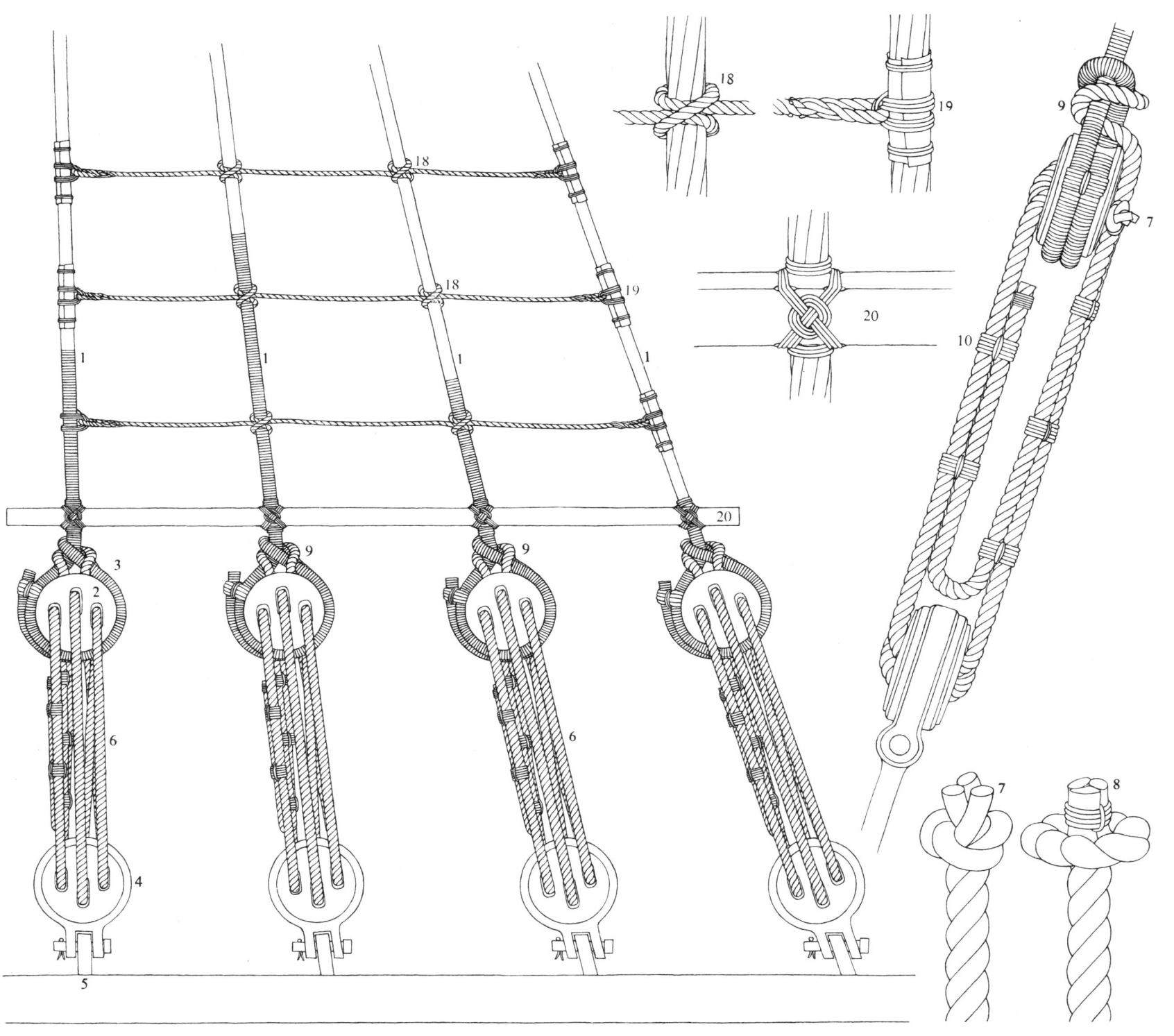

LOWER PART OF RIGGING, PORT SIDE

1. Shrouds, lower ends of which are served with spun yarn
2. Upper deadeye
3. Deadeye turned in cutter-stay fashion
4. Lower deadeye in iron strap
5. Chain plate
6. Lanyard, standing part with wall knot
7. Wall knot
8. Double wall knot
9. Hauling end of lanyard hitched
10. Surplus end of lanyard made up
11. Setting up a shroud by luff upon luff
12. Luff clapped on lanyard up and down
13. Selvagee on shroud parceled for protection
14. Selvagee strapped on lanyard with a toggle
15. Double Blackwall hitch
16. Lower block of burton from masthead
17. Standing end of lanyard passed around neck of deadeye
18. Ratlines in rigging
19. Seizing of ratline to shroud
20. Wooden batten secured to shroud with seizing wire

RIGGING SCREWS

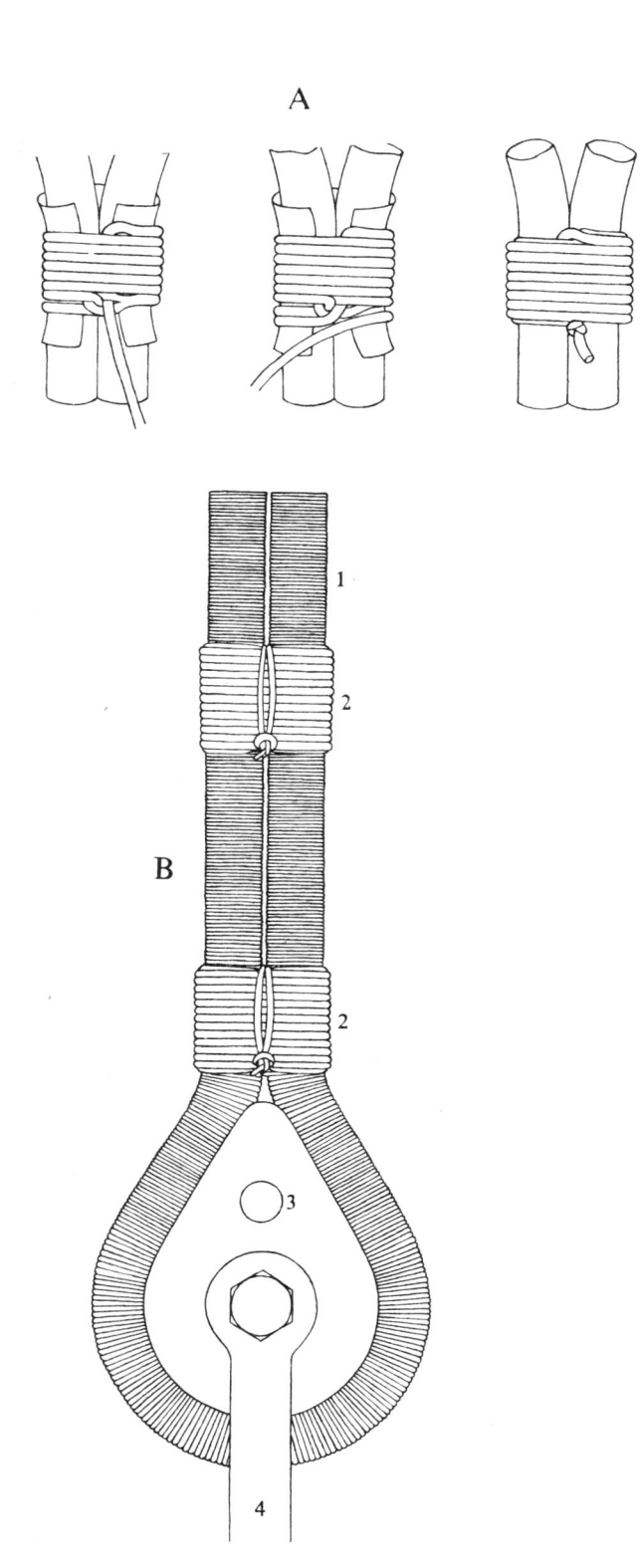

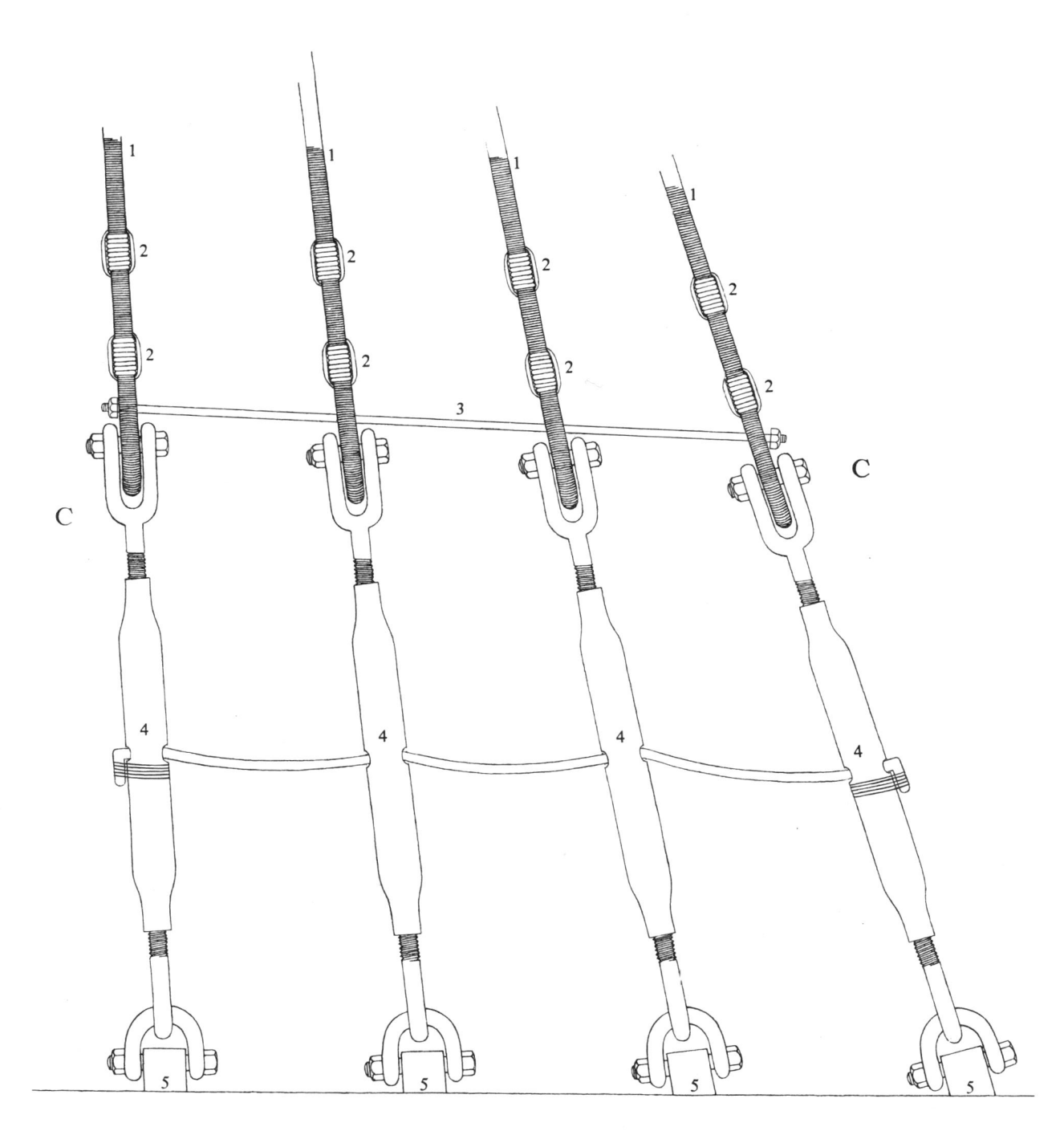

SEIZINGS AND RIGGING SCREWS

A Three stages of making an old-fashioned round seizing; formerly used on hemp shrouds

B 1 Shroud or backstay of wire served over with spun yarn
    2 Rigging seizings of galvanized wire
    3 Solid heart thimble with a hole for the sheer pole
    4 Upper end of rigging screw

C 1 Lower ends of four port side shrouds
    2 Rigging seizings
    3 Sheer pole
    4 Rigging screws or turnbuckles
    5 Upper ends of chain plates

BOWSPRIT

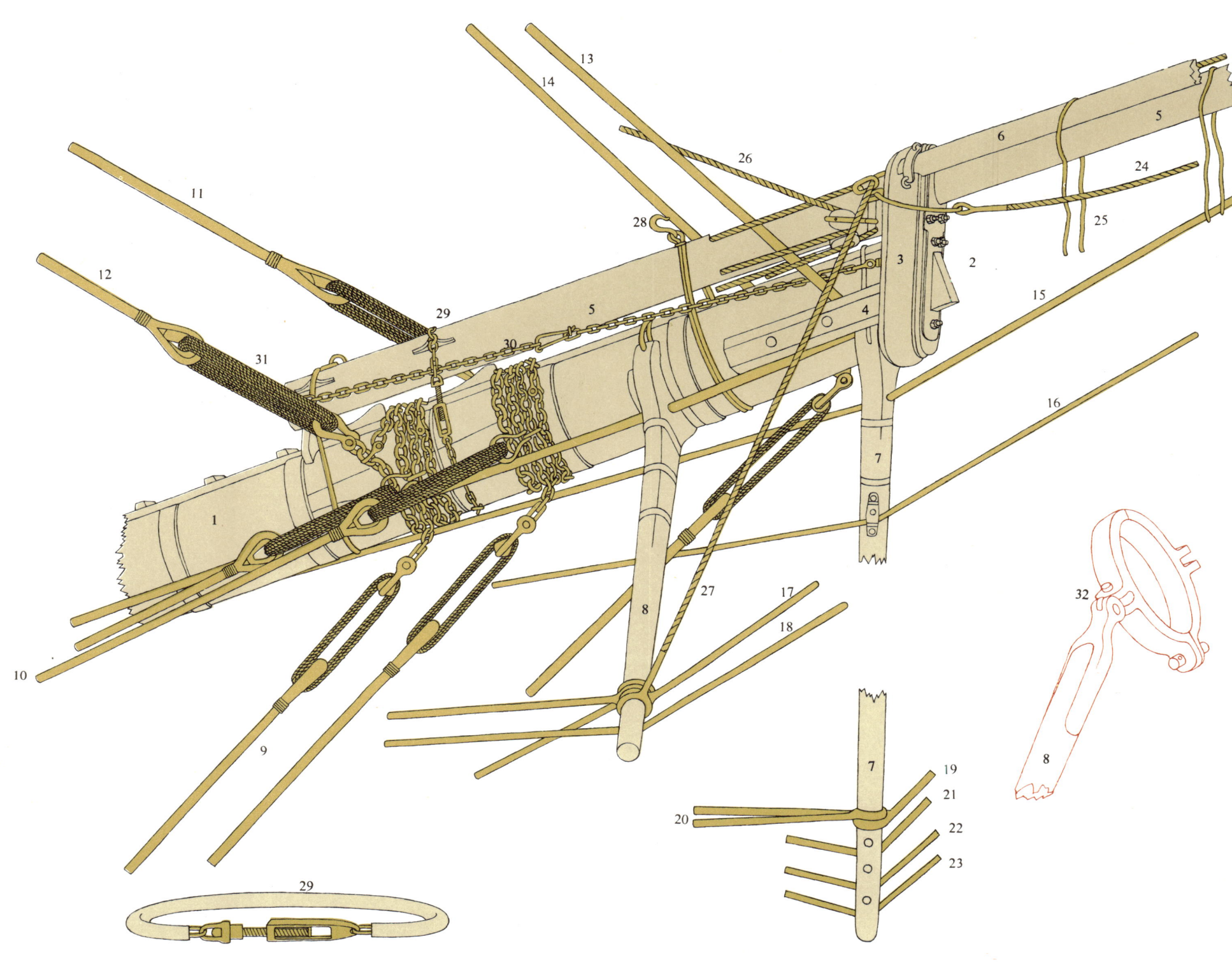

BOWSPRIT OF A FRIGATE, 1890

1. Bowsprit
2. Tenon for bowsprit cap
3. Bowsprit cap
4. Bowsprit bees
5. Jib boom
6. Heel of flying jib boom
7. Martingale boom or dolphin striker
8. Whisker
9. Inner and outer bobstays
10. Bowsprit shrouds
11. Forestay
12. Preventer forestay
13. Fore topmast stay
14. Fore topmast preventer stay
15. Jib stay
16. Jib outhaul
17. Jib boom guy
18. Flying jib boom guy
19. Martingale stay
20. Backropes or martingale guys
21. Flying jib stay
22. Fore topgallant stay
23. Fore royal stay
24. Jib boom horse, footrope
25. Gaskets
26. Fore topsail bowline
27. Whisker lift
28. Fore topmast staysail tack
29. Jib boom gammoning
30. Jib boom heel stay
31. Lanyards for stays
32. Iron fitting for whiskers

BOWSPRIT

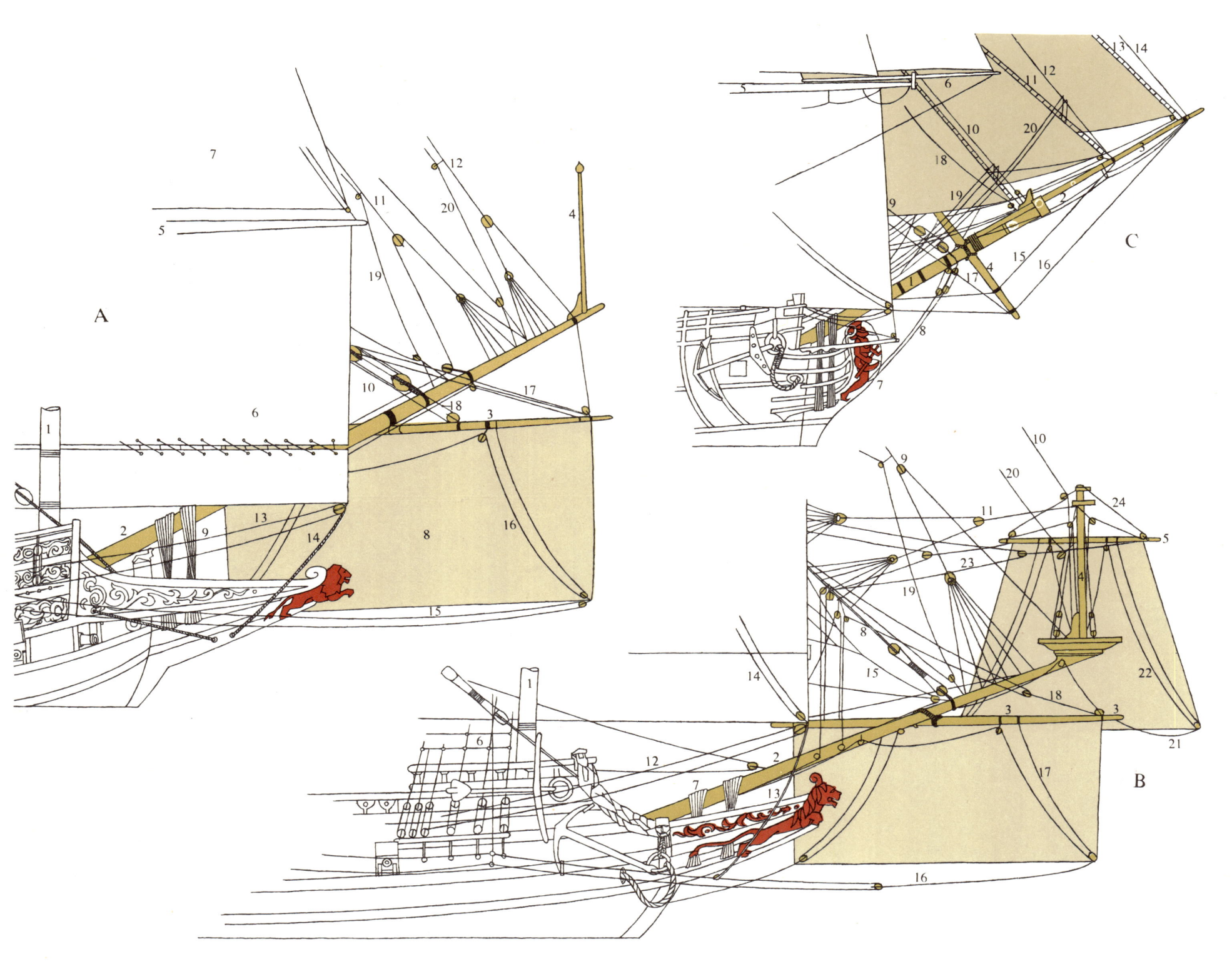

THE BOWSPRIT DURING THREE CENTURIES

A *The bowsprit and its rigging at the end of the 16th century*
1. Foremast
2. Bowsprit
3. Spritsail yard
4. Jackstaff
5. Foreyard
6. Foresail with bonnet
7. Fore topsail
8. Spritsail
9. Gammoning
10. Forestay lanyard
11. Fore topmast stay
12. Fore topgallant stay
13. Fore sheet
14. Fore tack
15. Spritsail sheet
16. Spritsail clewline
17. Spritsail braces
18. Spritsail lifts
19. Fore topsail bowline
20. Fore topgallant bowline

B *Bowsprit with spritsail topmast and rigging, from the 17th century*
1. Foremast
2. Bowsprit
3. Spritsail yard
4. Spritsail topmast
5. Spritsail topsail yard
6. Fore rigging
7. Gammoning
8. Forestay
9. Fore topmast stay
10. Fore topgallant stay
11. Spritsail topmast backstay
12. Fore sheet
13. Fore tack
14. Fore clewgarnet
15. Fore bowline
16. Spritsail sheet
17. Spritsail clewline
18. Spritsail braces
19. Fore topsail bowline
20. Fore topgallant bowline
21. Spritsail topsail sheet
22. Spritsail topsail clewline
23. Spritsail topsail braces
24. Spritsail topsail lift

C *Bowsprit with jib boom and rigging, end of the 18th century*
1. Bowsprit
2. Jib boom
3. Flying jib boom
4. Spritsail yard
5. Foreyard
6. Studdingsail boom
7. Fore tack bumpkin
8. Bobstay
9. Forestay
10. Fore topmast stay
11. Jibstay
12. Fore topgallant stay
13. Flying jibstay
14. Royal stay
15. Jib boom guy
16. Flying jib boom guy
17. Spritsail braces
18. Fore topmast staysail downhaul
19. Weather side jib sheet
20. Weather side flying jib sheet

87

BOWSPRIT

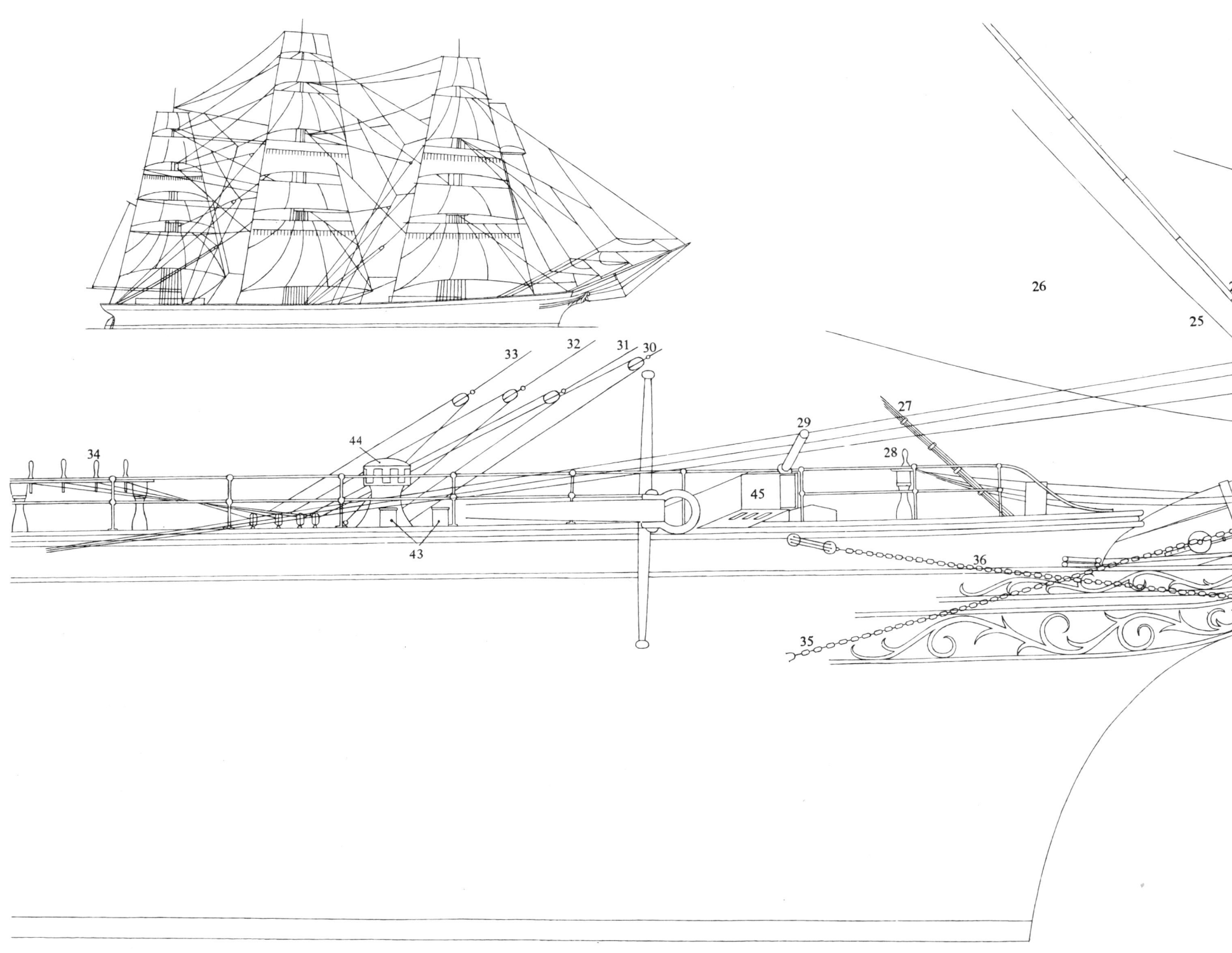

BOWSPRIT OF THE SHIP, PRINCE OSCAR, BUILT IN 1864

1. Shark's tail
2. Fore royal stay
3. Fore topgallant stay
4. Flying jib tack
5. Flying jib downhaul
6. Flying jib
7. Flying jib boom
8. Outer jib stay
9. Outer jib tack
10. Outer jib downhaul
11. Outer jib
12. Inner jib stay
13. Inner jib tack
14. Inner jib downhaul
15. Inner jib
16. Flying jib boom guy
17. Outer jib boom guy
18. Inner jib boom guy
19. Bowsprit cap
20. Swinging boom fore guy lead block
21. Jib boom
22. Bowsprit
23. Fore topmast stay
24. Fore topmast staysail tack
25. Fore topmast staysail downhaul
26. Fore topmast staysail
27. Fore stay
28. Pinrail for staysails' downhauls
29. Whisker boom
30. Flying jib sheet
31. Outer jib sheet
32. Inner jib sheet
33. Fore topmast staysail sheet
34. Pinrail
35. Bowsprit shroud
36. Martingale backrope (Martingale guy)
37. Bobstay
38. Martingale or Dolphin striker
39. Inner martingale (stay)
40. Middle martingale (stay)
41. Outer martingale (stay)
42. Foot rope
43. Bitts
44. Capstan working the windlass
45. Cathead

BOWSPRIT

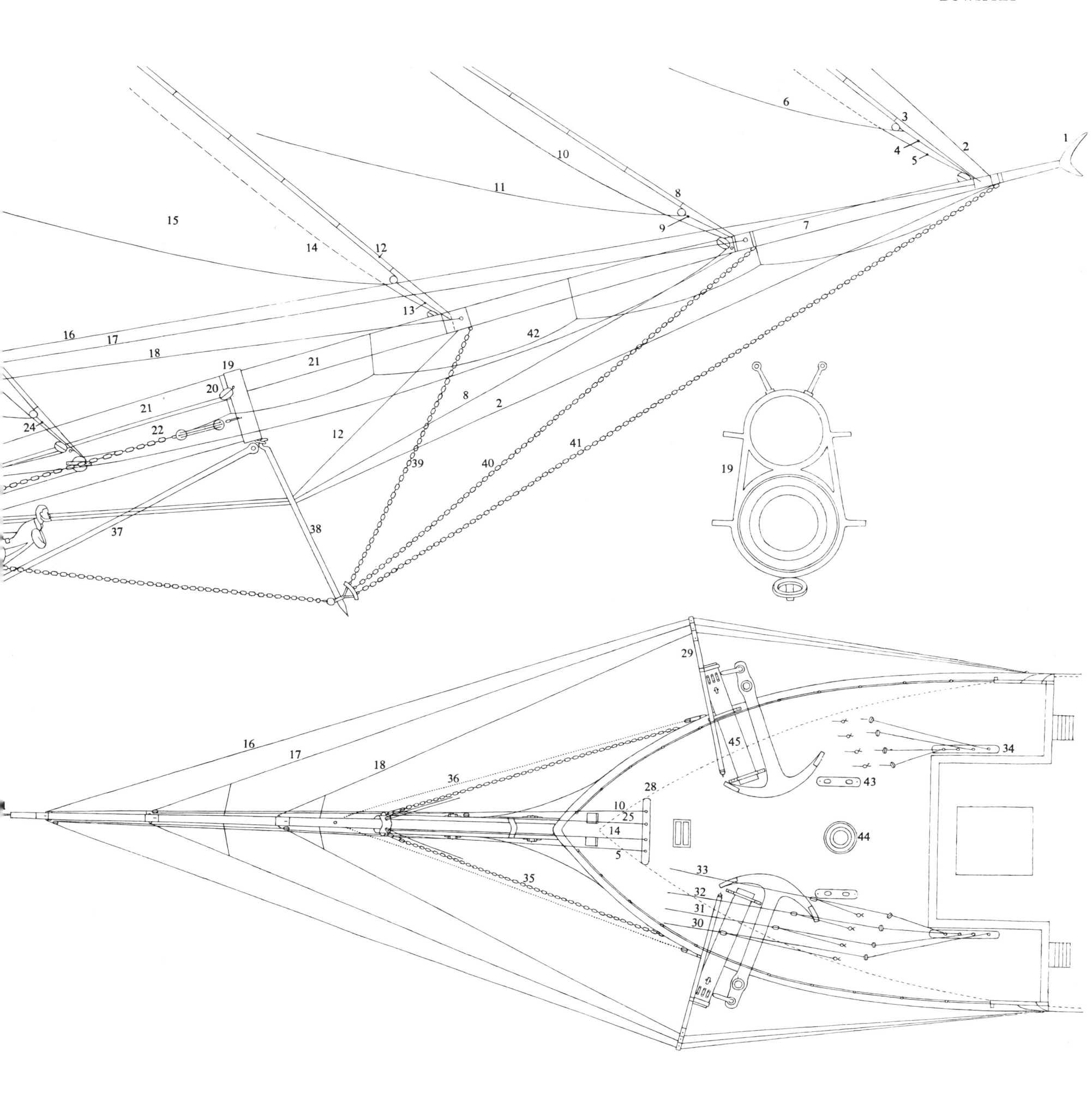

89

A SNOW

DETAILS OF MAINMAST AND MAINYARD OF A SNOW, ABOUT 1800

1 Mainmast	6 Main rigging	11 Main topsail	16 Mainyard footrope	21 Topsail sheet
2 Mainyard	or shrouds	12 Trysail	17 Mainyard stirrups	22 Topsail clewline
3 Main top	7 Futtock shrouds	13 Mainyard sling	18 Main clewgarnet	23 Topsail bowline bridle
4 Trysail mast	8 Topmast shrouds	14 Main lift	19 Reef tackle	24 Fore topsail brace
5 Trysail gaff	9 Mainstay	15 Main brace	20 Reef earing	25 Trysail brails
	10 Mainsail			

SHIP OF THE LINE

DETAILS OF MAINMAST HEAD, SHIP OF THE LINE, 1750

1. Mainmast
2. Trestle trees
3. Maintop
4. Lower masthead
5. Heel of topmast
6. Main cap
7. Mainyard
8. Main parrel
9. Parrel tackle
10. Main rigging or shrouds
11. Mainstay
12. Spring stay
13. Futtock shrouds
14. Topmast shrouds
15. Mizzen topmast stay
16. Main lift
17. Main footrope
18. Main clewgarnet
19. Main topsail sheet
20. Main jeers

91

OLDER STEAMERS

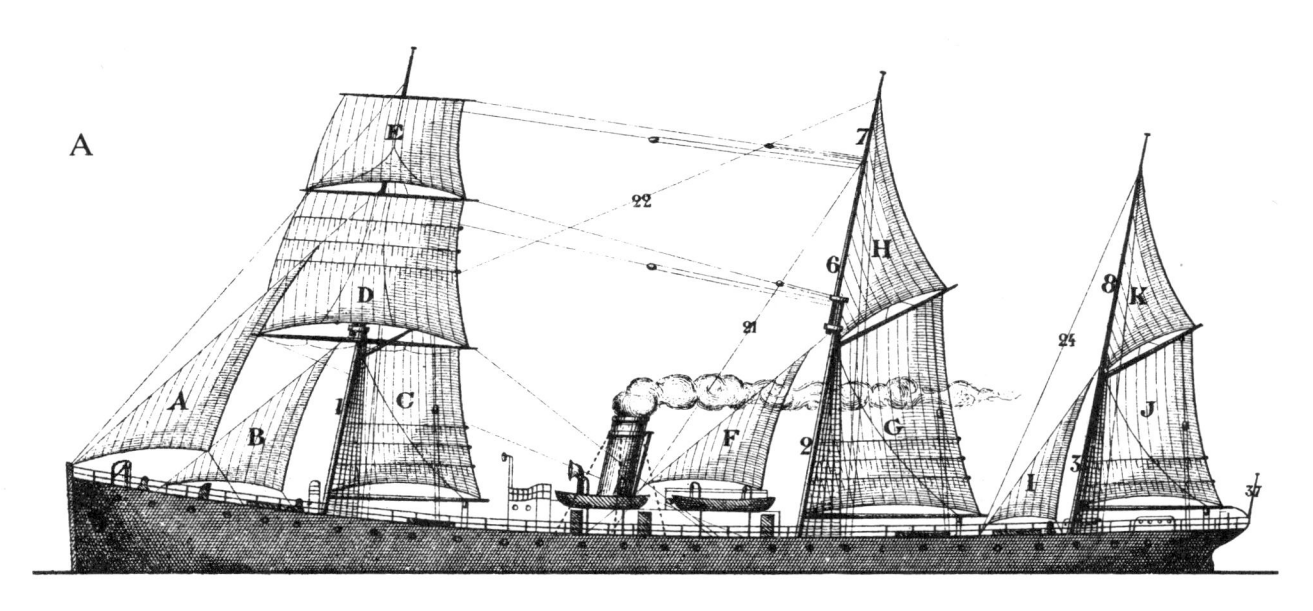

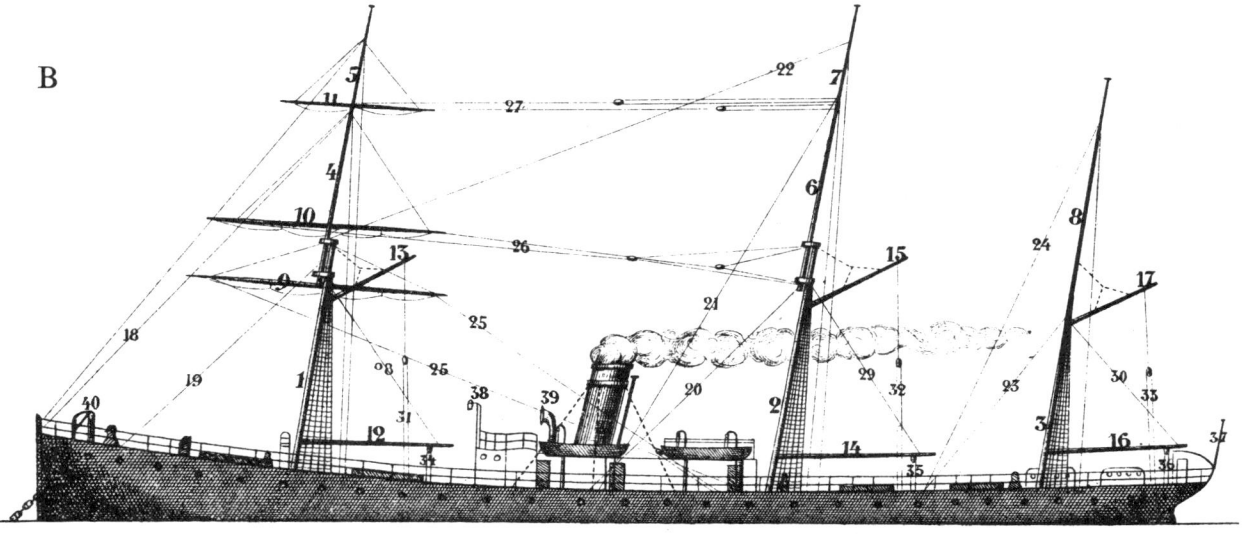

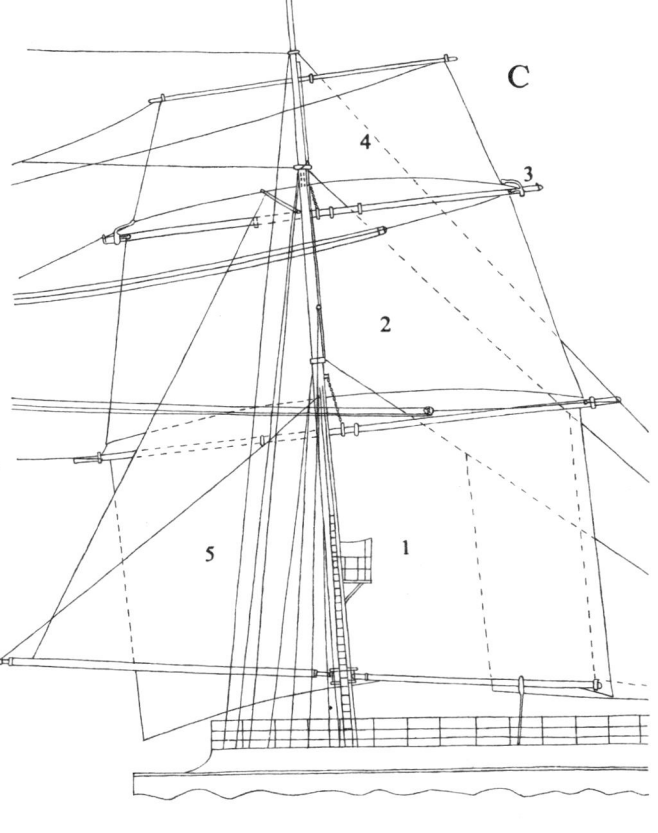

RIGGING OF OLDER STEAMERS

A, B *Steamer from about 1890, rigged as a three-masted topsail schooner*

- A Fore topmast staysail
- B Fore staysail
- C Foresail; Boom foresail
- D Topsail
- E Topgallant sail
- F Main staysail
- G Mainsail
- H Main gaff topsail
- I Mizzen staysail
- J Mizzen
- K Mizzen gaff topsail

1. Foremast
2. Mainmast
3. Mizzenmast
4. Fore topmast
5. Fore topgallant mast
6. Main topmast
7. Main topgallant mast
8. Mizzen topmast
9. Fore yard
10. Topsail yard
11. Topgallant yard
12. Fore boom
13. Fore gaff
14. Main boom
15. Main gaff
16. Mizzen boom
17. Mizzen gaff
18. Fore topmast stay
19. Fore stay
20. Main stay
21. Main topmast stay
22. Main topgallant stay
23. Mizzen stay
24. Mizzen topmast stay
25. Fore braces
26. Topsail braces
27. Topgallant braces
28. Fore boom topping lift
29. Main boom topping lift
30. Mizzen boom topping lift
31. Fore vang
32. Main vang
33. Mizzen vang
34. Boom foresail sheet
35. Main sheet
36. Mizzen sheet
37. Flagstaff
38. Pole compass
39. Ventilator
40. Anchor davit

C *Patent reefing topsails were not unusual in the old steamers carrying sails, because of the possibility of reefing without a man leaving the deck*

1. Foresail
2. Topsail with Collin's and Pinkney's Patent (3)
4. Topgallant sail
5. Bermuda-type trysail traveling on a bar abaft the mast

CARGO SHIP RIGGING

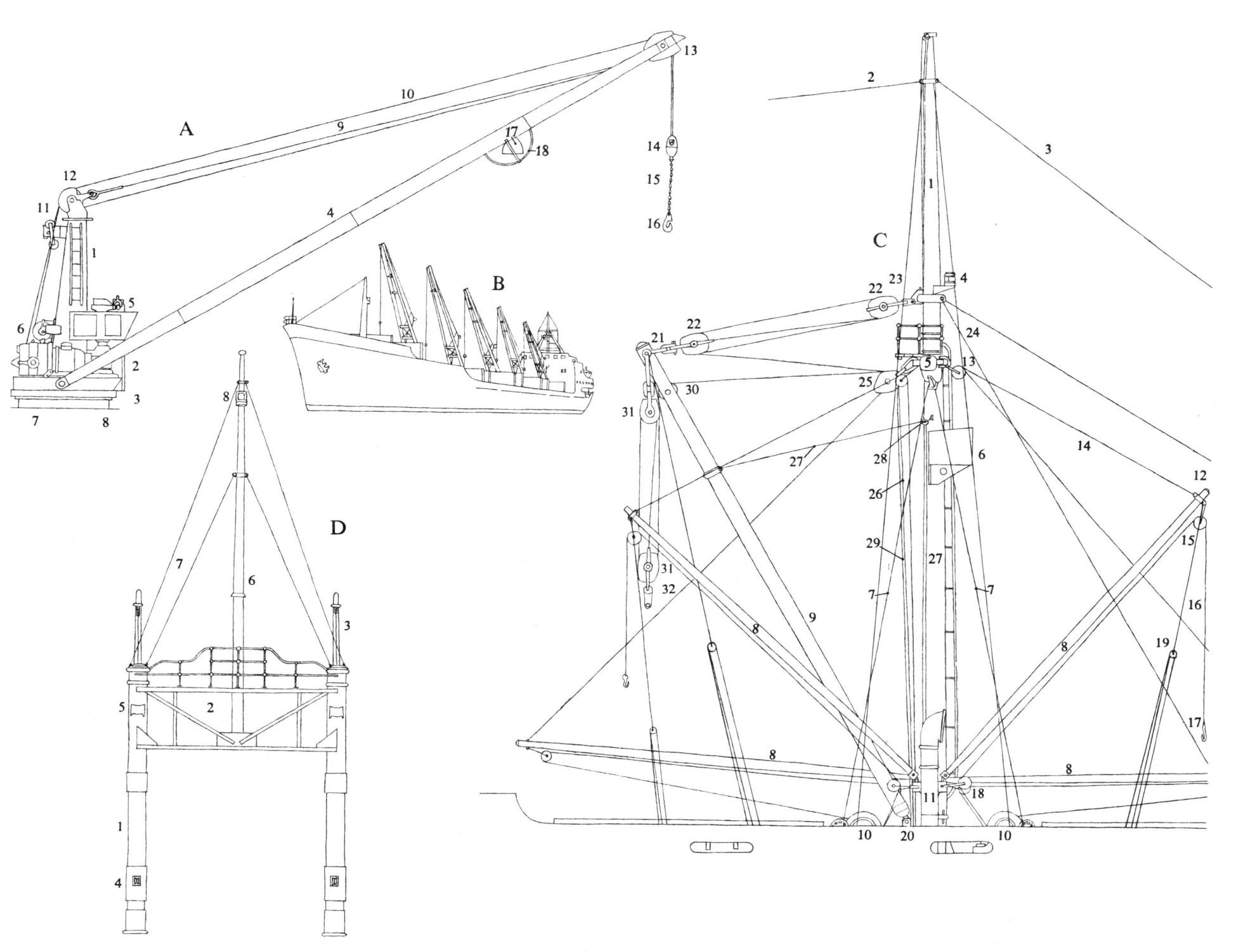

CARGO SHIP RIGGING

A *Electric deck crane*
1. Crane post
2. Electric equipment platform
3. Turning rim
4. Crane jib
5. Maneuvering stand
6. Topping motor
7. Hoisting motor
8. Slewing motor
9. Topping rope
10. Hoisting rope
11. Slack rope switch
12. Triple sheave block
13. Triple sheave block
14. Weight and swivel
15. Chain
16. Cargo hook
17. Electric light
18. Cage guard

B *Cargo vessel with deck cranes*

C *Rigging and derrick arrangement*
1. Foremast
2. Signal stay
3. Topmast stay
4. Masthead light
5. Outrigger
6. Crow's nest
7. Shrouds
8. 5-ton booms
9. 20-ton heavy boom
10. Topping and cargo winches
11. 5-ton boom, gooseneck
12. Boom band
13. Topping lift block
14. Topping lift
15. Cargo hoist block
16. Cargo fall
17. Cargo hook
18. Topping lift and cargo fall heel blocks
19. 5-ton boom guy
20. Heavy boom heel fitting
21. Boom head eye plate
22. Four-fold topping lift tackle
23. Mast band
24. Preventer stays
25. Topping lift and cargo fall block
26. Topping lift hauling part (wire)
27. Topper
28. Topper block
29. Cargo fall hauling part
30. Cargo fall sheave
31. Four-fold cargo tackle
32. 20-ton cargo hook

D *Goal-post mast, pair mast*
1. King post
2. Transverse girder
3. Boom (behind post)
4. Gooseneck fitting
5. Band for lashing boom
6. Topmast
7. Topmast shrouds
8. Masthead light

Opposite is a 1492 nao; it is Columbus' SANTA MARIA and it introduces the section about sails. The color in the picture illustrates the fact that the chapter deals with flags as well.

THE SAIL

THE SAIL

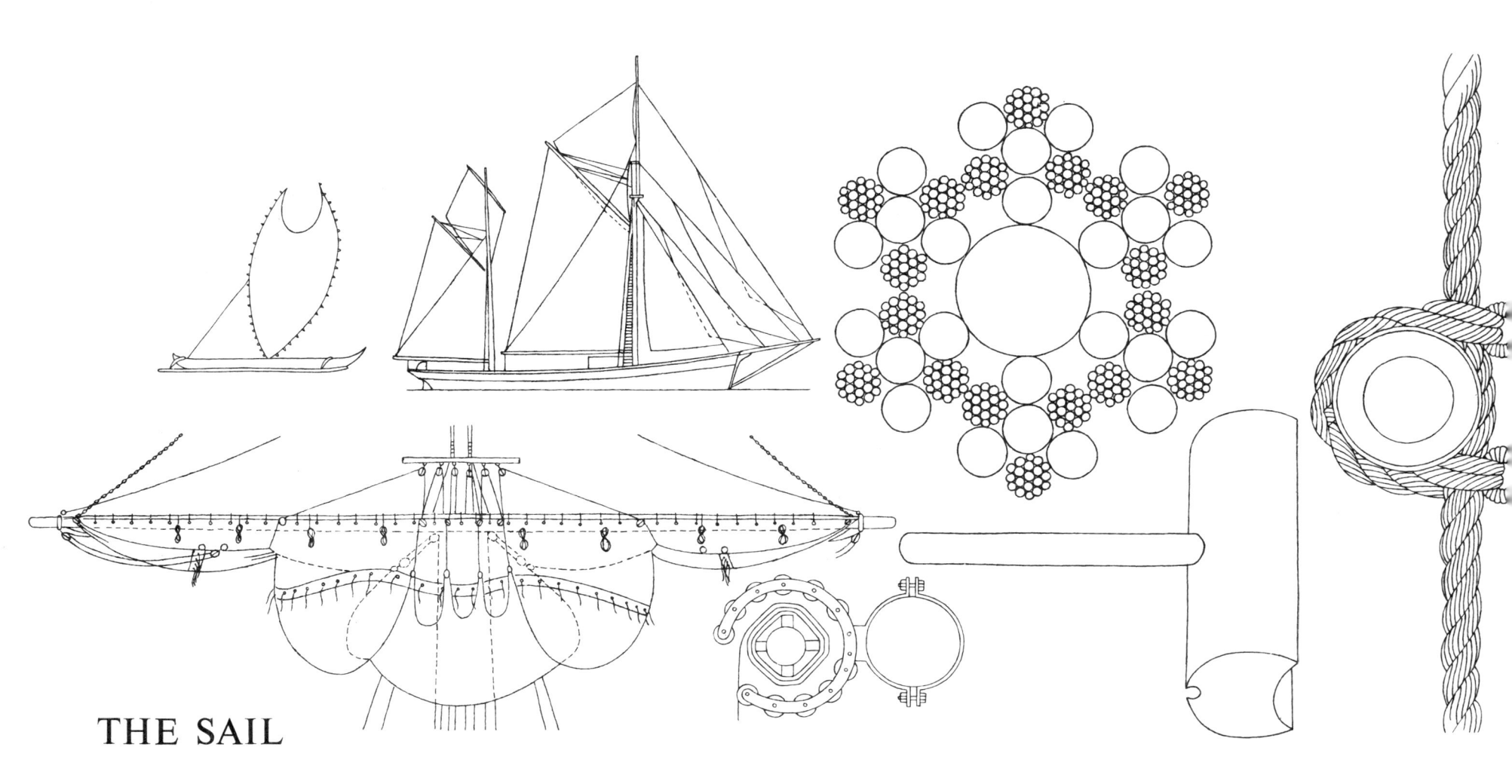

BY SAM SVENSSON

The oldest sail we know is the square sail. For many thousands of years no other types were used. The distinguishing feature of the square sail is that the same side is always turned to the wind. This is a simple, fundamental principle, and none of the aerodynamic inventions of recent years have changed the square sail or influenced its value for sailing on the high seas.

The fore-and-aft sail, which can face into the wind with either side, is a more recent development. What aerodynamics could not do for the square sail it has succeeded in doing for the fore-and-aft sail. The latter is very effective in close-hauled sailing and is superior for use while cruising. Today it is the sail most used for sport sailing among off-shore islands where winds are variable and the water is smooth. Because the fore-and-aft sail always has its forward bolt rope as the windward edge and the leech as the leeward edge, it can be cut with a favorable curvature. The square sail, on the other hand, has the starboard or port leech alternately as the windward edge, resulting in a different curvature. The value of the modern fore-and-aft sail on the wind is, however, outweighed by the advantages of the more secure square sail in running before the wind in stormy and high seas. Almost all sailing on the high seas has been done with the square sail. The oldest known reproduction of a boat equipped with a sail is painted on an Egyptian clay urn from the predynastic period. Estimated to be from about 4000 B.C., it could actually be even older. Furthermore, the evidence is not conclusive that this painting shows the world's first sail. Past cultures of which we have no knowledge may very well have had sailing vessels thousands of years before.

Contemporary writings and pictures prove that the sailors of ancient lands in the eastern Mediterranean used sails. In the twenty-seventh chapter of Ezekiel, the ships of Tyrus are described as having cedar masts from Lebanon, gay, embroidered sails of fine Egyptian linen, and awnings of blue and purple cloth from the Isles of Elisha. The decoration of the sails indicates that they were used both for propulsion and as a means of identification.

We have no record of when the art of sailing was brought to Scandinavia, but by the Viking Age it was certainly hundreds, perhaps even thousands, of years old. Early Nordic sails were made of homespun wool, and lacked the durability of linen sail. The cloth would stretch under the force of the wind, and the large sail would sag more and more until it burst. To strengthen the sail and hold it more evenly, a supporting net was fastened to the forward side. The net, often of a different color than the sail, was either of rope, of cloth bands, or of interwoven sennit. The foot of the sail was held down by a number of sheets, forming bridles, all to hold the sail flatter. By the Viking Age, linen sails were in use on larger ships. These sails could be set flatter, making for better sailing on the wind. The long journeys made by the Vikings in European waters and over the Atlantic Ocean would have been impossible, if their ships had not been able to sail with all kinds of wind. At the dawn of Swedish history, the cruising ability of the ships of the time is illustrated in the saga of the King of the Sveas, Erik Väderhatt, who, according to history, could turn the wind so that he never had a headwind.

The majority of ships continued to have only one mast and a single sail for many years. Only after the later Middle Ages did larger ships commonly appear with two or three masts and sails — one sail on each mast. By the end of the 15th century, however, a new sail was set at the head of the mainmast. It was originally very small, and was handled by the men in the top (an early masthead castle). It derived its name, the topsail, from this position. Another sail was added under the bowsprit; this was called the spritsail or blind, as it blocked the view ahead. Eventually a topsail was also added to the foremast. By the middle of the 16th century, then, a large three-masted ship carried six sails: the spritsail under the bowsprit, two sails on the foremast, two sails on the mainmast, and one sail on the mizzenmast. The sail on the mizzenmast was always a triangular lateen sail at this time.

The origin of the lateen sail is unknown. At the fall of the Roman Empire in 476 A.D., all ships had square sails. After that, sources of information on ships and navigation in the Mediterranean are not available for several hundreds of years. Not until the end of the 9th century do Greek manuscripts show some miniatures of ships with triangular sails under an inclined yard. Even today these sails are called lateen sails. These were probably introduced into the Mediterranean by the Arabs, but no one knows whether their origin is Arabian or Polynesian. Up to the 13th century the lateen sail was in use exclusively along the Mediterranean. But from that time on, the square sail began to make a comeback under western European impetus. The lateen sail was used, at this time, along the whole European coastline, especially as a mizzen on larger ships. It probably reached the Baltic by the latter half of the 15th century, about the same time as the carvel or smooth-sided shipbuilding technique came along. Down to the middle of the 18th century the lateen sail was in general international use as the mizzen. It was then replaced by the gaff mizzen. The coastal galleys of the Swedish navy continued to employ lateen sails as long as these ships were in use, the last one being built in 1749. But the development of sail went in the opposite direction in small barges and boats, and in the Mediterranean, the Red Sea, and the Persian Gulf. The lateen sail can be seen on these craft even today.

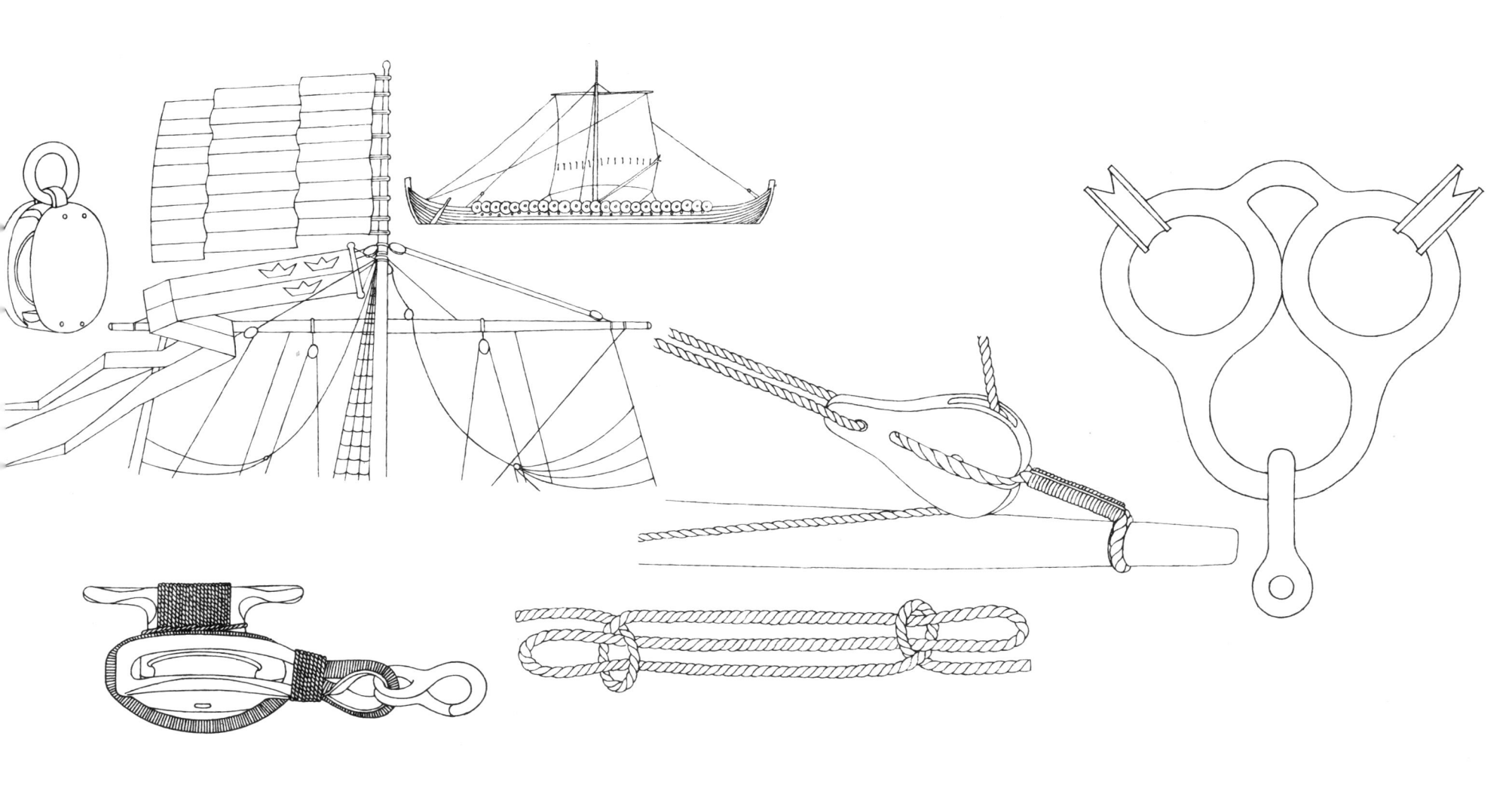

As the lateen sail has to be set on the leeward side of the mast, it is not suitable for tacking with short boards in a narrow channel. The rule is that lateen-rigged craft wear, and the sail is taken around forward of the mast and sheeted on the new lee side when the craft is wearing. Large Arab dhows still sail in this same manner from the Persian Gulf to East African ports, as far down as Zanzibar. They never beat against the wind, but run to Africa in the favorable wind of the northeast monsoon and return with the southwest monsoon to the Persian Gulf. They are, therefore, limited to only one such round trip a year, the same as the Indian grain carriers that make only one voyage a year to Rangoon to pick up rice for Ceylon.

The lateen sail was the world's first fore-and-aft sail. While it enjoyed great popularity in the Near East and Mediterranean for a long time, other types of sail began to appear in Europe. We can follow this development especially well in Holland and Friesland.

During the 16th century, Holland became the world's most powerful maritime nation, replacing the sea power of the Hanseatic League. Using the rich Rhineland inland waterways, the Dutch had developed navigation with small ships in canals and rivers and in the shallow coastal waters between the islands. The inability to beat and especially to tack in a narrow channel, when using a square sail, created the need for new types of sail, and Dutch art records two new fore-and-aft sails, the spritsail and staysail. The former was a simple rectangular sail with one side laced to the mast and extended by a diagonally placed sprit. The sail was found to be very practical, and, as a result, it became the most commonly used sail in small sailing boats of Northern Europe. It was eventually used in larger craft as well, and is now best known on the Thames River barges, which still use it today.

With the spritsail set abaft the mast, there was an empty space under the stay on the forward side of the mast, and it was only natural to set a triangular sail on that stay before the mast. By the middle of the first half of the 16th century, boats with a spritsail and fore staysail were in use in Holland. The development of the fore staysail was followed by a new staysail called the jib, which was set on a jib boom outside the stem. These staysails were soon in general use in small vessels in Western Europe, but it was not until the end of the 17th century that staysails appeared in the larger, square-sailed ships.

Another fore-and-aft sail, the lug sail, came to Europe somewhat later. The lug sail was a rectangular one that was hoisted with an inclined yard, with the halliard nearer the forward yardarm. Again there is evidence that the lug sail was known in the eastern Mediterranean about 100 A.D.

We are not sure whether the lug sail evolved from the lateen sail by cutting away the forward section or whether it came from the square sail by moving the halliard nearer one end of the yard and at the same time shifting the sail's tack amidships. The lug sail was used mostly in Western Europe, in the English and French waters of the English Channel. French fishermen and smugglers, as well as privateers and customs boats with sharp lines and fast hulls, were often rigged with lug sails; the type was sometimes called the *Chasse Marée*. English and Scottish fishermen in the North Sea also employed the lug sail, until they gave up the use of sails. Sailing ship's boats, both in the merchant marine and the navy, generally had lug sails as well, most often in one-masted, but also in two- or three-masted, rigs.

There were two types of lug sails: the standing and the dipping. The tack of the dipping lug was made fast a little before the mast, near the stem. It was always set to the lee of the mast and had to be shifted to the new leeward side at every tack. A standing lug had the tack at the mast and could take the wind from either side, though it was most effective when the yard was on the lee side of the mast. In ancient times it was very common for the masts of fishing boats to have no shrouds, and one sailed only "on the wood," as it was called. The sail was set on the lee side of the mast, with the halliards leading to the weather quarter and serving as a backstay to sail on. Coming about, the sail was shifted to the new lee and the halliard to the new weather side.

In addition to the fore-and-aft sail on fishing boats and smaller vessels, the lateen sail in the Mediterranean, the lug sail in Western Europe, and the spritsail in Northern Europe, there were many small craft that still used square sails. The "Roslagen" sloops from Stockholm's archipelago used square sails until the end of the 18th century, as did the Norwegian "Nordland" yachts—for as long as they used sails.

The original square sail, which had served maritime navigation for several thousand of years, was entirely different from the various kinds of fore-and-aft sails. When ships became larger and masts taller, the number of sails on each mast also increased. After the middle of the 16th century the larger ships set a third sail, the topgallant sail, which was rigged above the topsail. In the beginning of the 17th century a square sail, the spritsail topsail, was rigged on a topmast at the end of the bowsprit. An impractical square sail, its mast was very badly stayed and often prone to damage. It remained in use on larger ships, however, for more than a hundred years, before it was replaced by a more practical staysail, the jib.

The first staysails on larger ships were set between the masts as the main staysail, the main topmast staysail, and the mizzen staysail. In addition, there was the fore topmast staysail, which was placed on a special stay from the fore topmast head and parallel with the fore topmast stay. This stay was actually so cluttered with blocks and running gear for the spritsail that the additional rigging for the new staysail caused many difficulties. The fore topmast staysail was, however, a more effective headsail than either of the square sails on the bowsprit, and at the beginning of the 18th century the spritsail topsail disappeared. It was replaced, as was said earlier, by a new staysail called the jib. This was set on a new spar, the jib boom, which was rigged on the extension of the bowsprit.

By the beginning of the 18th century rigging became more functional. The sails could be reefed effectively, and the rigging allowed for better bracing, which meant better sailing to windward. The studding sail, which on occasion was already used in the previous century, became more common. It was used, when running free, to increase the sail area, much as the modern spinnaker functions on sailing yachts.

Toward the end of the 18th century larger ships began to use a fourth square sail above the topgallant sail. It was called the royal. In men-of-war it was always set flying, *i.e.,* it was set from the deck, and when furled, it was taken down on deck. But in merchant ships it became a standing sail with the royal yard left aloft.

An important improvement in types of sail was made at the beginning of the 19th century, as the jackstay on the yards came into use. The head of the sail was bent to the jackstay on the forward upper side of the yard instead of having lashings around the yard. This made the work easier when bending and unbending sail, and especially when furling sail. The sail could then be rolled up on top of the yards, where it could be easily secured under the gaskets. Without the jackstay on the yards, the larger steel ships of a later period could not have sailed with the small crews they had.

After the Napoleonic era larger ships were rigged with a fifth sail, the skysail, which was carried over the royal. It was never widely used, but was seen mostly at the time of the clipper ships, in the middle of the century. Some clippers carried still another sail, the moonsail, usually set only on the mainmast. Exaggerations could always be found, and one of the most unusual occurs in a story of the English corvette hunting for slavers in the steaming heat and calm waters of the Bay of Benin. Seamen tell of it carrying a royal, skysail, moonsail, heaven poker, angel poker, and cloud disturber—all over the topgallant sail.

Expanding 19th century industry gave rigging a more delicate look. Mechanical improvements in the rigging also influenced the sails. Thimbles and clasp hooks were introduced, and, later, shackles. Both square sail halliards and sheets were made of chain. Previously, the clews of square sails had been part of the bolt rope, which formed an eye in which the sheet and clewline were fastened. It now became common to put a thimble in the clew, and later to lead a cringle from the eye. Still later, a wrought-iron clew was spliced into the bolt ropes. In larger ships, with double topsail sheets, the clew was formed by a stropped block through which the sheet was reeved. The sheet was still made of hemp. In navy ships, where working the sails quickly became more and more important, all running gear was equipped with toggles, so that bowlines, buntlines, clewlines, and sheets could be let go in just a few seconds and a topsail shifted in just a few minutes.

When large ships began to be built of iron and then of steel, during the last half of the century, the standing rigging and then the running gear was made of wire. Even the sails were influenced. The huge square sails were given both leech and foot ropes of wire, and a bolt rope of wire could be used for foot and leech on the staysail but not for the luff, as this had to be folded along the stay when the sail was hauled down.

In addition to the fore-and-aft sails already mentioned—the lateen sail, spritsail, staysail, and lug sail—there is still another, the gaff sail, that gradually came to dominate all the others. It evolved from the spritsail by means of shortening the sprit, raising it, and fastening it to the sail's head. To keep it in place, with the forward end against the mast, the end was shaped as a throat or gaff with a branch fork, which partly covered the mast and gave both the spar and the sail its name, the gaff. To be able to hoist the gaff sail the mast had to be made higher than the sail, so that the gaff's halliards, the inner throat halliard, and the outer peak halliard could be fastened above the gaff.

Pictures of the gaff sail appear later than those of the spritsail, but also go as far back as the middle of the 17th century. Slowly, the gaff sail won out over the other fore-and-aft sails. Mail packets and other semi-official craft, which sailed with mail and passengers between specified ports, revenue cutters, the larger pilot boats, and similar craft were among the first to use the gaff sail. During the 18th century, smaller merchant ships and warships began more often to be rigged with the gaff sail. Various types of early schooners and sloops all had gaff sails.

During the 19th century, larger merchant ships, for example, the three-masted fore-and-aft schooners and barkentines, began to employ the gaff rig. Particularly in North America, by the end of the century, multi-masted fore-and-aft schooners began to show up. Many were four- or five-masted, several six-masted, and one was seven-masted. Some of them were extremely large sailing vessels that required steam winches to hoist their large gaff sails. They were at their best sailing on the wind in calm coastal waters; but they were difficult to run before the wind in hard weather. When they were used on deepwater voyages, their performance was usually much poorer than that of the square-riggers.

The gaff sail, however, soon became the most important sail for pleasure yachts. By the 17th century the Dutch, English, and even the Swedes had gaff-rigged pleasure yachts. With the development of sport sailing and yacht clubs in the maritime nations, the gaff-rigged cutter became more and more popular; though it was sometimes surpassed in size by two- and three-masted, gaff-rigged pleasure schooners. At the beginning of the 20th century the gaff sail was almost universally used in the yachting field.

Here, aerodynamic research performed a great service for sport sailing. As a result of new inventions, the wide gaff sail with a long boom is now almost as rare as the square sail. The only sail that has survived the extensive use of the motor yacht is the tall, narrow, gaffless boom sail, known as the Bermuda sail. Two hundred years ago fishermen in Bermuda were using a triangular mainsail without a gaff, but with a long boom. The modern yacht uses a sail which has only the name in common with that original Bermuda sail.

DIFFERENT SAILS

DIFFERENT SAILS

1 Spritsails
2 Standing lug sail
3 Gaff sail
4 Gunter rig
5 Bermuda sail
6 Staysail rig
7 Lateen sails
8 Square sail

99

SAILS

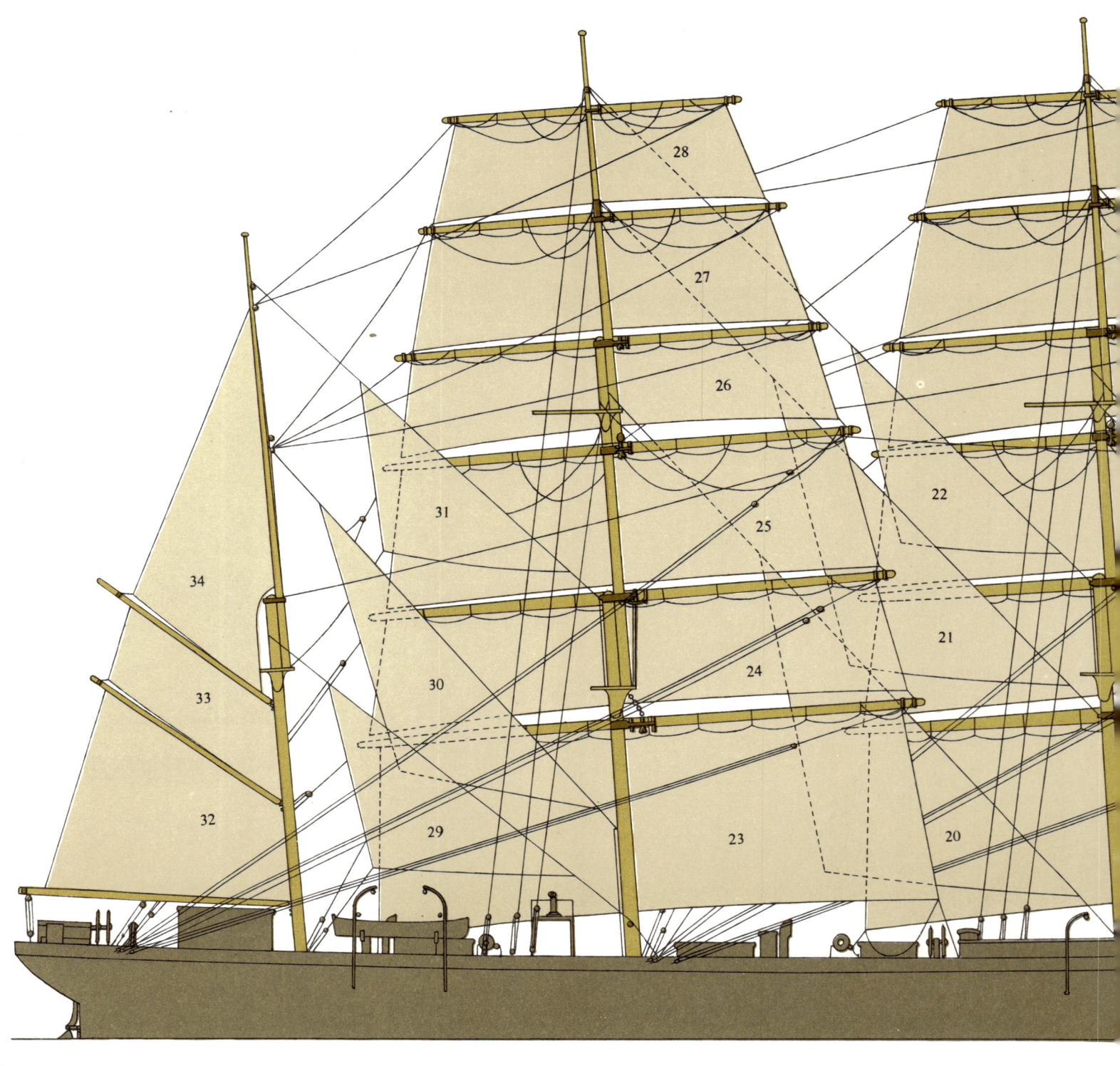

SAILS OF A FOUR-MASTED BARK

(Herzogin Cecilie)
This four-masted bark was built in 1902 by Rickmers ship yard at Bremerhaven for the Norddeutscher Lloyd at Bremen. It was a big sailing vessel of 3,242 gross tons or 4,350 dw. The Norddeutscher Lloyd, a large shipowner and in Germany second only to the Hamburg—America Line, employed the Herzogin Cecilie to train cadets as officers for their own fleet of ships. In addition to the officers, teachers, and a skeleton crew of tradesmen and seamen, she was fitted out to carry ninety cadets. She had the best possible equipment, but with plenty of man power on board to pull the braces she was rigged without any brace winches, as was customary at that time in big sailing ships of this class. She was a good sailer and made many excellent voyages. During World War 1 she was interned at Coquimbo, Chile. After the war she brought a cargo of nitrate to Ostend, and was there allocated to the French government. In November, 1921, she was purchased by Gustaf Erikson, Mariehamn, and under his flag was employed chiefly in the Australian grain trade. She foundered on April 25, 1936, off Salcombe, Devonshire, after running aground in heavy fog.

SAILS

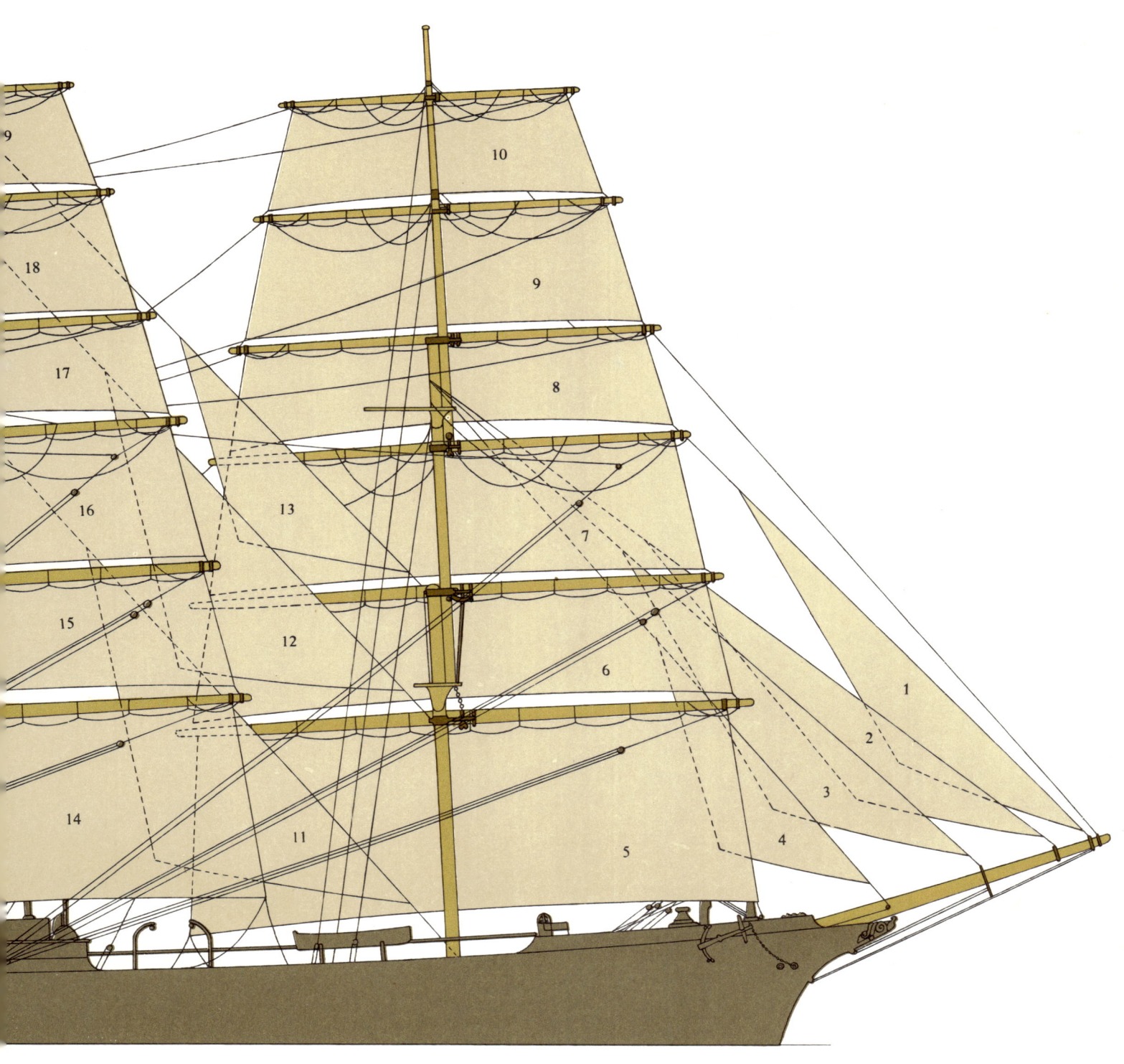

SAILS OF A FOUR-MASTED BARK

1. Flying jib
2. Outer jib
3. Inner jib
4. Fore topmast staysail
5. Fore sail, fore course
6. Fore lower topsail
7. Fore upper topsail
8. Fore lower topgallant sail
9. Fore upper topgallant sail
10. Fore royal
11. Main topmast staysail
12. Main topgallant staysail
13. Main royal staysail
14. Main sail, main course
15. Main lower topsail
16. Main upper topsail
17. Main lower topgallant sail
18. Main upper topgallant sail
19. Main royal
20. Mizzen topmast staysail
21. Mizzen topgallant staysail
22. Mizzen royal staysail
23. Crossjack, mizzen course
24. Mizzen lower topsail
25. Mizzen upper topsail
26. Mizzen lower topgallant sail
27. Mizzen upper topgallant sail
28. Mizzen royal
29. Jigger staysail
30. Jigger topmast staysail
31. Jigger topgallant staysail
32. Lower spanker
33. Upper spanker
34. Gaff topsail

SAILS

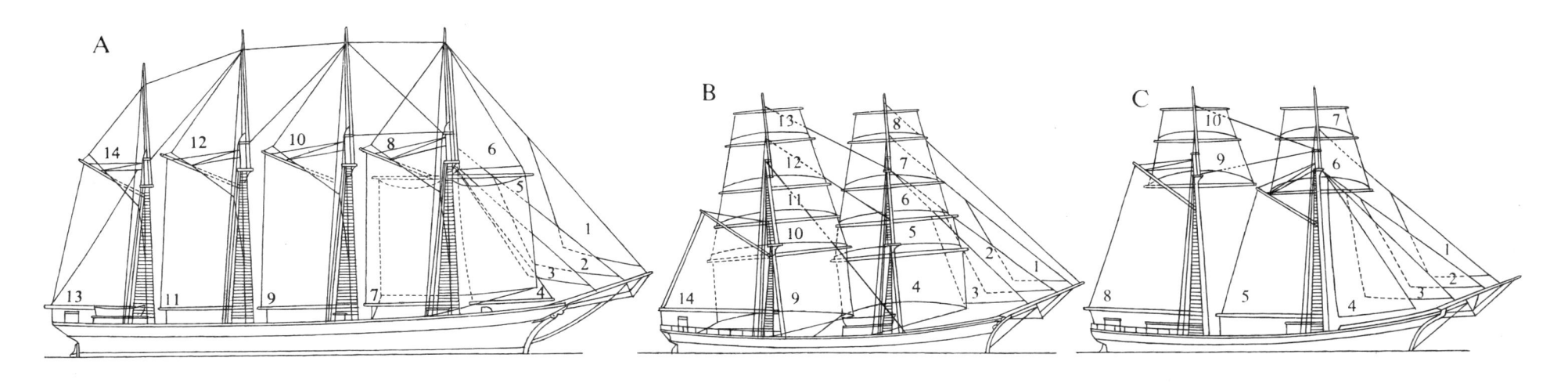

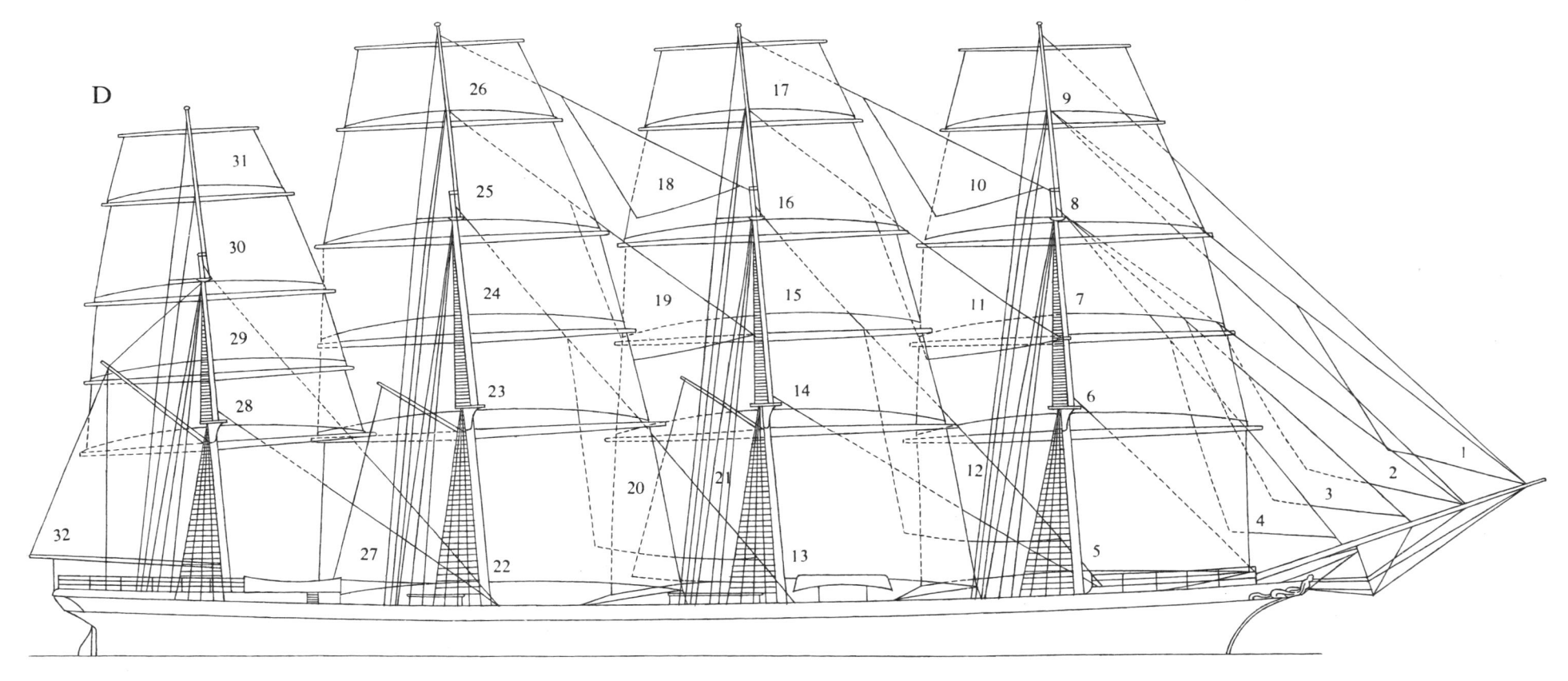

SAILS IN VARIOUS SAILING VESSELS

A *Four-masted fore-and-aft schooner*
1 Flying jib
2 Outer jib
3 Inner jib
4 Fore staysail
5 Square foresail
6 Raffee
7 Foresail
8 Fore gaff topsail
9 Mainsail
10 Main gaff topsail
11 Mizzen
12 Mizzen gaff topsail
13 Jigger or spanker
14 Jigger gaff topsail

B *Brig*
1 Flying jib
2 Jib
3 Fore topmast staysail
4 Foresail
5 Fore lower topsail
6 Fore upper topsail
7 Fore topgallant sail
8 Fore royal
9 Mainsail
10 Main lower topsail
11 Main upper topsail
12 Main topgallant sail
13 Main royal
14 Trysail

C *Two-topsail schooner*
1 Flying jib
2 Outer jib
3 Inner jib
4 Fore staysail
5 Foresail
6 Fore topsail
7 Fore topgallant sail
8 Mainsail
9 Main topsail
10 Main topgallant sail

D *Full-rigged four-masted ship*
1 Flying jib
2 Outer jib
3 Inner jib
4 Fore topmast staysail
5 Foresail
6 Fore lower topsail
7 Fore upper topsail
8 Fore topgallant sail
9 Fore royal
10 Main royal staysail
11 Main topgallant staysail
12 Main topmast staysail
13 Mainsail
14 Main lower topsail
15 Main upper topsail
16 Main topgallant sail
17 Main royal
18 Mizzen royal staysail
19 Mizzen topgallant staysail
20 Mizzen topmast staysail
21 Main spencer
22 Crossjack
23 Mizzen lower topsail
24 Mizzen upper topsail
25 Mizzen topgallant sail
26 Mizzen royal
27 Mizzen spencer
28 Jigger lower topsail
29 Jigger upper topsail
30 Jigger topgallant sail
31 Jigger royal
32 Spanker

SAILS

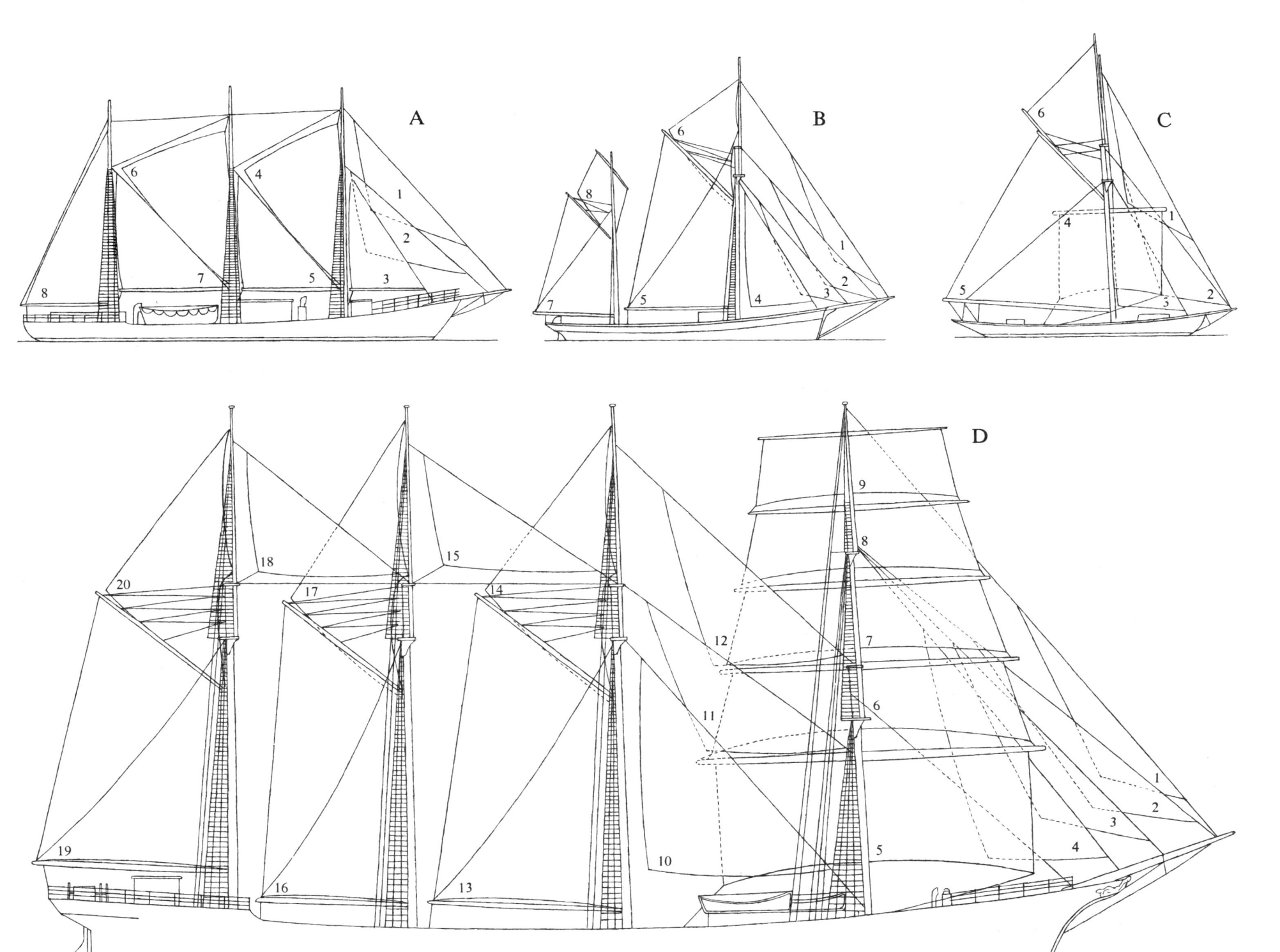

SAILS IN VARIOUS SAILING VESSELS

A *Three-masted staysail schooner*
1 Flying jib
2 Jib
3 Fore staysail
4 Fore trysail
5 Main staysail
6 Main trysail
7 Mizzen staysail
8 Jib-headed spanker

B *Ketch*
1 Flying jib
2 Outer jib
3 Inner jib
4 Fore staysail
5 Mainsail
6 Main gaff topsail
7 Mizzen
8 Mizzen gaff topsail

C *Sloop*
1 Jib topsail
2 Jib
3 Fore staysail
4 Square foresail
5 Mainsail
6 Gaff topsail

D *Four-masted barkentine*
1 Flying jib
2 Outer jib
3 Inner jib
4 Fore topmast staysail
5 Foresail
6 Fore lower topsail
7 Fore upper topsail
8 Fore lower topgallant sail
9 Fore upper topgallant sail
10 Main staysail
11 Middle staysail
12 Main topmast staysail
13 Mainsail
14 Main gaff topsail
15 Mizzen topmast staysail
16 Mizzen
17 Mizzen gaff topsail
18 Jigger topmast staysail
19 Jigger or spanker
20 Jigger gaff topsail

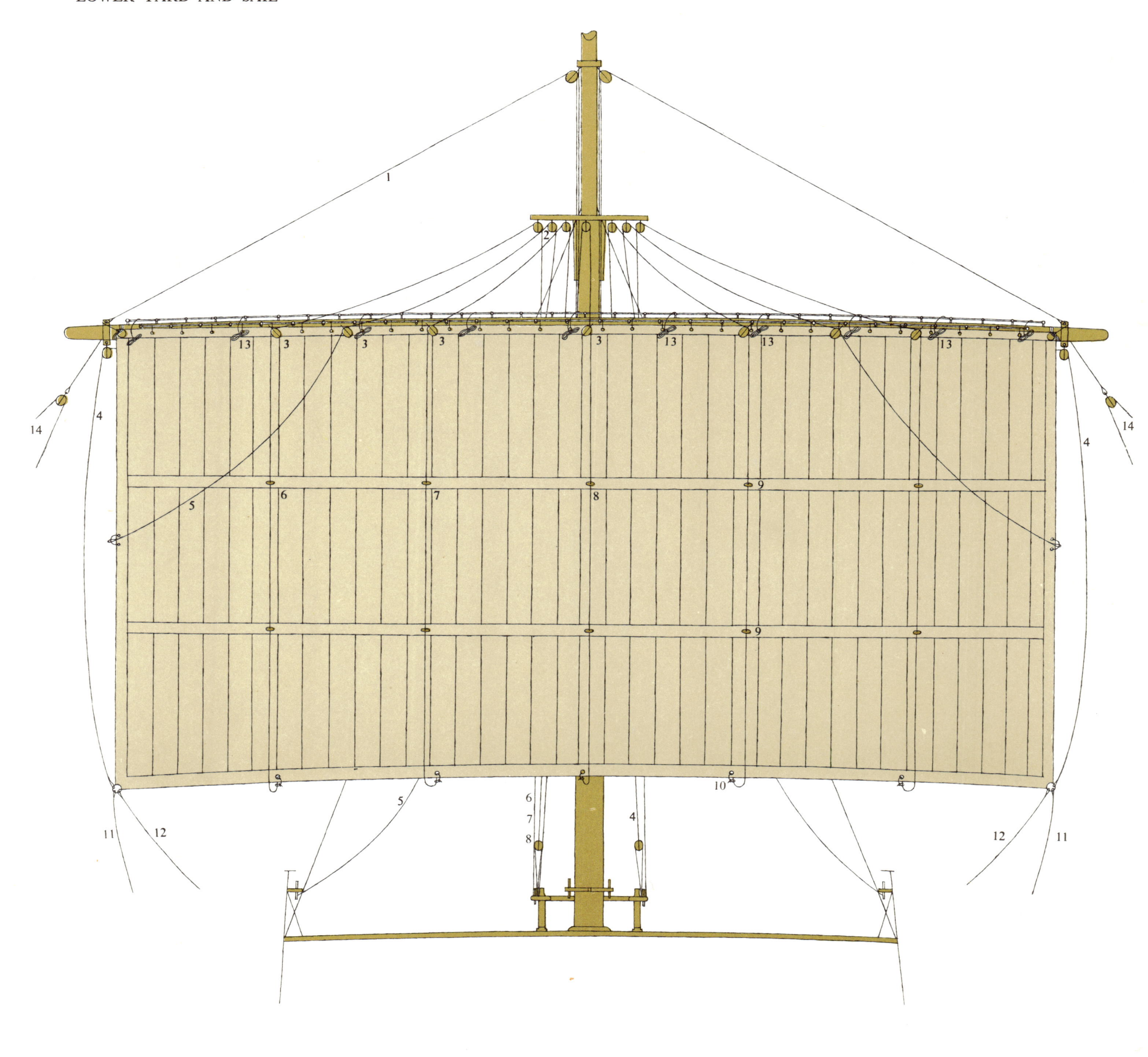

LOWER YARD AND SAIL

104

YARD WITH DETAILS

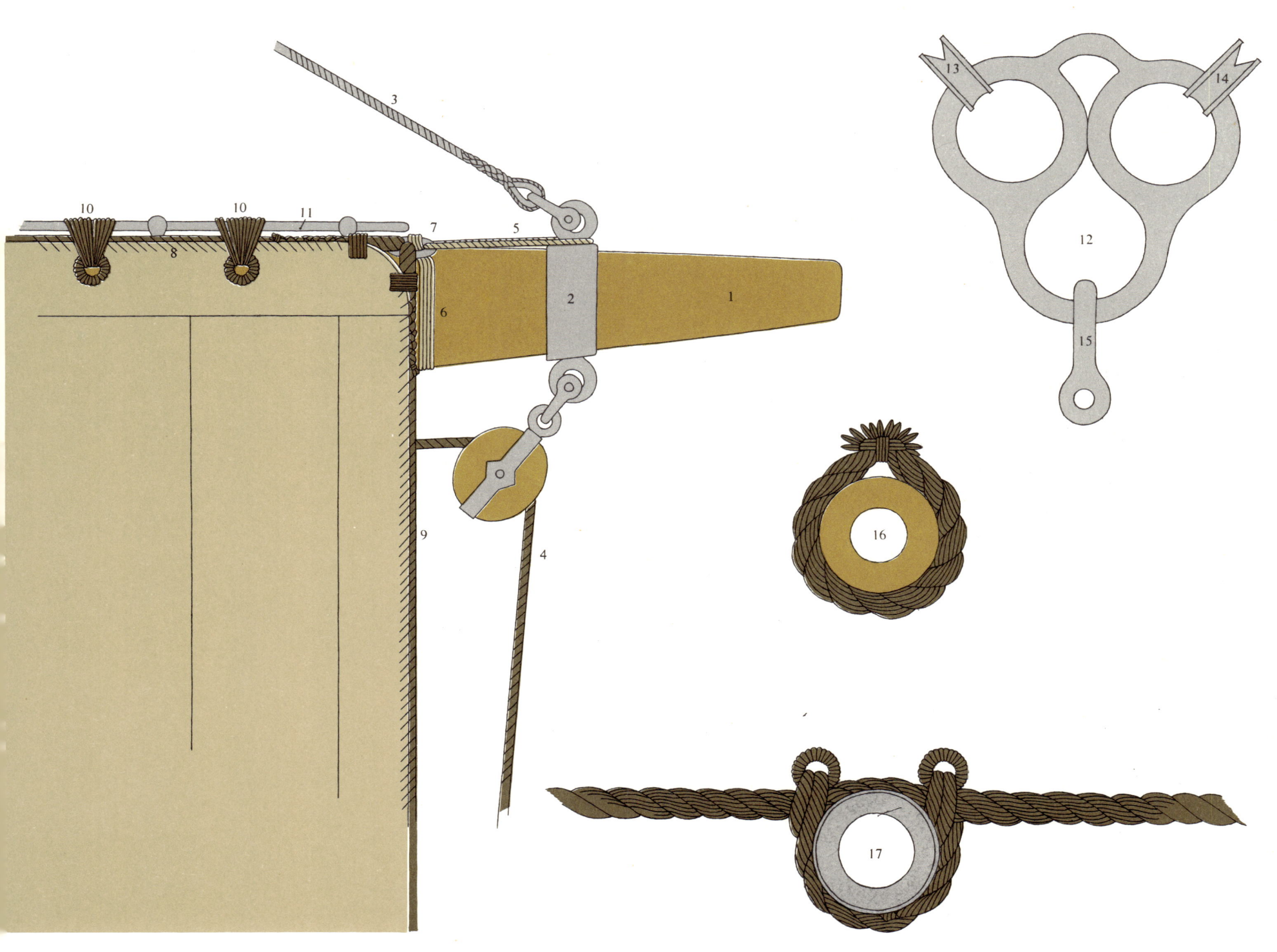

LOWER YARD AND SAIL, WITH RUNNING GEAR, IN A BIG SQUARE-RIGGED SHIP *(page 104)*

1. Lift by which the yard can be trimmed either way out of the horizontal. In port, this can be done independently of the yards above and to a considerable angle. At sea, when sails are set, the movement is restricted, but affects all the yards on the mast.
2. Buntline blocks under rim of top
3. Buntline blocks on yard seized to jack stay
4. Clewgarnet by which the clews of the sail are hauled up to the yardarms
5. Leech line
6. Outer buntline
7. Inner buntline
8. Middle buntline
9. Bull's eye sewn to the sail to lead the buntlines
10. Buntline hitch
11. Tacks leading forward
12. Sheets leading aft; the clews of the sail are trimmed to the wind by tacks and sheets
  When the sail is to be furled, the tacks and sheets are let go and the sail is hauled up to the yard by the clewgarnets and buntlines. Then the men go aloft, lie out on the yard, and roll up the sail tightly and secure it by tying the gaskets around yard and sail.
13. Gaskets
14. Braces leading aft, by which the yard is braced to different winds

PORT SIDE YARDARM OF LOWER YARD, WITH DETAILS

1. Yardarm
2. Yardarm band
3. Lift shackled to yardarm band
4. Clewgarnet
5. Hauling out part of head earing
6. Round turns of head earing
7. Ring for head earing
8. Head of sail
9. Leech of sail
10. Robands, tied with a square knot
11. Jack stay
12. Clew of galvanized iron
13. Thimble for foot of sail
14. Thimble for leech
15. Shackle for sheet
16. Bull's-eye sewed into sail
17. Cringle on bolt rope with round thimble

105

TOPMAST AND TOPSAIL

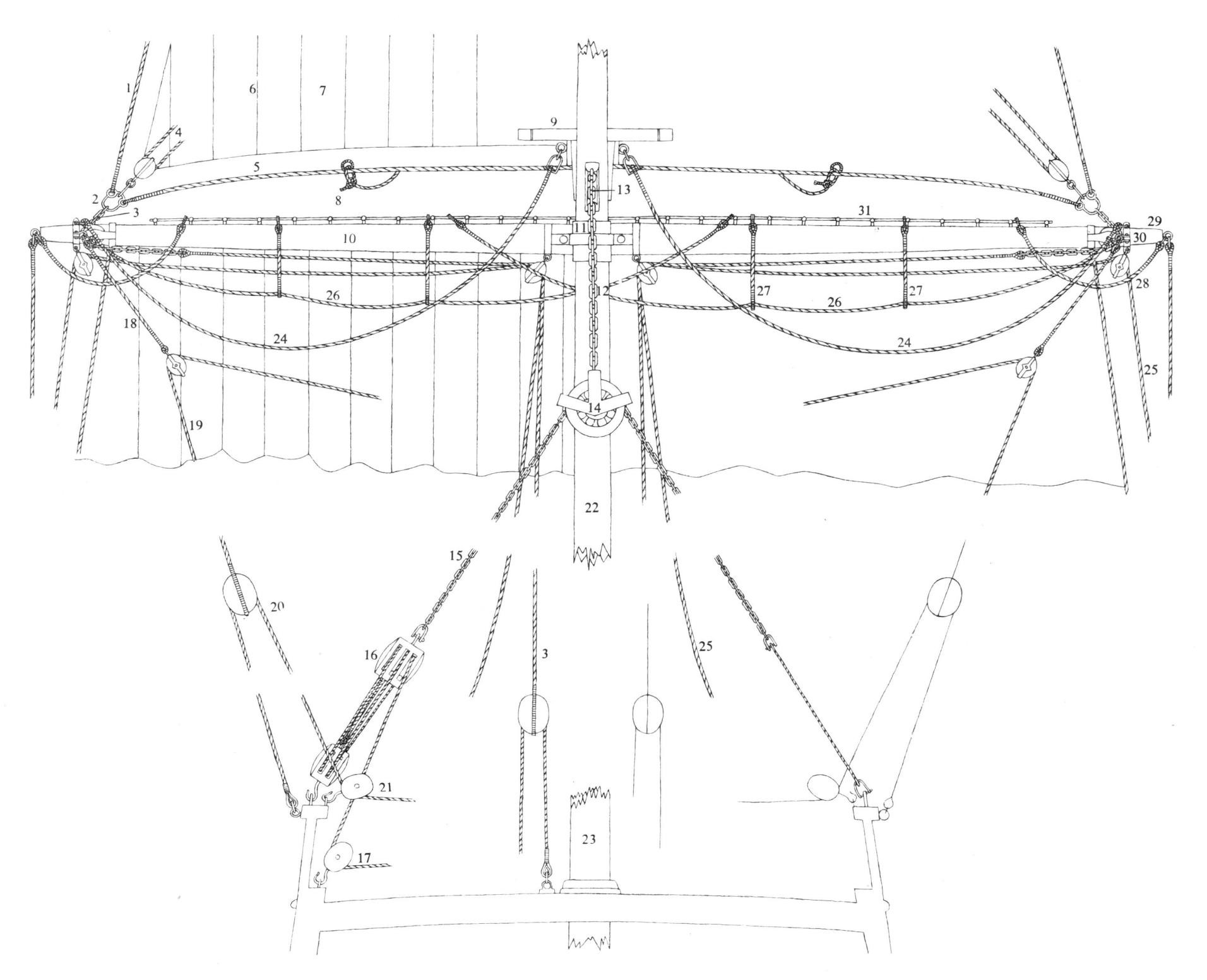

TOPMAST, TOPSAIL, AND TOPGALLANT SAIL WITH RUNNING GEAR

1. Topgallant leech, port side
2. Topgallant clew
3. Topgallant sheet
4. Topgallant clewline
5. Tabling on foot of topgallant sail
6. Flat seam between the cloths of the sail
7. Cloth of canvas, generally 2 feet wide
8. Topgallant buntline
9. Topmast crosstree
10. Upper topsail yard
11. Upper topsail yard parrel
12. Upper topsail yard tie
13. Sheave hole in topmast for the tie
14. Topsail tie gin block
15. Topsail halliard chain span
16. Topsail halliard tackle
17. Topsail halliard lead block
18. Upper topsail brace pendant
19. Upper topsail brace runner
20. Upper topsail brace falls
21. Leading block of upper topsail brace
22. Topmast
23. Lower mast
24. Topsail yard lift
25. Topsail yard downhaul
26. Foot rope of upper topsail yard
27. Stirrups to support foot rope
28. Yardarm horse
29. Yardarm
30. Yardarm band
31. Jack stay to which sail is bent

SQUARE SAIL

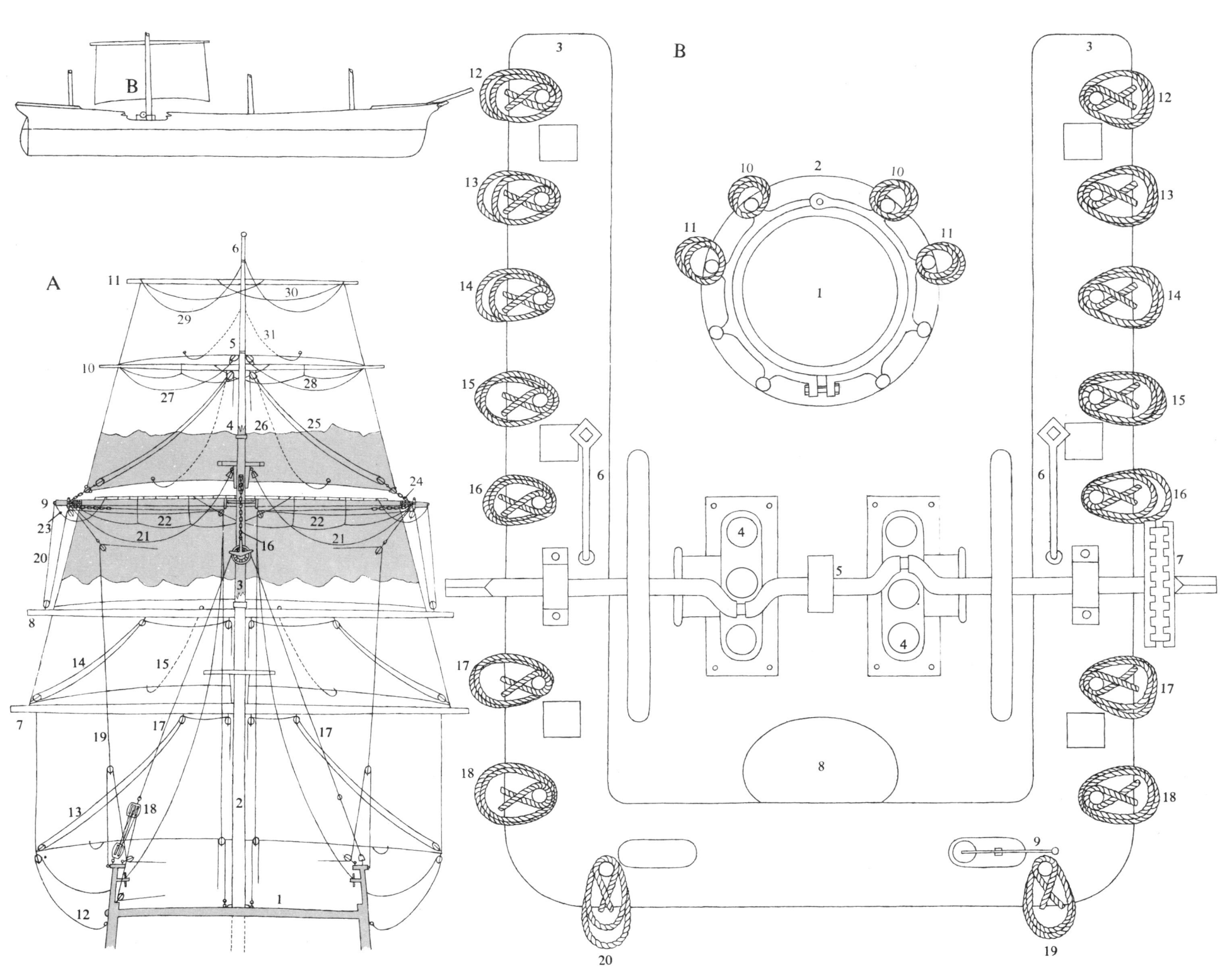

THE SQUARE SAIL

A *Square-rigged mast, seen from aft*
1 Deck
2 Lower mast with top
3 Topmast with crosstrees
4 Topgallant mast
5 Royal mast
6 Pole
7 Lower yard
8 Lower topsail yard
9 Upper topsail yard
10 Topgallant yard
11 Royal yard
12 Lower sheet
13 Clewgarnet
14 Topsail clewline
15 Lower topsail buntline, shown in broken lines forward of sail
16 Topsail halliard, tie
17 Topsail halliard, spanner
18 Topsail halliard, tackle or falls
19 Upper topsail brace
20 Topsail downhaul
21 Topsail lift
22 Upper topsail yard footrope
23 Upper topsail yardarm horse
24 Topgallant sheet
25 Topgallant clewline
26 Topgallant buntline
27 Topgallant lift
28 Topgallant yard footrope
29 Royal lift
30 Royal yard footrope
31 Royal buntline

B *Plan of fife rail at mizzenmast of a big sailing ship*
1 Section of mast with spider hoop
2 Mast coat at deck
3 U-shaped fife rail with belaying pins
4 Bilge pumps on deck
5 Pump axle with flywheels
6 Detachable pump cranks stowed on fife rail
7 Chain wheel for messenger from steam winch
8 Manhole from deck to pump well
9 Fresh water pump from tanks below deck
10 Lower topsail sheet
11 Upper topsail sheet
12 Crossjack clewgarnet
13 Inner crossjack buntlines
14 Outer crossjack buntlines
15 Crossjack lift
16 Mizzen topgallant sheet
17 Main lower topgallant brace
18 Main upper topgallant brace
19 Jigger topmast staysail downhaul
20 Jigger topgallant staysail downhaul

107

RUNNING RIGGING

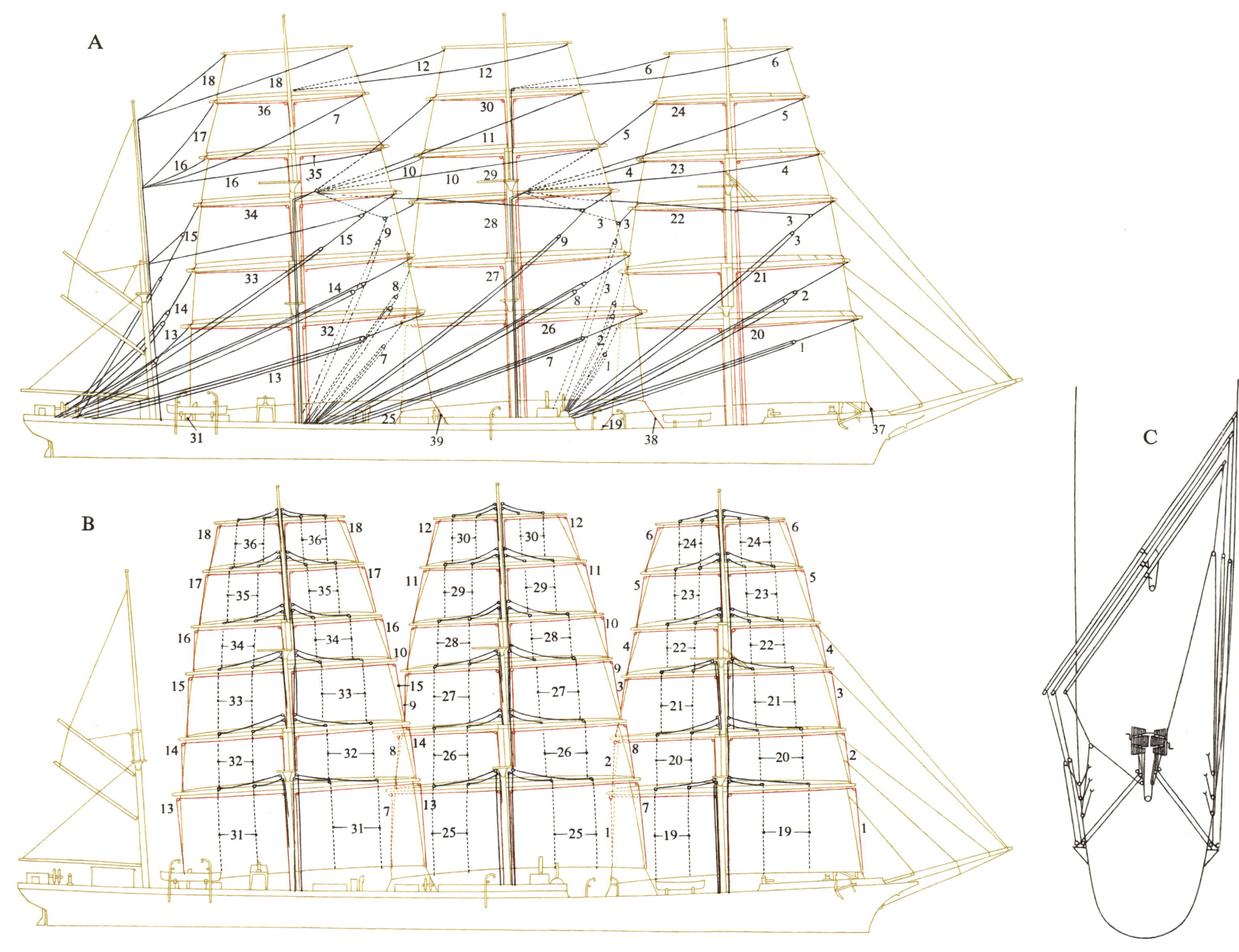

RUNNING RIGGING OF THE SQUARE SAILS OF A FOUR-MASTED BARK

A *Braces and sheets*
1. Fore brace
2. Fore lower topsail brace
3. Fore upper topsail brace
4. Fore lower topgallant brace
5. Fore upper topgallant brace
6. Fore royal brace
7. Main brace
8. Main lower topsail brace
9. Main upper topsail brace
10. Main lower topgallant brace
11. Main upper topgallant brace
12. Main royal brace
13. Crossjack brace
14. Mizzen lower topsail brace
15. Mizzen upper topsail brace
16. Mizzen lower topgallant brace
17. Mizzen upper topgallant brace
18. Mizzen royal brace
19. Fore sheet
20. Fore lower topsail sheet
21. Fore upper topsail sheet
22. Fore lower topgallant sheet
23. Fore upper topgallant sheet
24. Fore royal sheet
25. Main sheet
26. Main lower topsail sheet
27. Main upper topsail sheet
28. Main lower topgallant sheet
29. Main upper topgallant sheet
30. Main royal sheet
31. Crossjack sheet
32. Mizzen lower topsail sheet
33. Mizzen upper topsail sheet
34. Mizzen lower topgallant sheet
35. Mizzen upper topgallant sheet
36. Mizzen royal sheet
37. Fore tack
38. Main tack
39. Crossjack tack

B *Buntlines, clewlines, and downhauls*
1. Fore clewgarnet
2. Fore lower topsail clewline
3. Fore upper topsail downhaul
4. Fore lower topgallant clewline
5. Fore upper topgallant downhaul
6. Fore royal clewline
7. Main clewgarnet

Continued

108

HALLIARDS

TOPSAIL HALLIARDS AND WINCHES

A *Topsail halliard winch*
1. Flywheel with removable handle, which was removed after the sail was hoisted so as to be out of the way
2. Worm gear
3. Grooved barrel for the halliard, tapered to increase power as the yard ascends
4. Brake
5. Wheel with threaded shaft to control the brake. When the topsail yard was lowered, the brake was eased off and the flywheel was given a start with a push. This set the barrel revolving; the downward speed was regulated by the brake.

Continued

Continued

8. Main lower topsail clewline
9. Main upper topsail downhaul
10. Main lower topgallant clewline
11. Main upper topgallant downhaul
12. Main royal clewline
13. Crossjack clewgarnet
14. Mizzen lower topsail clewline
15. Mizzen upper topsail downhaul
16. Mizzen lower topgallant clewline
17. Mizzen upper topgallant downhaul
18. Mizzen royal clewline
19. Fore buntlines
20. Fore lower topsail buntlines
21. Fore upper topsail buntlines
22. Fore lower topgallant buntlines
23. Fore upper topgallant buntlines
24. Fore royal buntlines
25. Main buntlines
26. Main lower topsail buntlines
27. Main upper topsail buntlines
28. Main lower topgallant buntlines
29. Main upper topgallant buntlines
30. Main royal buntlines
31. Crossjack buntlines
32. Mizzen lower topsail buntlines
33. Mizzen upper topsail buntlines
34. Mizzen lower topgallant buntlines
35. Mizzen upper topgallant buntlines
36. Mizzen royal buntlines

C *Mizzenmast with braces leading to a brace winch at the foot of jiggermast*

Since this is an outline sketch only, see also page 245

DOUBLE TOPSAILS

EARLY METHOD OF RIGGING DOUBLE TOPSAILS, 1860

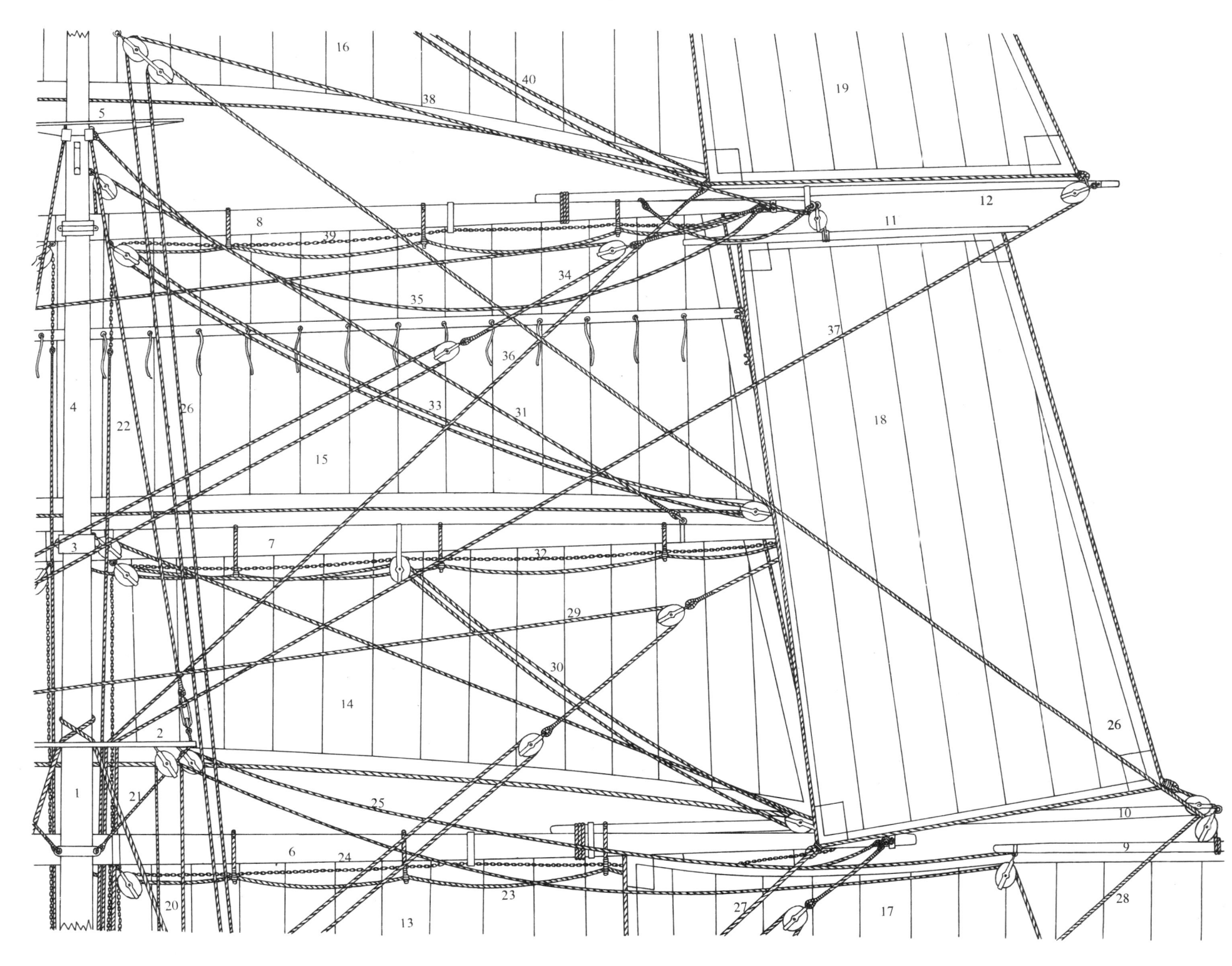

Continued

B *Topsail halliard of a barkentine*
1 End of chain span across the deck
2 Mousing on hook
3 Moving block, double
4 Becket, in one with the straps
5 Fall, two-fold purchase rove to advantage
6 Pin rail
7 Belaying pin
8 Main rail

C *Brace winch invented by Captain J. C. Jarvis of Tayport, Scotland. The winch controls the lower brace and the two topsail braces, one winch for each mast. The winch has three axles, each with two barrels, and is so arranged with cogwheels that when the winch is turned, braces on one side pay out as those on the other side wind on.*
1 Weather side brace paid out
2 Lee side brace hove in

1 Lower mast, foremast
2 Top
3 Cap
4 Topmast
5 Topmast crosstree
6 Lower foreyard
7 Lower topsail yard
8 Upper topsail yard
9 Lower studding sail yard
10 Topmast studding sail boom
11 Topmast studding sail yard
12 Topgallant studding sail boom
13 Fore course, foresail
14 Lower topsail
15 Upper topsail
16 Topgallant sail
17 Lower studding sail
18 Topmast studding sail
19 Topgallant studding sail
20 Lower rigging or shrouds
21 Futtock shrouds
22 Topmast rigging or shrouds
23 Lower yard footrope
24 Lower topsail sheet of chain
25 Inner lower studding sail halliard
26 Outer lower studding sail halliard
27 Topmast studding sail sheet
28 Topmast studding sail tack
29 Lower topsail brace
30 Lower topsail clewline
31 Lower topsail lift
32 Upper topsail sheet
33 Upper topsail clewline
34 Upper topsail brace
35 Upper topsail lift
36 Topgallant studding sail sheet
37 Topgallant studding sail tack
38 Topmast studding sail halliard
39 Topgallant sheet
40 Topgallant clewline

SQUARE AND STUDDING SAILS

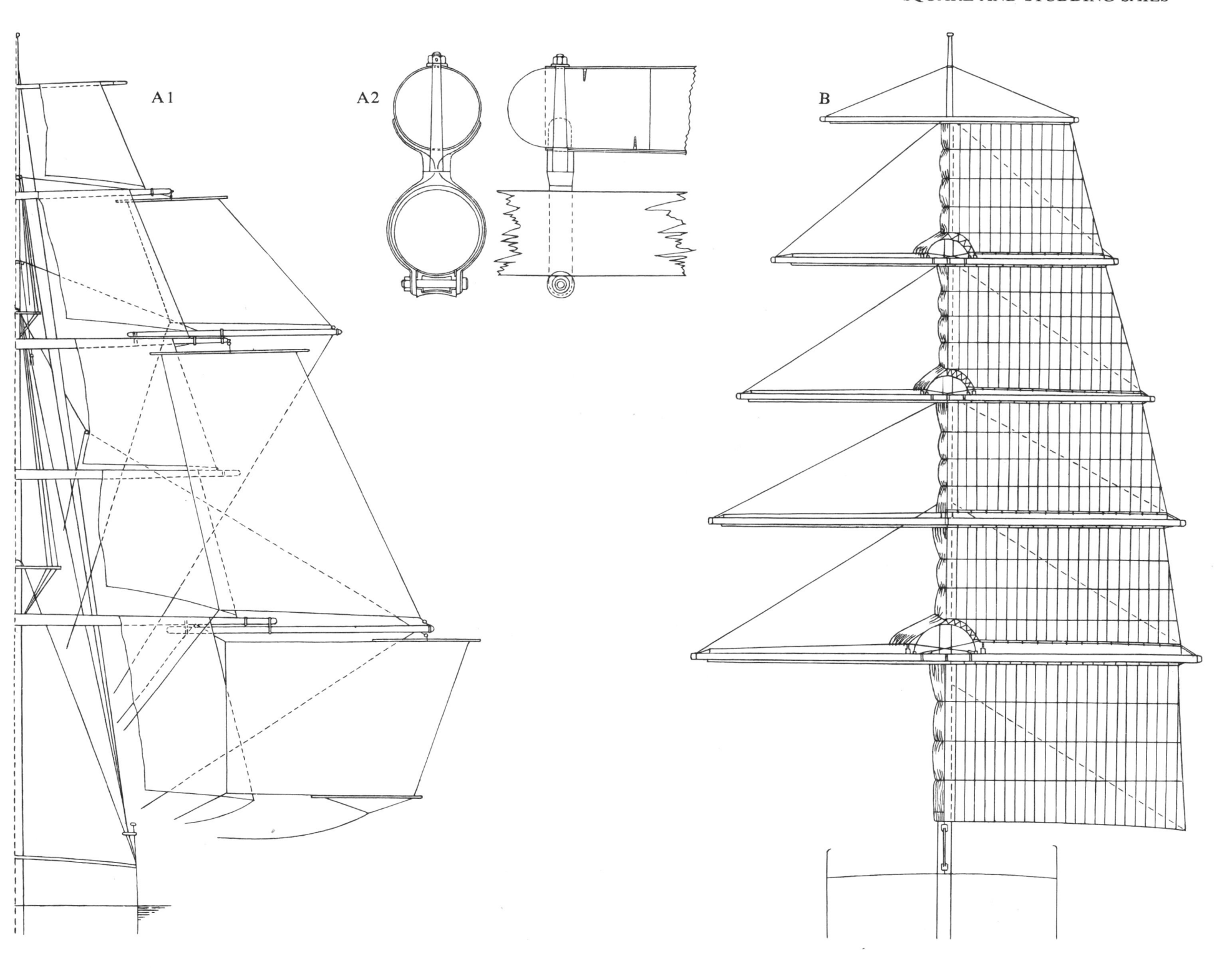

SQUARE SAILS AND STUDDING SAILS

A *Studding sails*
1. Outline sketch showing studding sails and their spars and rigging, looking aft
2. Band on the yardarm for the studding sail boom

B *Square sail by the Rägener system*
Many inventors have tried to improve upon the traditional square rig, which evolved empirically from centuries of experience gained the hard way. None did much to improve the old sailing ship, and this system by Rägener, with trussed yards and sails running on horizontal slides and brailed in to the mast, never got beyond the drawing board.

111

REEFING

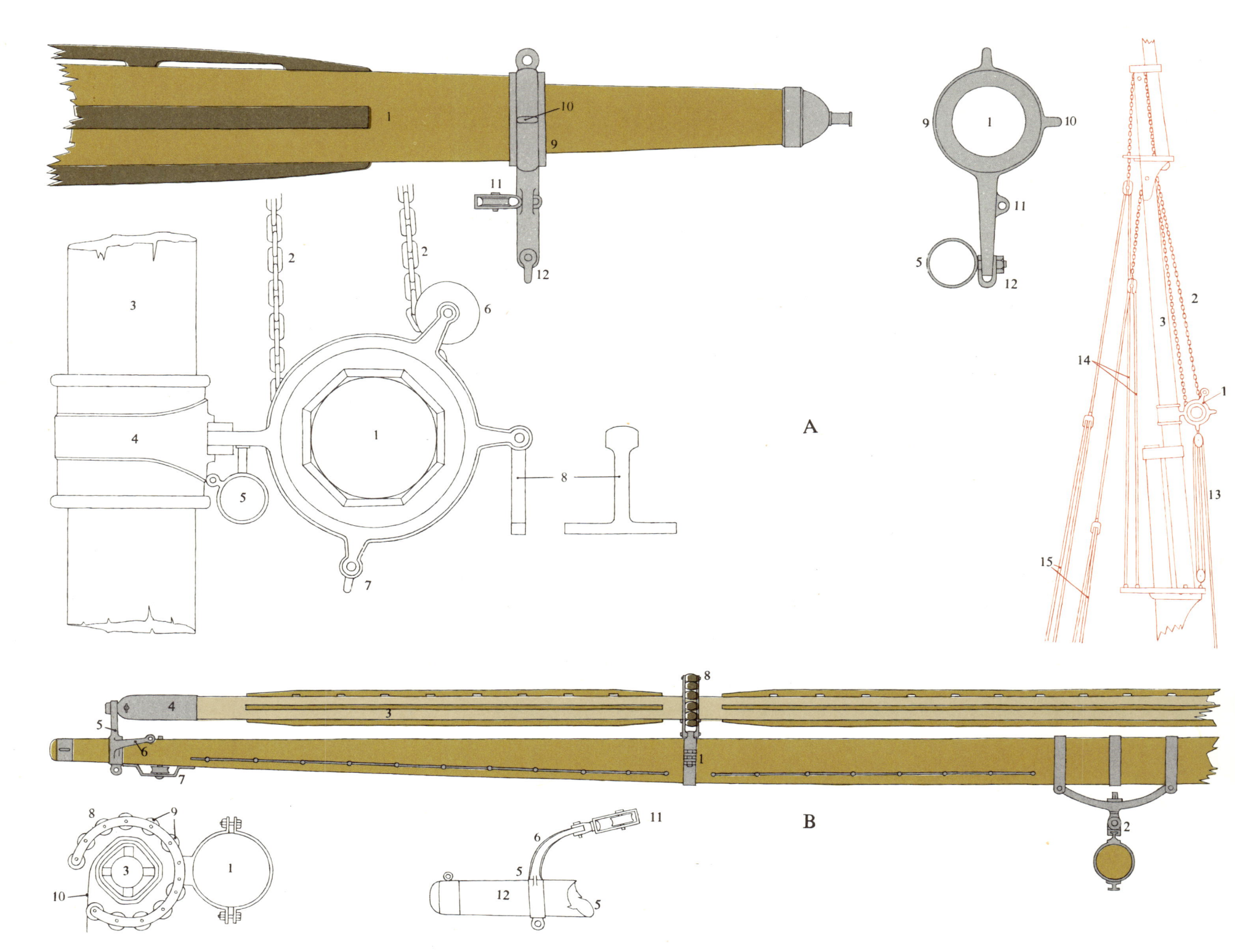

PATENT SELF-REEFING TOPSAILS

A *Cunningham's patent*
1. Revolving topsail yard
2. Bight of chain topsail tie
3. Topmast
4. Topsail yard parrel
5. Chafing spar to protect the sail when reefed
6. Roller lead for tie
7. Bolt for downhaul tackle
8. T-shaped bolt for the bonnet
9. Yardarm hoop within which the yard works
10. Bolt for topsail yard lifts
11. Leading block for topgallant sheet
12. Shackle to take the brace
13. Downhaul tackle
14. Twin runners of topsail halliards
15. Twin tackles of topsail halliards

B *Colling's & Pinkney's patent*
1. Topsail yard
2. Parrel
3. Rolling spar
4. Iron drum end of rolling spar
5. Yardarm hoop
6. Arm carrying reefing halliard block
7. Cheek block for topgallant sheet
8. Parrel crutch with lignum vitae rollers
9. Lignum vitae rollers
10. Topsail
11. Lead block for reefing halliards
12. Topsail yardarm

112

SQUARE SAILS

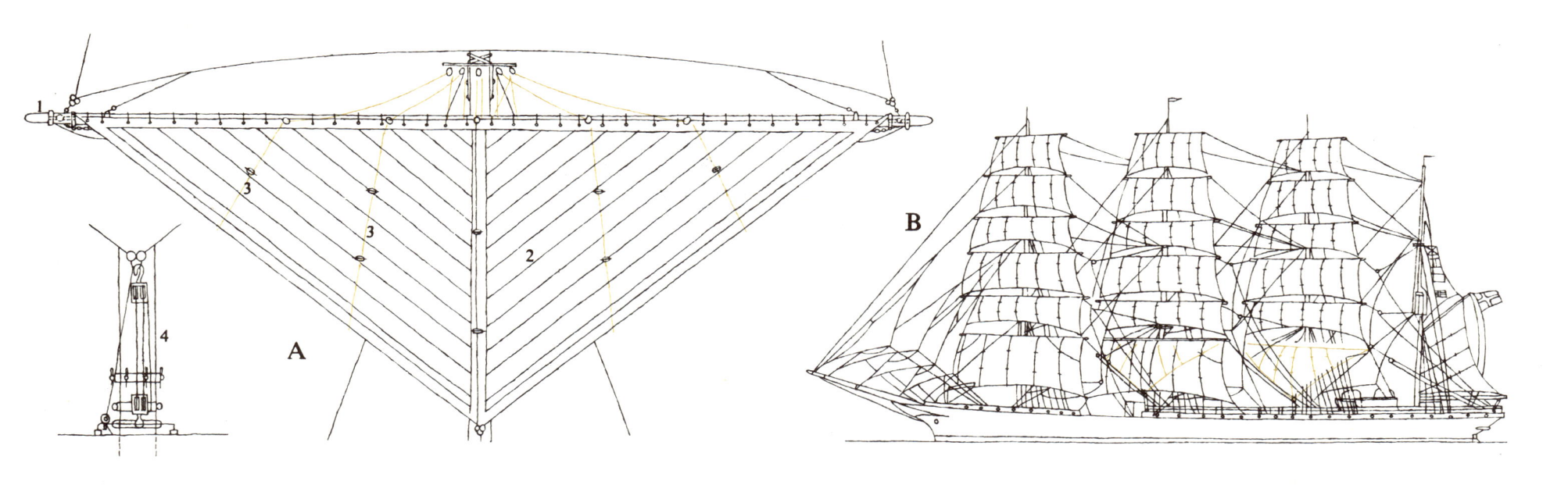

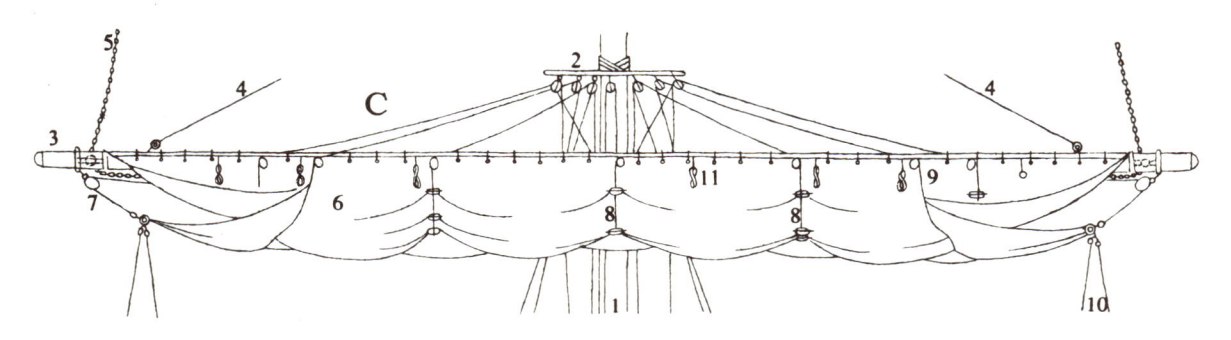

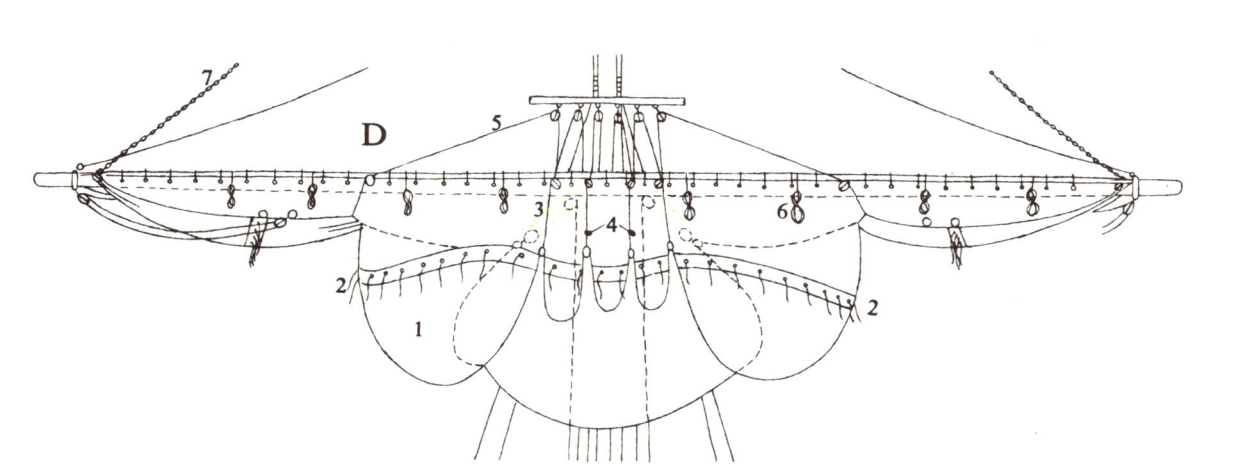

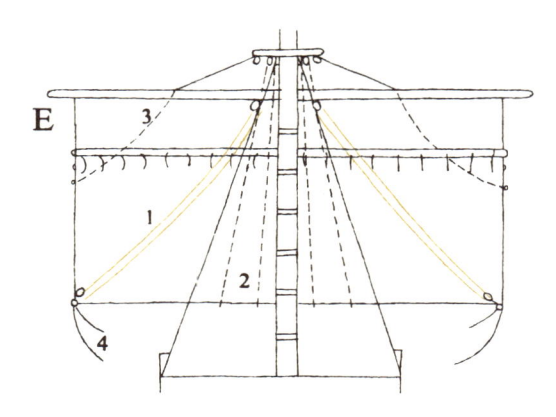

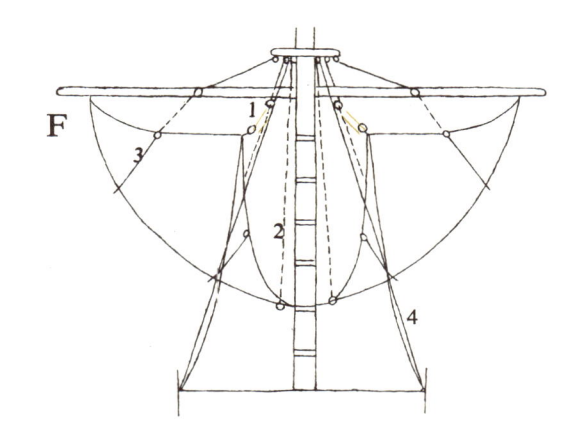

DIFFERENT RIGGING OF LOWER SQUARE SAILS

A Big square-rigged sailing ships could, sometimes, set a three-cornered mainsail or crossjack. Such a sail could be carried in a gale long after a square sail had to be taken in, but this advantage was counteracted by the fact that the three-cornered sail gave less spread of canvas in a moderate wind. In A the numbers indicate:
1. Lower yard
2. Three-cornered sail
3. Buntlines
4. Tackle sheet in front of mast

B A four-masted bark under all sail, setting a three-cornered crossjack, while the mainsail is drawn double showing both a square sail and a three-cornered sail

C A course, say, mainsail, clewed up to the yardarm, as seen from forward
1. Lower mast
2. The top
3. Lower yard
4. Lifts
5. Lower topsail sheet, sail clewed up to the yardarm
6. The sail, say, mainsail
7. Clewgarnets
8. Buntlines
9. Leechlines
10. Tacks and sheets
11. Gaskets

D A course, mainsail, clewed up in the bunt as seen from forward
1. The sail
2. Reef band
3. Clewgarnets abaft the sail
4. Buntlines
5. Leechlines
6. Gaskets
7. Lower topsail sheet, sail clewed up in the bunt

E A mainsail clewed up in the bunt as seen from aft
1. Clewgarnets
2. Buntlines
3. Leechlines
4. Sheet

F A mainsail with the clews hauled up as seen from aft
1. Clewgarnets
2. Buntlines
3. Leechlines
4. Sheets

113

GAFF SAIL

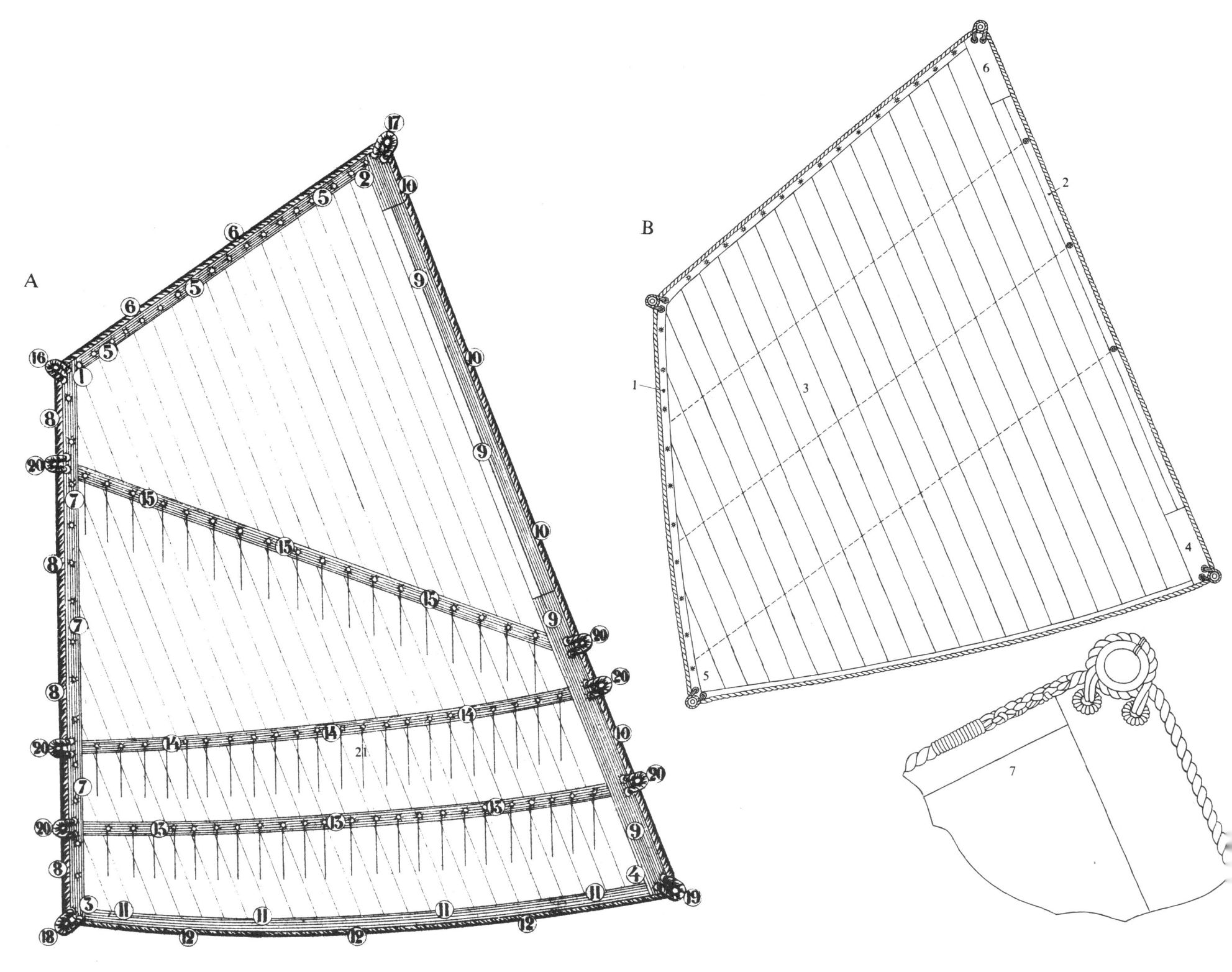

THE GAFF SAIL (FROM PAASCH)

A *Gaff sail*
1 Throat
2 Peak
3 Tack
4 Clew
5 Head
6 Headrope
7 Luff
8 Luff rope
9 Leech
10 Leech rope
11 Foot
12 Foot rope
13 First reef band
14 Second reef band
15 Balance reef band
16 Throat cringle
17 Peak cringle
18 Tack cringle
19 Clew cringle
20 Reef cringles
21 Reef points

B *A spanker, which sets under a standing gaff and brails in to the mast, (leeches and cringles made as in A)*
1 Half a cloth tabling on the luff
2 Folding on the after leech with three holes to take the brails
3 Lead of brails across the sail
4 Sheet patch
5 Tack patch
6 Peak patch
7 Detail of peak cringle

114

GAFF SAIL

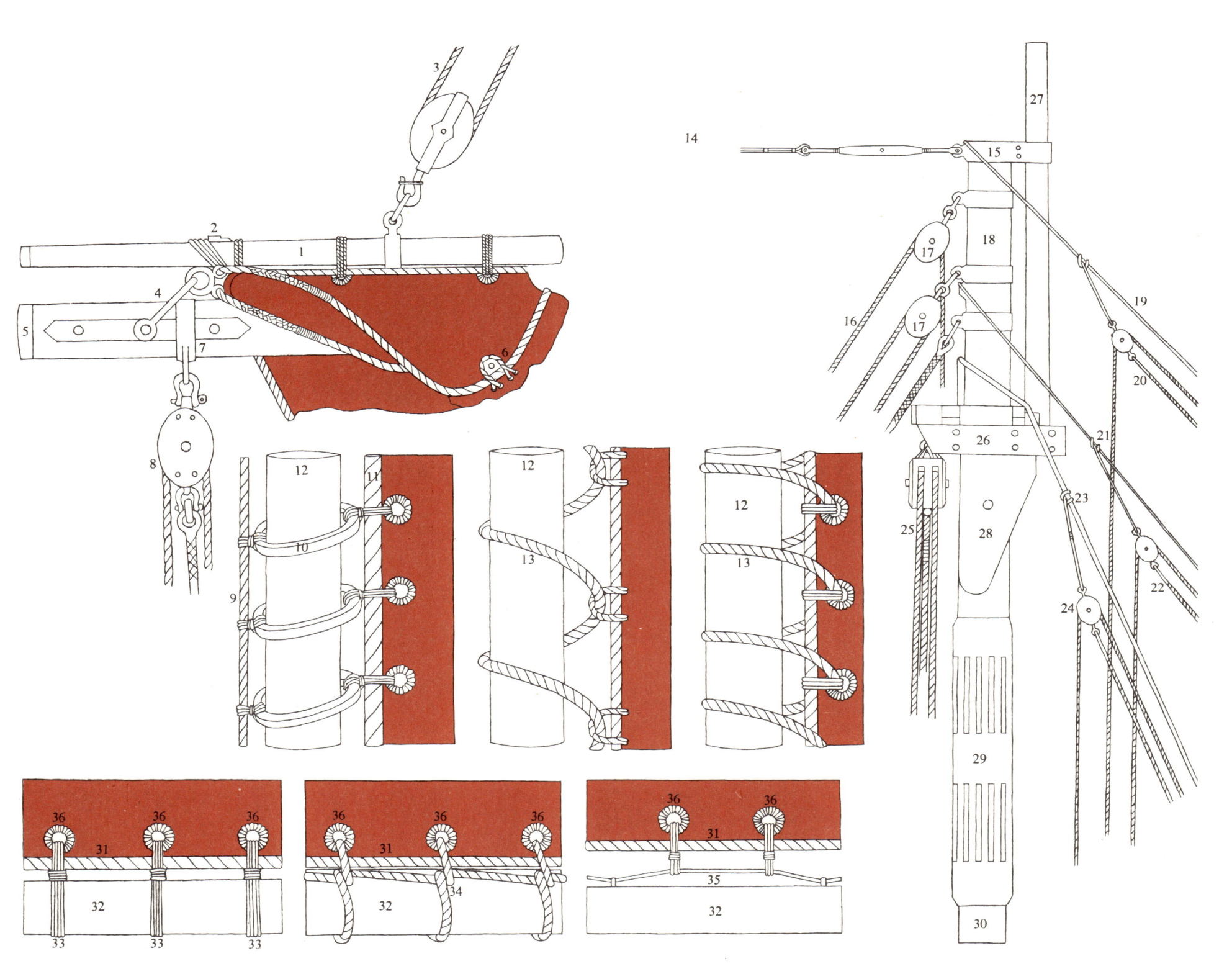

THE GAFF SAIL

1. Gaff
2. Head earing
3. Peak halliards
4. Clew shackle
5. Boom end
6. Reef cringle
7. Sheet band
8. Sheet
9. Distance line
10. Hoops
11. Bolt rope on luff of sail
12. Mast
13. Spiral lacing
14. Mainstay
15. Cap
16. Fore peak halliards
17. Peak halliard block
18. Foremast head
19. Outer jibstay
20. Outer jib halliard
21. Inner jibstay
22. Inner jib halliard
23. Forestay
24. Fore staysail halliard
25. Fore throat halliards
26. Trestletrees
27. Topmast
28. Cheeks
29. Mast battens
30. Foremast
31. Foot of sail
32. Boom
33. Seizings
34. Marline hitched lacing
35. Wire jack stay
36. Eyelet hole for lacing

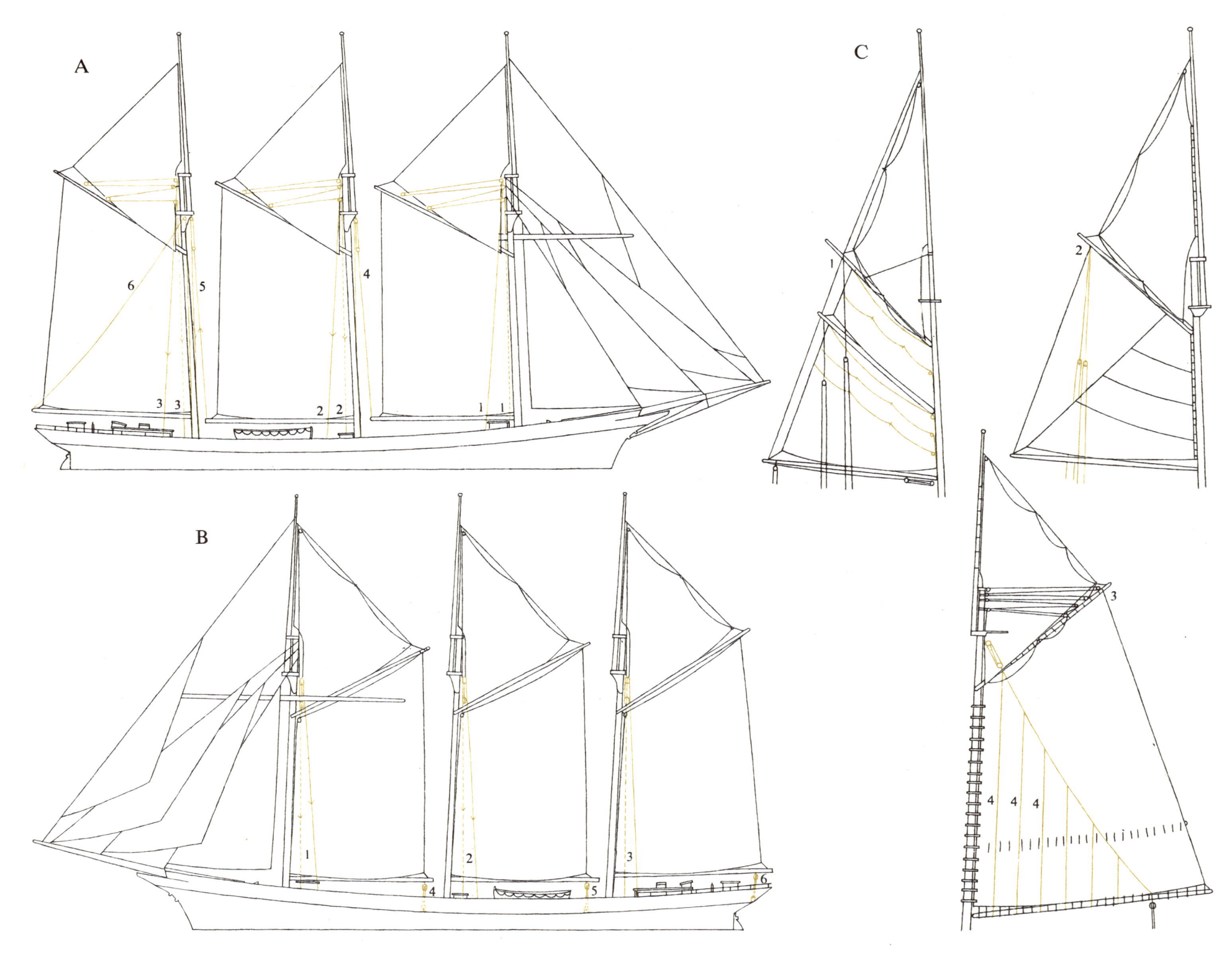

GAFF SAILS

GAFF SAILS

A *The peak halliards and topping lifts of the gaff sails on board a three-masted fore-and-aft schooner*
1. Fore peak halliard
2. Main peak halliard
3. Mizzen peak halliard
4. Fore topping lift
5. Main topping lift
6. Mizzen topping lift

B *The throat halliards and sheets of the gaff sails on board a three-masted fore-and-aft schooner*
1. Fore throat halliard
2. Main throat halliard
3. Mizzen throat halliard
4. Fore sheet
5. Main sheet
6. Mizzen sheet or spanker sheet

C *Different gaff sails*
1. Upper and lower spanker of the five-masted bark *Potosi*
2. Jigger of the four-masted bark *Archibald Russell*
3. Spanker of a big American fore-and-aft schooner. The vertical ropes (4) from the topping lift are called lazy jacks.

GAFF TOPSAIL

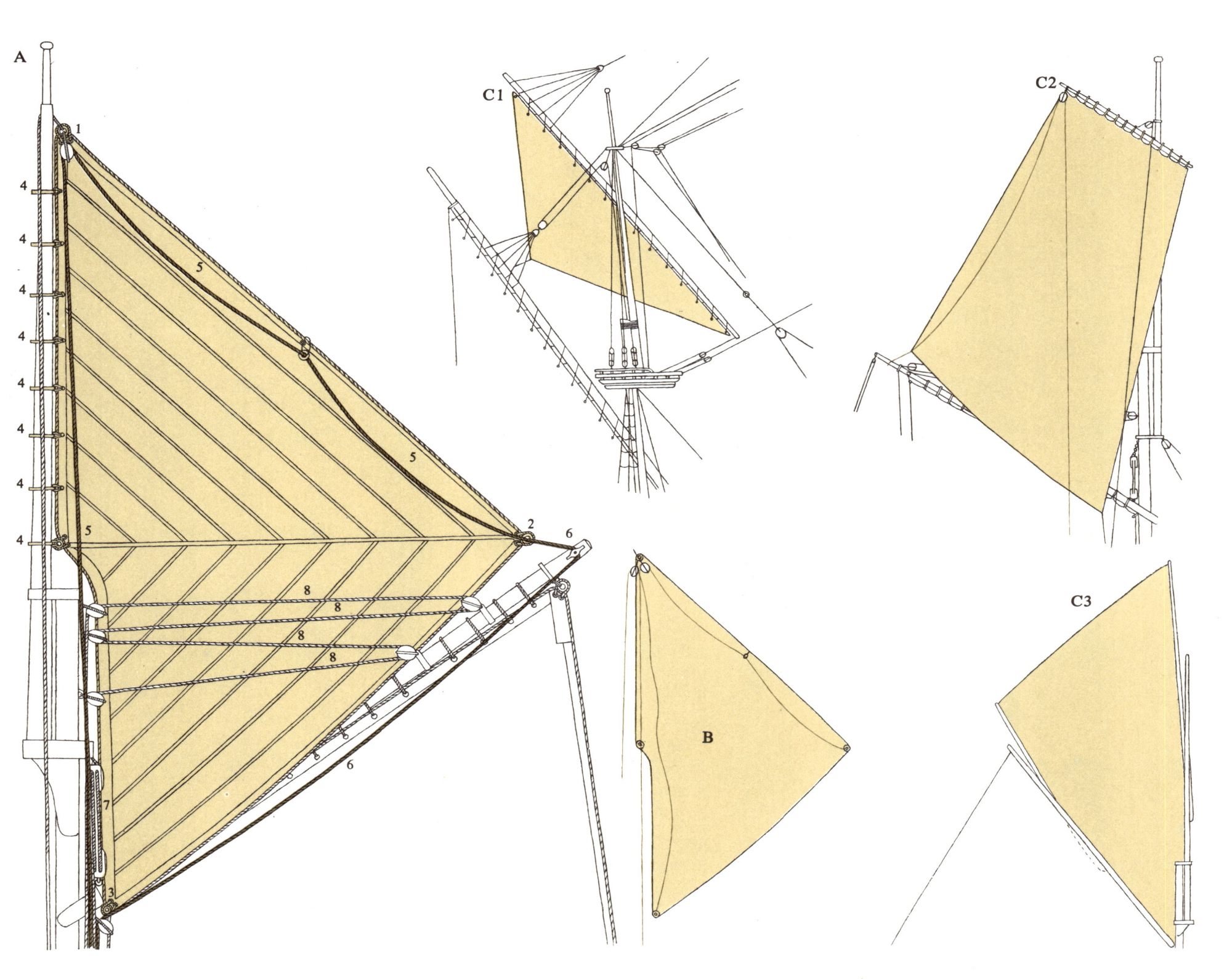

FORE-AND-AFT TOPSAILS

A *Jib-headed gaff topsail*
1. Head
2. Clew
3. Tack
4. Mast hoops
5. Clewline
6. Sheet
7. Throat halliard of the gaff sail
8. Peak halliard of the gaff sail

The gaff topsail is carried on the lee side of the peak halliard and the tack leads down to deck on the weather side of the gaff. When the ship is put about, one man has to go aloft and shift the sail over to the new lee side.

B *Another way of rigging the gaff topsail with two clewlines*

C *Different types of fore-and-aft topsails*
1. Lateen topsail from the middle of the 16th century
2. Square gaff topsail bent to a short yard
3. Jackyard topsail of a cutter from the 1890's

117

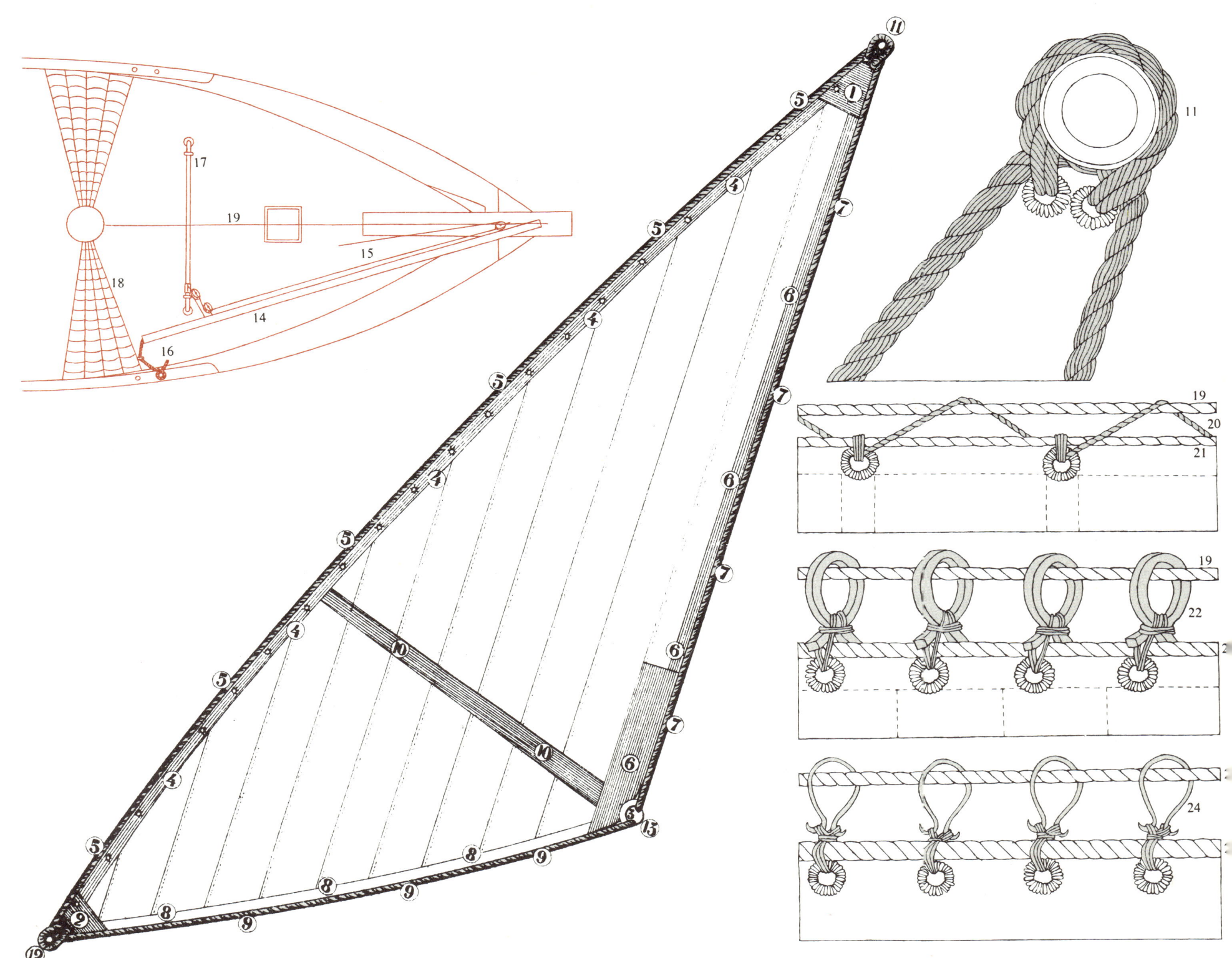

STAYSAIL

STAYSAIL

1 Head	6 Leech	11 Head cringle	17 Horse	21 Luff rope
2 Tack	7 Leech rope	12 Tack cringle	18 Shrouds	22 Wooden staysail hanks
3 Clew	8 Foot	13 Clew ring	19 Hemp stay	23 Wire stay
4 Luff	9 Foot rope	14 Staysail boom	20 Lacing	24 Iron staysail hanks
5 Luff rope	10 Girth band	15 Fore staysail sheet		
		16 Preventer sheet		

STAYSAIL

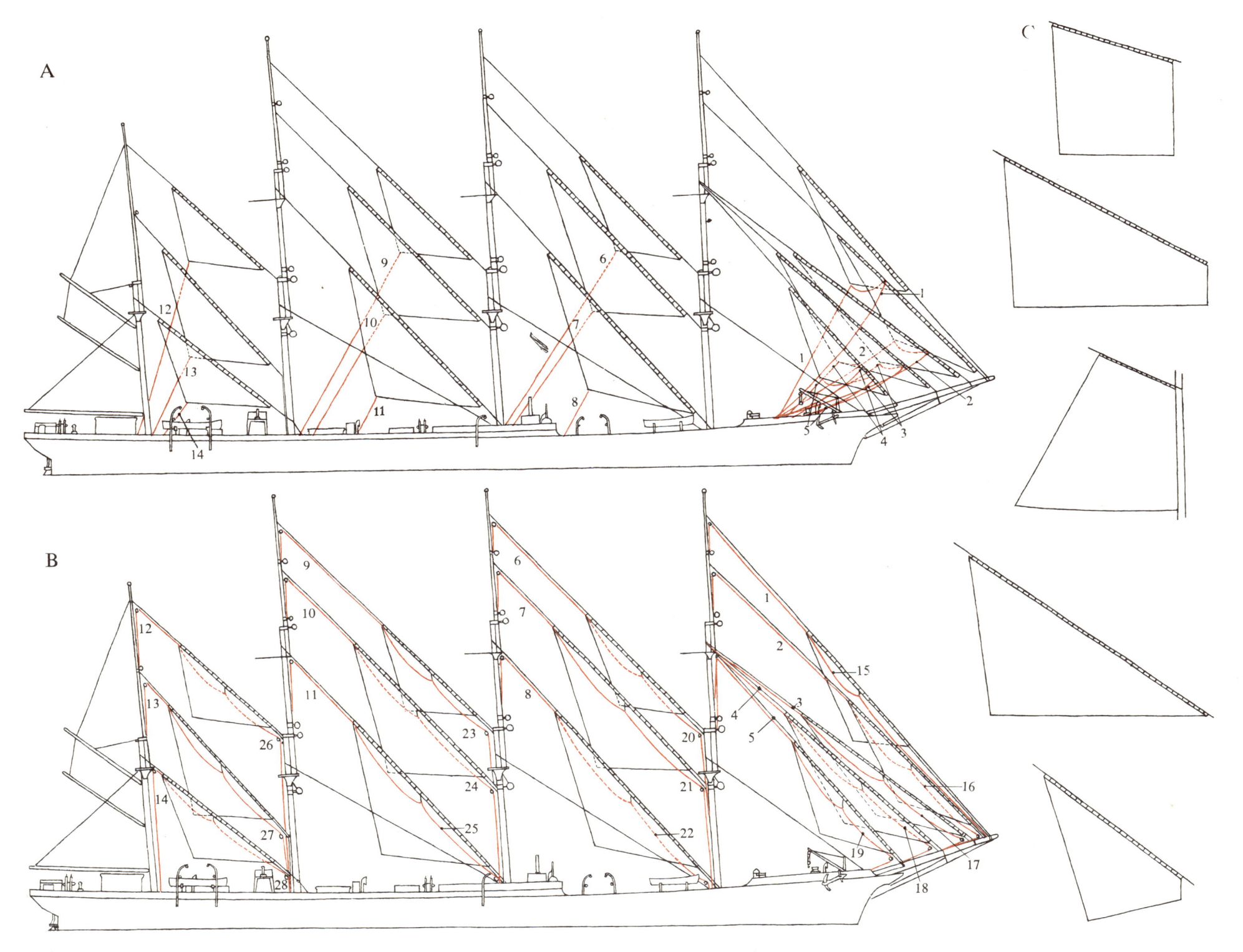

RUNNING GEAR OF STAYSAILS IN A FOUR-MASTED BARK, DIFFERENT TYPES OF STAYSAILS

A *Sheets*
1. Fore royal staysail sheets
2. Flying jib sheets
3. Outer jib sheets
4. Inner jib sheets
5. Fore topmast staysail sheets
6. Main royal staysail sheet
7. Main topgallant staysail sheet
8. Main topmast staysail sheet
9. Mizzen royal staysail sheet
10. Mizzen topgallant staysail sheet
11. Mizzen topmast staysail sheet
12. Jigger topgallant staysail sheet
13. Jigger topmast staysail sheet
14. Jigger staysail sheet

B *Halliards and downhauls*
1. Fore royal staysail halliards
2. Flying jib halliards
3. Outer jib halliards
4. Inner jib halliards
5. Fore topmast staysail halliards
6. Main royal staysail halliards
7. Main topgallant staysail halliards
8. Main topmast staysail halliards
9. Mizzen royal staysail halliards
10. Mizzen topgallant staysail halliards
11. Mizzen topmast staysail halliards
12. Jigger topgallant staysail halliards
13. Jigger topmast staysail halliards
14. Jigger staysail halliards
15. Fore royal staysail downhaul
16. Flying jib downhaul
17. Outer jib downhaul
18. Inner jib downhaul
19. Fore topmast staysail downhaul
20. Main royal staysail downhaul
21. Main topmast staysail downhaul
22. Main topmast staysail downhaul
23. Mizzen royal staysail downhaul
24. Mizzen topgallant staysail downhaul
25. Mizzen topmast staysail downhaul
26. Jigger topgallant staysail downhaul
27. Jigger topmast staysail downhaul
28. Jigger staysail downhaul

C *Different shapes of staysails*

119

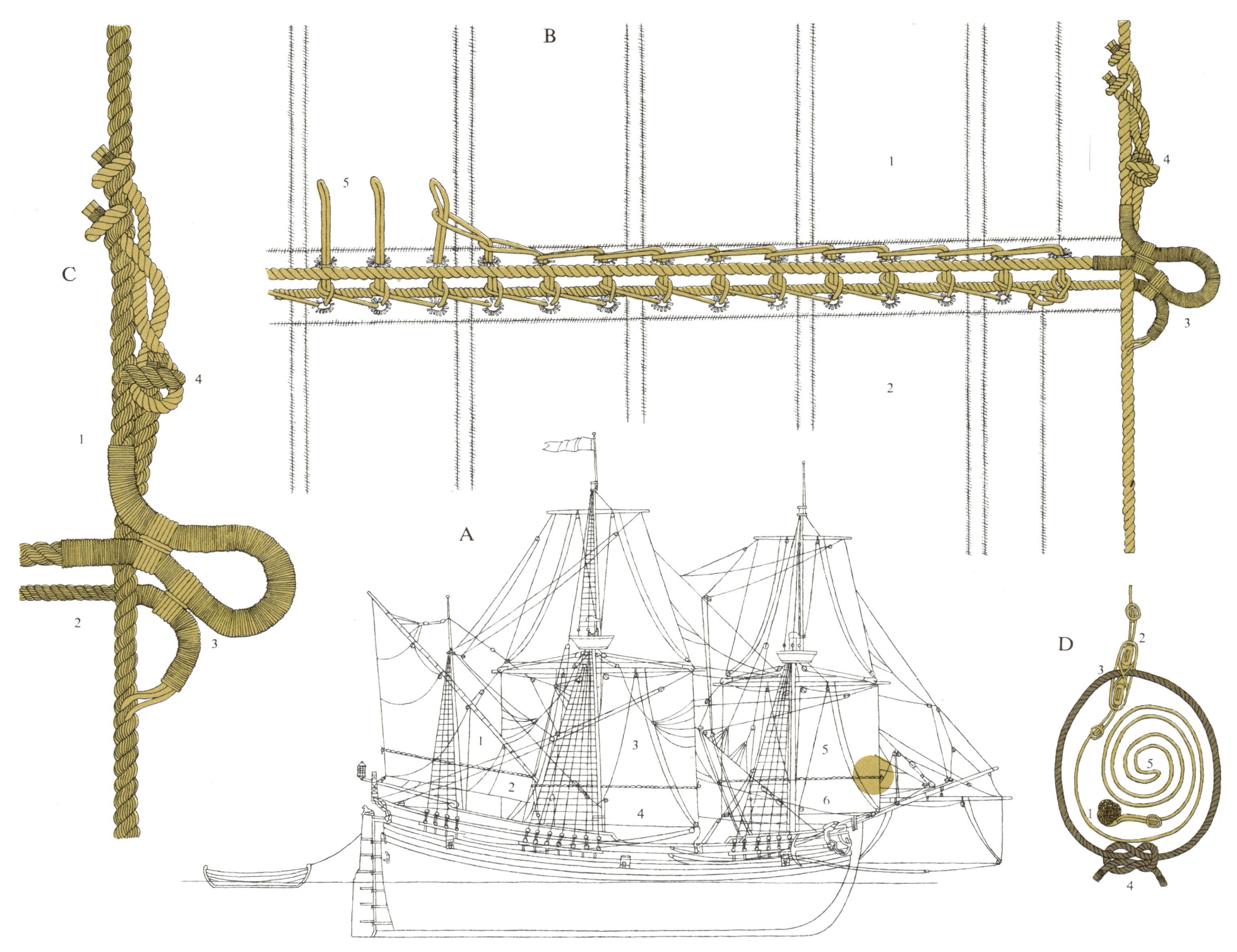

BONNETS AND REEFS

A *A merchant ship from the first half of the 17th century. Additional sails, called bonnets, are laced to the foot of her courses and lateen mizzen. Sail area can be reduced by unlacing the bonnets.*

1. Mizzen
2. Mizzen bonnet
3. Mainsail
4. Main bonnet
5. Foresail
6. Fore bonnet

B *The bonnets were laced to the sails in such a way as to make the lacing spill itself once it was started; this made quick work of shortening sail*

1. Lower sail
2. Bonnet
3. The clew of the sail seized to the earing of the bonnet
4. The leech rope of the bonnet, ending in a wall knot and stropped to the leech of the sail
5. Lacing of head of bonnet to foot of sail is made to spill once its stop is let go

C *Enlargement of clew of sail, showing details*

D *Sectional view of a reefed sail*

1. Foot of sail
2. Reef band
3. Reef point
4. Reef point knotted around reef with a reef knot
5. Rolled-up canvas in reef

120

SAIL DETAILS

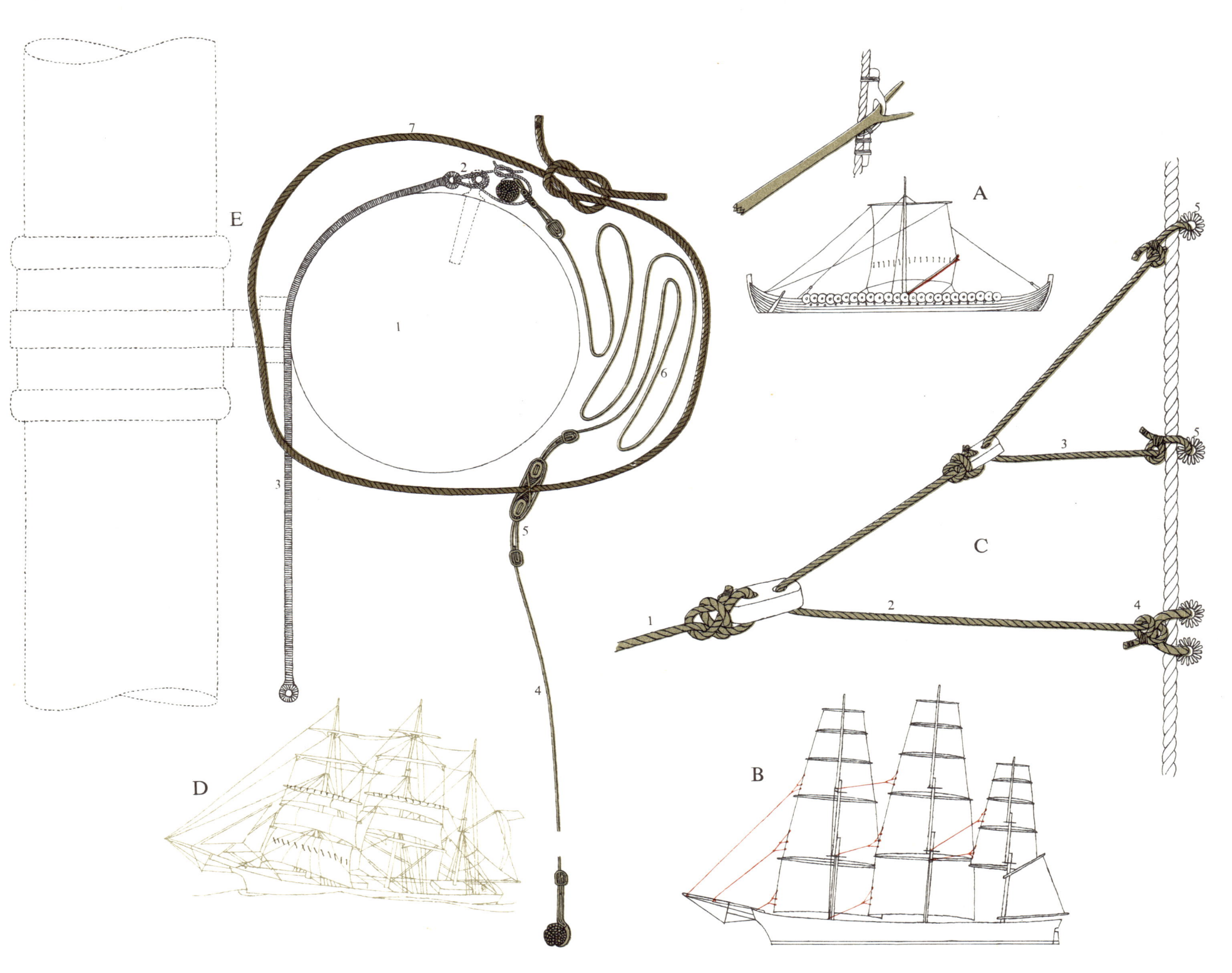

SAIL DETAILS

A *Norse Viking ship beating with a spar, known as a beatas, to hold the weather leech instead of a bowline; detail showing the spar's connection to sail*

B *Outline drawing of an American clipper close hauled on the port tack, with her weather bowlines picked out on her courses, topsails, and topgallant sails*

C *Detail of a bowline bridle*
1 Bowline hitched to the dead block with a bowline
2 Long bridle
3 Short bridle
4 Bowline cringle in sail
5 Eyelet-holes in sail for short bridle

D *Bark with double topsails, sailing by the wind under reefed upper topsails, lower topsails, and foresail*

E *Section of a yard showing a reefed sail*
1 Yard
2 Jack stay
3 Stirrup
4 Sail below the reef
5 Reef band
6 Reefed part of sail
7 Reef point tied around yard and sail with a reef knot

121

BLOCKS

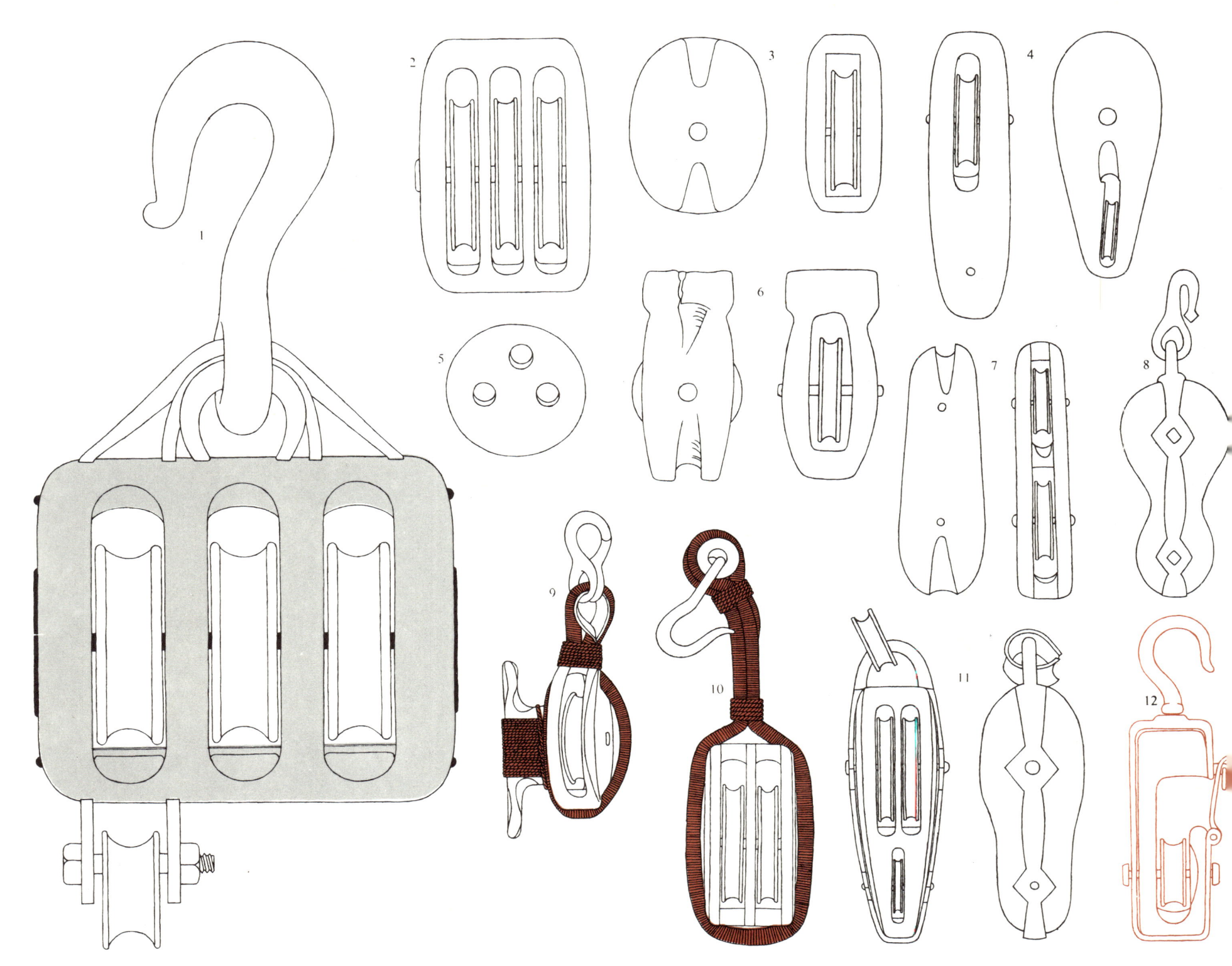

BLOCKS OF DIFFERENT TYPES

1. Large modern triple block, with internal straps and side hook; parts of the straps go through the block and form the becket for the standing part of the fall
2. Triple block for a hemp strop, 19th century
3. Single block, side view and front view, for a hemp strop, 18th century
4. Dutch style yardarm sheet block for topsail sheet and lower lift, front view and side view, 17th century
5. Deadeye, 19th century
6. Clewgarnet block, side view and front view; this block has been turned on a lathe; medieval or 16th century
7. Fiddleblock, side view and front view, with two sheaves, 18th or 19th century
8. Fiddleblock, with external strap and hook, 19th century
9. Wire-stropped sheet block, with clip hooks and a cleat for the sheet, so as to make the sheet block travel on a horse, 20th century
10. Double block with a double strop and hook, for masthead pendant, 19th century
11. Triple fiddleblock, with external strap and thimble for splicing the pendant, 19th century
12. Snatch block, with external straps and a swivel hook, 19th century

TACKLES AND BLOCKS

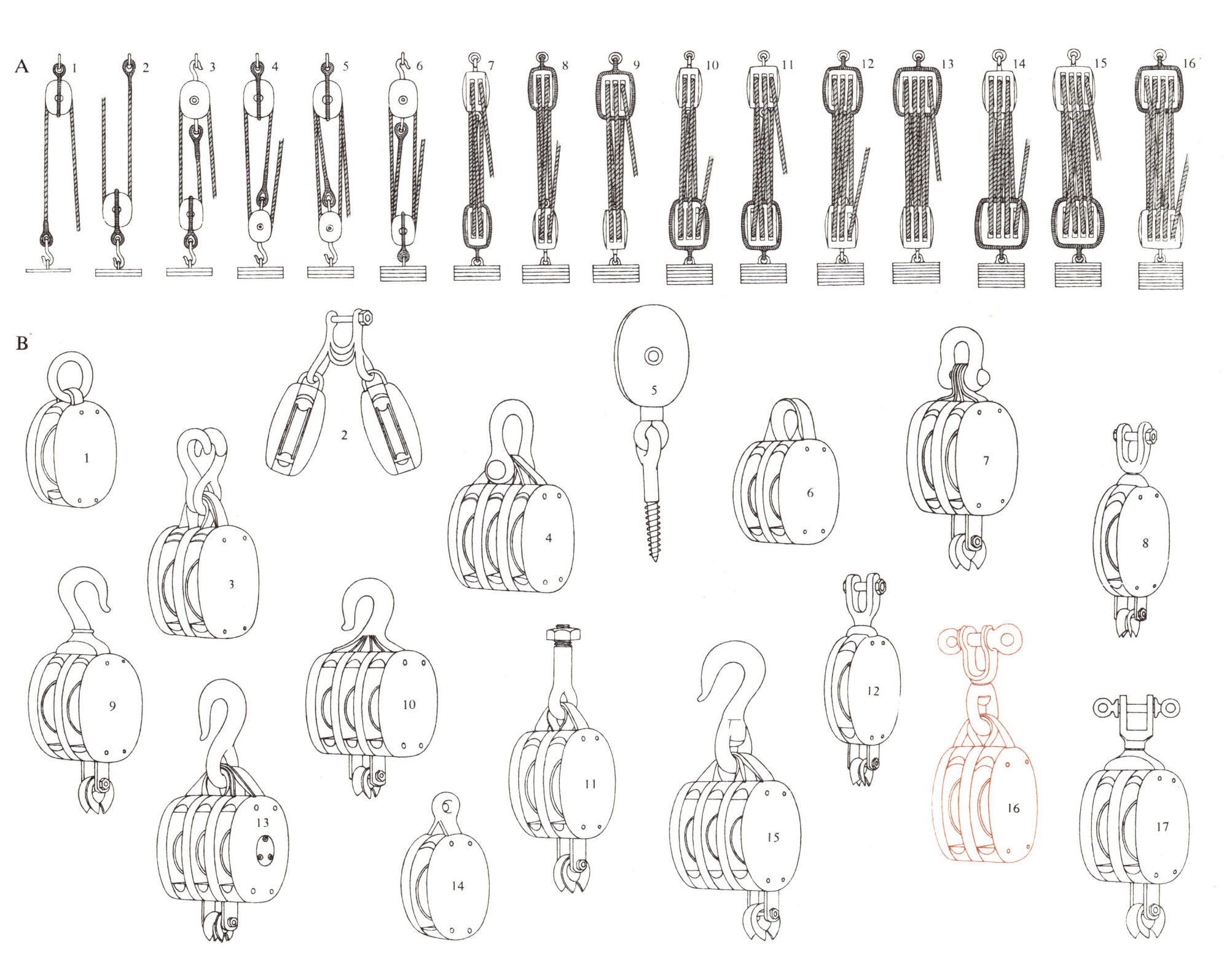

TACKLES AND BLOCKS

A *Tackles (the number of loads indicates the increase of power for each tackle)*
1. Single whip
2. Runner
3. Gun tackle
4. Gun tackle rove to advantage
5. Luff tackle
6. Luff tackle rove to advantage
7. Double purchase
8. Double purchase rove to advantage
9. Winding tackle
10. Reversed winding tackle
11. Triple tackle
12. Reversed triple tackle
13. Four-by-three tackle
14. Three-by-four tackle
15. Four-fold tackle
16. Quadruple tackle

B *Different blocks with internal iron straps*
1. Single block with a ring
2. Fore-and-aft jib sheet block
3. Double block with sister hooks
4. Triple block with a shackle
5. Single block with loose swivel screw eye bolt
6. Double block with an eye
7. Double block with shackle and becket
8. Single block with stiff swivel jaws and becket
9. Double block with stiff swivel hook and becket
10. Triple block with stiff fixed front hook and becket
11. Double block with eye bolt and nut and becket
12. Single block with stiff jaws and becket
13. Triple block with loose side hook and becket
14. Single block with a solid eye for gaff bands
15. Triple block with loose swivel hook and becket
16. Double block with loose swivel jaws with guy eyes
17. Double block with stiff swivel jaws with guy eyes and becket

RIGGING DETAILS

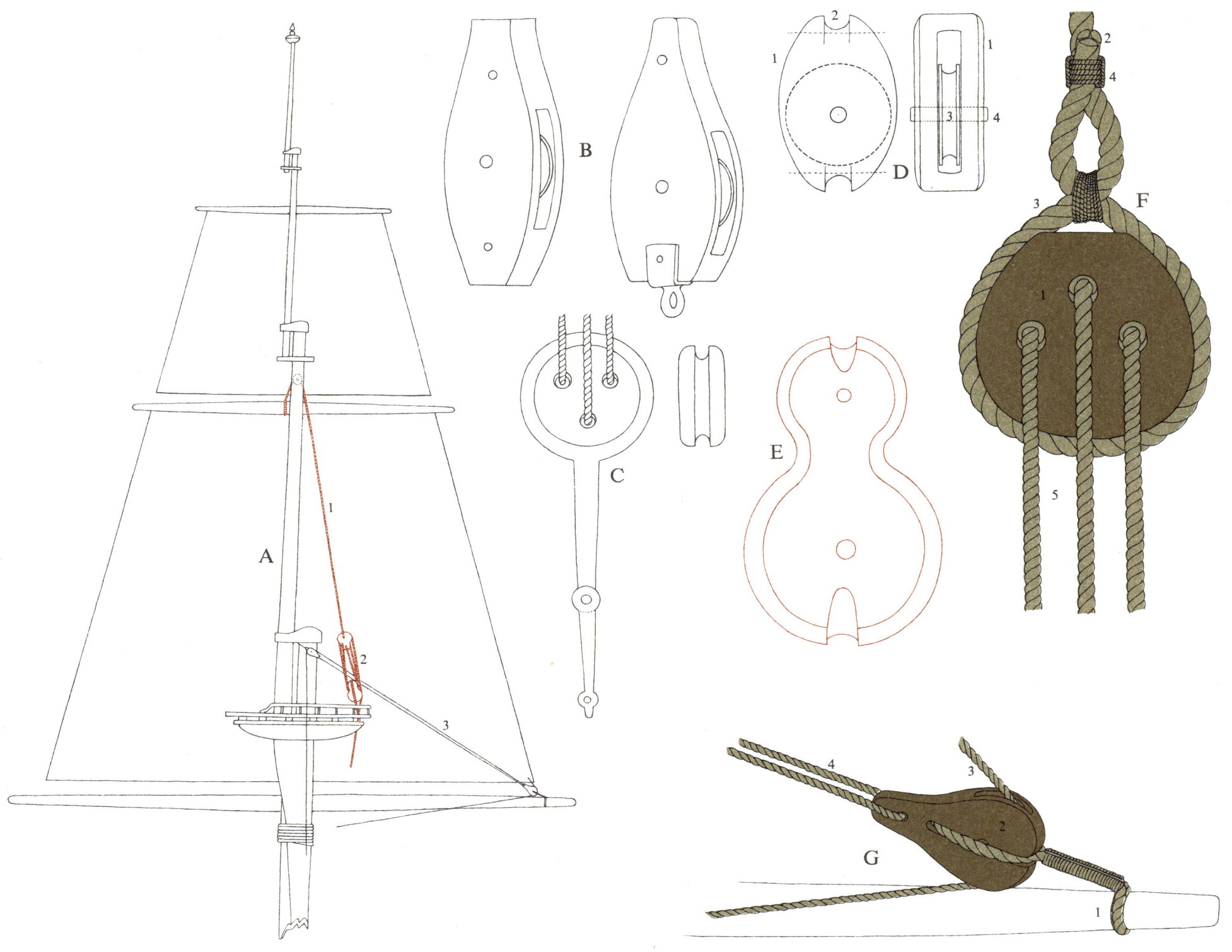

SOME OLD RIGGING DETAILS

A *Topsail halliard, end of 17th century*
1 Tie
2 Tackle
3 Lower lift

B *Wooden blocks without strops*

C *Chain plate with deadeye*

D *Block for hemp strop*
1 Shell
2 Score for the strop
3 Sheave
4 Pin

E *Fiddleblock with one sheave smaller than the other*

F *Deadeye, turned in a shroud*
1 Deadeye
2 Shroud
3 Throat-seizing
4 End-seizing
5 Lanyard

G *Lower yardarm with topsail sheet block*
1 Lower yardarm
2 Topsail sheet block
3 Topsail sheet
4 Lower lift

SAIL MAKING

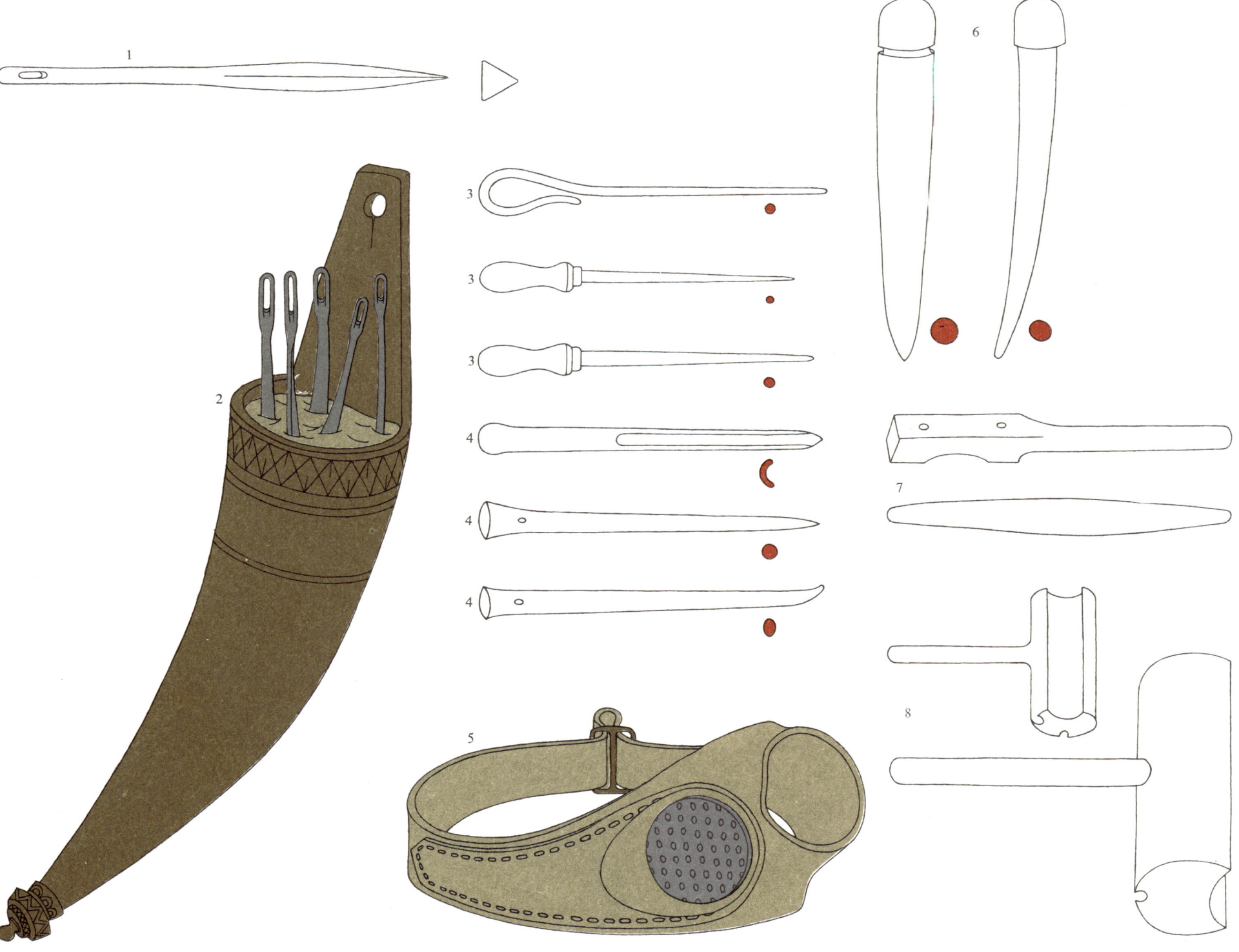

TOOLS FOR SAIL-MAKING AND RIGGING WORK

1 Big sail needle, roping needle
2 Carved bullock's horn with tallow for holding needles
3 Prickers for small work
4 Marlinespikes for splicing wire
5 Sail-maker's palm
6 Splicing fids
7 Turning fids or heavers
8 Serving mallets

125

SAILING SHIPS

OLD TYPES OF SAILING SHIPS

1. Egyptian sea-going ship, about 1500 B.C.
2. Roman trader, about A.D. 200
3. Viking longship, A.D. 900
4. Norman ship from the 13th century
5. Hulk of the Hanseatic League, about 1470
6. Spanish caravel, about 1490
7. Spanish ship, nao, about 1490
8. English carrack, about 1500
9. Swedish kravel, galleon, 1550
10. North European boeier, 1560
11. West European galleon, 1590
12. Dutch flute, 1640

SAILING SHIPS

OLD TYPES OF SAILING SHIPS

- 13 Dutch pinnace, middle of 17th century
- 14 Swedish packet, 1690
- 15 72-gun ship, 1746
- 16 Merchantman, 1770
- 17 Hooker, second half of 18th century
- 18 Algerian chebec, 18th century
- 19 Swedish krayer, second half of 18th century
- 20 Swedish East Indiaman, 1786
- 21 Swedish snow, 1783
- 22 Swedish bark, 1792
- 23 Baltimore clipper, 1820

ETHNOGRAPHICAL BOAT TYPES

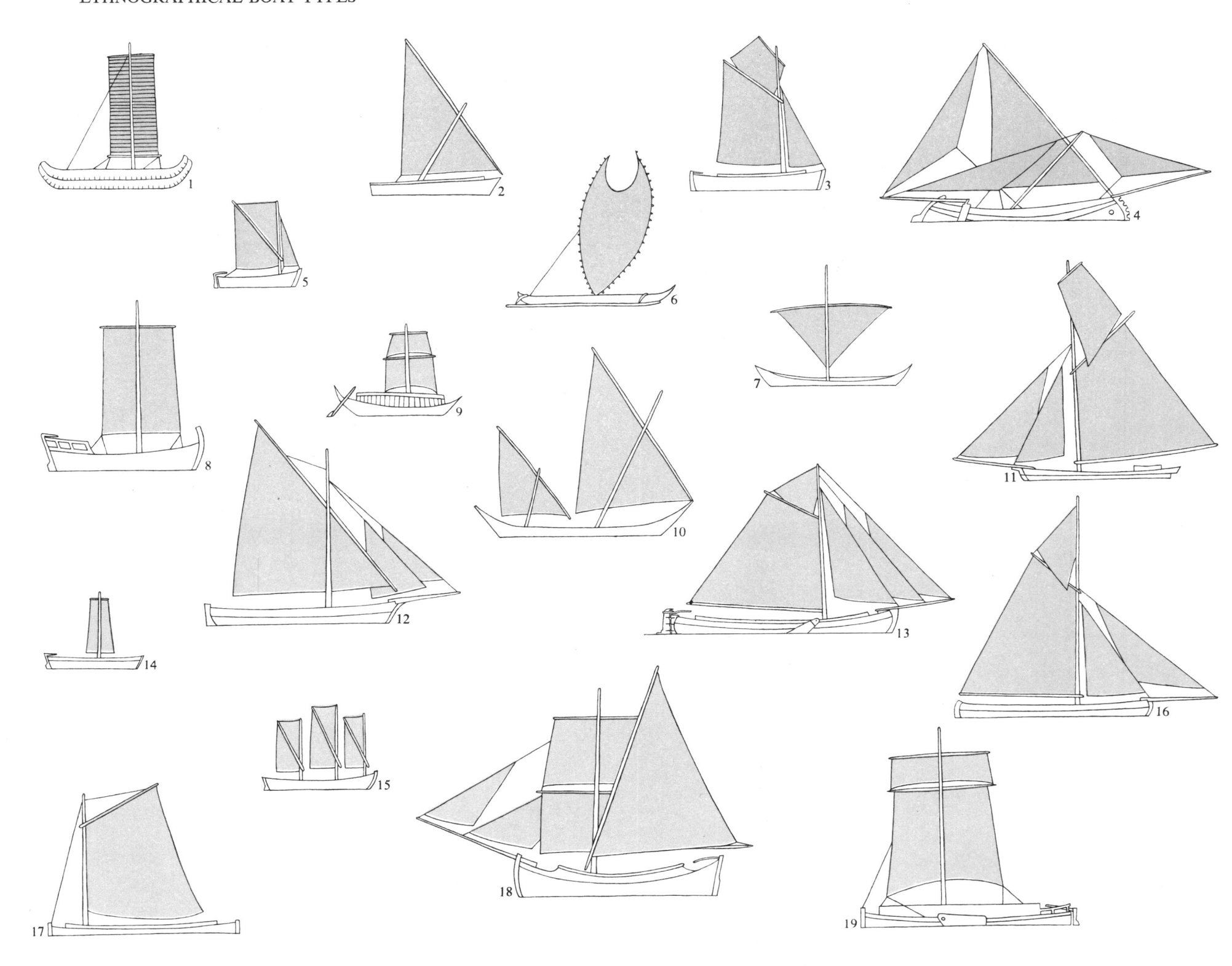

SOME ETHNOGRAPHICAL BOAT TYPES

1. Reed-boat from Lake Titicaca, South America
2. Boat from Lake Victoria
3. Koster boat from west coast of Sweden
4. Portuguese muleta
5. Small fishing boat from west coast of Sweden
6. Outrigger canoe from the South Pacific
7. Piragua from Tahiti
8. Norwegian jacht
9. Boat from East Pakistan
10. Boat from Kimari, India
11. Sloop from archipelago off Stockholm
12. Tartan, trading craft from western Mediterranean
13. Dutch barge
14. Boat from the Göta River, West Sweden
15. Fishing boat from the Åland Islands, Finland
16. Danish revenue cutter
17. Norfolk wherry
18. Turkish caique
19. Humber keel, Yorkshire

ETHNOGRAPHICAL BOAT TYPES

SOME ETHNOGRAPHICAL BOAT TYPES

- 20 Dutch koff
- 21 Boat from Bahia, Brazil
- 22 Bilancella, Italian fishing craft
- 23 Bovo, Sicilian coaster
- 24 Arabian dhow
- 25 Egyptian markab
- 26 Paduakan, coasting craft from Celebes
- 27 Scow schooner, New Zealand
- 28 Thames barge
- 29 Ketch, Åland Islands, Finland
- 30 Junk, Amoy, South China
- 31 Velocera, Sicilian, lateen-rigged barkentine
- 32 Old barge, Lake of Vänern, Sweden

SAILING SHIPS

DIFFERENT RIGS

1. Five-masted ship
2. Four-masted ship
3. Ship
4. Brig
5. Snow
6. Main topsail brigantine
7. Five-masted bark
8. Four-masted bark
9. Bark

SAILING SHIPS

DIFFERENT RIGS

10 Brigantine or hermaphrodite brig
11 Four-masted jackass bark
12 Jackass bark
13 Six-masted barkentine
14 Five-masted barkentine
15 Four-masted barkentine
16 Barkentine
17 Five-masted two-topsail schooner
18 Four-masted topsail schooner
19 Three-masted topsail schooner
20 Topsail schooner
21 Main-topsail schooner or two-topsail schooner

131

SAILING SHIPS

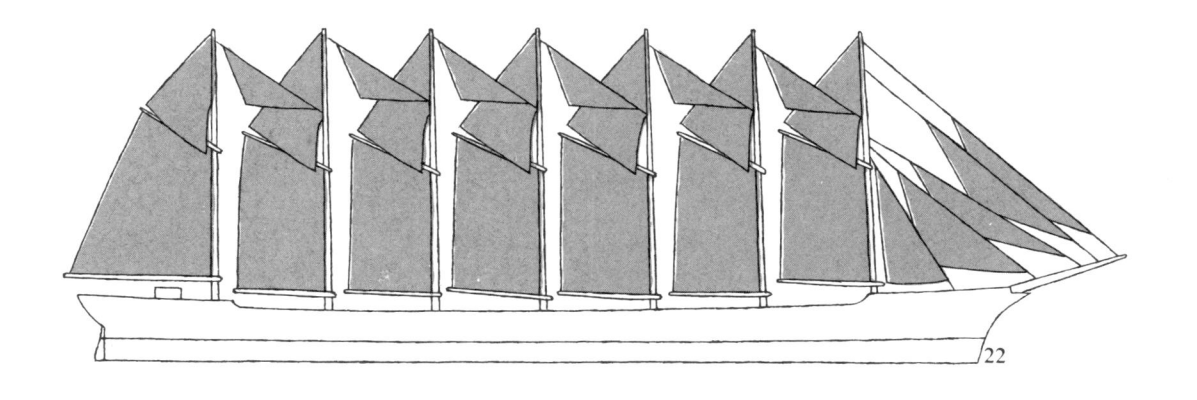

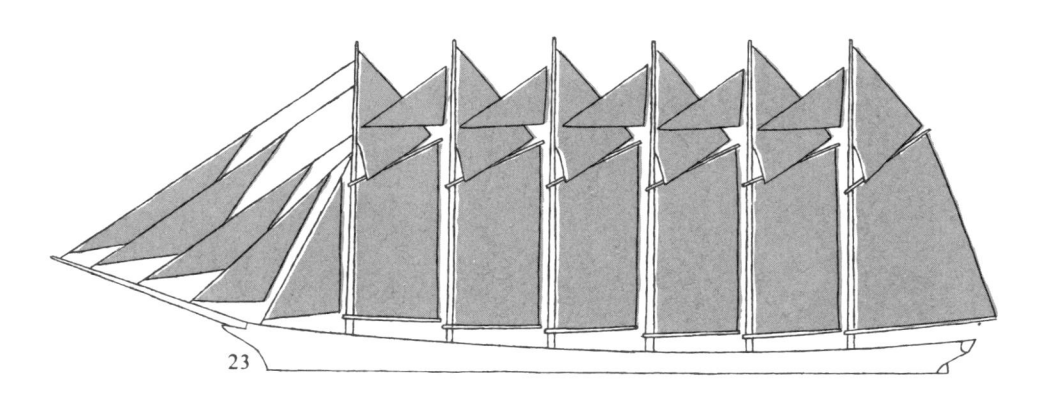

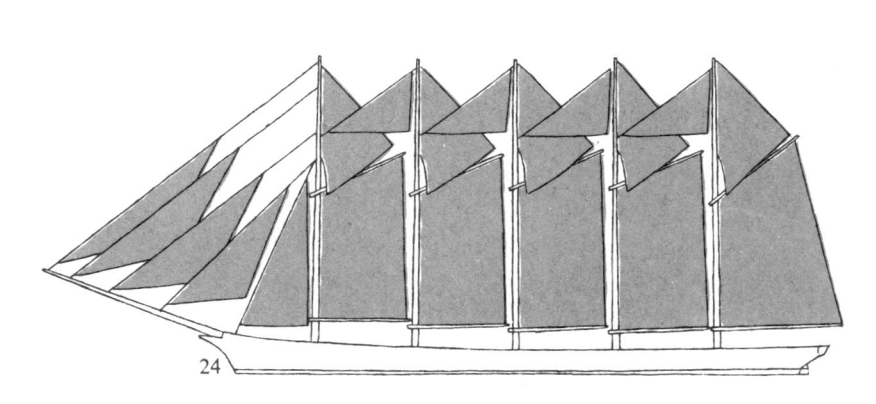

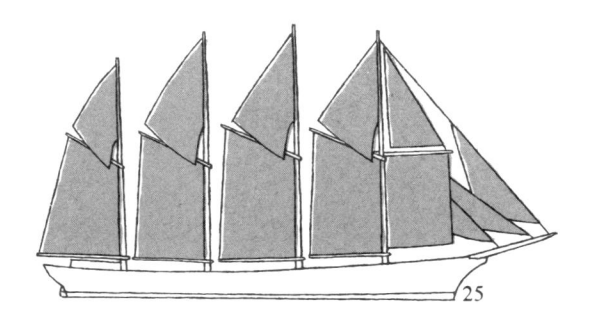

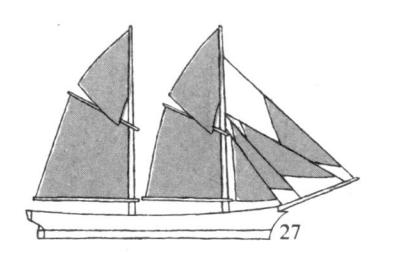

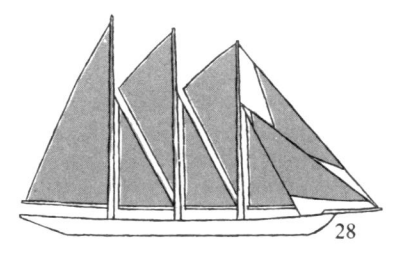

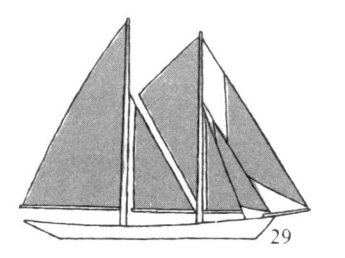

DIFFERENT RIGS

22 Seven-masted fore-and-aft schooner
The only seven-masted schooner ever built was the American schooner THOMAS W. LAWSON built at Quincy, Mass., 1902. According to a letter from the captain the masts were named as follows: Fore, Main, Mizzen, Number 4, Number 5, Number 6 and Spanker. This letter is kept in Peabody Museum, Salem, Mass.

23 Six-masted fore-and-aft schooner
24 Five-masted fore-and-aft schooner
25 Four-masted fore-and-aft schooner rigged with a flying foresail
26 Three-masted fore-and-aft schooner
27 Two-masted fore-and-aft schooner
28 Three-masted staysail schooner
29 Two-masted staysail schooner

SAILING SHIPS

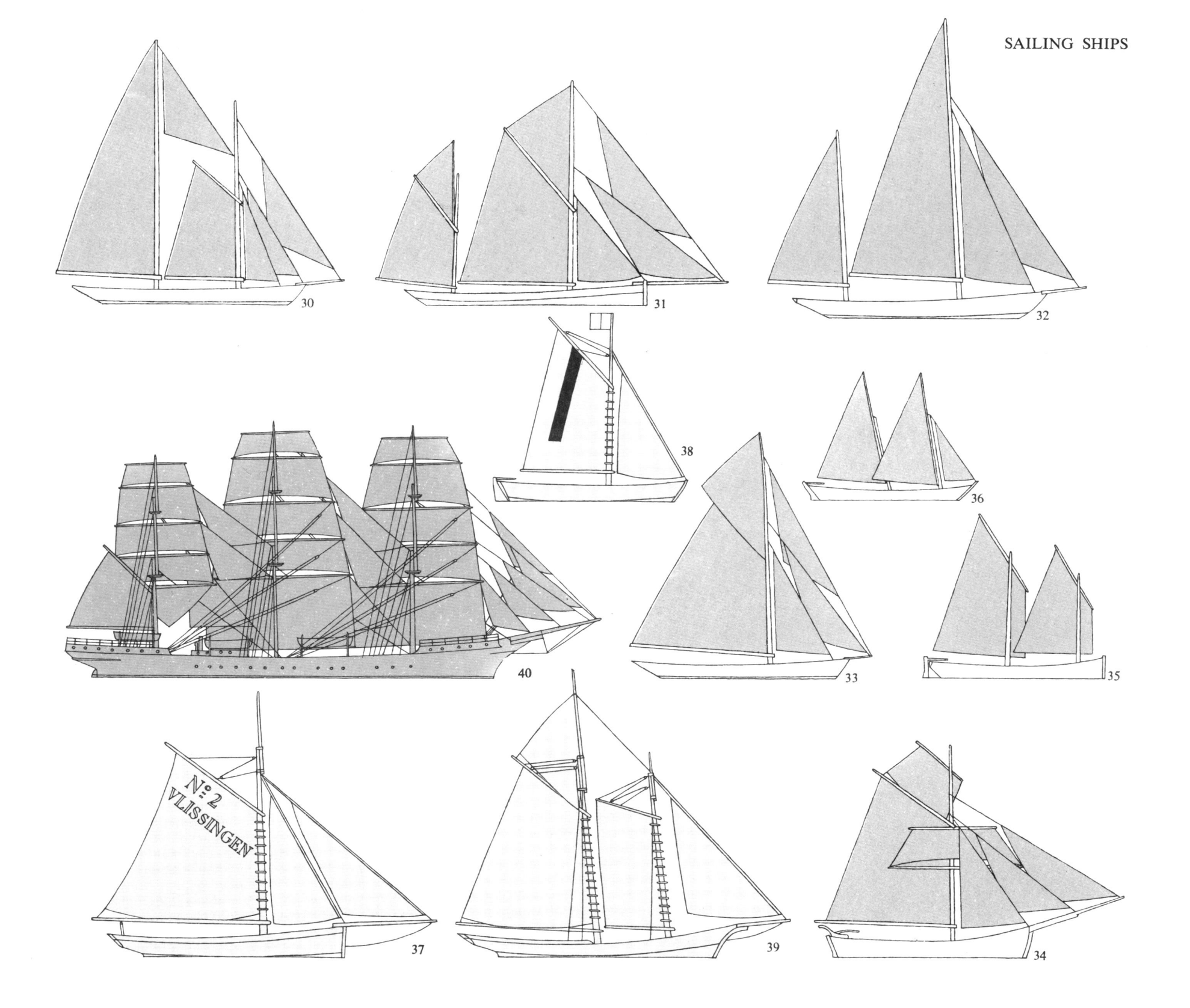

DIFFERENT RIGS AND AUXILIARY SAILING VESSELS

30 Two-masted schooner with Bermuda mainsail
31 Ketch
32 Bermuda-rigged ketch
33 Gaff-rigged cutter
34 Baltic sloop
35 Launch rigged with dipping lugsails
36 Gunter-rigged gig
37 Dutch pilot cutter, 1880's
38 Old Swedish sailing pilot cutter
39 New York pilot schooner
40 Training ship, *Denmark*, three-masted full-rigged ship

133

FLAGS

MERCHANT FLAGS

1. Norway
2. Finland
3. West Germany
4. Belgium
5. Netherlands
6. France
7. Eire
8. Portugal
9. Spain
10. Italy
11. Greece
12. Turkey
13. Israel
14. Canada
15. New Zealand
16. Panama
17. Honduras
18. Costa Rica
19. Liberia
20. Japan
21. Brazil
22. Argentina
23. Mexico
24. Colombia
25. Venezuela
26. Chile
27. South Korea
28. Republic of South Africa
29. India
30. China, Formosa

FLAGS

FIVE FLAGS

A *Sweden*
1. In the second half of the 16th century the present Swedish flag was not yet in use. Instead Swedish men-of-war flew a blue-and-white striped flag. The pennant at the masthead, however, carried the three Swedish crowns.
2. The three-tongued blue flag of the fleet of the army, 1761-1813
3. The ensign of 1658, from the oldest preserved Swedish flag, now in Rijksmuseum, Amsterdam
4. Merchant flag, 1815-1844, with the canton of the Swedish-Norwegian Union
5. The ensign with the canton of the Union, 1844-1905
6. Merchant flag, after 1905

B *Great Britain*
1. Union flag
2. Cross of St. George
3. Cross of St. Andrew
4. Cross of St. Patrick
5. Merchant flag (red ensign)

C *Denmark*
According to a legend, the Danish flag fell from the sky in front of the army in 1219 and lead the army to victory. It is probably the oldest flag in the world, and has been Denmark's colors since the 14th century.

D *United States of America*
1. The U.S. flag of today. The stars represent the 50 states and the stripes the original 13 states.
2. The 13 stars of 1777
3. 1795
4. 1818
5. 1846
6. 1848
7. 1912
No official design for placement of the stars existed before 1912

E *Australia*
The five stars in the field are the principal stars in the Southern Cross constellation. The large star below the canton is the symbolic "Commonwealth Star"
1. National flag
2. Merchant flag

135

HOUSE FLAGS

FLAGS

A *House flags from sailing ship days*
1. The Hanseatic League, Lübeck (the Middle Ages)
2. The East India Company, London
3. Black Ball Line, New York (1816)
4. Enoch Train White Diamond Line, Boston (1820's)
5. Grinnell, Minturn & Co., New York, Swallow Tail Line for Liverpool
6. Grinnell, Minturn & Co., New York, Swallow Tail Line for London
7. Arthur Sewall, Bath, Me.
8. Alaska Packers Association, San Francisco
9. Money Wigram & Sons, London
10. George Thompson & Co., Aberdeen White Star Line, Aberdeen
11. John Willis & Son, London
12. Devitt & Moore, London
13. John Hardie & Co., Glasgow
14. Thomas Law & Co., Shire Line, Glasgow
15. John Stewart & Co., London
16. Andrew Weir & Co., Bank Line, Glasgow
17. Soc. Anon. Des Voiliers Nantais, Nantes
18. Ferdinand Laeisz, Hamburg
19. S. O. Stray & Co., Kristiansand
20. Gustaf Erikson, Mariehamn

B *Other house marks:* Black Ball Packet Besides flags, proud owners often had marks on the sails similar to the funnel marks of today. The Black Ball Line, New York, carried a black ball on the fore topsail, which was visible from far away.

C *Flags of a merchant ship*
1. Jack, often a small house flag or coat of arms, only flown in port
2. When in port abroad: the color of the country. In ports at home: when loading, the color of the country where bound, or when discharging, the color of the country from which the ship has arrived
3. Code flag, the Blue Peter, if vessel is to proceed to sea
4. Mail flag, if vessel carries mail
5. House flag
6. National colors, when in port
7. National colors, when at sea, if ship is fitted with an ensign gaff on the mainmast

D *Flags of man-of-war*
1. Union Jack
2. Naval flag
3. Commander's flag or pennant

136

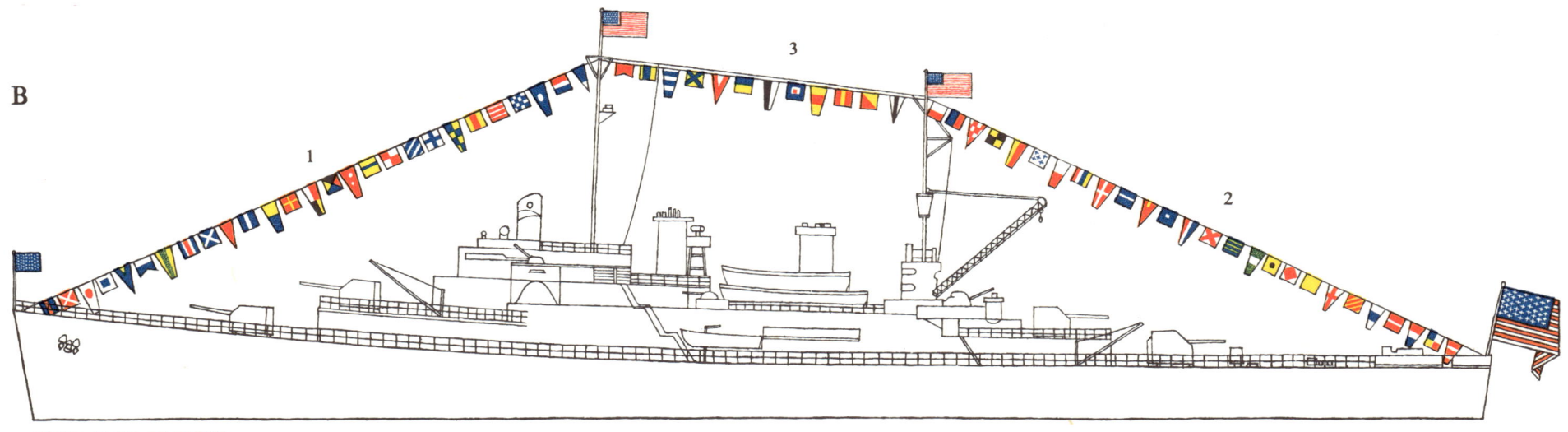

HOUSE FLAGS

HOUSE FLAGS OF TODAY

1. P & O Steam and Nav. Co., London, 1834
2. Cunard Steamship Co., Liverpool, 1840
3. Matson Nav. Co., San Francisco
4. United Fruit Co., Boston, New York
5. American President Line, San Francisco
6. United States Lines, New York
7. British India Co., London
8. Royal Mail Steam Packet Co., London
9. Pacific Steam Nav. Co., Liverpool
10. Canadian Pacific Railways Co., London
11. Blue Star Line, London
12. British Tankers Co., Ltd., London
13. Cie de Messageries Maritimes, Paris
14. Rotterdamsche Lloyd, Rotterdam
15. Hamburg American Line, Hamburg
16. Norddeutscher Lloyd, Bremen
17. Det Forenede Dampskibselskab, Copenhagen
18. J. Lauritzen, Esbjerg
19. Norwegian American Line, Oslo
20. Wilhelm Wilhelmsen, Oslo
21. Swedish American Line, Gothenburg
22. Johnson Line, Stockholm
23. Nippon Yusen Kaisha, Tokyo
24. China Merchant Nav. Co., Hong Kong

B *How to dress a ship Dressing a ship means that national ensigns shall be displayed from the flagstaff and from each masthead. When full dressing a ship, a rainbow of signal flags and pennants is also displayed. The order of flags in the U.S. Navy is shown above. In the Royal British Navy the order shall be:*

1. Fore-down. Beginning at jack staff: E, Q, Desig, G, p3, Z, Negat, W, p9, 7, p4, R, p8, P, p4, i, p1, T, p7, 6, Corpen, 8, p2, X, Preparative, H, Code, 5, Starboard, X, pØ, F, Church pennant, Division, Form, O, Sub Division.

2. Main down. Beginning at Ensign Staff: 3, L, p2, 4, p7, X, Church pennant, Ø, Interrogative, B, pØ, V, p4, K, pQ, N, Code, J, Form, R, Turn, M, Corpen, P, p7, 3, p3, 2, Desig, 5, p8, 9, Speed Flag.

3. Fore to Main: Station, Y, Third Substitute, U, First Substitute, D, Fourth Substitute, 3, Emergency, 1, Third Substitute, L, Emergency, 7, Second Substitute, Squadron, First Substitute, C.

SIGNALS CODE

THE INTERNATIONAL CODE OF SIGNALS

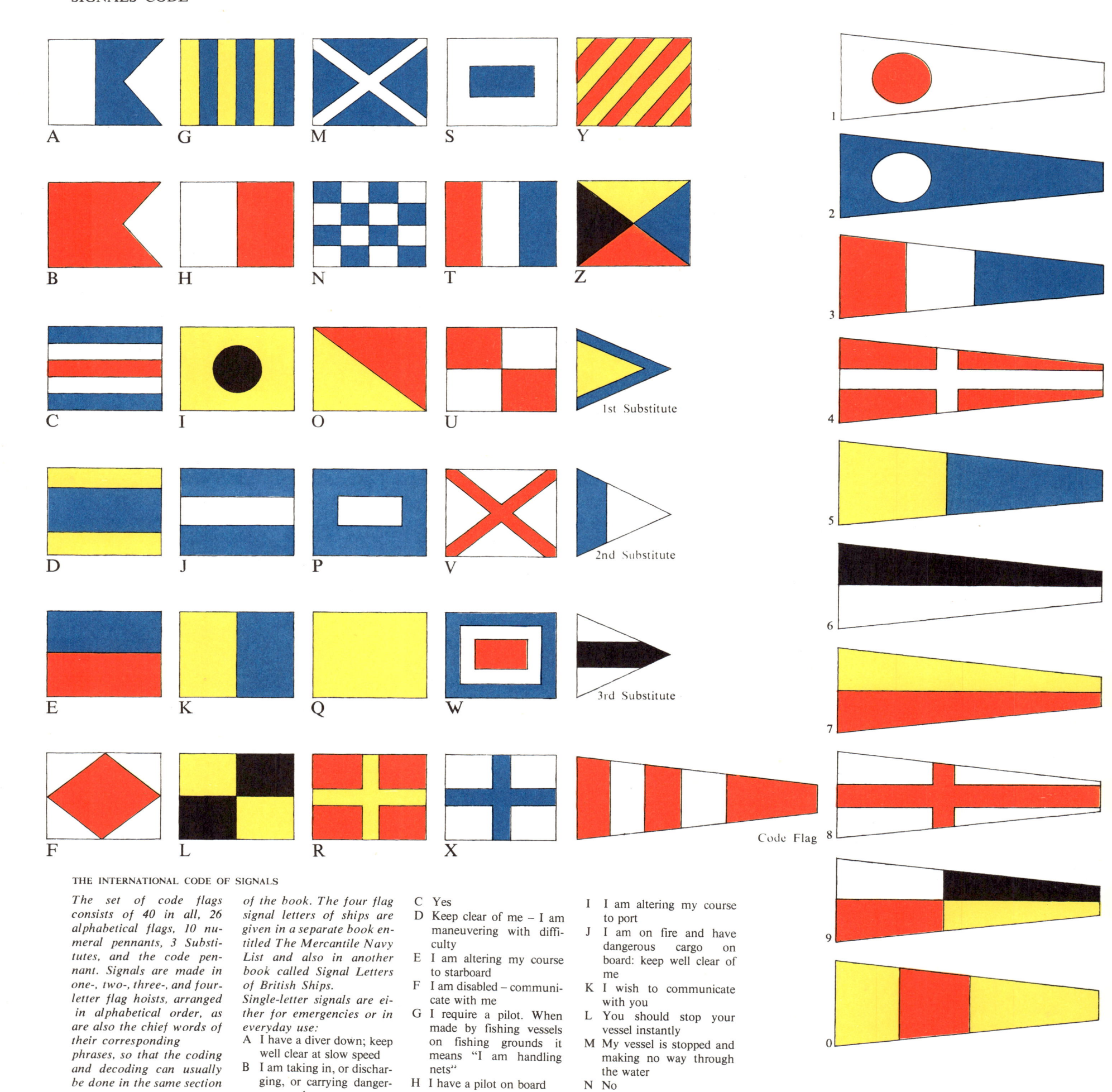

The set of code flags consists of 40 in all, 26 alphabetical flags, 10 numeral pennants, 3 Substitutes, and the code pennant. Signals are made in one-, two-, three-, and four-letter flag hoists, arranged in alphabetical order, as are also the chief words of their corresponding phrases, so that the coding and decoding can usually be done in the same section of the book. The four flag signal letters of ships are given in a separate book entitled The Mercantile Navy List and also in another book called Signal Letters of British Ships.

Single-letter signals are either for emergencies or in everyday use:

A I have a diver down; keep well clear at slow speed
B I am taking in, or discharging, or carrying dangerous goods
C Yes
D Keep clear of me – I am maneuvering with difficulty
E I am altering my course to starboard
F I am disabled – communicate with me
G I require a pilot. When made by fishing vessels on fishing grounds it means "I am handling nets"
H I have a pilot on board
I I am altering my course to port
J I am on fire and have dangerous cargo on board: keep well clear of me
K I wish to communicate with you
L You should stop your vessel instantly
M My vessel is stopped and making no way through the water
N No

Continued

138

SIGNALS CODE

Continued

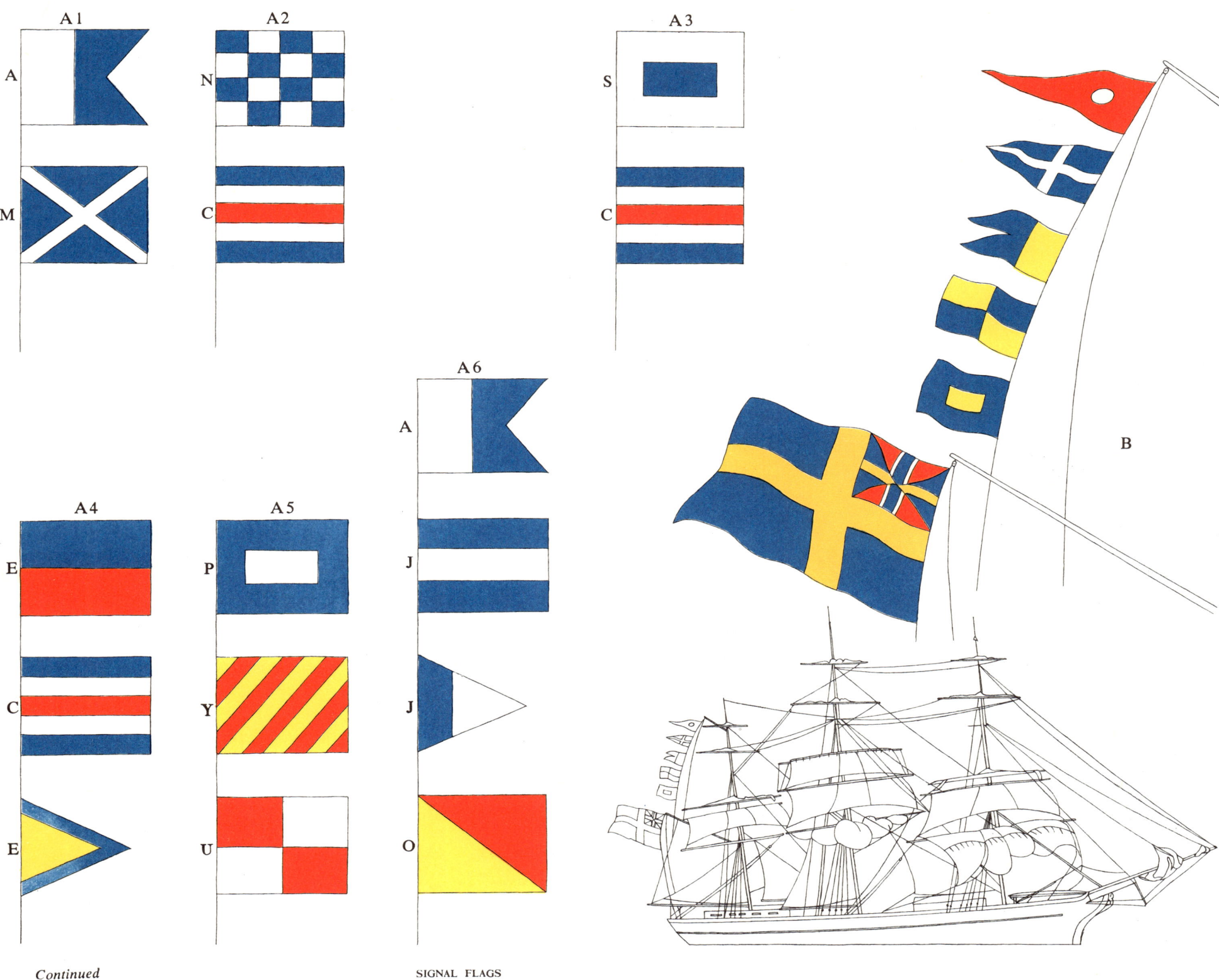

- O Man overboard
- P *In harbour.* All persons should report on board as the vessel is about to proceed to sea. *At sea.* It may be used by fishing vessels to mean: "My nets have got caught on an obstruction"
- Q My vessel is healthy – I request a free pratique
- R The way is off my ship you may feel your way past me
- S My engines are going full speed astern
- T Keep clear of me; I am engaged in pair trawling
- U You are standing into danger
- V I require assistance
- W I require medical assistance
- X Stop carrying out your intentions and watch for my signals
- Y I am dragging my anchor
- Z I require a tug. When made by fishing vessels on fishing grounds it means "I am handling nets"

SIGNAL FLAGS

A *The international signal code*
Selection of two-letter signals
1 AM – Have you a doctor?
2 NC – I am in distress and require immediate assistance
3 SC – I am under way. SC1 – I am ready to get under way. SC2 – I shall get under way as soon as the weather permits

A selection of three-letter signals
4 ECE – What course are you steering? *(When 1st flag is to be repeated, it is indicated by the 1st Substitute)*
5 PYU – Good voyage!

Example of a four-letter signal
6 AJJO – Liverpool (When the 2nd flag is to be repeated, it is indicated by the 2nd Substitute)

B *Earlier signal systems During a few decades in the middle of the 19th century. Marryat's code was in use before the Commercial Code became universal. The number in Marryat's Code of the Swedish three-masted ship Indiaman of Gävle, 1856, is shown above the ship.*

139

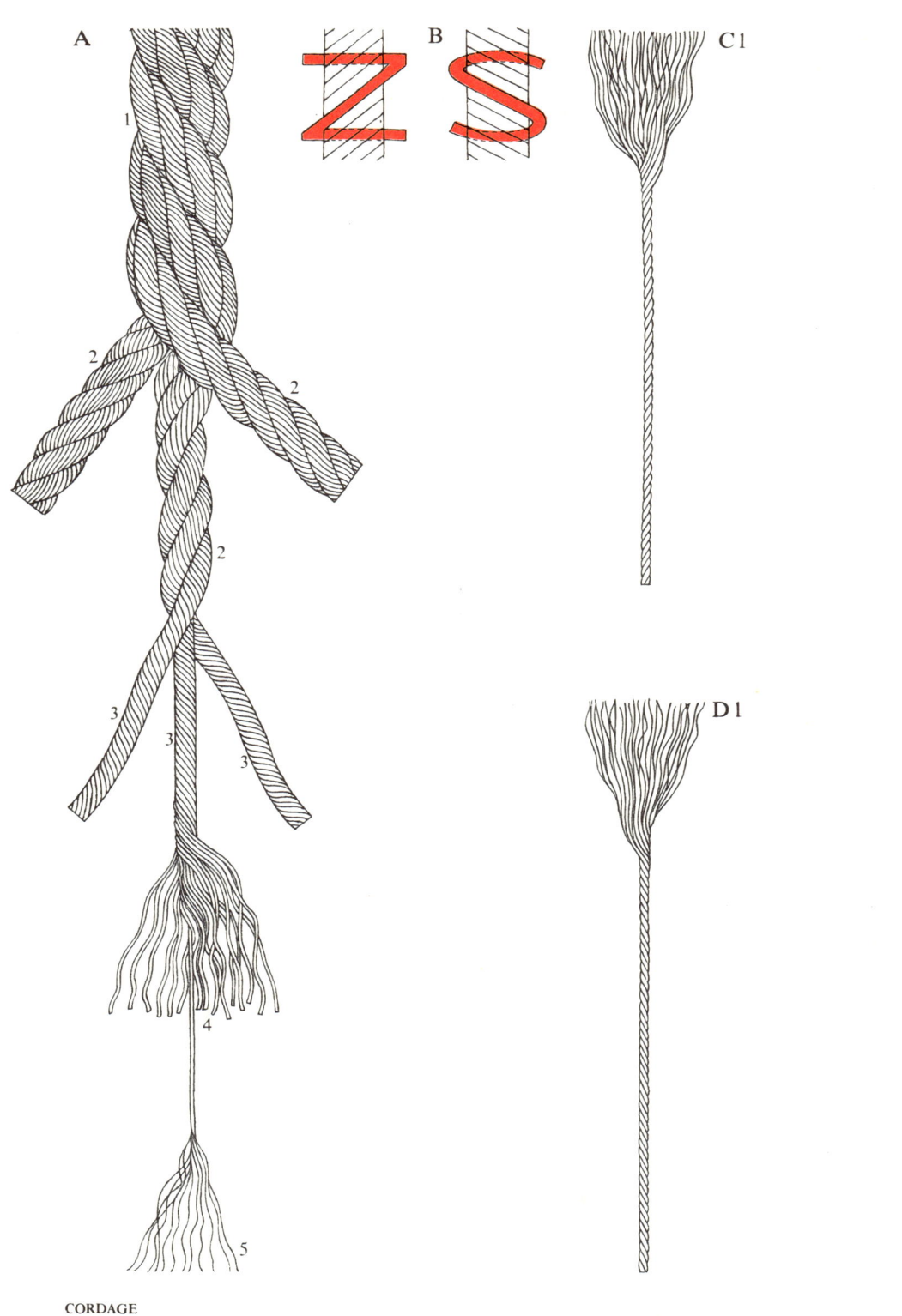

CORDAGE

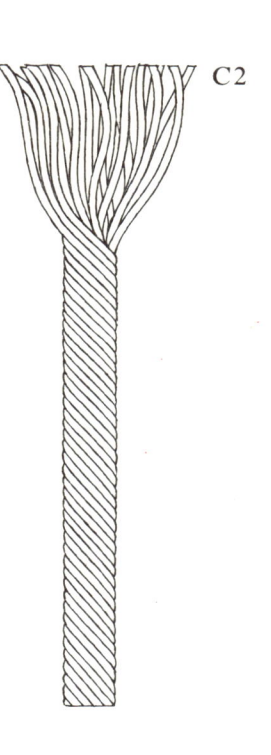

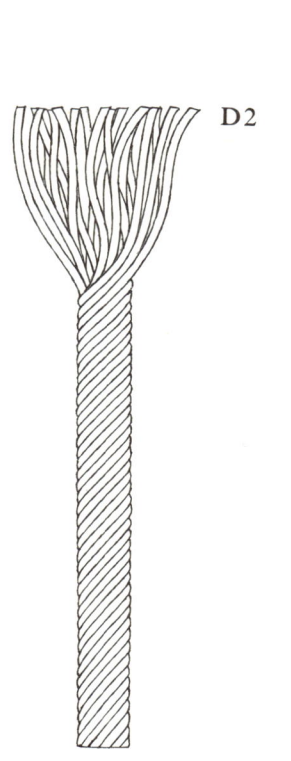

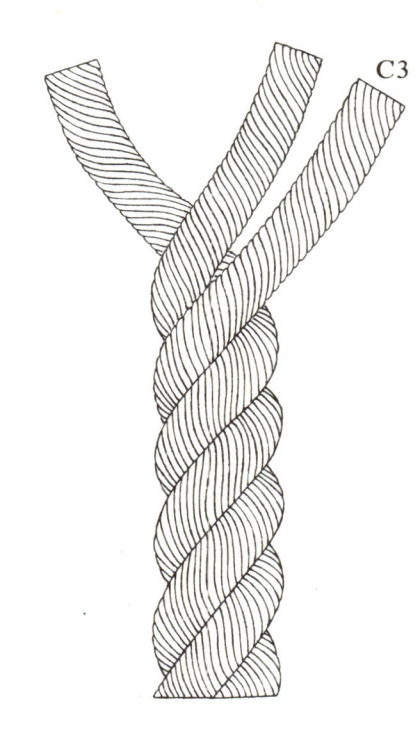

CORDAGE

- **A** *Cable-laid rope*
  1. Cable, laid up left-handed
  2. Hawser, laid up right-handed
  3. Strands
  4. Yarn
  5. Fiber

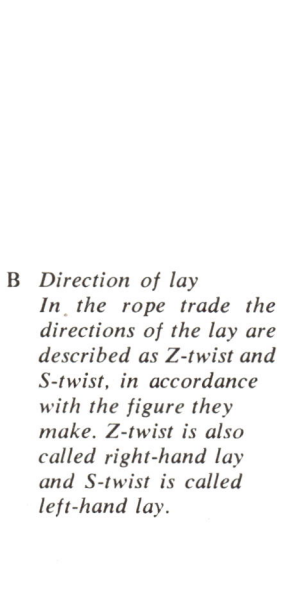

- **B** *Direction of lay*
  In the rope trade the directions of the lay are described as Z-twist and S-twist, in accordance with the figure they make. Z-twist is also called right-hand lay and S-twist is called left-hand lay.

- **C** *Z-laid, hawser laid, right-handed rope is the most used*
  1. Z-spun yarn
  2. S-twisted strand
  3. Z-laid rope

- **D** *S-laid, hawser laid, left-handed rope is rather uncommon*
  1. S-spun yarn
  2. Z-twisted strand
  3. S-laid rope

WIRES

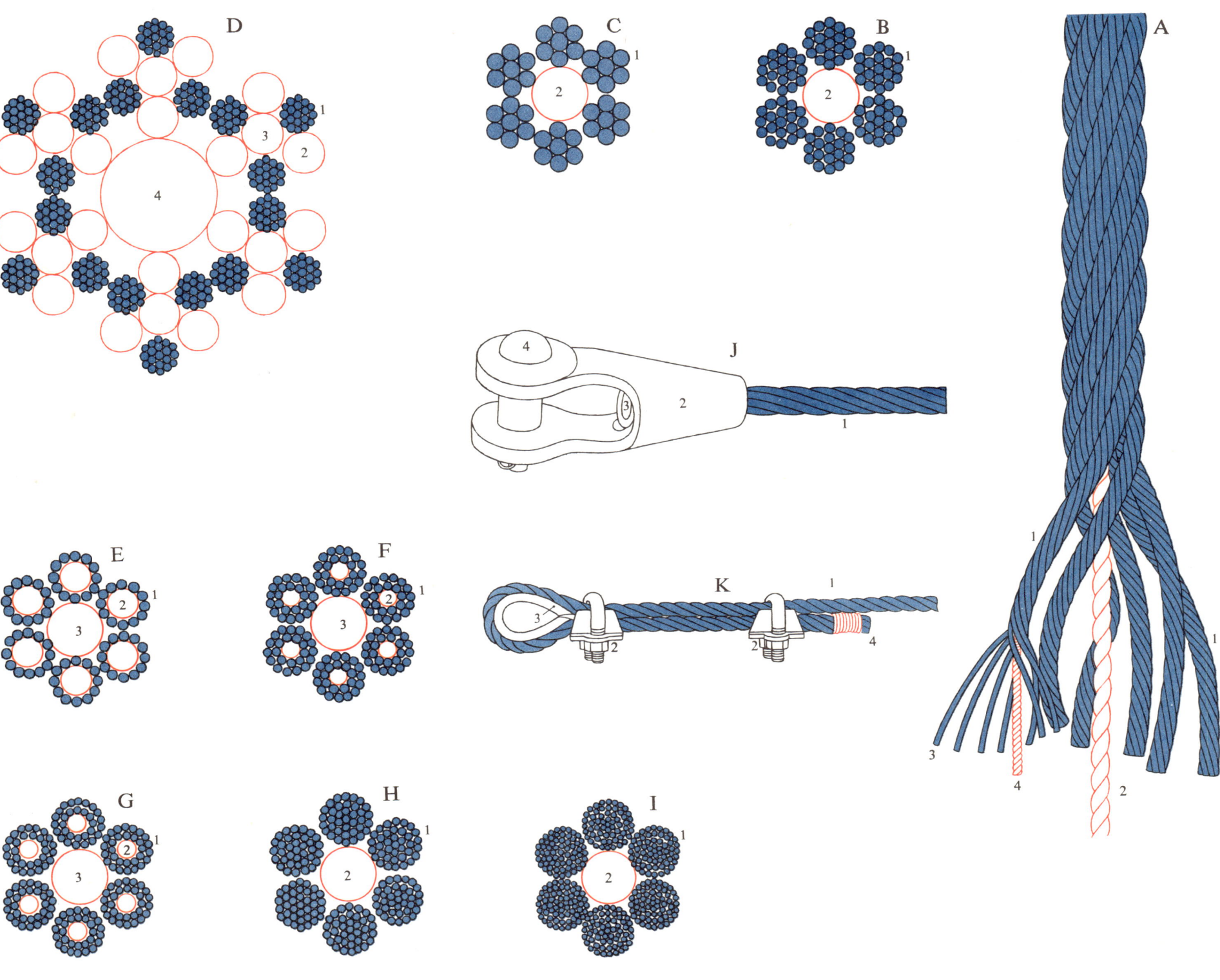

WIRES

A *Regular lay, right lay steel wire rope*
 1 Left-handed twisted strand
 2 Heart of hemp
 3 Steel wires
 4 Hemp or jute core

B *Standard hoisting wire rope, 6×19+1*
 1 Strand of 19 steel wires
 2 Heart of hemp

C *Standing rigging wire rope, 6×7+1*
 1 Strand of 7 steel wires
 2 Heart of hemp

D *Hemp-clad wire rope, 6×(3+4)+1*
 1 Wire rope
 2 Hemp string
 3 Jute core
 4 Heart of hemp

E *Running wire rope, 6×12+7*
 1 Wire
 2 Jute core
 3 Heart of hemp

F *Mooring line and hawser, 6×24+7*
 1 Steel wire
 2 Jute core
 3 Heart of hemp

G *Mooring line and hawser, 6×30+7*
 1 Steel wire
 2 Jute core
 3 Heart of hemp

H *Tiller wire rope, 6×37+1*
 1 Galvanized steel or bronze wire strand
 2 Heart of hemp

I *Tiller wire rope, 6×61+1*
 1 Strand (like H)
 2 Heart of hemp

J *Open wire-end socket*
 1 Wire rope
 2 Socket
 3 End spread and soldered
 4 Bolt with cotter pin

K *Temporary wire rope eye*
 1 Wire rope
 2 Wire rope bulldog grips
 3 Thimble
 4 Whipping

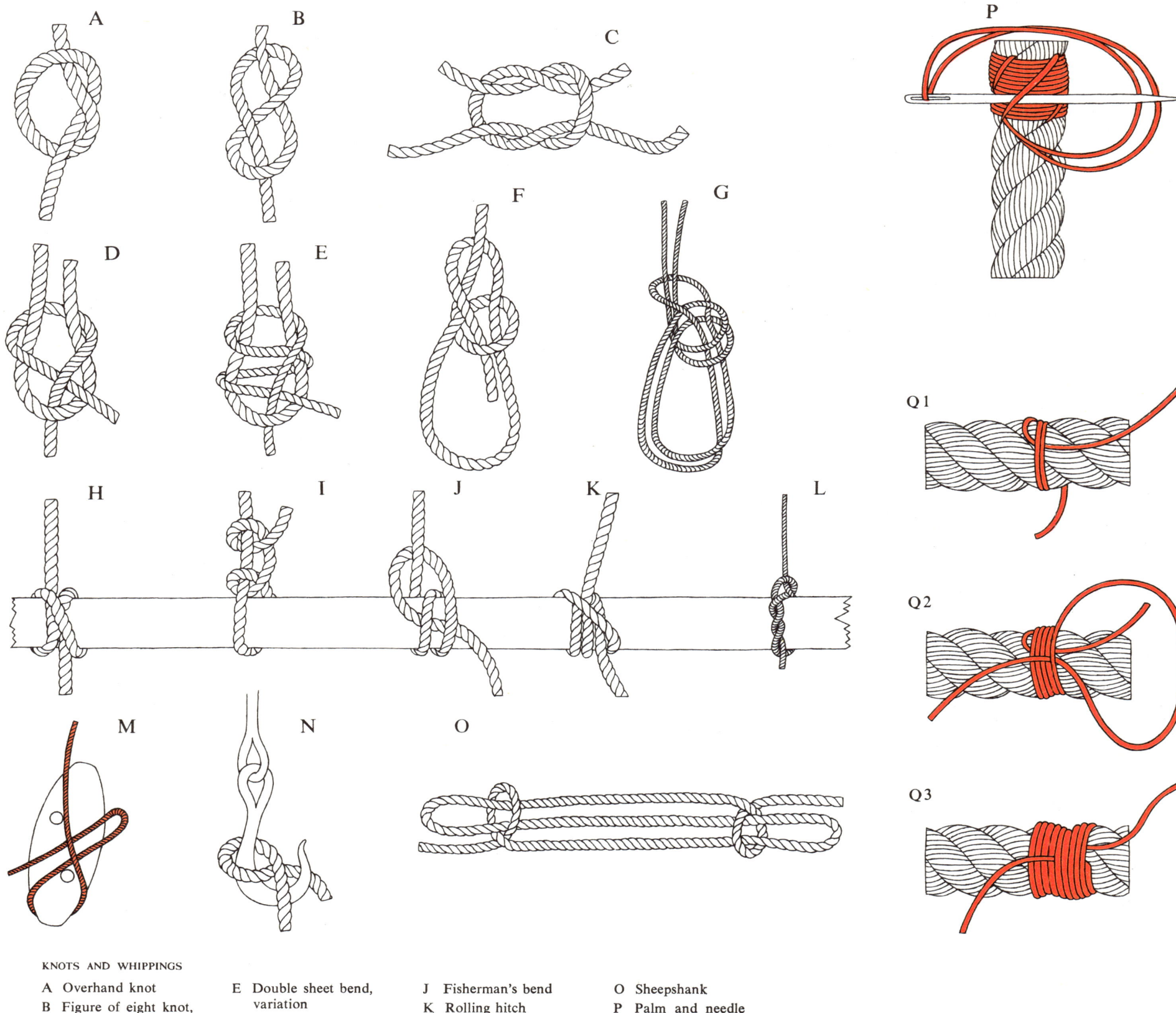

KNOTS

KNOTS AND WHIPPINGS

- A Overhand knot
- B Figure of eight knot, Flemish knot
- C Square knot, reef knot
- D Sheet bend
- E Double sheet bend, variation
- F Bowline
- G Bowline on the bight
- H Clove hitch
- I Two half-hitches
- J Fisherman's bend
- K Rolling hitch
- L Timber hitch
- M Slippery hitch
- N Blackwall hitch
- O Sheepshank
- P Palm and needle whipping
- Q Common whipping

SPLICES

SPLICES

When splicing cordage the strands are tucked against the lay. Each strand is taken over the strand on its left and then under the next one.

A Short splice, ropes put together before beginning to splice

B Long splice
1 The ropes laid up before beginning to splice
2 Way of knotting the strands
3 Way of tucking the strands

C Eye splice
1 Way of placing the strand before commencing the splice
2 Way of tucking the two first strands

D Eye splice on a wire rope, one tuck made on each strand.

When splicing wire rope each strand is generally tucked around the same strand all the time, in the same direction, as the single wires are laid.

Columbus' stately ship can no longer serve as the introductory note for the up-to-date chapter on propulsion. Instead, a rough print of the cylinder top in a diesel motor has been used.

PROPULSION

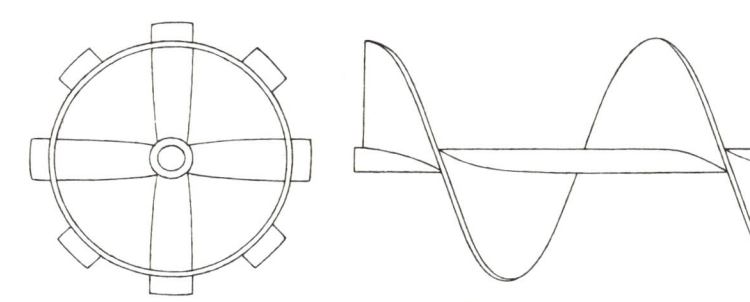

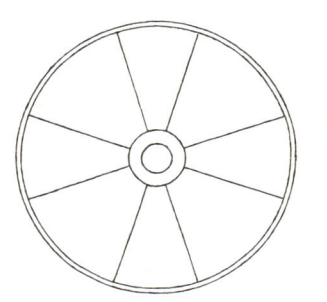

PROPULSION

BY TAGE BLUM

The first primitive craft, hollowed-out tree trunks or skin-covered boats built on light frames, were propelled by a paddle which was held with both hands and had no support by the gunwale. If there were many paddles on each side a considerable speed could undoubtedly be obtained. Even quite large ships have been paddled, which is apparent from many Egyptian reproductions. The "Hjortspring boat" in the National Museum in Copenhagen is a good example of a ship which had been built for propulsion by paddles. The invention of the oar with a fixed support on the gunwale was a very great advancement. The "Nydam boat" (Gottorp Castle) was an effective and fast "rowing ship" of slender shape and with twenty-eight oars. In Scandinavia the sail came into use early, and even though the Norsemen's Viking ships and longships were very easily rowed, sail was always used when making long voyages.

It was different in the Mediterranean, where the rowing vessel had a unique development. Here, they were not content with one line of oars or one man to an oar, but built vessels with two, three, and possibly more tiers of oars banked over each other. Probably the largest vessels employed several men to an oar. They were named biremes, triremes, quadriremes, quinquiremes, and so on even to one huge "40." Of these, the trireme was the best (170 oarsmen, maximum speed 8—9 knots). To give some idea of its efficiency, it was not until the time of Napoleon III that there was a faster postal service by steamship over the Mediterranean than that which the triremes maintained during Roman times. A factor should, however, be pointed out: while it was an honor to row an oar in a Viking ship, it was the slaves who rowed the Mediterranean galleys.

The idea of using paddle wheels appeared comparatively early. Appius Claudius is said to have experimented with hand-driven paddle wheels as early as the year 263 B.C. During the course of time, the idea appeared again and "walking drivers" by horses and oxen were tried. About the year 1200 mention is made of Chinese naval battles, where the warships were driven by slaves at capstans. As far as pure muscle power was concerned, the oar was undoubtedly the most effective means of propulsion. From the Middle Ages we have several illustrations of paddle-wheel ships, and in 1543 we hear of Blasco Garay's ship, which was tested in the harbor of Barcelona. But here also the paddle wheel was activated by man-power. A stronger source of propulsion was needed before mechanically driven vessels would have any practical use. Steam became the source of power that solved the problem. The name of James Watt will always be associated with the first practically applicable steam engine, where the movement of the piston was changed into a rotary motion. Watt was an instrument maker and was born in 1736. It cannot be said that he invented the steam engine, as Thomas Newcomen's atmospheric engine was already in existence, but Watt improved Newcomen's engine. It had been a clumsy device; now it was a really usable engine which could be used where a rotating shaft was required. Watt invented the condenser and made an engine where the piston was operated by the steam pressure and not, as in Newcomen's engine, where the steam was only used to lift the piston while the atmospheric pressure above it pushed it down. Hence the name "atmospheric engine."

Now the steam engine began to be used in ships. The first name in this connection was Denis Papin, the inventor of "Papin's Pot." In the year 1707 Papin is said to have sailed down the Fulda river in a steamboat from Kassel to the Weser. Here, his boat was destroyed by the boatmen who had a monopoly of navigation on the Weser. It is doubtful if this boat was anything other than a hand-powered paddle boat. In the year 1736 the Englishman Jonathan Hull obtained a patent on a steam tugboat, but there is doubt if it ever came into being. In 1776 the Marquis Claude de Jouffroy built a steamboat in which the engine drove paddle feet. In 1783 he built a larger, paddle-wheel boat, which forced the current on the Saône river as witnessed by many spectators. In 1788—1789 the Scotsman William Symington built two less successful steamboats; all of these experiments, however, were of no significance.

About the same time, in 1785, in America, the clockmakers, John Fitch and Henry Voigt, built a steam engine in a boat which had twelve oars. This experiment was successful, and with his third boat Fitch carried on a regular passenger service on the Delaware river between Philadelphia and Trenton, a distance of thirty miles. Fitch, however, never received any recognition. It was Robert Fulton who succeeded commercially and reaped riches and fame. Originally he was an artist, but with technical interests. About this time, in 1801, William Symington built the steam tugboat, *Charlotte Dundas,* which in many ways was before its time. Its engine differed from others by having a horizontal cylinder, with the piston rod, crosshead, guides, and connecting rod acting directly on the crankshaft. It was direct-acting as compared with the beam engine. The paddle wheel was placed in the stern and was fitted with wheel rims. The helm was situated on the foredeck. Fulton studied this boat, and in 1802 built a steamboat in France. The machinery was from Boulton and Watt. At a trial on the Seine he succeeded in winning the confidence of the American Ambassador in Paris, Robert Livingston, and in 1806 he returned to America. Here, he built the paddle steamer *Clermont,* with an engine from Boulton and Watt, and in 1807 he made his historic and successful voyage up the Hudson river. Even if Fulton was not the inventor of the steamship, it was he who made the first steamship which had any practical value. The *Clermont* will always be considered a milestone in the development of the steamship. In spite of its successful voyages in 1802 it was not the *Charlotte Dundas* that opened a new era. Instead, it was forbidden the use of the Clyde canal for fear it would damage its banks. Henceforth, all steamship traffic in Great Britain was stopped until years later. In America, under more favorable circumstances, development of steamships on the big rivers was rapid. Five years after the *Clermont's* journey there were fifty steamships in regular service. The high speeds attained by these paddle steamers are rather surprising: for example, the fastest ship at that time, the *Daniel Drew* of 1860, was able to maintain an average speed of 22 knots. However, these were large ships! For instance, the *New World* was 380 feet long, had a paddle wheel of 46 feet in diameter, and had no less than 680 berths.

Not until 1812 did the building of steamships begin in Europe. This was when Henry Bell launched the *Comet,* a ship with a length of 40 feet and a beam of 10½ feet. The engine was a single cylinder unit of 3—4 horsepower and the speed was only 4—5 knots. It differed from other paddle steamers by having two wheels on each side. The whole engine installation was much more primitive than that of the *Charlotte Dundas,* but, in spite of this, the *Comet* became the model for practical steamship service in England.

At first, steamships were looked upon as only suitable for river and coastal traffic; possibilities for development were a lot greater in America with its large waterways. It is therefore notable that it was an American steamship that first crossed the Atlantic. On May 26, 1819, the *Savannah* left Savannah, Georgia, and arrived at Liverpool twenty-five days later. *Savannah* was a full-rigged ship, fitted with a 90 horsepower engine that drove the wheel shaft directly. The paddle wheels were sixteen feet in diameter and were fitted with chains instead of wheel rims, so that the paddle wheels could be folded up when the sails were in use. From the logbook it can be seen that the steam engine was used for eighteen days of the voyage, while only the sails were used during the remaining seven days. The *Savannah's* dimensions were: length 100 feet; beam 27 feet 9 inches; draft 14 feet. The vessel held seventy-five tons of coal and three-thousand cubic feet of wood bunkers.

The ships mentioned up to now, with the exception of the *Charlotte Dundas* and the *Savannah,* were all fitted with beam engines on which the piston rod was joined to one end of a center pivoted rocker beam and the crankshaft to the other end. There were many variations of the beam engine: engines with the beam above, and engines with the beam below; also the "grasshopper engines," with the beam pivoted at one end. In Europe a low-location beam was mostly used, as this gave a low center of gravity. Paddle wheels, in the beginning, had fixed paddles, but these were inefficient. Soon, movable paddles came into being. These paddles could, by means of a series of rods, operated by a cam, stand almost vertical during the whole time they were under water (Morgan's patent paddle wheel).

As early as about 1770 the French scientist, Daniel Bernoulli, had suggested the propeller as a means of propulsion. There were both corkscrew and windmill types. In 1836 the Englishman, E. P. Smith, made a propeller that resembled a corkscrew, while the Swede, John Ericsson, experimented with a propeller that resembled the sails of a windmill. Smith's propeller had a pitch of 1½–3 turns to start with, but during one of the test runs part of it was knocked off and it was then found that it was much more effective. John Ericsson, who was born in 1803 and died in 1889, built a successful propeller-driven boat, the *Francis B. Ogden,* which was demonstrated on the Thames in 1837. His idea, however, was not popularly received, so he left for America where he quickly met with great success. Among the early propeller ships, Samuel Owen's *The Witch of Stockholm,* 1816, should be mentioned.

The engines used in paddle steamers were much too slow to drive propellers, and attempts were made to increase the speed by means of gears or chain transmission (*S/S Great Britain,* 1839), but these gearings did not solve the problem. Although the propeller had many advantages over the paddle wheel it was a long time before the propeller became a real success. The majority preferred the paddle steamer for passenger traffic and were responsible for the building of the last of the large paddle steamers: *Persia* (1855) and *Scotia* (1862). Especially interesting was the tug of war carried out by the British Navy between H.M.S. *Rattler* (propeller) and the equally large and powerful H.M.S. *Alecto* (paddle wheel). It was a great victory for the propeller.

A unique change was represented by the gigantic ship *Great Eastern* (trials, 1859), which was equipped with both propeller (24 feet in diameter) and paddle wheels (56 feet in diameter, each weighing 92 tons). Commercially, the ship was a failure, but even so, it will always be looked upon as a milestone in the history of shipbuilding.

The first boilers were very primitive, with an external firebox and often with large flat surfaces. These potboilers could not stand high pressures. They were then developed into boilers with internal fireboxes, and then into fire tube boilers with combustion chambers and several fire tubes. This increased the heating area and used the fuel more effectively. Fire tube boilers (the Scotch boilers) became the commonest type in merchant ships about 1900 and later. Development continued with water tube boilers, where the water (as opposed to the fire tube boilers) is contained inside the tubes and the furnace and combustion gases are outside. Water tube boilers contain less water than fire tube boilers. Steam can be raised much more quickly with a water tube boiler than with a Scotch boiler. They became even more economical with the introduction of the superheater, artificial draft created by fans, preheating of the water, and so on. The engine went through a comparable development, to direct-acting vertical steam engines with the crankshaft placed under the cylinders. The expansion of steam became more efficient with the use of a three-cylinder engine with high, medium, and low pressure cylinders. The triple-expansion engine became the most usual type in the merchant navy.

A really powerful engine had been developed in the shape of the reciprocating steam engine, but it was, however, of rather complicated construction. It was, therefore, obvious that an engine where the energy was directly transformed into rotation had to be built.

As far back as two-thousand years ago, Hero of Alexandria described such a machine. It was the famous Hero steam ball, which was a complete reactive turbine. In 1629 the Italian, Johann Branca, described a machine where a jet of steam drove a bladed wheel. This was also a turbine, an active turbine. Both were only curiosities, and it was to take centuries before the first usable turbine was designed by the Swede, de Laval.

De Laval's turbine was an active one where the expansion of the steam took place in a stationary turbine casing. This is called an equal pressure turbine because the steam acts directly on the rotor. With high rotor speed, about 30,000 r.p.m., and consequently, great centrifugal force, it was difficult to transmit the power to slower rotating shafts. It was necessary to expand steam pressure through several stages. This brings us to multistage turbines and such inventors as Zoelly, Curtis, and Parsons, who used several rotors on the same shaft but separated them with stationary guide blade rings.

The most important figure in the development of the steam turbine as a marine-power plant was Sir Charles Parsons, who built the first turbine-powered ship, the steam yacht *Turbinia,* powered by a 2,000 s.h.p. turbine, which drove a propeller at approximately 1,800 r.p.m. The first trials were a disappointment: a speed of 19³/₄ knots at 1,780 r.p.m. The trouble was that at such high revolutions cavitation occurred at the propeller, a problem of which little was then known.

In 1893, the *Turbinia's* power plant was rebuilt with three turbines, each driving its own shaft, and with a total of nine propellers. With this change came success: a maximum speed of up to 34 knots — a rather incredible speed at that time. The Admiralty, however, showed no interest in it. This led to Parsons' historical demonstration, in 1897, at the naval review at Spithead. Parsons sailed at a speed of over 30 knots past the warships at anchor. A naval vessel was sent out to stop the unwelcome visitor, but the speed of the *Turbinia* only made the naval ship look ridiculous. This demonstration resulted in an order for the first turbine-powered destroyer, H.M.S. *Viper.* The steam turbine had many advantages compared with the reciprocating engine, such as no vibration and less space required for the same amount of power. Nevertheless, while direct drive was used, trouble with propeller cavitation was encountered. This trouble was not overcome until gears, which could transmit high power, were developed. Naval ships, as well as large passenger ships, where vibration had to be kept to a minimum quickly changed to steam turbines.

Just before the steam engine and the steam turbine reached the peak of their development a new source of power appeared: the diesel engine. Even the best steam plant is still an external combustion engine in which the fuel's energy is converted into dynamic energy through an intermediate means. If an engine could be made where the actual combustion took place inside the cylinder, greater power for the same amount of fuel could be attained. It was this which Rudolf Diesel (1858–1913) did when he invented the engine which now bears his name all over the world. Diesel soon decided to make such an internal combustion engine. In 1893 he described in a treatise the theory and construction of an internal combustion engine, and this put him in contact with the two well-known concerns of Krupp and M.A.N., which then did everything to complete the task. The first usable diesel engine was completed in 1897. Its main principle was the ignition of the fuel itself in the cylinder when highly compressed with air. The temperature rose to about 800°C. During combustion (not explosion), the piston was pushed down the cylinder. The diesel engine used about thirty-five per cent of the energy in the fuel, while the steam engine used only fifteen per cent.

The person who was of the greatest importance in the development of the marine diesel engine was, however, the Dane, Ivar Knudsen, the Director of A/S Burmeister & Wain, who, in 1897, succeeded in producing a directly reversible engine. On February 12, 1912, the first ocean-going motor ship the *Selandia,* sailed on its maiden voyage, introducing a new era in international shipping. Here, the manager of B. & W.'s diesel engine design department, Dr. H. H. Blacke, must be mentioned as another important man in the development of the diesel engine. Blacke was awarded the James Watt medal, a very rare honor for non-Englishmen.

Development progressed from the *Selandia's* four-stroke engine, with compressed air for the injection of fuel oil, to double-acting four-stroke engines (in the first *Gripsholm*), two-stroke engines, double-acting two-stroke engines with fuel pressure feed pump to the modern two-stroke engine with exhaust-driven superchargers, which is the most popular engine today. The large diesel engine was a source of power which could be competitive with the steam turbine, even when the great power needed for supertankers and fast cargo liners was considered.

The diesel engine, even so, is a piston engine, with many heavy reciprocating mechanical parts. The need was therefore obvious for a combustion turbine, where the energy from the combustion gases was directly transferred to a gas turbine. The greatest difficulty was in overcoming the very high temperatures. Materials have now been discovered which can stand up to such great heat, and today there are ships powered by gas turbines with combustion chambers, heat exchangers, superchargers etc., as well as gas turbines in connection with free piston engines.

Ever since the atom was successfully split, scientists have been searching for ways to put this mighty power to practical use. In the reactors, where the fission of atoms takes place, heat is produced; this is used to produce steam, which is then used in steam turbines. It may seem rather primitive, generally speaking, to use a reactor instead of fuel for a boiler. For the present, however, it would seem to be the only method of utilizing this tremendous energy. The difference between combustion and fission is that when one unit of nuclear fuel (uranium or similar material) is split, two million times as much heat is produced as when one unit of fuel oil is burned.

The reactor in which actual fission takes place is a very strong steel container. By means of a coolant, the heat of nuclear fission is transferred to a heat exchanger in which pipes filled with water receive the heat and produce steam. The steam is used to drive a turbine and then returns to the heat exchanger via a condenser. This is, roughly speaking, the principle used in a ship's reactor. To be able to use nuclear power safely it is necessary to have an effective screen against radiation. This screening is always very heavy (in the N/S *Savannah* about 1,900 tons) and even though the nuclear fuel is light, it is very expensive (about $16,000 per kg.). A nuclear installation cannot, therefore, compete with a diesel or turbine installation because of its prohibitive cost, in spite of great operational range.

With the first American nuclear submarine, the *Nautilus,* and the first nuclear-powered merchant vessel, the *Savannah,* we stand on the threshold of an enormous development of one of the greatest sources of power in the history of mankind.

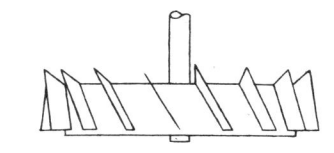

OARS

A 1

A 2

B

C

D

E 2

E 1

F

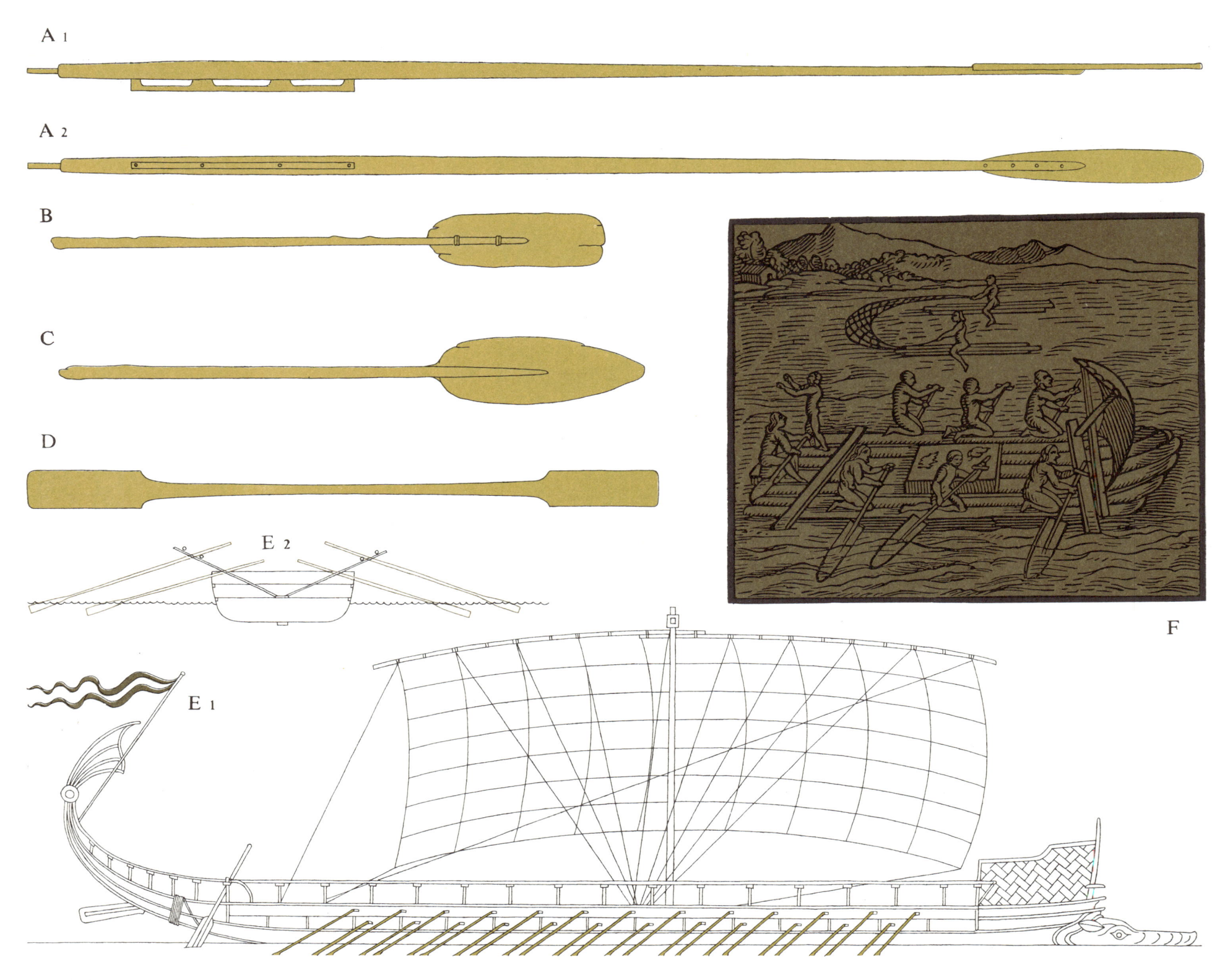

OARS

A *Old galley oar*
Because of their size, these oars were always built with the blade bolted to the shaft. They had handles so that four men could pull each oar.

B *Old Indian paddle*
C *Old Egyptian paddle*
D *Eskimo paddle*

E *Greek warship from 500 B.C.*
1 Drawing from a vase painting
2 Sketch showing the position of oars in a bireme, that is, a boat with two banks of oars on each side

F *Peruvian raft of balsa wood, with sail and paddles (from Benzoni)*

148

OARS

OARS

A *Oars from a book on shipbuilding by Rålamb, Å.C., 1691*
1, 2 The longest oar that can be pulled by one man should not exceed 16½ feet. An oar should never be more than three times the beam of the boat.
3 A handy oar for one man is 14 feet in length
4 When sculling, the oars should not be more than 9 feet and not more than 1½ times the beam of the boat
5 A pulling boat, 20 feet long, pulling ten oars

B *Medieval boat with paddle wheels*

C *Modern competition rowing*
1 Four oars with outriggers, no coxswain
2 Position of oarsman when pulling
3 The path of the oar blade during a stroke

D *The oar*
1 Grip
2 Loom
3 Leather-covered seat
4 Shaft
5 Blade
6 Copper-banded tip

PADDLE WHEEL

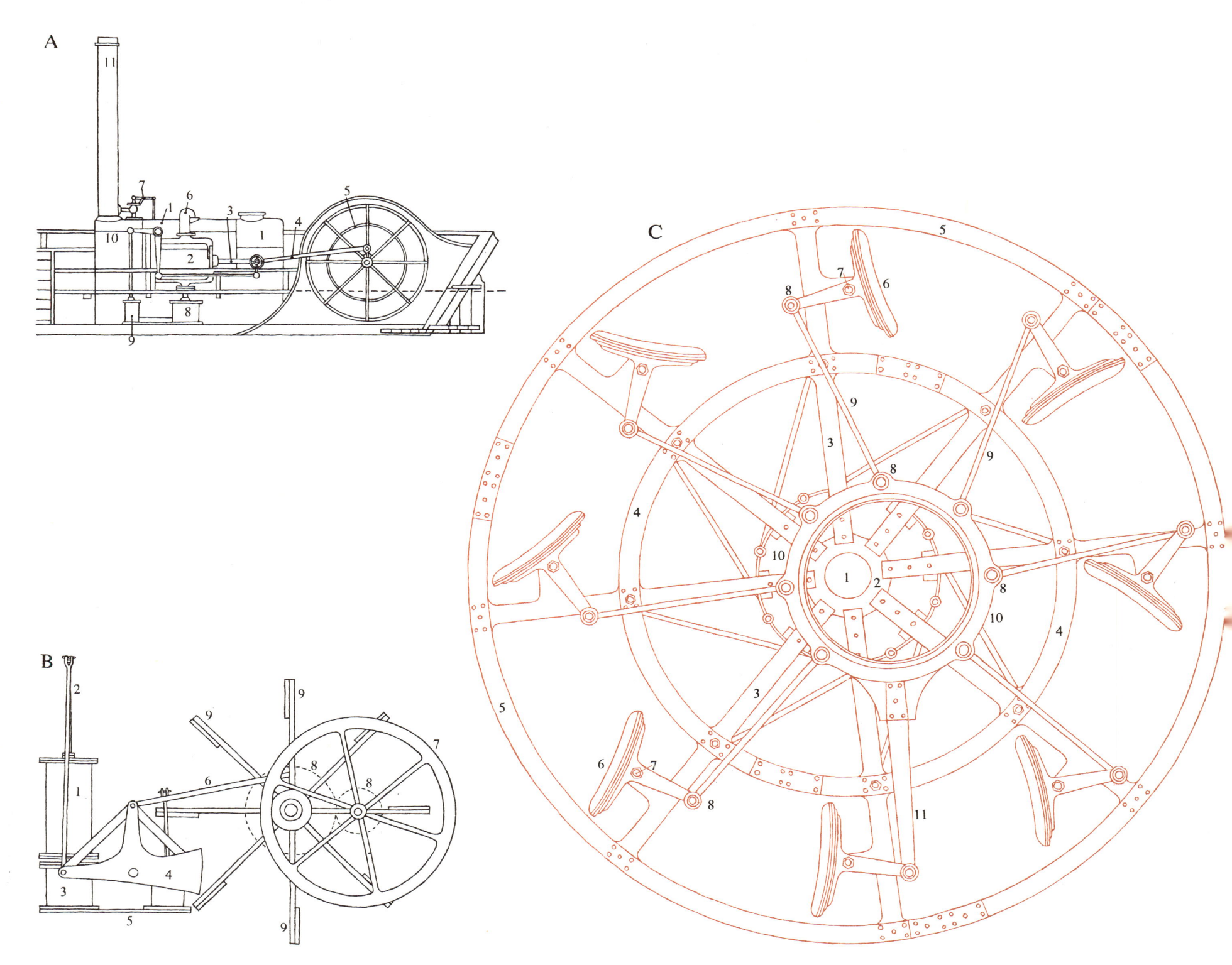

PADDLE WHEEL AND OLD PADDLE ENGINES

A *Symington's direct-drive steamship engine, 1802*
1. Boiler
2. Cylinder
3. Piston rod
4. Connecting rod
5. Paddle wheel
6. Steampipe
7. Safety valve
8. Condenser
9. Pump
10. Smoke box
11. Funnel

B *Geared steam engine of the Clermont by Fulton, 1807*
1. Cylinder
2. Piston rod
3. Condenser
4. Balance
5. Bearing
6. Connecting rod
7. Flywheel
8. Gear
9. Paddle wheel

C *Paddle wheel*
1. Paddle shaft
2. Hub
3. Spoke
4. Inner rim
5. Outer rim
6. Paddle
7. Wrist pin
8. Limbs
9. Drag link
10. Eccentric strap
11. King rod

PADDLE WHEEL ENGINE AND PROPELLERS

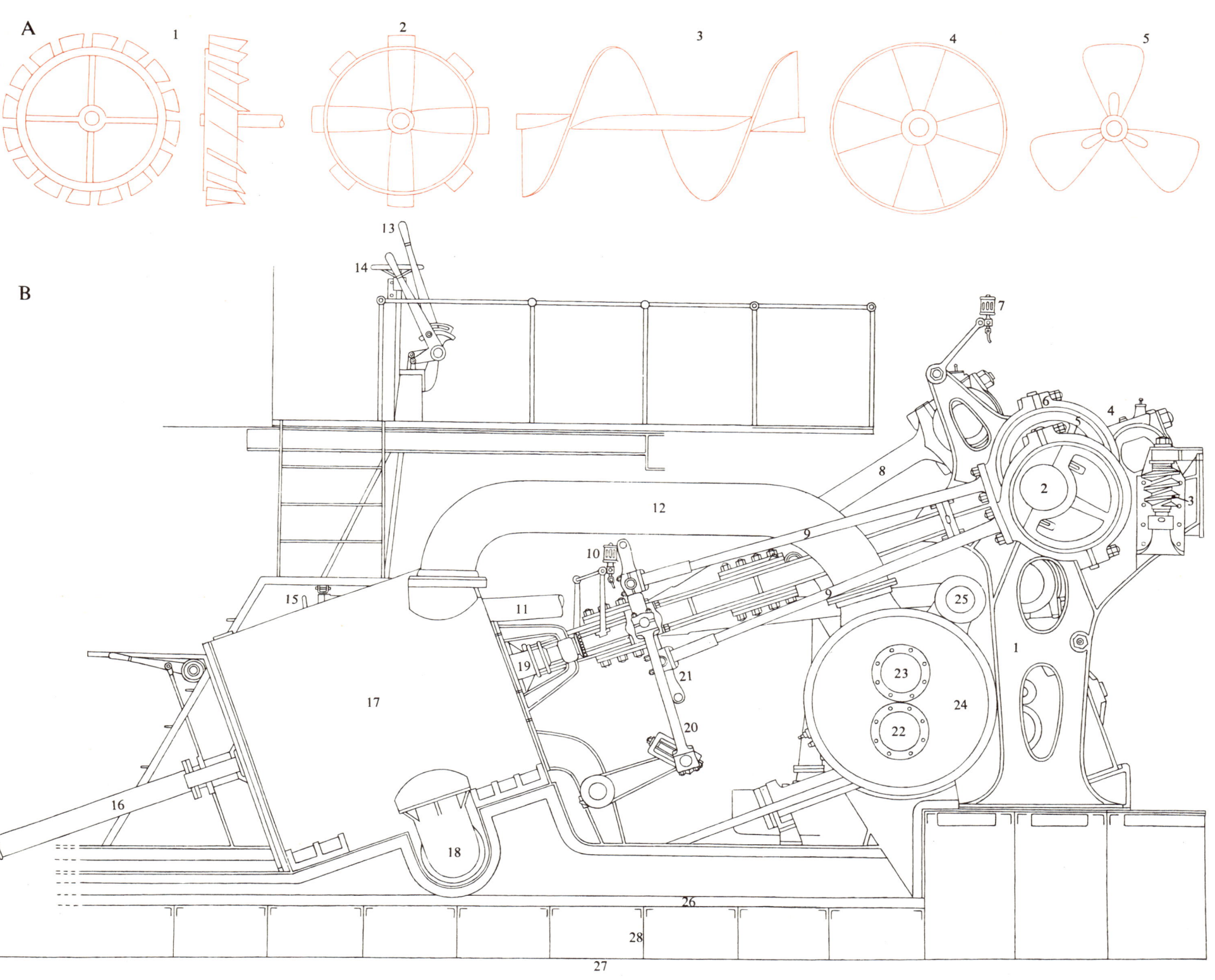

PADDLE WHEEL ENGINE AND OLD PROPELLERS

A *Propeller development*
1. 1785
2. 1800
3. 1812
4. 1840
5. 1860

B *Triple-expansion paddle wheel engine*
1. Foundation
2. Crank shaft
3. Turning gear
4. Connecting rod
5. Eccentric
6. Eccentric strap
7. Oil cup
8. Connecting rod
9. Eccentric rods
10. Oil cup
11. HP-cylinder steam inlet
12. LP-cylinder exhaust pipe
13. Reversing lever
14. Throttle valve wheel
15. Throttle valve wheel
16. Tail rod
17. LP-cylinder
18. LP-cylinder steam inlet
19. Valve-spindle guide
20. Link operating bar
21. Double-bar link
22. Cooling water, inlet
23. Cooling water, outlet
24. Condenser
25. Pipe to vacuum pump
26. Tank top plating
27. Bottom plating
28. Plate floor

OLDER BOILERS

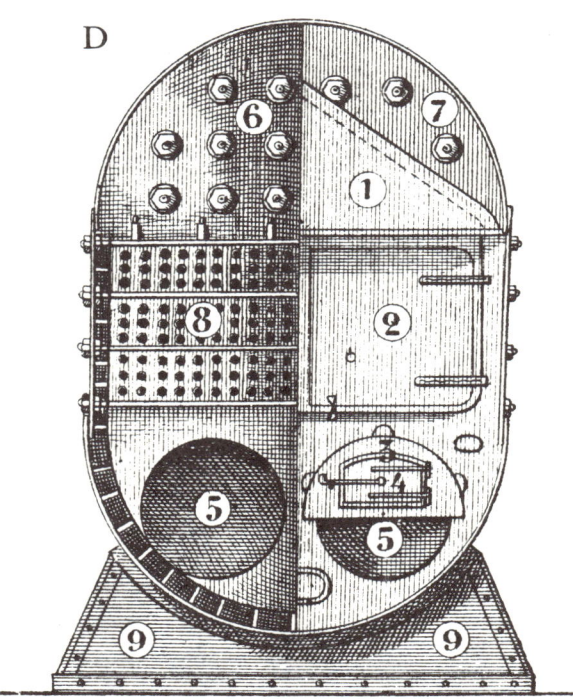

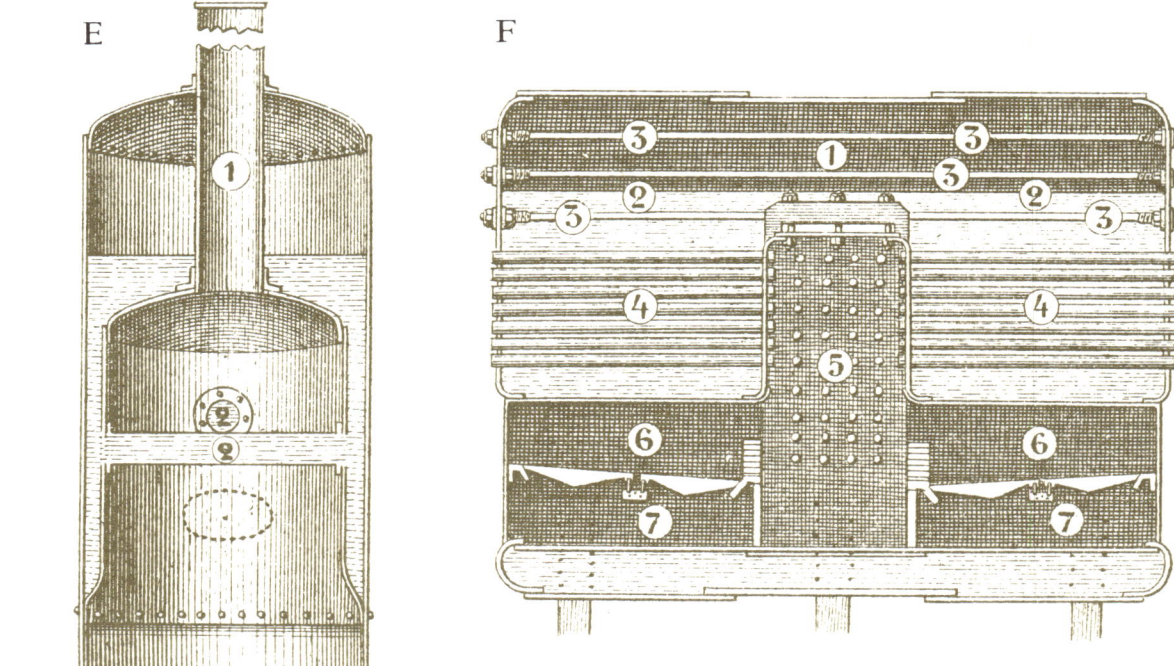

VARIOUS TYPES OF OLDER BOILERS

A *Rectangular or box boiler*
1. Uptake
2. Steam space
3. Water level
4. Boiler tubes
5. Combustion chamber
6. Furnace
7. Ash pit
8. Furnace bars
9. Furnace bridge

B *Vertical donkey boiler*
1. Donkey funnel
2. Crown of donkey boiler
3. Manhole door
4. Sludge hole doors
5. Furnace door
6. Safety valve
7. Steam pipe
8. Gauge glass
9. Feed pipe

C *Cylindrical boiler (Scotch type)*
1. Dome
2. Uptake and smoke box
3. Furnaces
4. Shell of boiler

D *Oval donkey boiler*
1. Uptake and smoke box
2. Smoke box door
3. Furnace front
4. Furnace door
5. Furnace and ash pit
6. Back plate
7. Front plate
8. Back tube-plate
9. Boiler bearer

E *Water tube donkey boiler*
1. Funnel
2. Water tubes

F *Double-ended boiler*
1. Steam space
2. Water level
3. Boiler stays
4. Boiler tubes
5. Combustion chamber
6. Furnaces
7. Ash pits

OLDER STEAM ENGINES

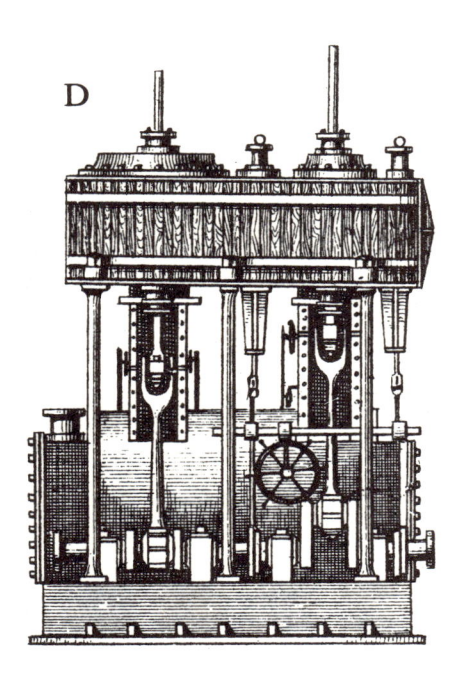

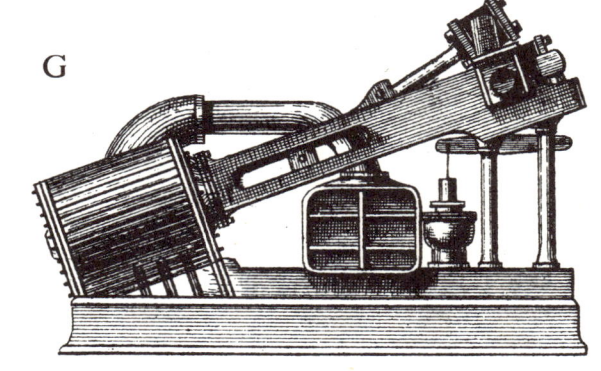

VARIOUS KINDS OF OLDER STEAM ENGINES

A *Side lever engine*
B *Overhead beam engine*
C *Grasshopper engine*
D *Inverted vertical reciprocating compound engine*
E *Steeple engine*
F *Oscillating engine*
G *Diagonal engine*
H *Horizontal (trunk) engine*

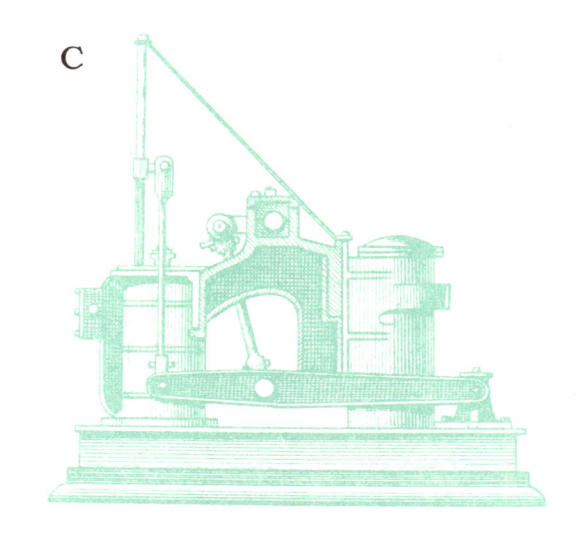

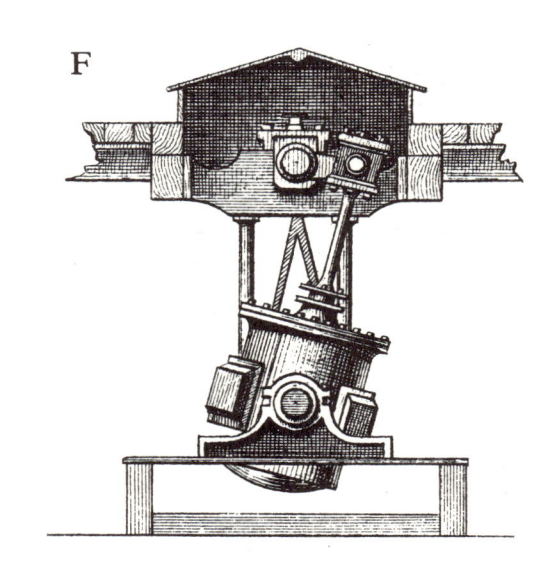

ENGINE AND BOILER

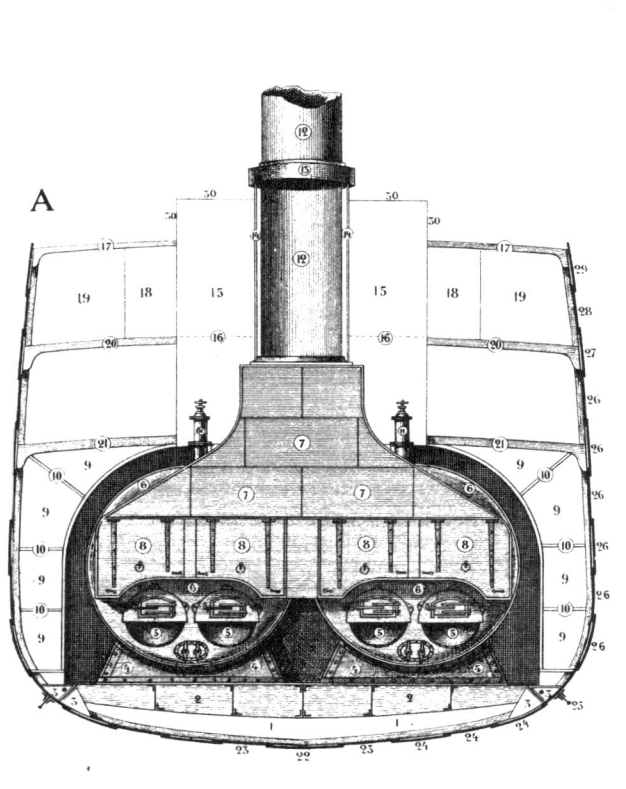

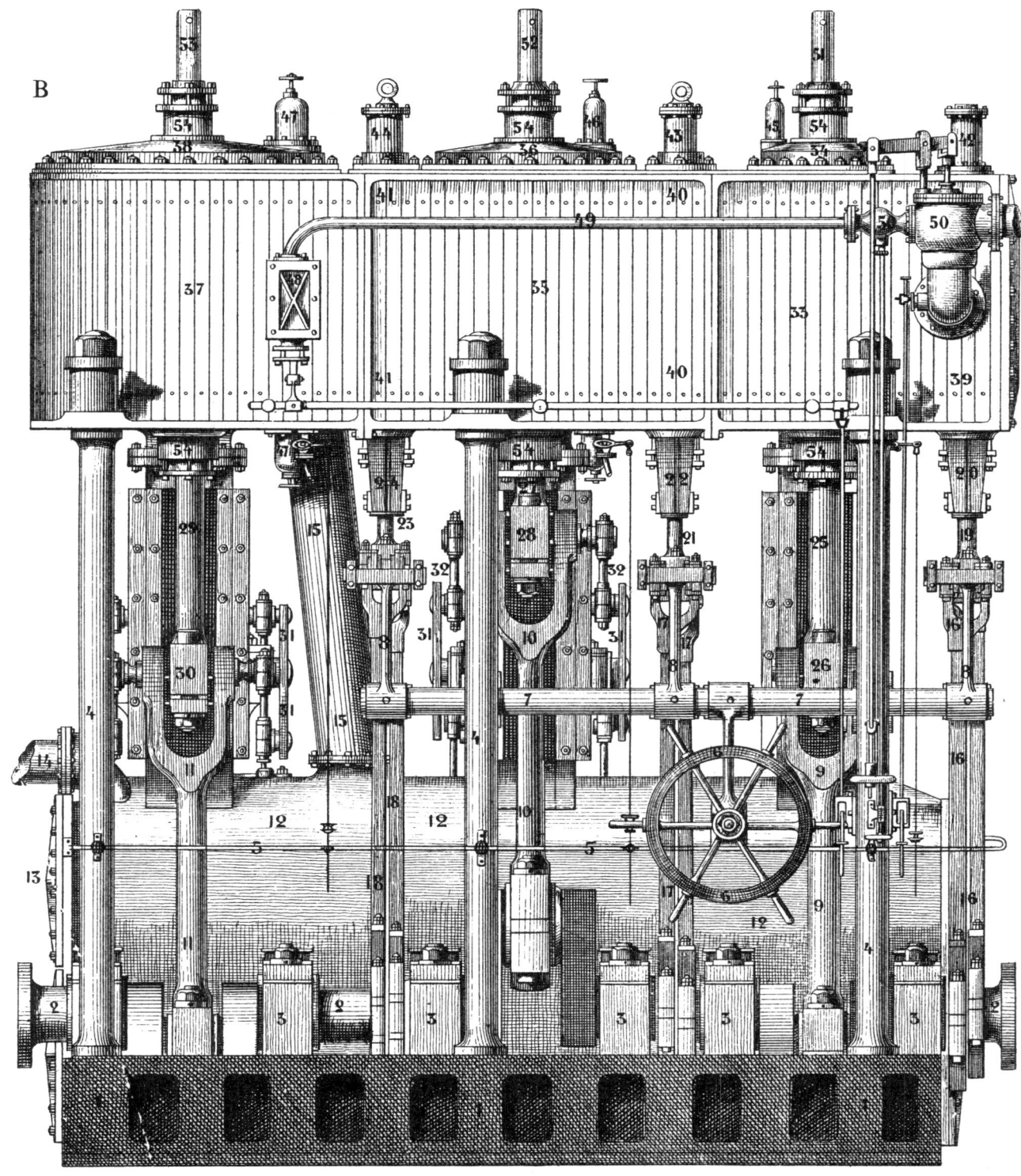

ENGINE AND BOILER, 1880

A *Midship section of a steamer, showing boiler room*
1. Floor
2. Water ballast in double bottom
3. Brackets
4. Boiler bearers
5. Ash pits
6. Front tube plates
7. Smoke box, uptake
8. Smoke box doors
9. Side coal bunkers
10. Bunker stays
11. Safety valves
12. Funnel
13. Funnel cape
14. Air casing of funnel
15. Fidley
16. Fidley gratings
17. Bridge deck beam
18. Alley-way, in bridge-house
19. Officer's room
20. Upper deck beam
21. Lower deck beam
22. Flat plate keel
23. Garboard strakes
24. Bottom plating
25. Bilge keel
26. Side plating
27. Sheer strake
28. Side plating of bridge
29. Sheer strake of bridge
30. Fidley top

B *Triple-expansion engine*
1. Bedplate
2. Crank shaft
3. Main bearings
4. Cylinder columns
5. Hand rail
6. Reversing wheel
7. Weigh shaft
8. Weigh shaft arms
9. High-pressure connecting rod
10. Intermediate-pressure connecting rod
11. Low-pressure connecting rod
12. Condenser
13. Condenser head
14. Circulating-pump discharge pipe
15. Exhaust pipe
16, 17, 18 Eccentric rods
19, 21, 23 Valve spindles
20, 22, 24 Valve spindle guides
25, 27, 29 Piston rods
26, 28, 30 Piston rod crossheads
31. Pump levers
32. Pump links
33. High-pressure cylinder
34, 36, 38 Cylinder covers
35. Intermediate cylinder
37. Low-pressure cylinder
39, 40, 41 Valve casings
42, 43, 44 Balance cylinders
45, 46, 47 Escape valves
48. Starting valve
49. Starting valve pipe
50. Throttle
51, 52, 53 Tail rods
54. Stuffing boxes

OLD STEAM ENGINE

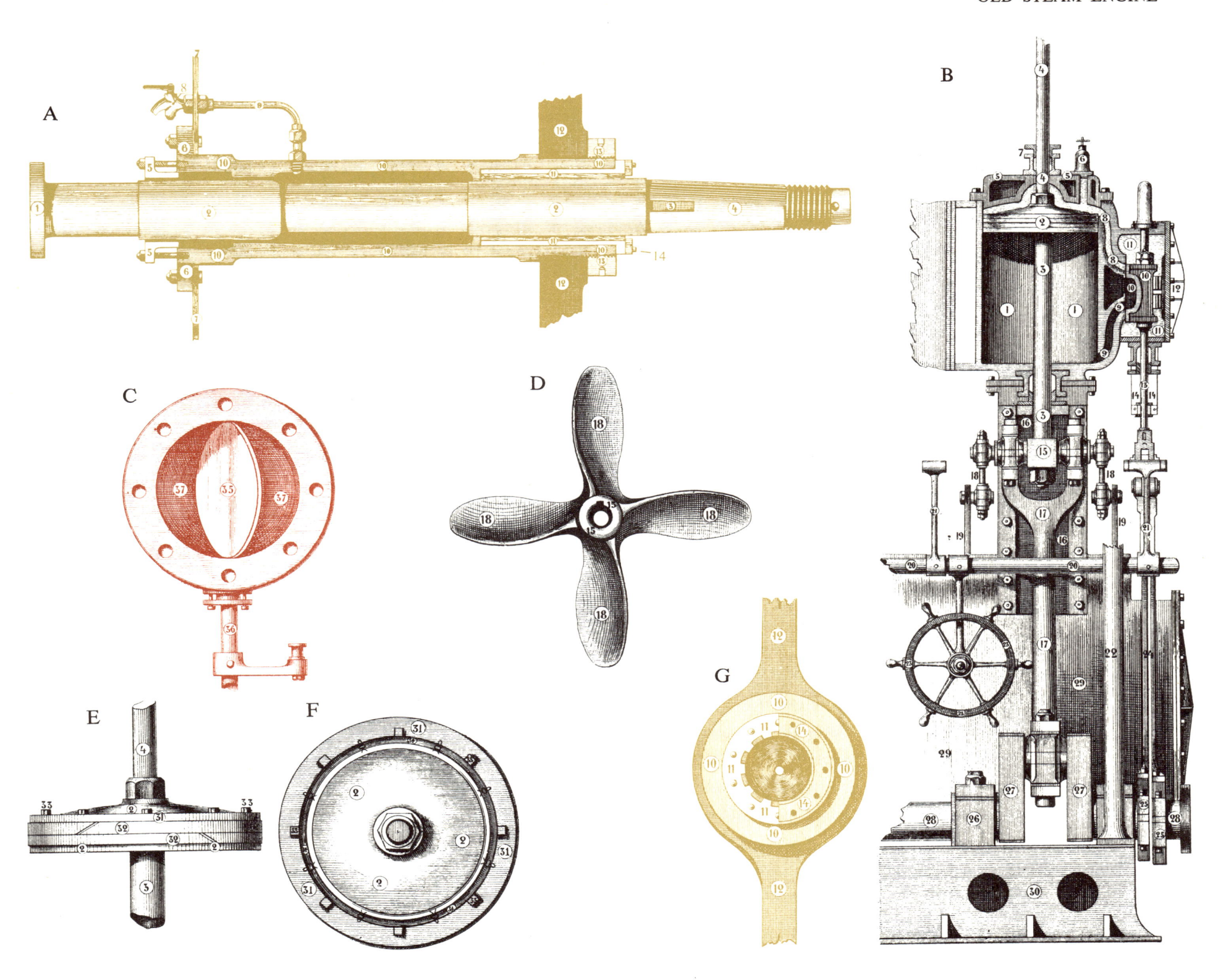

OLD STEAM ENGINE AND ANCILLARY DETAILS, FROM AN OLD DRAWING

A *Propeller tail shaft*
 1 Coupling flange
 2 Sleeve
 3 Keyway
 4 Tail end
 5 Stuffing-box gland
 6 Stern tube flange
 7 Stuffing-box bulkhead
 8 Tunnel cock
 9 Water pipe
 10 Stern tube
 11 Stern tube bushing
 12 Stern post
 13 Stern tube nut
 14 Guard ring

B *Piston steam engine*
 1 Cylinder
 2 Piston
 3 Piston rod
 4 Tail rod
 5 Cylinder cover
 6 Escape valve
 7 Stuffing box
 8 Steam ports
 9 Steam ports
 10 Slide valve
 11 Slide valve casing
 12 Slide valve casing door
 13 Slide valve rod
 14 Valve rod guide
 15 Piston rod crosshead
 16 Crosshead guide
 17 Connecting rod
 18 Pump links
 19 Pump levers
 20 Weigh shaft
 21 Weigh shaft arms
 22 Cylinder column
 23 Reversing wheel
 24 Eccentric rods
 25 Eccentric straps
 26 Main bearing
 27 Crank web
 28 Crank shaft
 29 Condenser
 30 Bedplates

C *Throttle valve*
 35 Throttle valve
 36 Throttle valve spindle
 37 Steam pipe

D *Propeller*
 15 Propeller hub
 18 Propeller blades

E *Piston*
 2 Piston
 3 Piston rod
 4 Tail rod
 31 Junk ring
 32 Packing rings
 33 Junk ring bolts

F *Piston, seen from above*
 2 Piston
 31 Junk ring
 33 Junk ring bolts
 34 Guard ring tail

G *Propeller shaft, end view*
 10 Stern tube
 11 Stern tube bushing
 12 Stern post
 14 Guard ring

BOILER AND ENGINE

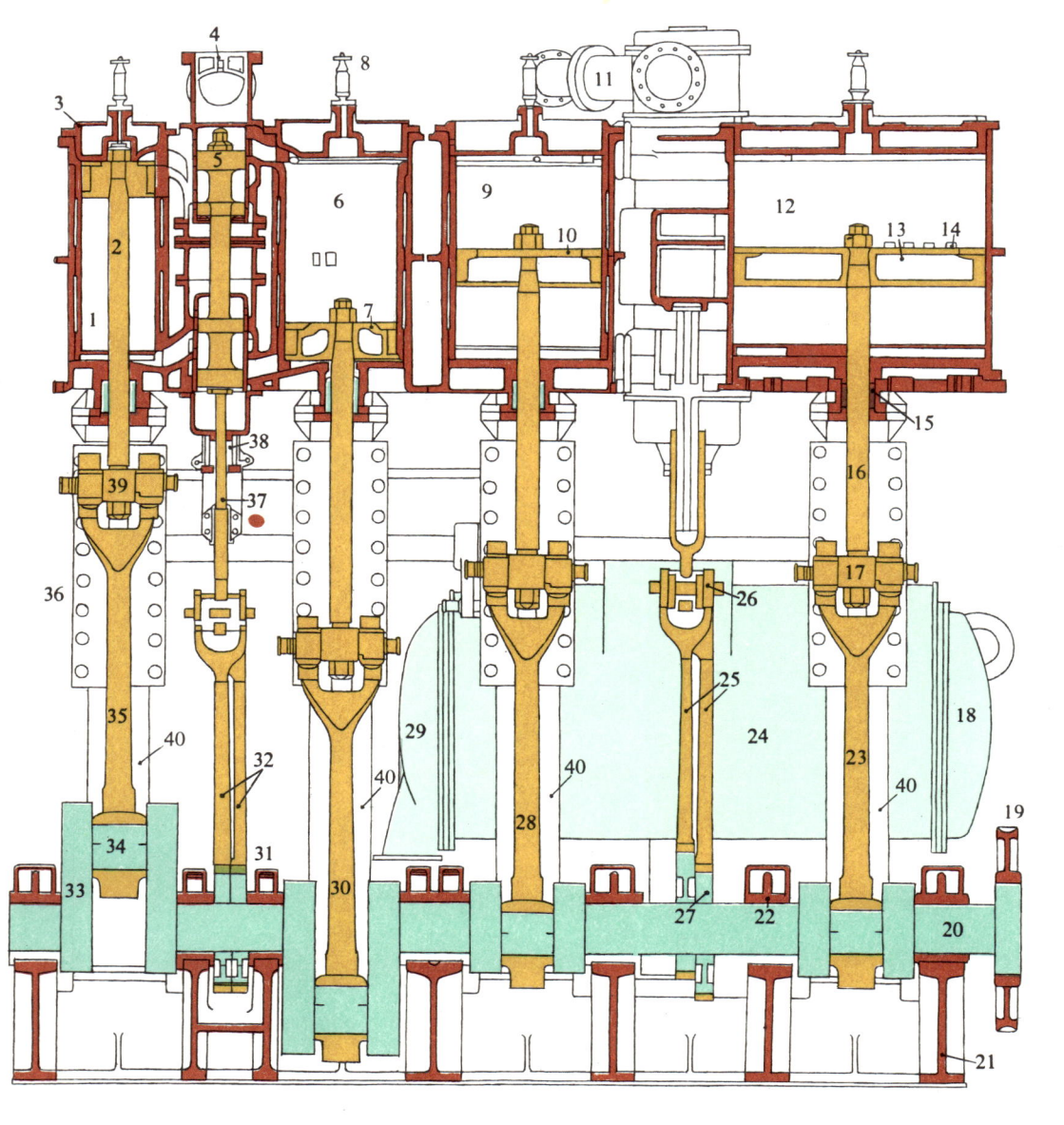

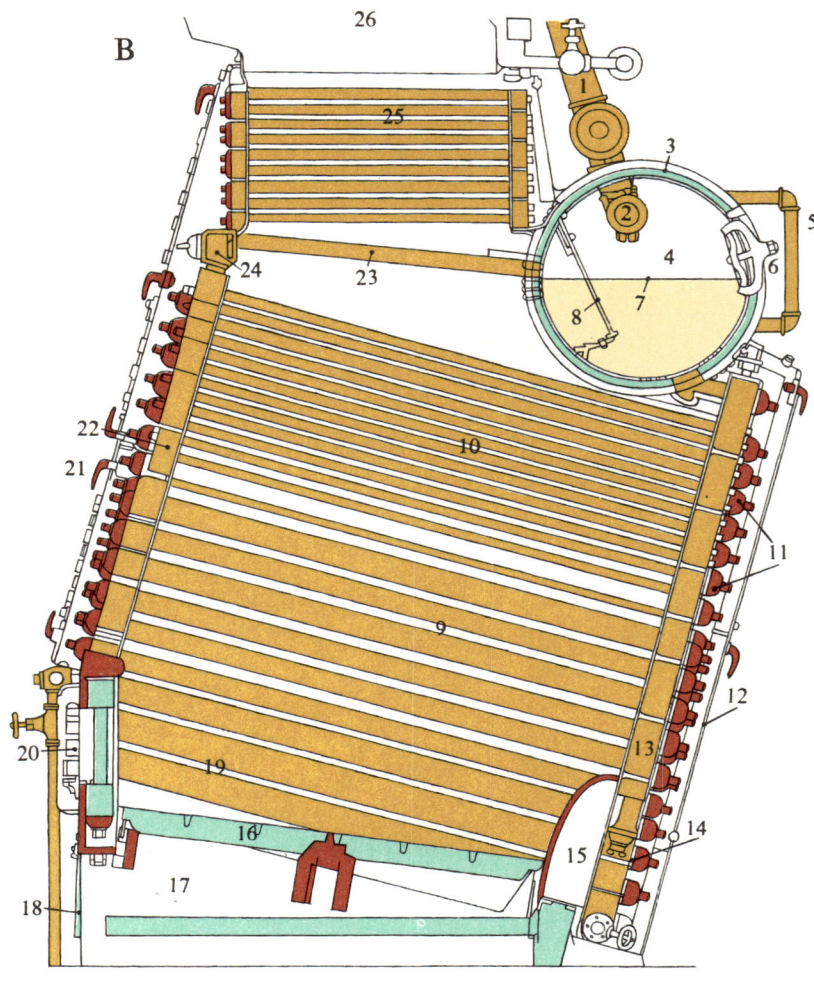

MODERN BOILER AND ENGINE

A *Quadruple steam engine, starboard engine of a twin-screw steamer*
1 HP-cylinder
2 Piston rod
3 Cylinder cover
4 Steam line to intermediate reheater
5 Piston valve
6 1st IP-cylinder
7 Piston
8 Safety valve
9 2nd IP-cylinder
10 Piston
11 Steam line from turbocompressor
12 LP-cylinder
13 Piston
14 Extraction steam ports
15 Piston rod box
16 Piston rod
17 Crosshead
18 Condenser head
19 Turning gear
20 Crank shaft
21 Bedplate
22 Main bearing
23 LP-connecting rod
24 Condenser
25 Eccentric rods
26 Double-bar link
27 Eccentrics and straps
28 2nd IP-connecting rod
29 Condenser head
30 1st IP-connecting rod
31 Eccentrics and straps
32 Eccentric rods
33 Crank web
34 Crank pin
35 HP-connecting rod
36 Crosshead guide plates
37 Valve spindle
38 Stuffing-box
39 Crosshead
40 Engine frame

B *Water-tube boiler, header boiler*
1 Steam outlet
2 Dry pipe
3 Steam drum
4 Steam space
5 Feed-water pipe
6 Manhole
7 Water level
8 Steam collecting baffle
9 1st tube bank
10 2nd tube bank
11 Hand hole plates
12 Boiler casing
13 Rear header
14 Mud drum
15 Furnace bridge
16 Furnace-bars (-grate)
17 Ash pit
18 Ash pit door
19 Furnace
20 Furnace door
21 Locking handle
22 Front header
23 Return tubes
24 Cross box
25 Economizer
26 Uptake

STEAM TURBINE

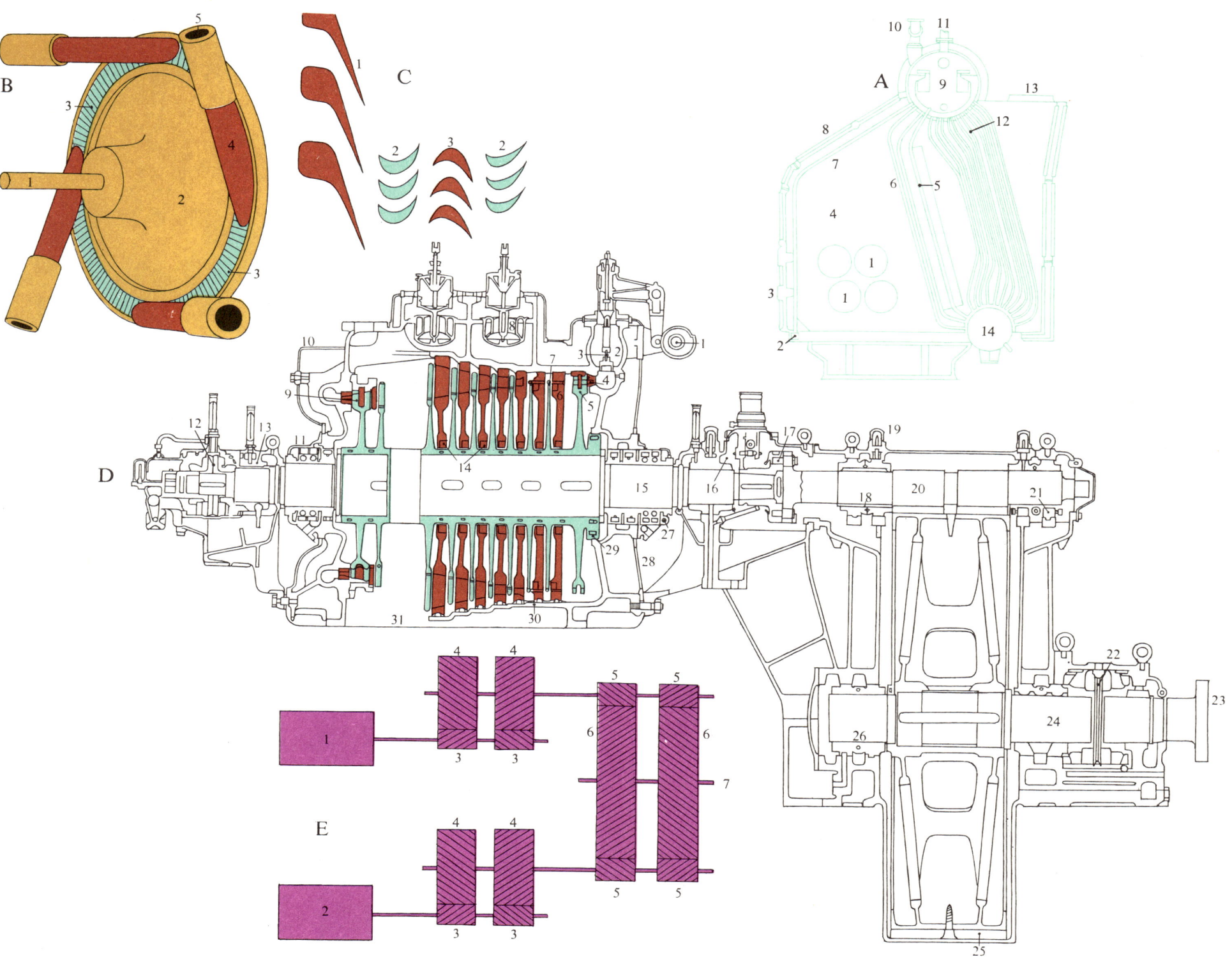

STEAM TURBINE

A *D-boiler*
1. Oil burner
2. Wall header
3. Furnace peepholes
4. Furnace
5. Superheater tubes
6. Furnace tubes
7. Water wall
8. Boiler casing
9. Steam drum
10. Steam outlet
11. Relief valve
12. Boiler generating tubes
13. Uptake
14. Water drum

B *Simple impulse turbine*
1. Shaft
2. Blade wheel
3. Blading
4. Laval nozzle
5. Steam supply

C *Velocity stage (Curtis)*
1. Nozzle block
2. Moving blades
3. Fixed blades

D *Minesweeper turbine*
1. Cam shaft
2. Steam inlet
3. Nozzle control valve or throttle valve
4. Nozzle block
5. Velocity stage (Curtis)
6. Diaphragm
7. Wheel
8. By-pass valve
9. Astern turbine elements
10. Shield
11. Steam-sealed packing
12. Thrust bearing
13. Bearing
14. Shaft packings
15. Turbine shaft
16. Bearing
17. Coupling
18. Bearing
19. Sight glass
20. Pinion
21. Gear
22. Thrust bearing
23. Line shaft flange
24. Shaft
25. Gear
26. Bearing
27. Turbine gland
28. Shield
29. Shaft packing
30. Casing
31. Foundation

E *Double-reduction gear*
1. HP-turbine
2. LP-turbine
3. 1st reduction pinion
4. 1st reduction gear
5. 2nd reduction pinion
6. 2nd reduction gear (main gear)
7. To propeller shaft

157

ENGINE-ROOM TELEGRAPH

ENGINE-ROOM TELEGRAPH AND MODERN PROPELLERS

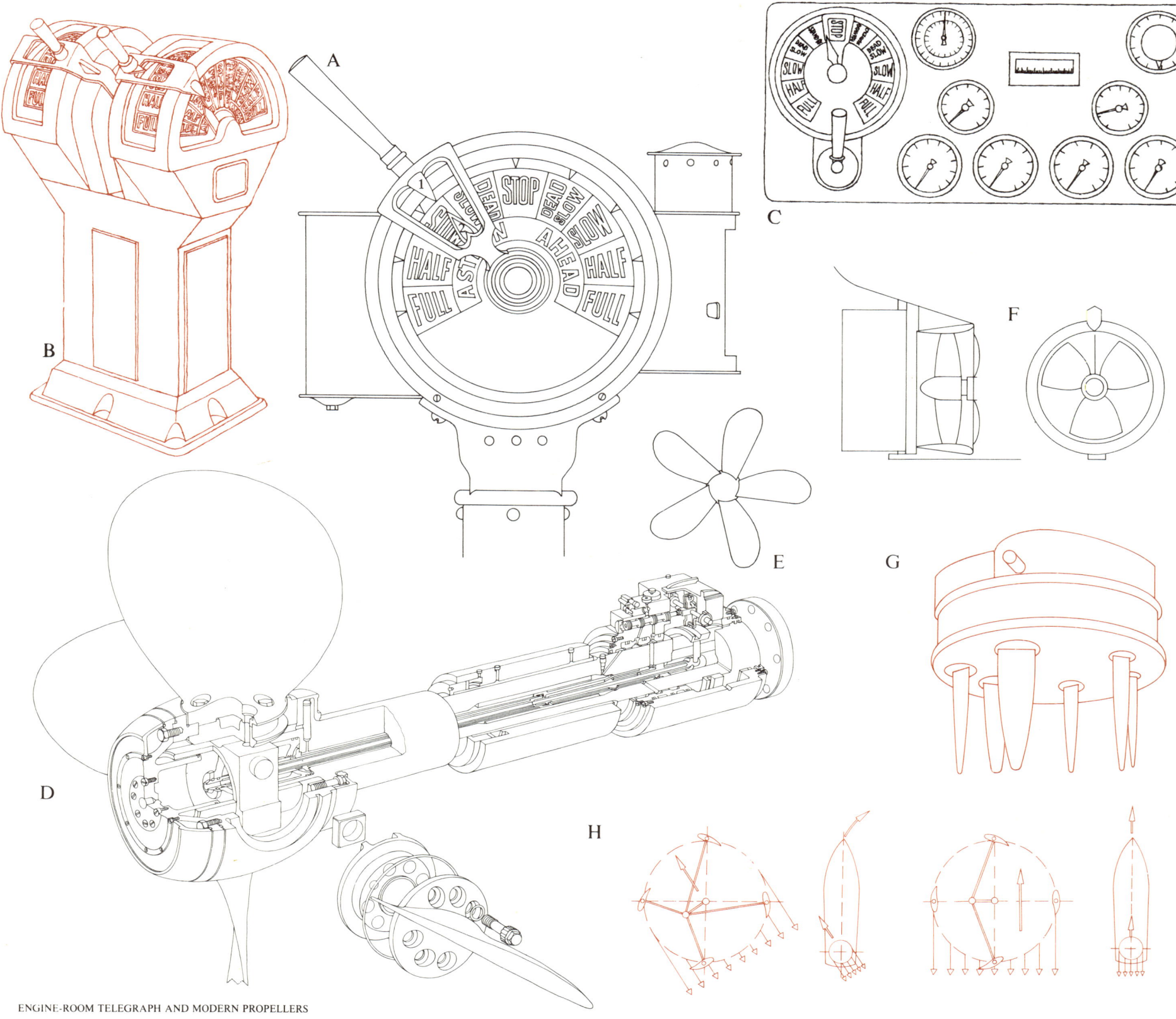

Orders are transmitted from the bridge to the engine room by means of a wire and chain telegraph on the bridge and another in the engine room, so that orders from the bridge can be repeated in the engine room for confirmation. In a twin-screw ship there is one telegraph for each engine.

A Wire-operated telegraph
1 When the lever is moved to, say, STOP on the bridge telegraph the pointer on the engine room telegraph moves to that same position. The engineer then replies by moving the lever of his telegraph to STOP. By so doing, the correponding pointer on the bridge (2) moves to STOP, thus indicating that the order has been understood and is being executed.

B Electrical telegraph for a twin-screw vessel, worked on this same principle but by electricity

C Control panel of the engine room, with the engine room telegraph shown on the left on the panel

D Controllable pitch propeller (Kamewa propeller). By changing the angle of the propeller blades the propelling power and the thrusting direction can be altered without changing the shaft-revolutions or shifting the gear from forwards to backwards

E Five-bladed propeller. Widely used in larger ships. A five-bladed propeller of a 300,000 tons tanker has a weight of approx. 50 tons and a diameter of about 9 m (29 ft).

F Nozzle-propeller

G Cycloidal propeller with rotating blades, called the Voith-Schneider propeller (in the U.S.A., the Kirsten-Boeing propeller).

H The principle behind the functioning of the Voith-Schneider propeller

NUCLEAR POWER

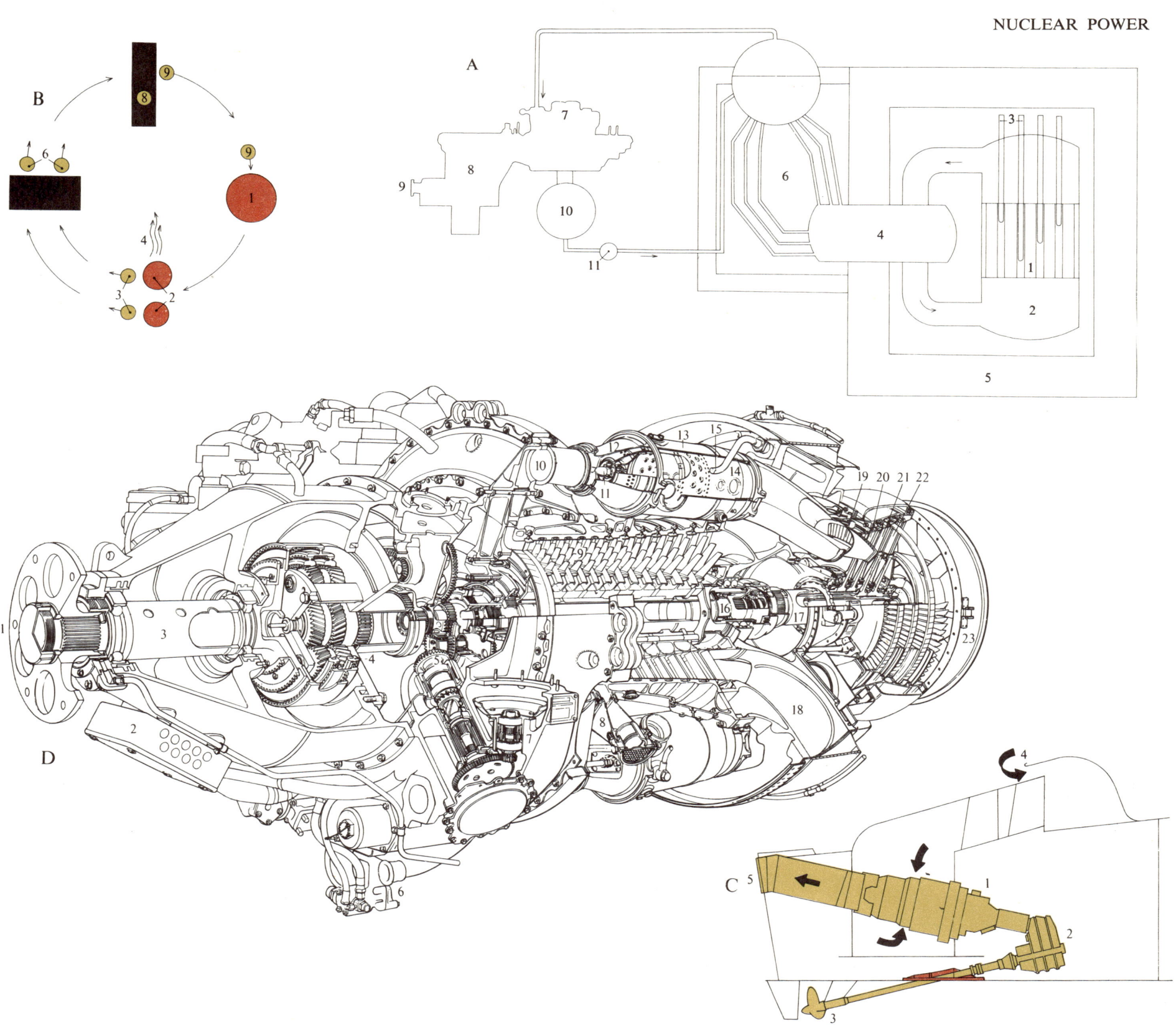

GAS-TURBINE AND NUCLEAR POWER

A *Nuclear ship plant*
1. Nuclear fuel elements
2. Heated fluid
3. Control rods
4. Heat exchanger
5. Lead radiation shielding
6. Boiler
7. Steam turbine
8. Gear
9. Driving shaft
10. Condenser
11. Feedwater pump

B *Principle of atomic fission*
1. Uranium atomic nucleus
2. Nucleus fragments
3. High speed neutrons
4. Heat energy
5. Moderator
6. Low speed neutrons
7. Control rod
8. Absorbed neutron
9. Low speed neutron on its way to split atomic nucleus

C *Engine room installation, SPICA torpedo boat*
1. Three Proteus gas-turbines
2. Reduction gearbox
3. C.p. propeller
4. Air intake
5. Exhaust

D *Marine gas-turbine (Rolls Royce Marine Proteus). This turbine engine has a maximum power rating of 4250 bhp, and features the compactness and light weight that has made the gas-turbine the competitive engine for units that crave immediate and high power output in a small size. The first ship powered by a gas-turbine was the British motor gunboat 2009, launched in 1948.*

1. Power output shaft coupling flange
2. Electrical services junction box
3. Power output shaft
4. Internal gear rings
5. Starter bevel gear
6. Fuel drain unit
7. Starter bevel gear unit
8. Blow-off valve unit
9. Compressor rotor blades
10. Compressor air delivery unit
11. Burner
12. Expansion chamber
13. Combustion chamber casing
14. Flame tube
15. Cooling air supply pipe for compressor turbine
16. Power turbine coupling shaft
17. Compressor turbine shaft
18. Air intake duct
19–22. 1st-4th stage rotor
23. Exhaust annulus

STEAMERS

EARLY STEAMERS

1. *Pyroscape*, built by Marquis Claude de Jouffrouy d' Abbans, 1783.
2. *Charlotte Dundas*, built for the Forth and Clyde Canal in 1802.
3. *Clermont*, built in 1807 by Robert Fulton for the Hudson River between New York and Albany.
4. *Comet*, built in 1812 by James Watt for service on the Clyde.
5. *The Witch of Stockholm*, built by Samuel Owens in 1816.
6. *Savannah*, built in 1818. As the first steamship she crossed the Atlantic in 1819. It is worth mentioning that she used her engine for only short periods during the voyage.
7. *Great Western*, built in 1838. First steamer in transatlantic service.
8. *Rob. F. Stockton*, built in 1839. The first iron hulled vessel to cross the Atlantic.
9. *Hamburger Paquet*, built in Gothenburg in 1858.
10. *Great Eastern*, built in 1858, length 692 ft., displacement 27,400 tons, speed 15 knots, crew 400, passengers 4,000. In her time she was the biggest ship in the world, and was not surpassed in size until 1899.

160

STEAMERS

EARLY STEAMERS

11 Side-wheeler *Natchez*. Until 1870 the fastest boat on the Mississippi River.
12 A paddle steamer from 1873.
13 The passenger steamer, *Odin*, built in 1875.
14 The tank steamer *Gluckauf*, built in 1886 in Great Britain for German owners. The first modern tanker.
15 The passenger vessel, *Deutschland*, built in 1900, length about 670 ft., speed 24 knots.
16 Turret deck steamer from 1907.
17 *Mauretania*, 1913, 33,000 gross tons register, speed 25.8 knots, length about 760 ft.

MERCHANT AND PASSENGER SHIPS

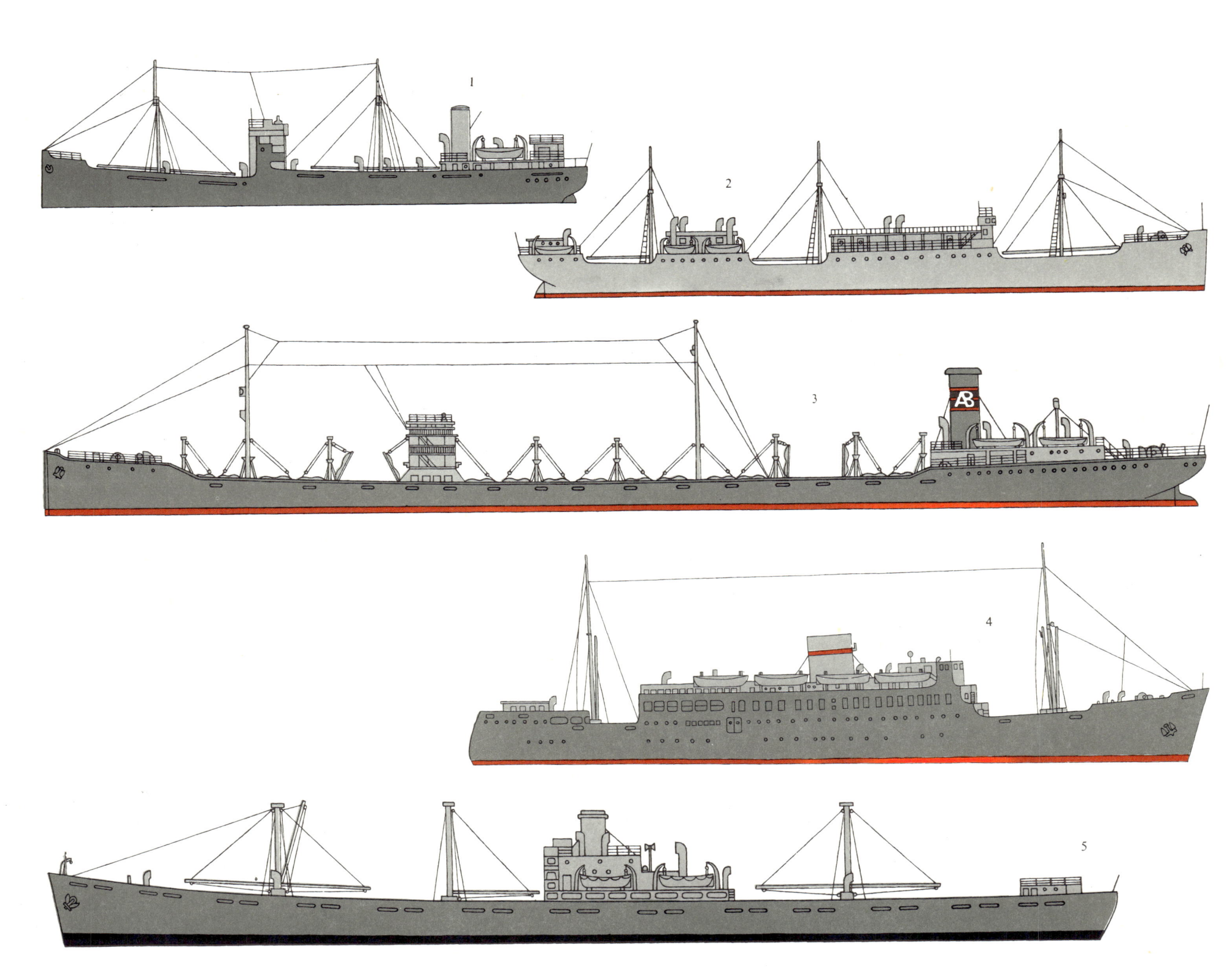

MERCHANT AND PASSENGER SHIPS

1. British collier, a ship that chiefly carries North Country coal to London
2. *Selandia*. The first ocean-going cargo diesel motorship in the world, built in Denmark in 1911
3. *Amerikaland*. Swedish ore-carrying vessel, built in 1925 for service between South and North America, 22,800 tons dwt.
4. Passenger ship used on short sea routes, for instance, the cross Channel service, about 3,000 gross tons
5. U.S. Liberty standard vessel, displacement 14,000 tons

MERCHANT AND PASSENGER SHIPS

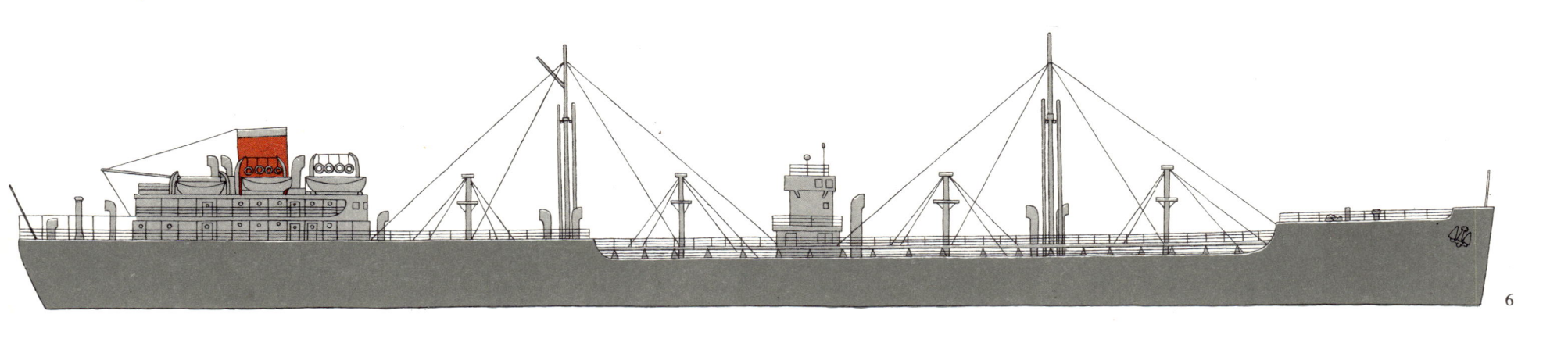

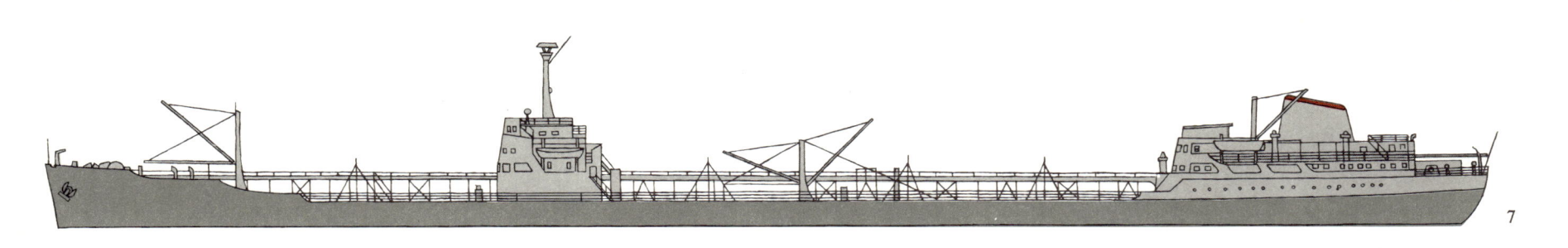

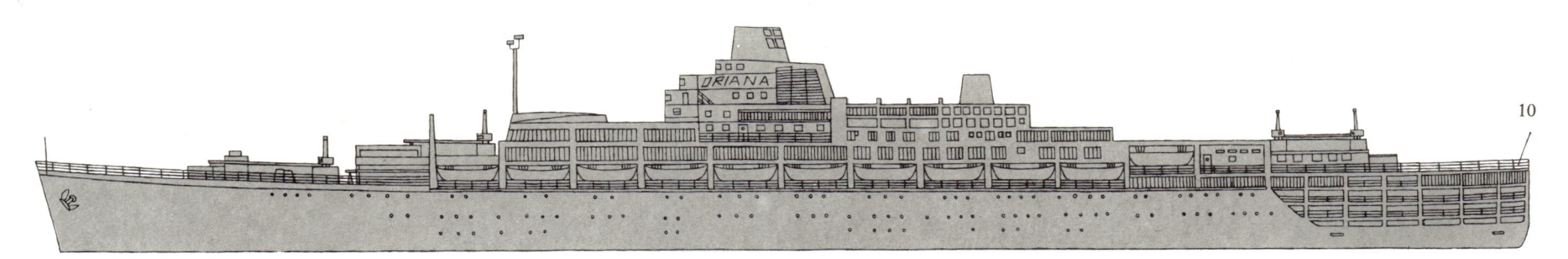

MERCHANT AND PASSENGER SHIPS

6 Ore tanker, 1950
7 Motor tanker of 40,000 tons dwt, speed 16½ knots. (At the time she was built, 1958, she was the largest motor tanker in the world)
8 A coastal tanker of about 800 tons dwt.
9 A small Dutch motor coaster
10 *Oriana*. Turbine passenger vessel, 40,000 gross tons

163

MODERN SHIPS

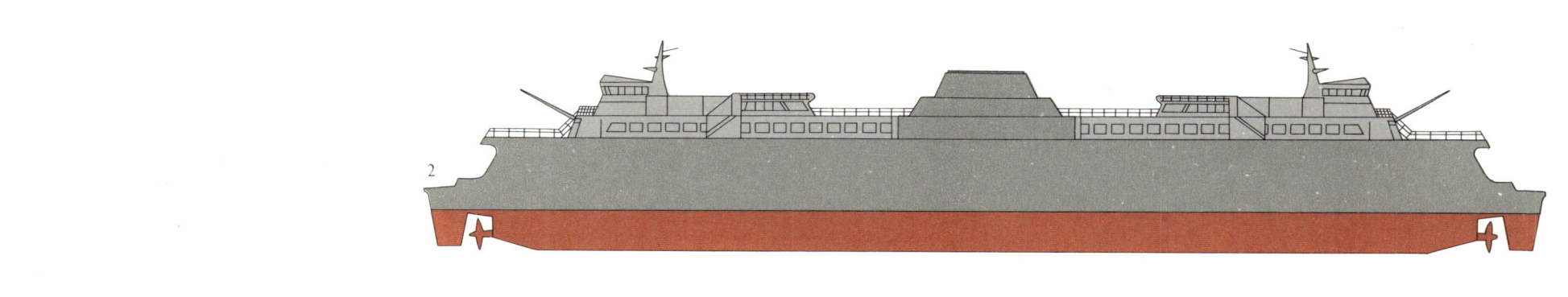

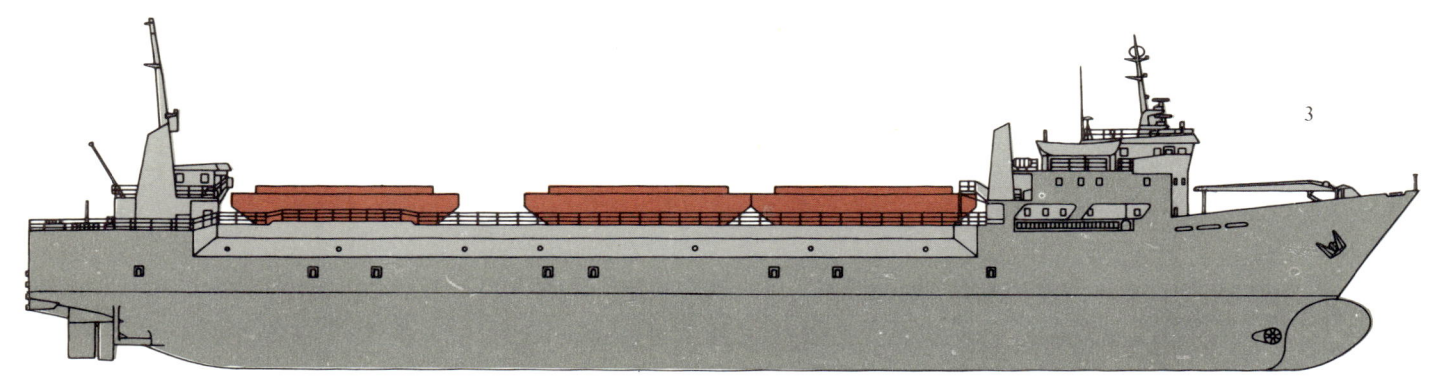

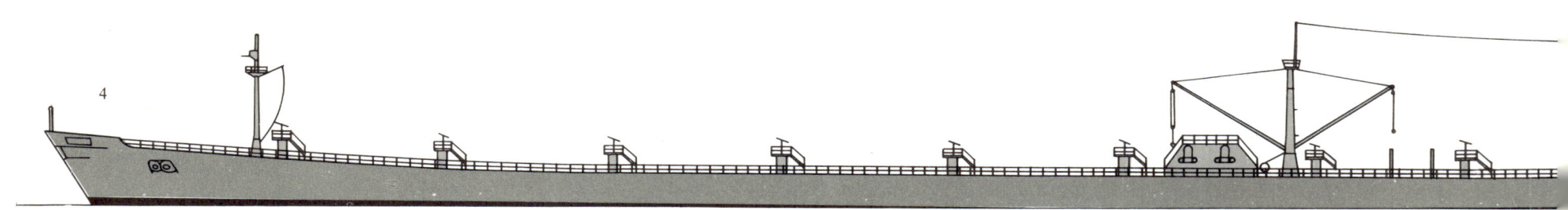

SOME MODERN SHIPS

1 Modern passenger liner, *France,* gross tonnage 66,000, length 1,035 ft., breadth 110 ft., 2,044 passengers, service speed 30 knots

2 American double-ender-ferry, the *Spokane,* designed for short routes. Launched in 1974

3 *Bacat 1.* Barge carrying semi-catamaran vessel with conventional forepart and twin hulls extending from aft of superstructure. Barges, specially designed to offer connection between inland British towns and the continent, are loaded on to the deck by an elevator lowered 3 meters (10 ft) below the water level between the hulls

4 Danish-built super-tanker of 495,000 tons, length 387.9 m (1,272 ft), breadth 67.1 m (214 ft), draught 25.6 m (85 ft), speed 16.1 knots, total tank capacity 600,000 m³

MODERN SHIPS

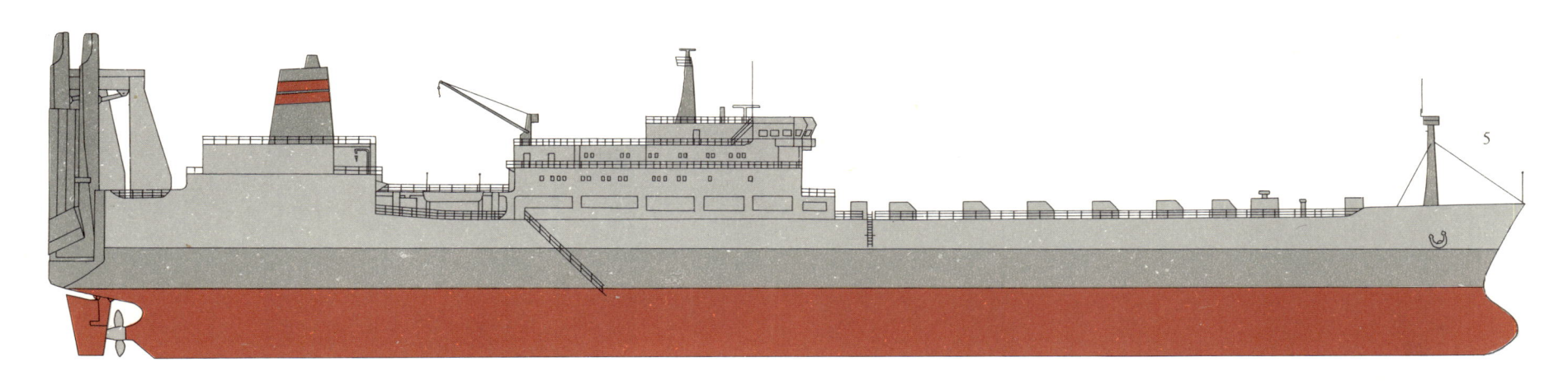

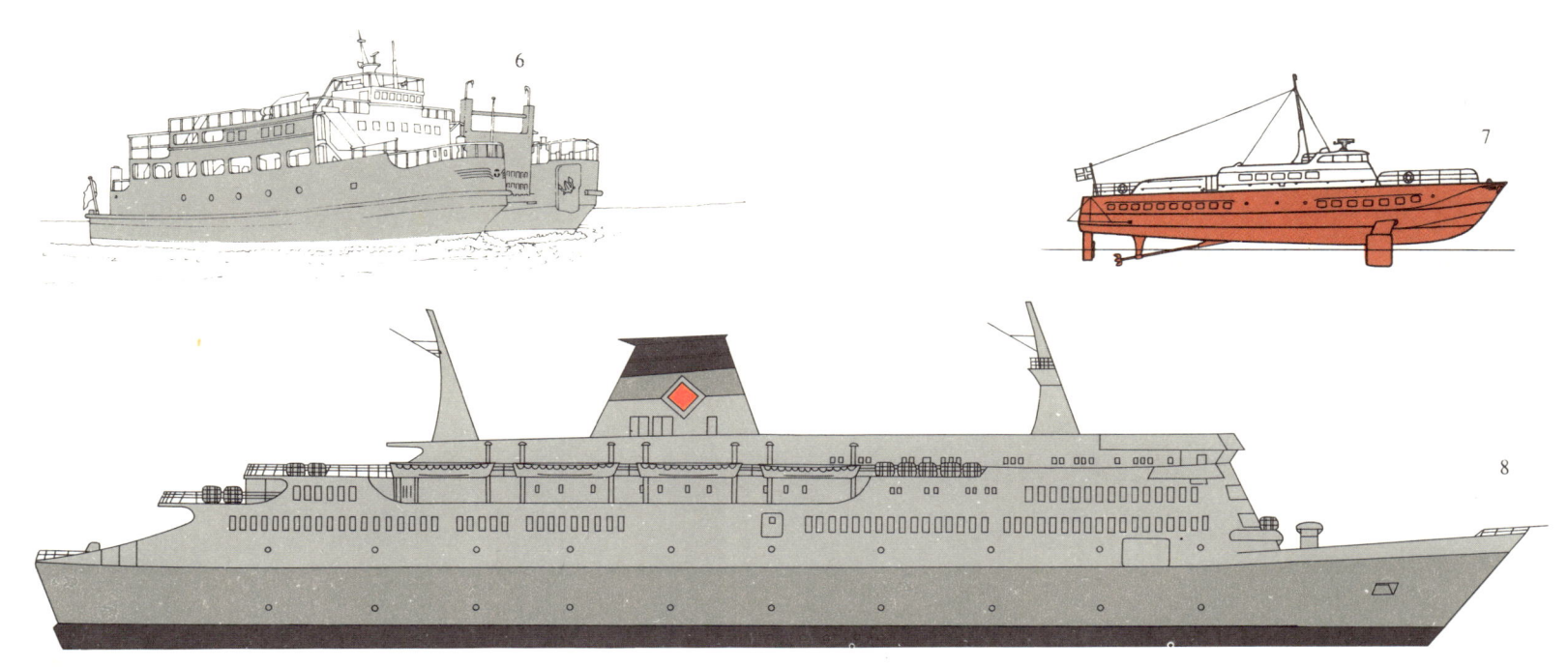

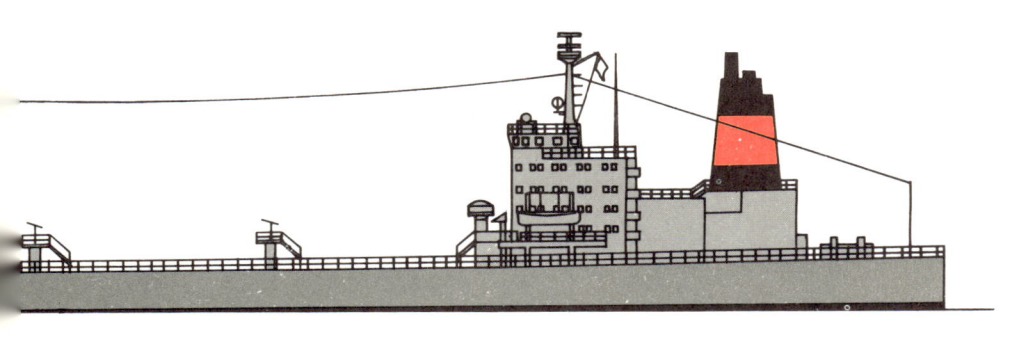

SOME MODERN SHIPS

5 The world's first heavy-duty gas-turbine powered cargo liner, the *Iron Monarch*, launched in Australia in 1973

6 The Japanese catamaran-ferry *Asashio*, on the Kawasaki-Kisarazu run

7 Modern Italian hydrofoil

8 Modern passenger and car ferry on the Sweden-Finland route, the *Aurella*, launched in 1973

165

DIESEL ENGINE

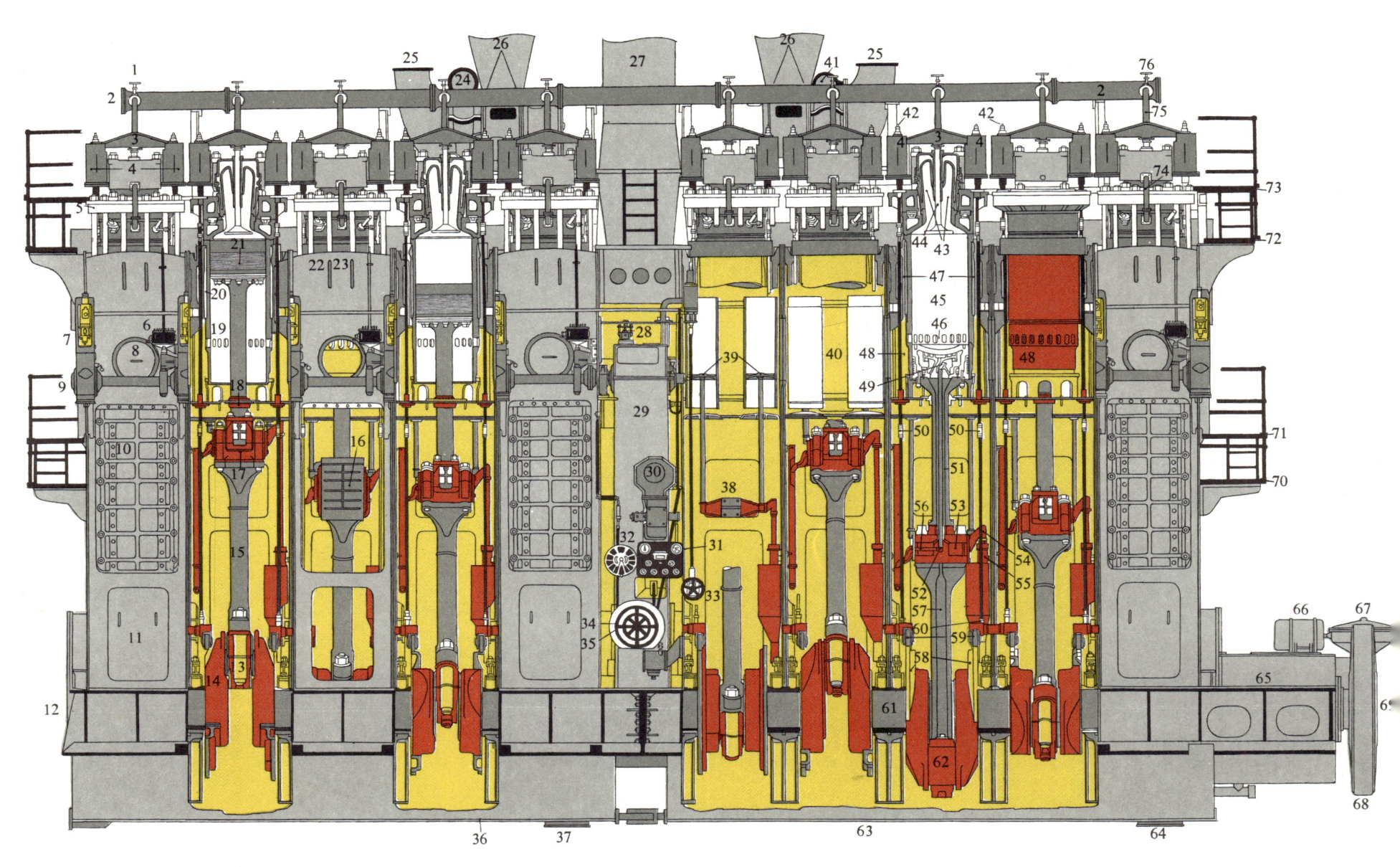

LONGITUDINAL VIEW OF A 10-CYLINDER, TURBOCHARGED 2-STROKE, CROSSHEAD, DIRECT DRIVE, PROPULSION DIESEL ENGINE

1. Fore end cylinder
2. Overhead cooling water pipe
3. Exhaust gas valve yoke
4. Encased valve springs
5. Cylinder cover
6. Cylinder lubricator
7. Fuel injection pump
8. Air receiver access
9. Cam shaft
10. Door to crosshead guide
11. Crankcase access door
12. Fore end of crankshaft
13. Crank pin bearing
14. Crank web
15. Connecting rod
16. Crosshead shoe
17. Crosshead bearing
18. Piston rod stuffing box
19. Scavenging ports
20. Cylinder liner
21. Working piston with rings
22. Fuel valve
23. Indicator valve
24. Forward turbocharger
25. Air compressor intake
26. Gas turbine outlet to boiler
27. Turbocharger by-pass pipe
28. Chain transmission stretcher
29. Chain transmission casing
30. Over-speed governor
31. Gauge board
32. Engine room telegraph
33. Master starting air valve wheel
34. Maneuvering hand-wheel
35. Telegraph reply wheel
36. Forward oil pan
37. Oil pan drain
38. Scavenging air pumps connecting arms
39. Scavenging air double-acting pumps
40. Scavenging air receiver
41. Aft turbocharger
42. Top end of valve drag links
43. Exhaust gas pipe
44. Exhaust gas valve
45. Cylinder in position for scavenging
46. Scavenging ports
47. Water cooling jacket
48. Scavenging air receiver
49. Oil cooling channels
50. Valve drag links
51. Piston rod oil cooling pipes
52. Crosshead pin
53. Cooling oil entrance
54. Telescope arm
55. Telescope pipe
56. Cooling oil drain
57. Connecting rod lubricating pipe
58. Exhaust valve cam segment
59. Cam rollers
60. Exhaust valve levers
61. Crankshaft journal and main bearing
62. Crank pin and connecting rod bearing
63. Aft oil pan
64. Oil pan drain
65. Propeller thrust bearing
66. Electric turning motor

DIESEL ENGINE

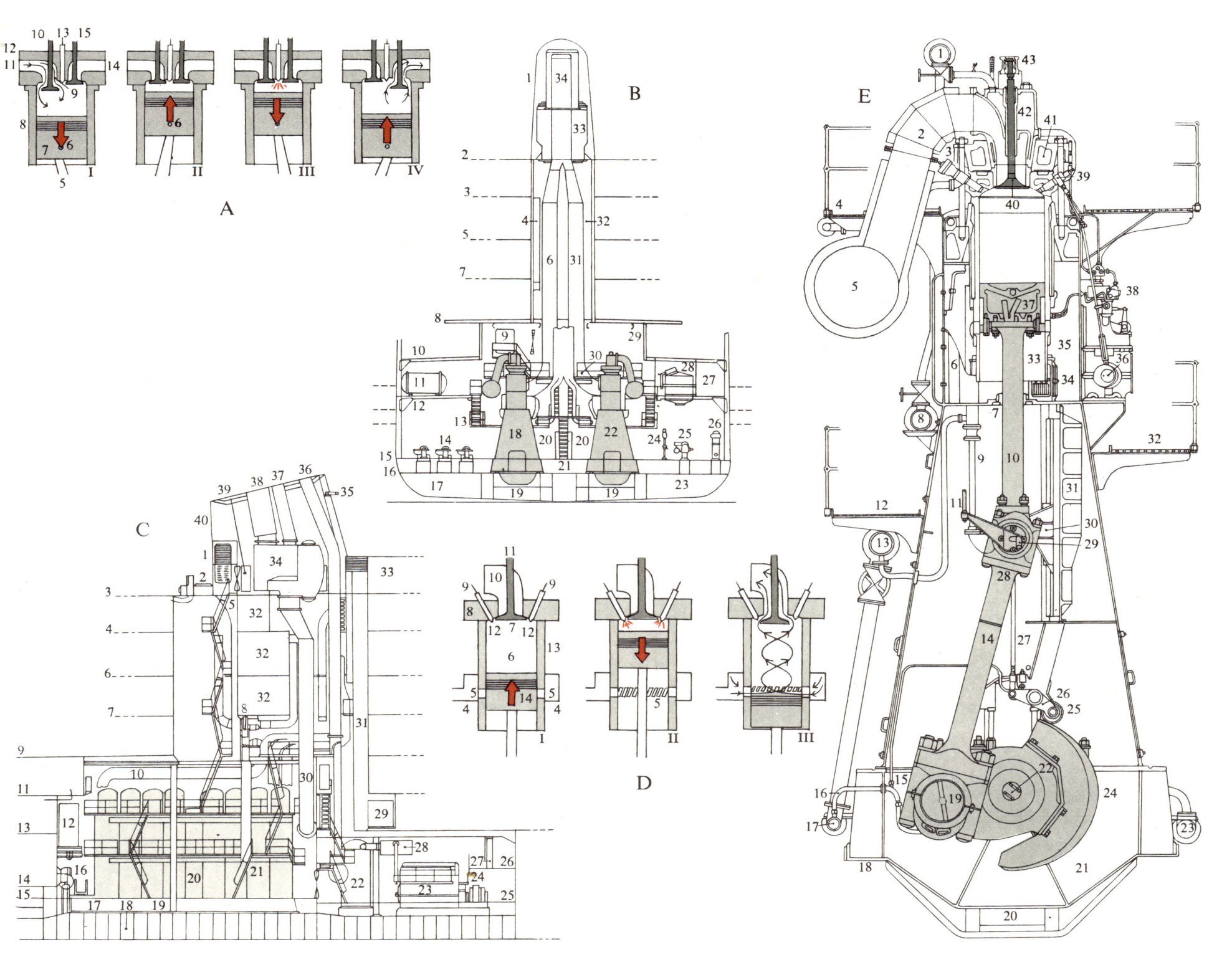

Continued

67 Turning gear
68 Turning wheel
69 Propeller shaft coupling flange
70 Lower platform starboard side
71 Lower platform port side
72 Upper platform
73 Turbochargers platform
74 Cooling water pipe
75 Cooling water pipe
76 Aft end cylinder

MOTOR SHIP ENGINES, ENGINE DETAILS AND LAYOUT

A *4-stroke diesel engine principle*
 I Intake stroke
 II Compression stroke
 III Power stroke
 IV Exhaust stroke
 5 Connecting rod
 6 Piston pin
 7 Working piston
 8 Cylinder liner
 9 Fuel valve
 10 Inlet valve
 11 Inlet manifold
 12 Cylinder cover
 13 Fuel pipe
 14 Exhaust manifold
 15 Exhaust-gas valve

B *Transverse section through passenger vessel's engine room, looking forward*
 1 Funnel
 2 Sun deck
 3 Boat deck
 4 Ventilation duct
 5 Promenade deck
 6 Exhaust pipe port engine
 7 Bridge deck
 8 Shelter deck
 9 Engine room entrance
 10 Main deck
 11 Lubricating oil cooler
 12 Lower deck
 13 Lower platform
 14 Lubricating oil pumps, salt and fresh water pumps
 15 Engine room flooring
 16 Tank top
 17 Fuel oil tanks
 18 Port main diesel engine
 19 Lubricating oil circulating tanks
 20 Maneuvering stands
 21 Ladder
 22 Starboard main diesel engine
 23 Fuel oil tanks
 24 Drilling machine
 25 Lathe
 26 Fuel oil pumps
 27 Engineer's storeroom
 28 Evaporator
 29 Traveling crane
 30 Upper platform
 31 Exhaust pipe starboard engine
 32 Exhaust pipe casing
 33 Exhaust gas boiler
 34 Spark arrester

C *Longitudinal section through passenger vessel's engine room*
 1 Air intake
 2 Skylight
 3 Sun deck
 4 Boat deck
 5 Ventilating fan suction duct
 6 Promenade deck
 7 Bridge deck (A deck)
 8 Ventilating fan

Continued

167

This rock carving from Kville Parish in the Province of Bohus shows how two men of the Bronze Age are fishing with a hook after anchoring their boat. This photograph is from the Gothenburg Museum of Archeology, and introduces the chapter on fishing.

Continued

9 Shelter deck (B deck)
10 Ventilation duct
11 Main deck (C deck)
12 Daily use fuel tanks
13 Lower deck (D deck)
14 Shaft tunnel
15 Propeller shaft
16 Turning gear
17 Propeller thrust bearing
18 Double bottom tanks
19 Tank top
20 Starboard main diesel engine
21 Ladder
22 Boiler
23 Auxiliary diesel engine
24 Electric generator
25 Engine room flooring

26 Platform
27 Main switchboard
28 Silencers, auxiliary engines
29 Diesel oil tanks
30 Main diesel exhaust pipe
31 Boiler exhaust pipe
32 Walking passages
33 Navigating bridge
34 Exhaust boiler
35 Tyfon
36 Boiler exhaust
37 Exhaust boiler outlet
38 Exhaust boiler by-pass and spark arrester
39 Exhaust casing entrance
40 Funnel

D *2-stroke diesel engine principle*
I Compression stroke
II Power stroke
III Scavenging
4 Scavenging air-receiver
5 Scavenging ports
6 Combustion chamber
7 Exhaust gas valve
8 Cylinder cover
9 Fuel pipe
10 Exhaust manifold
11 Valve spindle
12 Fuel valve
13 Cylinder liner
14 Piston

E *Cross section of a 2-stroke, crosshead, direct drive, propulsion diesel engine*
1 Overhead cooling-water pipe
2 Exhaust pipe
3 Starting air valve
4 Top platform
5 Exhaust receiver
6 Suction valves
7 Piston rod stuffing box
8 Bottom cooling water pipe
9 Piston cooling oil telescopic pipe
10 Piston rod
11 Scavenging air pump connecting arm
12 Lower platform (starboard side)

13 Lubricating and cooling oil main pipe
14 Connecting rod
15 Crank end bearing
16 Main-bearing lubricant pipe
17 Main lubricant pipe
18 Bedplate
19 Crank pin
20 Cast steel saddles
21 Crank case
22 Crank shaft
23 Lubricating and cooling oil return pipe
24 Exhaust valve cam segment
25 Cam roller
26 Exhaust valve lever
27 Exhaust valve pull rod
28 Crosshead bearing
29 Crosshead pin

30 Crosshead shoe
31 Crosshead guide
32 Lower platform (port side)
33 Scavenging air compression chamber
34 Scavenging air delivery valve
35 Scavenging air receiver
36 Cam shaft
37 Oil-cooled working piston
38 Fuel-injection pump
39 Fuel valve
40 Exhaust-gas valve
41 Water-cooled cylinder cover
42 Cooling water
43 Exhaust-gas valve yoke

168

FISHING

FISHING

BY GERHARD TIMMERMANN

It is not really known when man started collecting living creatures from the sea as part of his food. Probably fish and other sea creatures were at first caught with the bare hands. This is still done in some places even today. This primitive method of catching fish is little used now even though sponges, mussels, oysters, and other boneless animals are often taken in this manner. It is quite possible that early man watched animals catching fish for food and then imitated them.

The oldest fishing equipment known has come from the early European Stone Age (20,000-8,000 B.C.) in the form of small fish spears or harpoons that were hand-thrown. Similar spears are still used today in the tropics, where they are usually driven from a blowgun instead of being thrown. In some tropical areas one can also come across natives fishing with the bow and arrow; this is an ancient fishing method. The use of guns or small cannon for shooting harpoons dates from about the middle of the 19th century.

Catching fish with bait can be traced a long way back in time, as fish hooks made of stone have been found in layers of earth dating from Europe's middle Stone Age, *i.e.*, around 8,000-3,000 B.C. The fishing rod has been gradually developed in a large number of different forms and sizes, rods with lines having one hook, rods with lines having several hooks, etc. Long anchored or drifting lines to which numerous short lines with hooks are attached have also been used in bait fishing. Big hooks up to fifteen inches in length are used for catching large fish, while moderate-sized hooks are used for catching smaller fish. When fishing for sharks or tunny, hooks fitted with electrical stunning devices have been used for several years.

From the point of view of profit, the most important line fishing is found on the Grand Banks off Newfoundland. Here, French-Canadian, Portuguese, and, formerly, American fishermen catch cod from small boats called dories. Their daily catches are taken to a depot ship, usually a schooner or motor schooner, where the fish are preserved by salting and drying. These cod fisheries are of considerable importance to the economics of the fish-eating Catholic countries of southern Europe.

Bait is also used in setting various types of traps, where the fish is lured by the bait into a compartment from which it cannot possibly escape. Equipment of this type can be found in many different forms. Traps can be of woven or bound branches, or they can consist of nets stretched over wooden or metal frames, and so on. The oldest historical reproductions of this kind of equipment are shown on Egyptian reliefs from the 5th Dynasty, 3160-2920 B.C. In some places, traps of this kind are used without bait. These are usually permanent traps of very complicated form having long trap arms consisting of branches or wire netting. In spite of different forms of construction, the principle is always the same. A trap is placed where the fish, for hydrological reasons (tides or currents) or biological reasons (spawning season and the search for food), is compelled to travel in a certain direction. The historian, Pliny, (23-70 A.D.) described how walls were made of branches and were placed along the German coast during the ebb tide.

Fishing nets were used as early as the Stone Age, and their use is portrayed on early Egyptian reliefs from the 4th Dynasty (3430-3160 B.C.). When making nets, it is necessary to produce square or rhombic-shaped meshes, with knots that cannot slip sideways. Permanent nets can be anchored to the sea bed as floating vertical walls or be tied like sacks to posts having wooden or metal frames. There are a great number of such devices used almost entirely in coastal fishing. When setting out such nets comparatively small boats are used. In the beginning these boats were made of hollowed-out tree trunks, evidence of this is available from as early as about 6000 B.C. During the course of time, this method of boat building developed into clinker-built boats. In the Mediterranean area the raft was probably the boat's origin. This supposition is strengthened by relief pictures from Egypt dating from about 3000 B.C. In Greenland, Ireland, and Wales, where there is a shortage of wood, boats were, and still are, built of bone or wood frames and animal hides were stretched over these. Carvel-built vessels originated in the Mediterranean and, after modification in Northern Europe, were used all over the world. In some cases fishing boats were equipped with wells through which water flowed to keep the catch alive until the boat reached shore. Modern fishing boats have insulated holds in which the catch is kept on ice. Over the years there has been a great variety of fishing boats, and their appearance has differed both in hull and rig.

Drift nets are used when fishing for large shoals of fish. They have been employed since the Middle Ages. These nets hang vertically near the surface suspended from floats of cork, glass, plastic, and so on. One end of the drift net is attached to the fishing vessel. It is said that this type of net was first used by the Dutch, about 1416, for herring fishing in the North Sea. Since then, the herring has been of great importance in the food supply of middle Europe. In this kind of fishing, the Dutch, French, and Germans first used round, bilged, square-rigged boats called busses, which were later replaced by small luggers. The catch was salted down in barrels on board, which were also used to transport the fish over long distances inland. This method of preservation was not so essential in Scandinavia and England, where there are usually no great distances between the fishing grounds and the consumer; it was used mainly for fish which were to be exported. Drift nets were originally about 1,700 to 2,000 yards long, but since the introduction of steam and motor-driven vessels the length has been increased to about 5,500 yards.

Another type of net used for herring fishing is the ring net. It encloses the shoal and is then pulled together around the fish. The net usually hangs down near the sea bed. In coastal fishing the net is laid out in a semicircle from the beach, and when drawn in toward the shore, the encircled fish are caught. At sea, ring-netting is accomplished by two ships which pay out the net while steaming away from each other; they then come together again after completing a semicircle. When ring-netting with one boat, one end of the net is anchored and the boat then steams in a large circle back to the anchoring place.

The largest net of this type is a ring net which was invented in America at the beginning of the 19th century. It is now also common in Europe. This net is laid out in a circle around a previously located shoal of fish. At the lower edge of the net there is a rope line strung through rings, by which the net can be pulled together at the bottom to form a cone. Then the catch can be taken into the boat. This form of net is commonly called a purse seine.

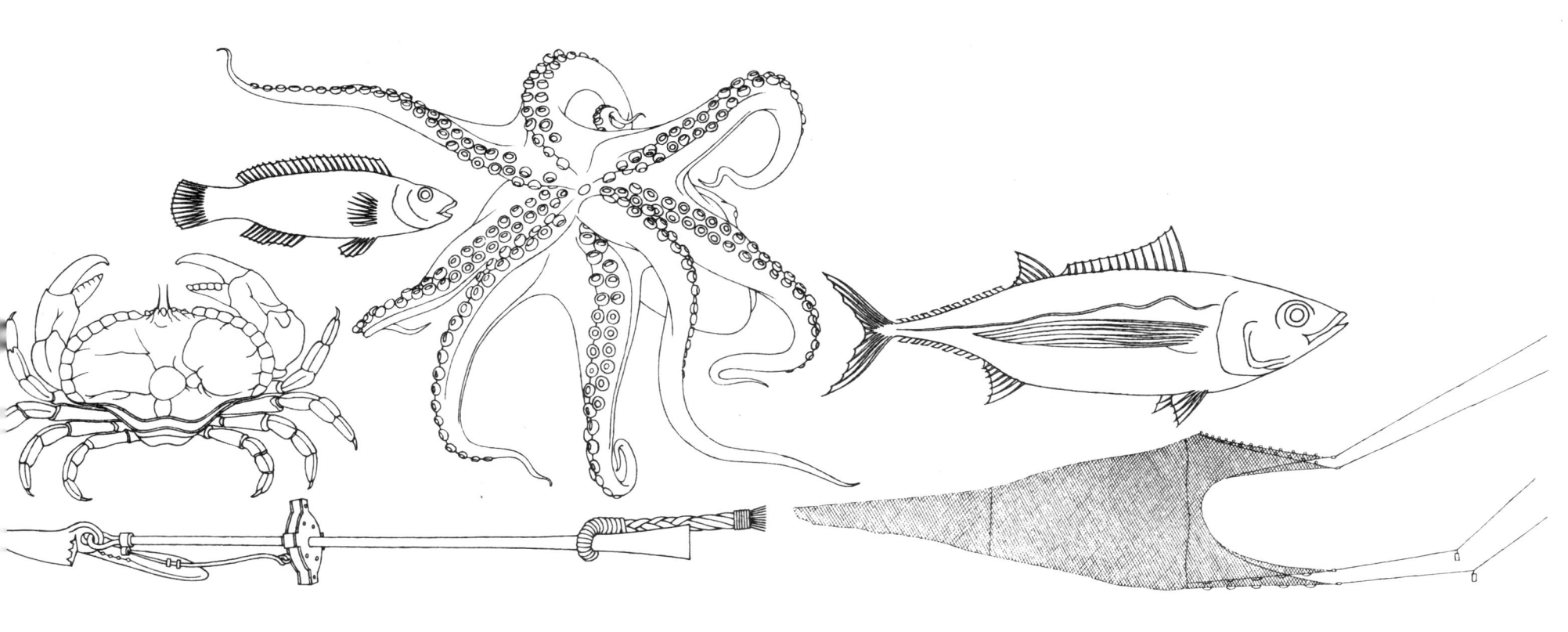

The most important method of fishing, however, is with the trawl. As long ago as the Middle Ages fishing was done with a boom trawl, *i.e.,* a net bag held open by a boom or pole was dragged along the sea bottom. It was not, however, until the end of the 19th century that trawl fishing had been developed to the point where its economic advantages became apparent. It was the British invention of the otter board, a kind of rudder that replaced the boom, and the introduction of steam and motor trawlers during this century that proved the economic superiority of trawl fishing. Although the French first used steam trawlers, it was mainly in England and Germany that mechanically propelled trawlers were developed and improved.

To make trawling even more profitable, trawls were fitted with a second otter board at the head of the trawl, thus achieving a greater width of net opening. Trawling with two vessels is also a useful method. This kind of trawling has been in existence in the Baltic since the 16th century, to a certain extent by Spanish fisherman through the ages, and since 1940 in the North Sea.

All fish are not caught on the sea bed. For catches at shallow depths, trawls, which can be set for changing depths, have been used for some years. The trawling depth is altered by varying the speed of the ship, and also by using different lengths of trawl line.

After the Second World War deep-sea fishing was spurred by the echo sounder, which not only made it possible to measure the depth of water but to locate shoals of fish as well. This has almost insured that a catch will be made and since 1945 has led to the development of the factory vessel, where the trawl is taken aboard over the stern and the catch is then immediately sorted and cleaned, ready for marketing or deep freezing.

Apart from ordinary fishing, man has also hunted the great mammals of the sea for about a thousand years.

There are old representations of dolphins which, however, do not prove that these mammals were caught. Our oldest information on whaling comes from Norway in about the year 900 A.D. A medal from the town of Biarritz describes whaling by the Basques in the year 1351. This, however, tells of small whales only, in addition to fishing for blackfish in the Faroe Islands. After William Poole, in 1583, and William Barents, in 1596, reported a great number of Greenland whales off Spitzbergen during their searches for the Northwest Passage, the British, in 1611, and the Dutch, in 1612, began an intensive hunt for whales. The Germans, in 1643, and the Americans, in 1650, also joined the hunt. Whale blubber was boiled to produce whale oil, at first on the Arctic islands, later in the homeland and also on shipboard. The actual pursuit of whales was carried out from small, strongly built rowing boats which carried crews of six to eight. The men used hand harpoons as weapons. Dead whales were stripped of their blubber and the remains were then allowed to drift away.

In about the year 1863 a Norwegian whaler mounted a newly invented harpoon gun on a steam vessel, and this made it possible to harpoon the faster-moving blue whales and rorquals. The harpoon was fitted with an explosive charge so that a quick killing of the whales was possible, and in 1935 the harpoon was further improved by fitting it with an electrocuting device. In today's whaling, steam or motor-driven vessels with powerful engines are used. After the whales are harpooned, they are towed to a large mother ship (factory ship) where they are winched up a slipway in the stern onto the whale deck. A large whale which, with its 100-foot length, is the biggest mammal ever to have been seen on earth, is cut up mechanically and completely disposed of in less than an hour. The largest of these factory ships, the *Unitas,* has a capacity of 30,000 tons. Whale oil is kept in large tanks aboard such vessels.

Besides whaling, seal hunting on the ice was conducted in Polar regions. The same sort of vessel was used for this as for whaling. As in the development of whaling boats, barks and steamers and, after 1914, motor-driven ships were built for seal hunting. Formerly killed by being clubbed, these fur-bearing animals are now shot.

Because of its importance to the food supply, fishing has become an international economic pursuit. Many nations draw in the harvest of the sea. Their shipping must be protected from piracy even in restricted areas, and the catches should be worth while as to size. So that this can be accomplished, fishermen must have knowledge of the sea and its creatures. The surveys carried out by the International Commission for Marine Research, based on systematic deep-sea expeditions since 1872, serve this end. The International Commission, organized in 1902 by the Northern European countries, co-ordinates research on the basis of the following program:

1. Hydrographic work
2. Testing of equipment to be used
3. Biological work
4. Fishery statistics

Since 1945 this task has been taken over by the FAO (Food and Agricultural Organization) inside OEEC (Organization for European Economic Co-operation) and OECD (Organization for Economic Co-operation and Development), respectively.

Furthermore, all countries with an interest in fishing carry out marine research in varying degrees with vessels of different sizes. These research ships make extensive observations and echo-sounding examinations of the fishing grounds. In addition to other forms of information gathering, research is carried out which should one day provide man with new kinds of food, such as the utilization of plankton.

OLD FISHING IMPLEMENTS

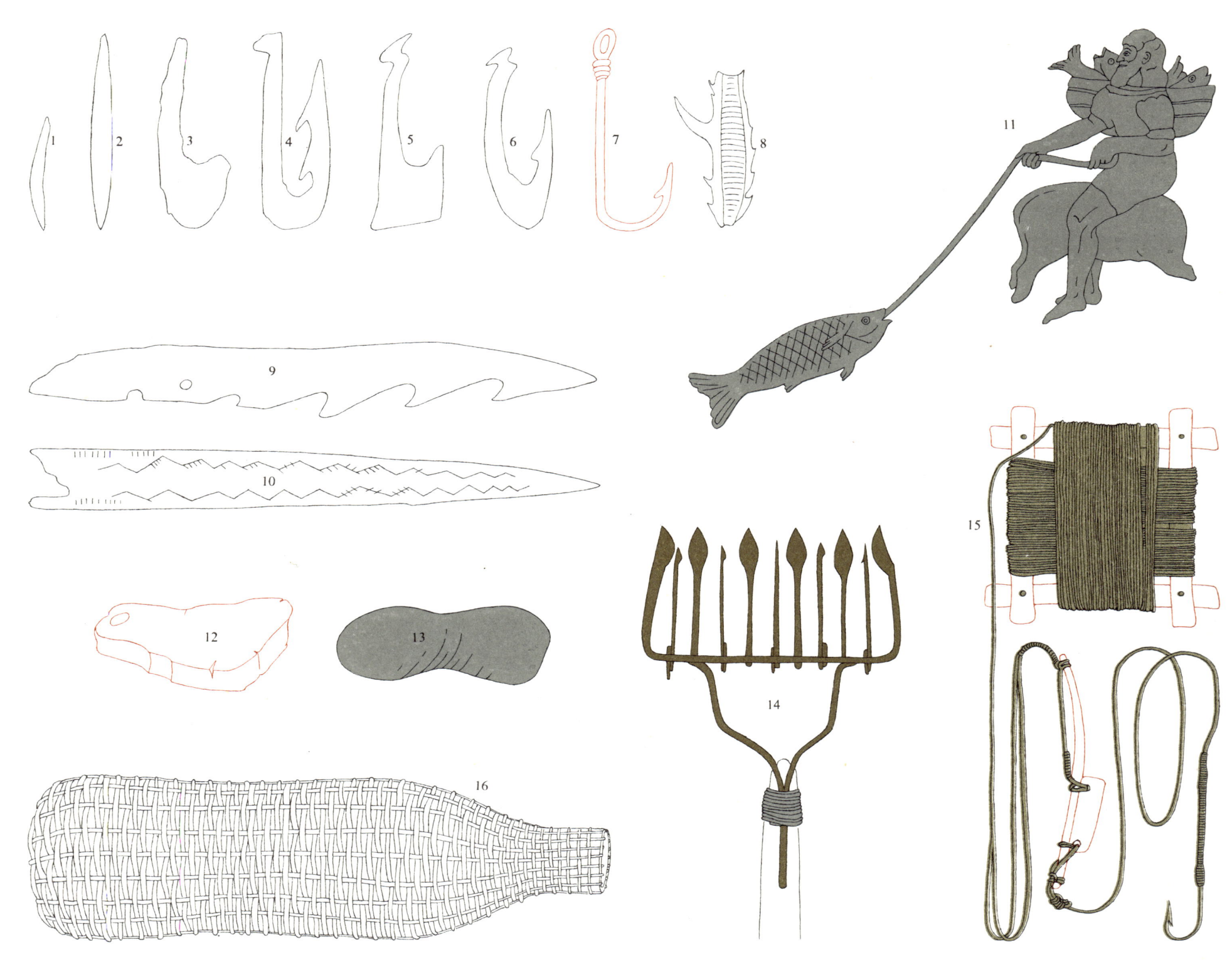

OLD FISHING IMPLEMENTS

1, 2 Primitive bone gorges or bait holders (The slight curving of 1 may possibly be the first step toward the more rounded gorge and, eventually, the bent hook)

3, 4 Bone hooks from the Paleolithic Age in Sweden, circa 4000 B.C.

5, 6 Hooks from the Neolithic Age in Sweden, circa 2000 B.C.

7 The oldest Mycenaean hook in the British Museum in London

8 Hook ready-made from the spur of an insect, Eurycantha Latro, New Guinea

9 Harpoon from the Paleolithic Age in Sweden, circa 4000 B.C.

10 Paleolithic narpoon with ornament; the flukes are worn off

11 Man fishing, sitting astride a blown-up goatskin (From Assyrian sculptures in the British Museum)

12 Carved piece of bark that has been used as a float for a net with coarse meshes

13 Stone sinker belonging to the same net (12 and 13 are finds from the Ancylus period in Finland, circa 6000 B.C.)

14 Old grain for spearing eels

15 Hand line, one of the oldest and most practical implements for codfishing

16 Wickerwork creel for catching eels; herring or mackerel spawn were used for bait

FISHING BOATS

TYPES OF FISHING BOATS

1. German heur boat
2. Greek fishing boat from Mykonos
3. Open Spanish fishing boat (Felucca)
4. Small Norwegian sailing fishing boat
5. French lugger (chasse marée)
6. Line fishing boat, Swedish west coast, 1880
7. German North Sea ketch
8. Portuguese barkentine for the Grand Banks
9. American Bank schooner, 1900
10. French Grand Bank schooner
11. British steam trawler
12. Large French motor trawler

FISHING BOATS

TYPES OF FISHING BOATS

13 British sailing trawler, about 1900
14 British motor trawler
15 American dragger
16 Swedish west coast trawler
17 Portuguese sardine steam drifter
18 British steam drifter
19 Norwegian motor fishing boat
20 German motor trawler
21 American seiner
22 British seiner
23 Dutch motor fishing boat
24 Fishing boat from the Sound
25 Danish motor fishing boat
26 American troller
27 Japanese bonito boat
28 Norwegian motor fishing boat (Ottring)

FISHING BOATS

TYPES OF FISHING BOATS

29 American tuna clipper
30 Norwegian sealer
31 French tunny yawl
32 Stern freezer-trawler, *Arctic Buccaneer*, built in Poland in 1974 for British owners. Length 85.5 m (280 ft), breadth 12.9 m (42 ft), draught 5.3 m (17 ft), displacement 1,120 tons, speed 15.5 knots, total freezing capacity 1,192 m³
33 Modern whaler
34 Spanish steam tunny boat
35 Sailing whaler, a three-masted bark, 1850
36 Whaling factory ship

175

OLD FISHING METHODS

OLD FISHING METHODS AND IMPLEMENTS

- A *Mark buoy*
  1. Flag
  2. Pole
  3. Cork float
  4. Shackle for buoy line
- B *Torch lamp*
- C *Trawling for mackerel, about 1880*
  1. Fishing smack
  2. Quarter pole
  3. Main pole
  4. Bow pole
  5. Trawling lines
  6. Lead sinkers
  7. Snells
- D *Shark hook*
- E *Whaling harpoon with hinged barb*
- F *Whaling harpoon*
- G *Cod bow net*
  1. Cod end
  2. Rattan rings
  3. Headline
  4. Leading net
  5. Footrope

SEINE NET AND PURSE SEINE

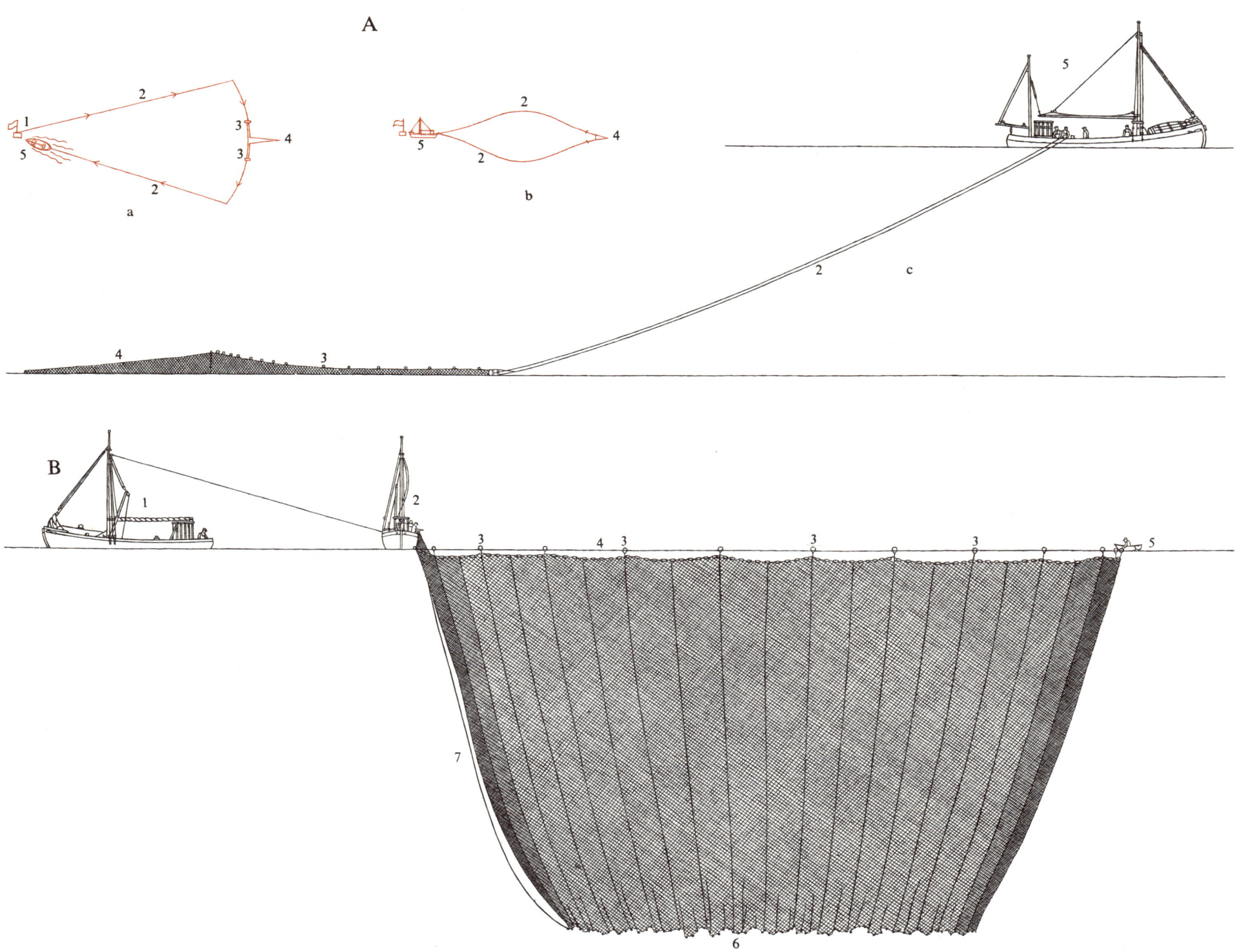

FISHING METHODS

A *Fishing with seine net of Scandinavian type*
a Setting the seine
b Hauling the warps
c Before hoisting the seine on board

1 Anchor buoy
2 Warps
3 Net tails
4 Seine purse
5 Seine netter

B *Fishing with purse seine*
1 Carrier
2 Purse seine netter
3 Floats
4 Cork line (headline)
5 Skiff
6 Leadline (footrope)
7 Purse line

177

LINES AND NETS

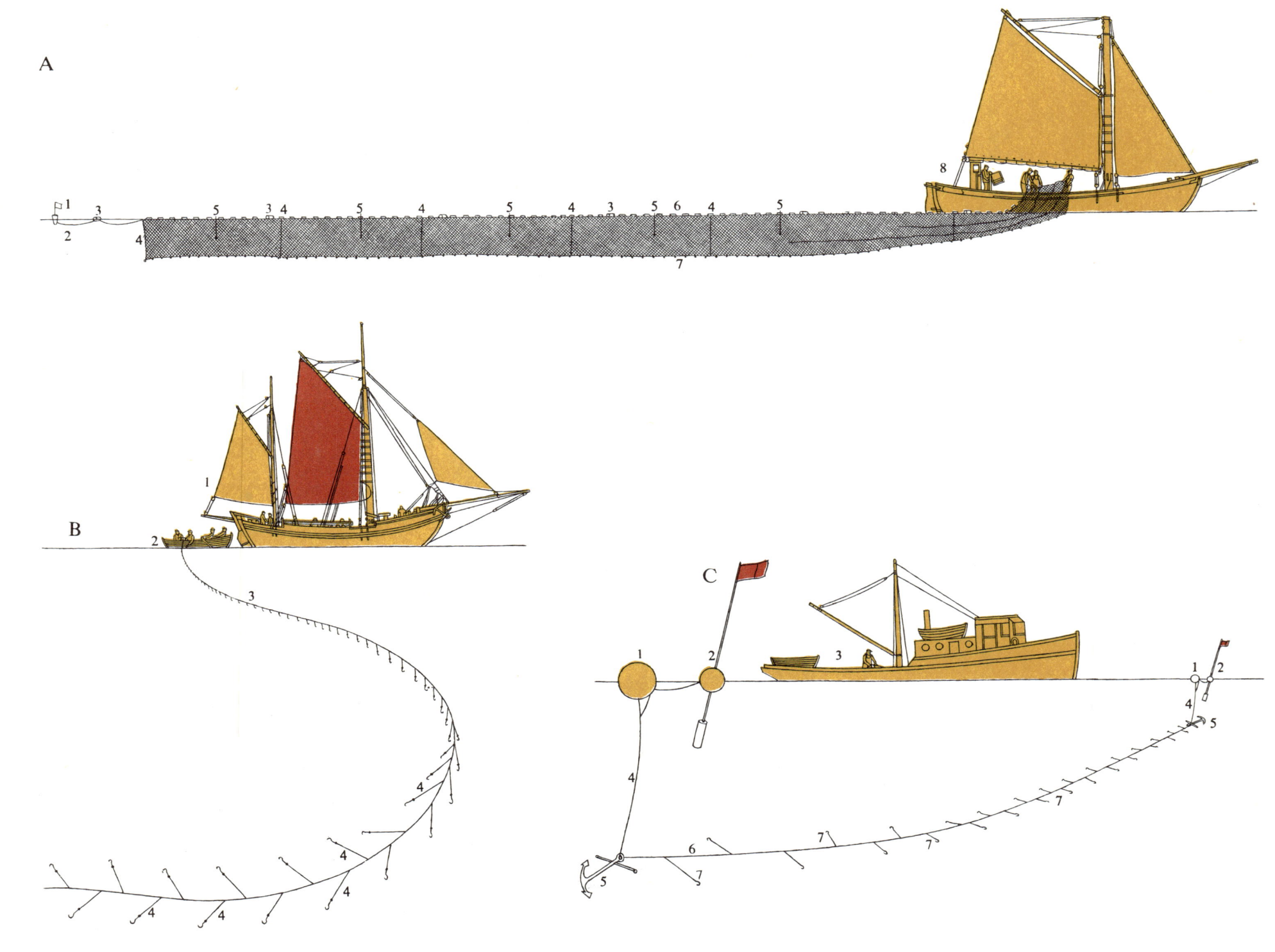

FISHING METHODS

A *Fishing for mackerel with drift nets*
1 Mark buoy with flag
2 Buoy line
3 Floats
4 Net ends ("heads")
5 Nets
6 Headline ("back")
7 Footrope ("foot")
8 Drifter shooting nets

B *Long line fishing from dories*
1 Attending vessel
2 Dory with fishermen
3 Ground line
4 Snells

C *Long line fishing for halibut*
1 Buoy
2 Mark buoy
3 Motor fishing boat
4 Buoy rope
5 Anchor
6 Ground line
7 Snells

178

TRAWLS

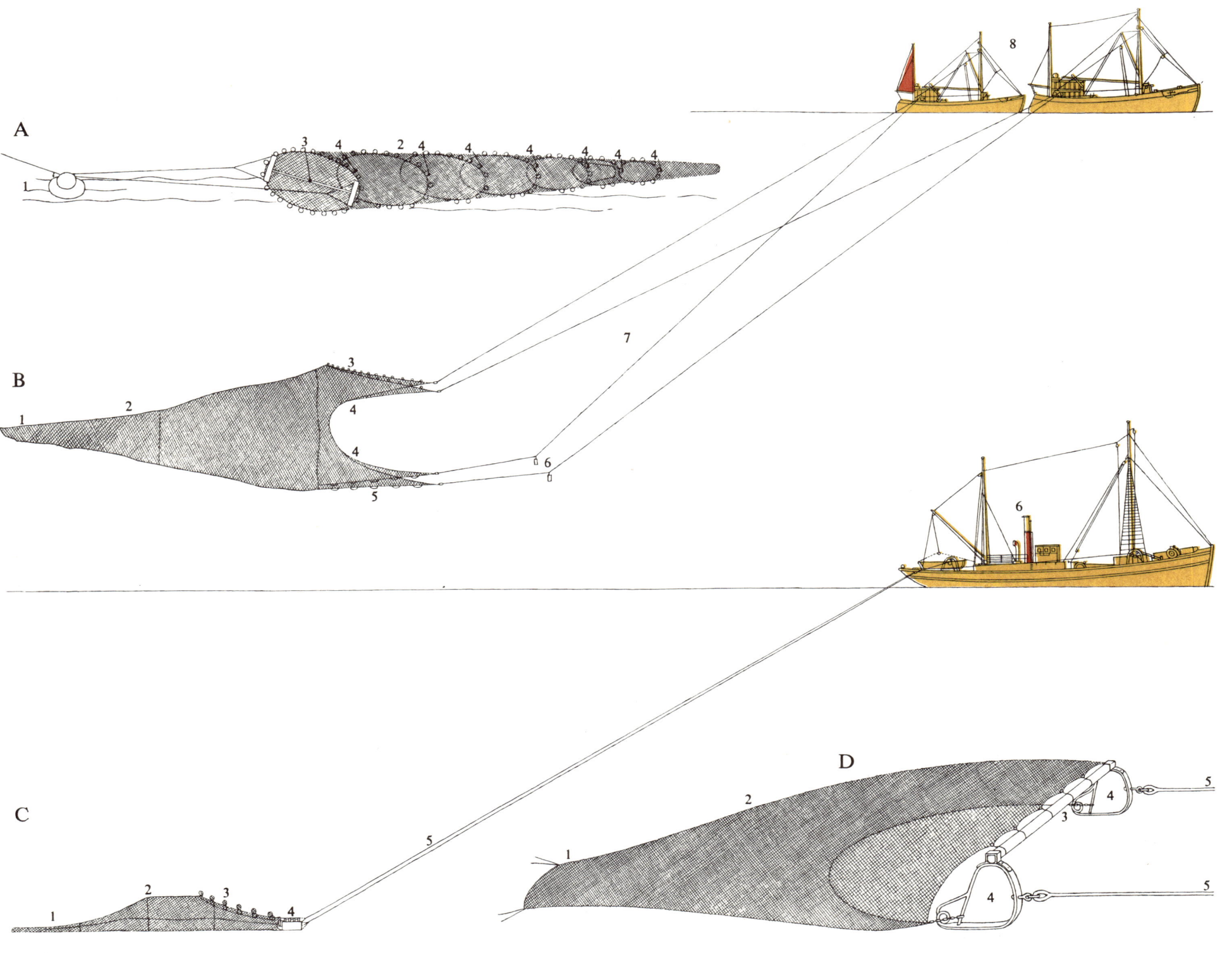

FISHING METHODS

A *Beam trawl, about 1800*
1 Stone weight
2 Belly
3 Beam
4 Wooden hoops

B *Modern floating trawl*
1 Cod end
2 Belly
3 Headline
4 Wings
5 Footrope
6 Weights
7 Towing warps
8 Motor trawlers, trawling in pairs

C *Otter trawl*
1 Cod end
2 Belly
3 Headline
4 Otter boards
5 Trawl warps
6 Steam trawler, about 1900

D *Beam trawl, from the 19th century*
1 Cod end
2 Belly
3 Beam
4 Trawl heads
5 Towing warps

179

FISH

FISH AND OTHER MARINE CREATURES

1. Seal
2. Bluefish
3. Tunny
4. Albacore
5. Angler
6. Ray's bream
7. Wrasse
8. Bergylt
9. Ray
10. Greenland whale
11. Polyprion Americanum
12. Salmon
13. Octopus
14. Red snapper
15. Conger eel
16. Great barracuda
17. Dogfish
18. Sole
19. Shark

FISH

FISH AND OTHER MARINE CREATURES

- 20 Mackerel
- 21 Turbot
- 22 Cod
- 23 Herring
- 24 Whiting
- 25 Brill
- 26 Lobster
- 27 Sea cat
- 28 Prawn
- 29 Halibut
- 30 Plaice
- 31 Crab
- 32 Hake
- 33 Oyster
- 34 Haddock
- 35 Burbot
- 36 Ling
- 37 Coalfish
- 38 Sprat
- 39 Sardine

The picture of Star boats in a race, taken by KEY L. NILSSON, *introduces the chapter on yachting.*

YACHTING

YACHTING

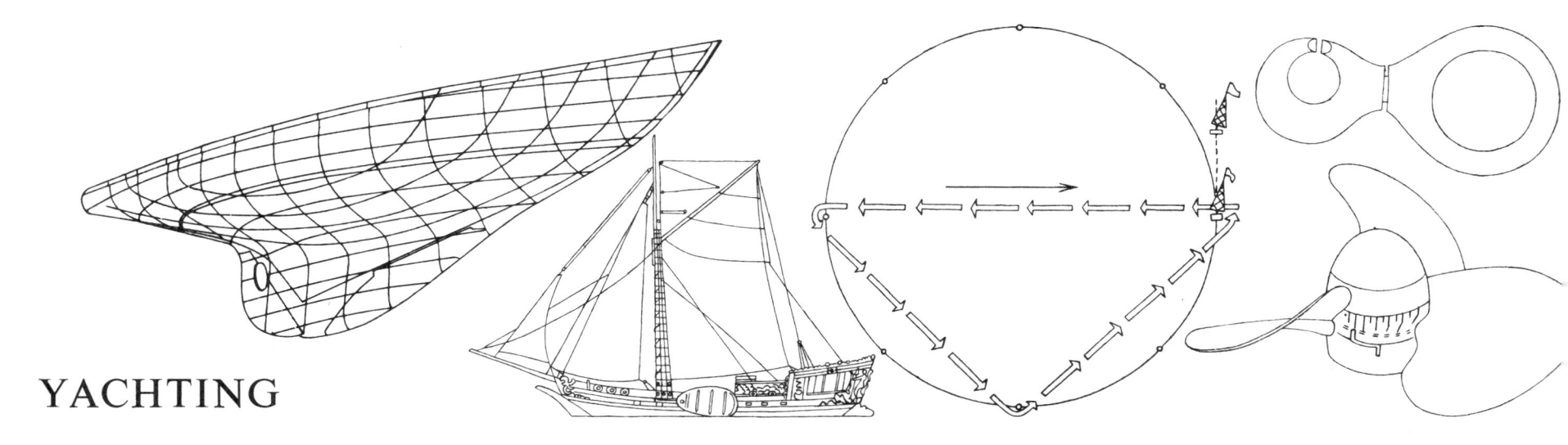

BY GEORGE P. B. NAISH

The word yacht nowadays usually refers to privately owned pleasure craft, used either for racing or cruising. There are still royal or state owned yachts, but before the 19th century the word usually referred to vessels publicly owned and used for the conveyance of princes, ambassadors, or other great personages from one kingdom to another. The word yacht came into the English language from the Netherlands at the time of the restoration of King Charles II to the throne in 1660. But, of course, ships and boats had been used for purposes of state and for pleasure from earliest times.

Thus, the model of a yacht used on the river Nile by an Egyptian nobleman of the 18th Dynasty, some 1500 years B.C. has been found in a tomb. It is represented as a vessel of a hundred feet in length over all, elaborately decorated and painted, with a deckhouse for a cabin. This yacht was probably used by the nobleman while traveling up and down the Nile valley on business. Egyptian tombs also depict small pleasure craft, which could be towed either from the bank or astern of other vessels. Perhaps Cleopatra's barge, which she used when she first met Antony, should be classed as a yacht. Plutarch tells us that the poop was of gold, the sails of purple, and the oars of silver. In English history we read of King Edgar, who reigned from 959 to 975 A.D., being rowed on the river Dee by a crew of eight lesser kings. But on the whole, in early times people seldom went to sea for pleasure, for there were too many dangers either from storms or from pirates.

The modern pleasure yacht was first developed as a type in Holland, with its maze of rivers and meres, on which, according to the many pictures painted in the seventeenth century, scores of shallow draft sailing boats, gaily carved and decorated, were raced and shown. There were also large state-owned yachts, and in 1660 one of these, originally built for the East India Company, was bought by the City of Amsterdam for presentation to the restored King of England. Both James I and Charles I had taken a great interest in shipbuilding and naval affairs generally and Charles II first learned to sail as a boy in a pinnace off the island of Jersey. He had continued to distract himself with sailing during his exile in Holland. The gift yacht from Amsterdam was named the *Mary,* and was a typical Dutch state yacht of a hundred tons, broad in the beam and of shallow draft with lee boards. The stern cabin had a high coach roof and windows. The stern was decorated with the royal arms, surmounted by three poop lanterns, and the figurehead was a unicorn. Eight little guns could be fired from circular gunports, each decorated with carved and gilded port wreaths. The *Mary* was cutter, or yacht rigged, and carried a boomless mainsail with a long standing gaff, called a half-spreet. The next year the Dutch gave Charles a smaller yacht, the *Bezan,* with the bezaan rig, well known in Holland, with a boomed mainsail and a short gaff. Charles soon set English shipwrights to building yachts which for English waters were an improvement in that they had deeper draft instead of leeboards. The new English royal yachts were much like small warships, but retained the fore-and-aft rig

When Charles tired of a yacht it was received into the fleet as a dispatch vessel or survey ship. Charles took much pleasure in his yachts, either for racing or making trips, and his brother James, Duke of York, as well as certain private gentlemen, followed his example and became owners of yachts. Several private individuals explored the English coast or visited the Continent in the second half of the 17th century.

When Peter the Great, Tzar of Russia, studied shipbuilding in Holland and England he learned his seamanship in yachts, and the French king, Louis XIV, had yachts built for him in England.

Although yachting for pleasure showed no signs of becoming a popular sport in the 18th century, it managed to hold its own in English waters despite the many long wars. There were river pageants, and in 1775 the Cumberland Fleet or sailing society was founded by the royal Duke of that name, who offered a cup for a regatta between some twenty small yachts of from two to five tons which was held on the river Thames above London Bridge. The Royal Thames Yacht Club claims descent from this Cumberland Fleet. The Fleet's yachts were distinguished by special pennants and the owners wore smart nautical uniforms.

We find William Hickey sailing in a cutter yacht of fifty tons in 1768: "a heavy dull sailer, but with capital accommodation, having a spacious cabin aft her whole width with sash windows astern."

Greenwich was considered the harbor for royal yachts during the century, and from Greenwich the royal family sailed for Hanover. George III reviewed his fleet at the Nore in 1781, sailing down the Thames with a flotilla of three or four royal yachts. In the National Maritime Museum at Stockholm the stern and king's cabin of Gustav III's schooner, the *Amphion,* built in 1778, is preserved, along with its furniture. The King held many councils of war in this cabin, when fighting the Russians in 1790.

The 19th century marked the beginning of yacht racing as a great international sport. In 1815 the peace with France no doubt encouraged the formation in England of the Royal Yacht Squadron, under royal patronage, with its headquarters at Cowes, Isle of Wight, which faced the sheltered waters of the Solent. The members were rich men owning large yachts, which were designed to resemble the brigs and schooners and cutters of the royal navy. The members considered, in fact, that one of their duties was to improve the design of sailing ships for the benefit of the royal navy. Mr. Dixon Kemp, a famous writer on yachting subjects, who died in 1899, estimated there were some 50 British yachts afloat in 1800 and as many as 503 in 1850. These yachts averaged some fifty tons apiece; they were mostly cutters with bluff bows and lines which fined off aft, the well-known "cod's head and mackerel's tail" fashion.

In 1851, the American schooner *America* was sailed to Cowes and raced around the Isle of Wight for a cup presented by the Royal Yacht Squadron. The *America* had her dazzling white cotton sails cut to stand flat as boards, in opposition to the very full cut English flax sails. And she had a light displacement and fine lines fore and aft. She won the cup and her example helped to revolutionize yacht design in European waters. In particular, her long hollow bow was copied.

Racing yachts were now built with deeper and narrower midship sections. The iron ballast was replaced by lead, and this lead began to be put on the keel instead of being interior ballast. A famous and successful yacht was the *Jullanar,* built in 1875, the design concentrating on a short keel, a long water line, and the smallest frictional surface. By the end of the century the old, narrow vessels, with their heavy weight and deep forward section and lean bow water lines, were useless when racing against the new lighter, broader boats. These new racing boats were becoming veritable skimming dishes, until a sensible compromise was effected; then the profile was rounded up forward and a raking sternpost was built aft so as to cut down the wetted surface.

It was calculated there were some 2,000 yachts in the British Isles by 1881 amounting to 100,000 tons, that is, an average of 50 tons a yacht. These were built at a cost of some £50 a ton, and were only half the tonnage of sailing yachts. By now, the steam yacht had become popular, and Lord Brassey's auxiliary three-masted schooner, the *Sunbeam* made a number of world cruises, the first in 1878, which were popularized by the narratives published by Lady Brassey.

By the beginning of the 20th century yachting had become an international sport, as popular in the United States as in the British Isles, and was spreading to the Mediterranean and Baltic and the great sheltered harbors of Australia and New Zealand. Anglo-American yachting rivalry is most well known in the America's Cup races.

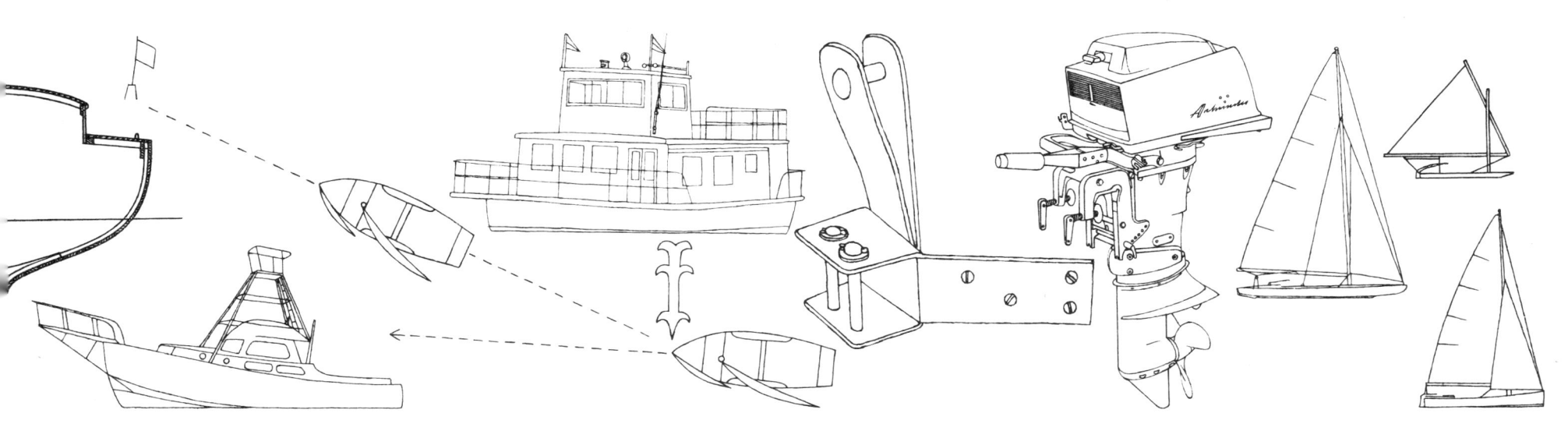

The first of these was held under the auspices of the New York Yacht Club in 1870.

Yachting in America had begun a rapid expansion once the Civil War was over, and in 1866 three rival schooners, the *Vesta, Henrietta,* and the *Fleetwing,* raced from Sandy Hook to Cowes Roads, arriving within nine hours of each other, although the *Fleetwing* had had six men swept out of her cockpit by a heavy sea. Naturally the great schooners caught the public eye and their doings were recorded in the press.

To many people the word yachting summoned up a picture of a fashionable gathering, for example, Cowes Week, with the roads full of large steam yachts, house parties on board, and fleets of sailing craft racing by day and returning to their moorings each night, so that the owners could attend social gatherings at the various yacht clubs. Serious yacht racing in the big classes had no more keen supporters than King Edward VII and King George V, who owned the famous racing cutter *Britannia,* designed by George Watson, between 1893 and 1935.

The German Kaiser came over to England to race, manning his yachts with English crews. Principally owing to the enthusiasm of King George V, the splendid great "J" Class cutters were raced again after the 1914-1918 war. These large yachts were generally manned by professional crews and became increasingly expensive to run. Therefore, it was not surprising that the trend turned toward building smaller, cheaper yachts, which could be manned and often partially maintained by amateur crews. And at the same time, racing in really small boats became increasingly popular; this popularity has become very obvious since World War II, because it is possible to race the modern dinghy on such small stretches of water as are formed by reservoirs and old gravel pits. It is now quite usual to sight a mass of small white sails earnestly engaged in yacht racing although they are far from the open sea.

In 1963 the International Yacht Racing Union consists of more than fifty different countries, including the Union of Soviet Socialist Republics and the United Arab Republic. There are eight international classes, including the 12-meters, the famous Dragons of Norwegian design, and the 14-foot international racing dinghy. Popular classes of small yachts, which can be used for racing or cruising, include the Folkbåts, a very popular and successful Swedish design, and the Vertue, product of a Solent yard.

While yacht racing is more likely to figure in the newspapers, cruising yachts have existed certainly from the 17th century, when we find an English naval officer fitting out his ship's boat and proceeding up the Channel with his dog for crew and company. He armed his boat with a swivel gun against pirates, and fired this off as a salute when entering Rye harbor in the early morning, so that the townsfolk manned their defences under the impression that the man and dog were themselves marauders. Since then, cruising yachtsmen have included many odd characters, including men who chose to sail single-handed, sometimes crossing oceans, sometimes exploring difficult coastlines. The more famous of them include Captain Joshua Slocum, who sailed alone around the world in the *Spray,* 1896 to 1898. He was a citizen of the United States who built his own ship in Fairhaven, Massachusetts, by carefully copying an old hull pulled up into a field. Captain Voss made his venturesome voyages in a converted Indian dugout canoe, looking for heavy weather so that he could try out a sea anchor and the effects of pouring oil on troubled waters. Frank Cowper wrote of enchanting sailing tours, combining near-fiction and detailed sailing directions for the coasts of the United Kingdom and Brittany. McMullen sailed heavy luggers up and down the English Channel, "single-handed," for when his wife sailed with him he did not care to count her as his crew. Rob Roy MacGregor not only popularized a type of canoe but built himself a small yawl and wrote a narrative which inspired others to follow his example. These men were on the scene in the closing years of the 19th century, and their example has proved infectious.

Dr. Claud Worth was one of the first of the amateur yachtsmen who turned his scientific training—for he was an eye specialist—toward inquiry into the proper design for yachts and the best materials from which to build them, the proper fastenings and all the details of the fittings connected with the rigging, the ground tackle—everything, in fact, upon which the safety of the yacht at sea depended. Dr. Worth wanted an ocean-going cruising yacht.

The rapid increase of interest in ocean racing and the problems this has posed has also had an important and beneficial effect on the sport as a whole. The object has been to produce small yachts intended to race on the open sea in all weathers. Early successes—the first Fastnet Race was held in 1925—went to converted pilot cutters.

The typical Bristol Channel pilot cutter had a large beam and draft, interior ballast only, and had been developed to establish sea-kindliness and the ability to keep the sea in all weathers. As these cutters had to be worked with a small crew, the mast was stepped well aft, which required a large fore staysail, perhaps the easiest sail in the ship to handle. In a breeze, these cutters were fast and weatherly, but often wet because of over ballasting. But they were very slow in light weather, so that when the specially designed light displacement ocean racers were built, the heavy old pilot cutters soon went out of business as ocean racers. The new ocean racers had all their ballast in the keel, many suits of headsails, such as genoas and spinnakers, and beautifully cut Bermudan mainsails, which did away with the weight of the gaff aloft. However, the influence of the older pilot cutters is still great on cruising yachts, a famous example being the *Dyarchy,* built in Sweden in 1939 to the design of Laurent Giles and partners. Nowadays, some small yachts with amateur crews will be racing across oceans, while others, perhaps crewed by a man and his wife, will be circumnavigating the world. The sport is on the increase and the meres and rivers of Holland are as busy with small craft as they were in the 17th century.

The sheltered waters of the Baltic are ideal for yachting, while in the Mediterranean the age-old harbors of Venice or Alexandria have their yacht berths in the same way as do the more modern harbors of New York or Sydney. Motor yachting, which can be quickly learned, attracts as many persons as does the sailing yacht. There are a great many standard craft on the market, and the outboard motor enables many hulls to be quickly converted into power boats. Materials, such as fiber glass, make it possible for hulls to be mass-produced. Fabrics, such as Dacron, prolong the life of sails. And the twin hulls of the catamaran have provided new thrills by letting small yachts sail very fast indeed with just a beam wind. There may be something new coming out every month, but the conditions of wind and weather remain the same, and it is important that the many yacht clubs exercise some sort of control to insure that yachtsmen sail the seas in seaworthy craft. Seamanlike precautions are to be preferred to foolhardy risks.

No doubt the general introduction of the auxiliary motor into most large sailing yachts has diminished the risk of shipwreck or collision, but it has also made it possible for yachts to cruise very much further in a given period.

DRAGON CLASS

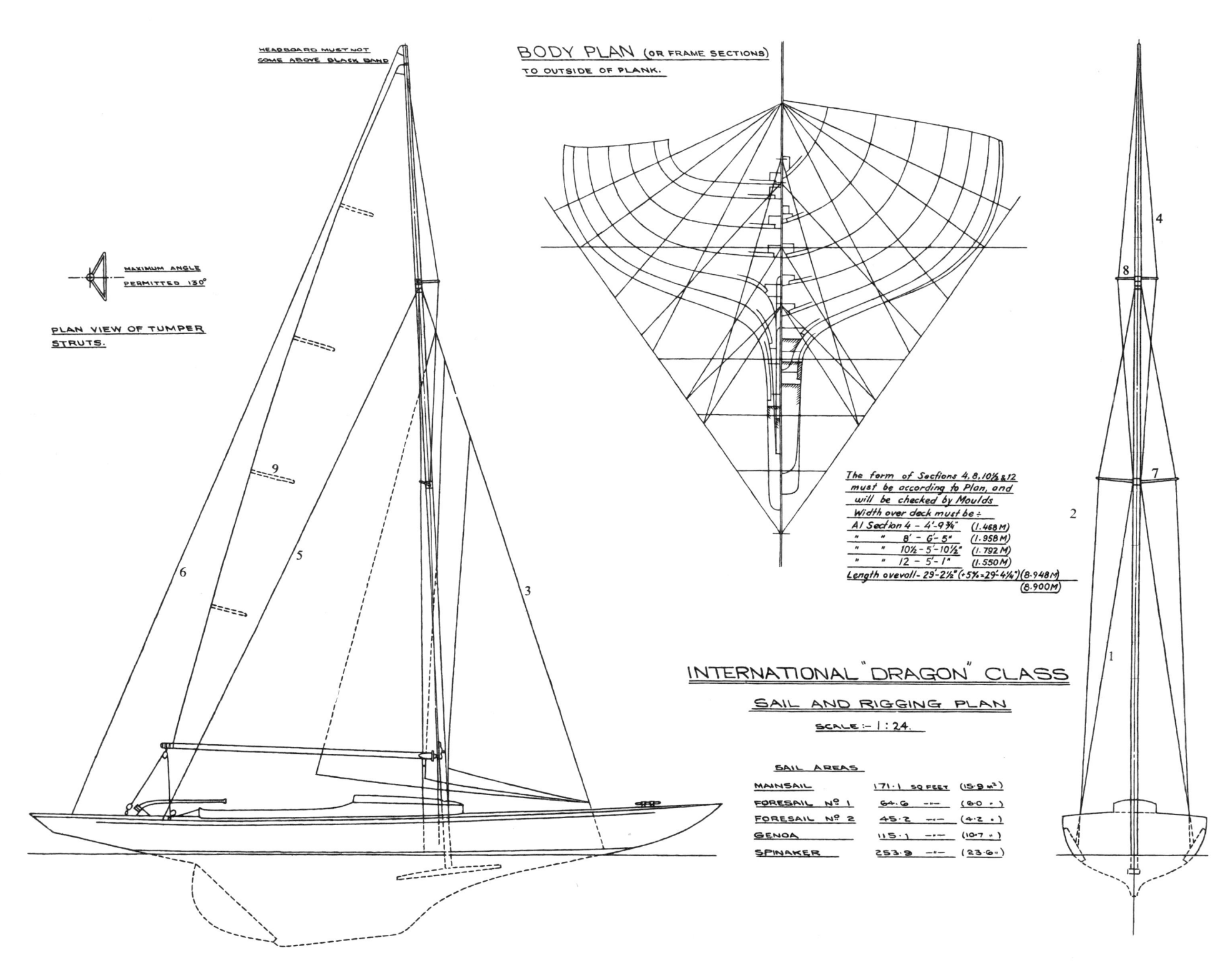

THE INTERNATIONAL DRAGON CLASS

The Dragon is a very popular class of one-design, fixed-keel boat, and in Europe today the International Dragon class is probably the largest group of such boats. It was designed as early as 1929 by the Norwegian designer, Johan Anker, at the request of the Royal Yacht Club of Gothenburg. The class soon spread to all Scandinavia and Germany, and in 1935 it was introduced into Great Britain. The control of the class is administered by the International Yacht Racing Union.

The aim of the Dragon was to get a racing cruiser with a high speed and a cabin for two. At the same time, the boat is very seaworthy and able to carry her large sail, even in strong winds. The hull of the Dragon has not been altered, but the rigging was changed in 1946.

DRAGON CLASS

INTERNATIONAL "DRAGON" CLASS CONSTRUCTION PLAN

MATERIALS AND SCANTLINGS

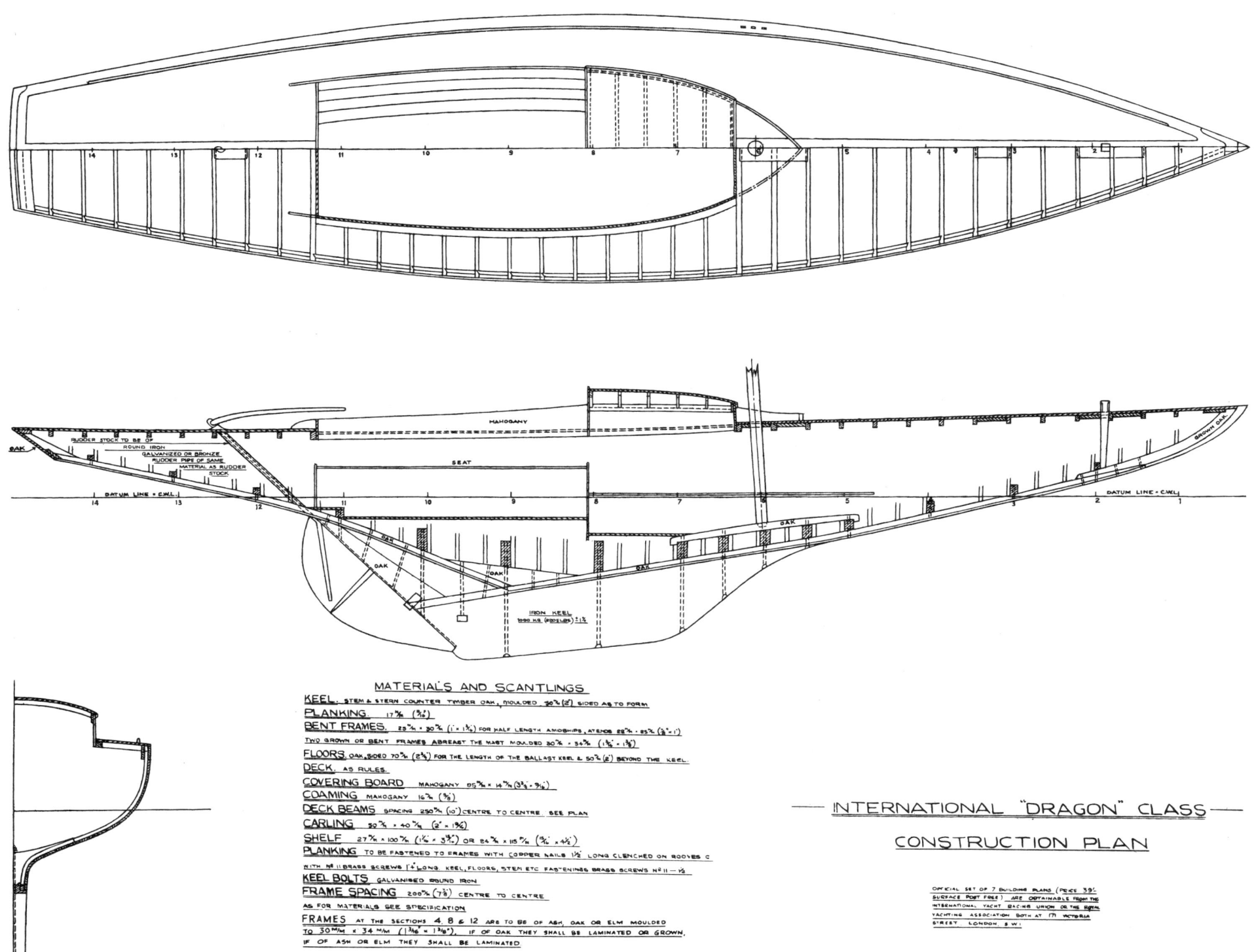

KEEL: STEM & STERN COUNTER TIMBER OAK, MOULDED 50 ㎜ (2") SIDED AS TO FORM

PLANKING. 17 ㎜ (¾")

BENT FRAMES. 25 ㎜ × 30 ㎜ (1" × 1¼") FOR HALF LENGTH AMIDSHIPS, AT ENDS 22 ㎜ × 25 ㎜ (⅞" × 1")
TWO GROWN OR BENT FRAMES ABREAST THE MAST MOULDED 30 ㎜ × 34 ㎜ (1³⁄₁₆" × 1⅜")

FLOORS. OAK, SIDED 70 ㎜ (2¾") FOR THE LENGTH OF THE BALLAST KEEL & 50 ㎜ (2") BEYOND THE KEEL

DECK. AS RULES.

COVERING BOARD MAHOGANY 85 ㎜ × 14 ㎜ (3⅜" × 9⁄16")

COAMING MAHOGANY 16 ㎜ (⅝")

DECK BEAMS SPACING 250 ㎜ (10") CENTRE TO CENTRE. SEE PLAN

CARLING 50 ㎜ × 40 ㎜ (2" × 1⅝")

SHELF 27 ㎜ × 100 ㎜ (1⅛" × 3⅞") OR 24 ㎜ × 115 ㎜ (⅞" × 4½")

PLANKING TO BE FASTENED TO FRAMES WITH COPPER NAILS 1½" LONG CLENCHED ON ROOVES C WITH No 11 BRASS SCREWS 1¼" LONG. KEEL, FLOORS, STEM ETC FASTENINGS BRASS SCREWS No 11 – 1½"

KEEL BOLTS GALVANISED ROUND IRON

FRAME SPACING 200 ㎜ (7⅞") CENTRE TO CENTRE

AS FOR MATERIALS SEE SPECIFICATION

FRAMES AT THE SECTIONS 4, 8 & 12 ARE TO BE OF ASH, OAK OR ELM MOULDED TO 30 ㎜ × 34 ㎜ (1³⁄₁₆" × 1⅜"). IF OF OAK THEY SHALL BE LAMINATED OR GROWN. IF OF ASH OR ELM THEY SHALL BE LAMINATED

OFFICIAL SET OF 7 BUILDING PLANS (PRICE 39/- SURFACE POST FREE) ARE OBTAINABLE FROM THE INTERNATIONAL YACHT RACING UNION OR THE ROYAL YACHTING ASSOCIATION BOTH AT 171 VICTORIA STREET, LONDON, S.W.1.

DRAGON RACES

The International Dragon Gold Cup was initiated in 1936, and is competed for annually in Britain, Norway, Sweden, or Denmark. Since 1948, the Dragon has been used at the Olympic Games, where the class now is the most popular.

The Edinburgh Cup was presented by the Duke of Edinburgh in 1949 for competition in Britain. The Herriot Cup was offered by the Yacht Club of France in 1948.

187

OLD YACHTS

OLD YACHTS

A The American schooner, *Sappho*, defender of the America's Cup in 1871

B *Jolie Brise*, winner of the first Fastnet Race and founder of the R.O.R.C. Rule

C The Swedish state barge, *Vasaorden*, constructed in 1774 by af Chapman for King Gustavus III

D Dutch yacht, 1678

E The famous schooner yacht, *America*, which in 1851 won the Queen's Cup, later known as the America's Cup. The *America* was a development from the American East Coast pilot schooner.

F *Shamrock IV*, owned by Sir Thomas Lipton, the British challenger in the Cup race of 1920

G H.M. Yacht, *Britannia*, in her first rig; she was built in 1893 for the Prince of Wales, later Edward VII

OLD AND NEW YACHTS

OLD AND NEW LARGE YACHTS

1. The *Drott*, built in 1877 and rebuilt in 1883 for the Swedish king, Oscar II
2. The British Royal yacht, *Victoria and Albert*, built in 1899
3. The Royal Danish yacht, *Dannebrog*, built in 1931
4. The motor yacht, *Vedette*, built at Copenhagen in 1924 for Fred W. Vanderbilt, New York
5. The *Stella Polaris*, for tourist cruises
6. The British Royal yacht, *Britannia*, built in 1954
7. The three-masted fore-and-aft schooner, *Sunbeam II*, built in 1929 for Lord Runciman; now a Swedish training ship under the name *Flying Clipper*, rigged as a topsail schooner

MODERN PLEASURE-BOATING

BY JANNE LUNDBLADH

Sailing for the pleasure of it is, as has been seen earlier, by no means something new. The first sailing club in the world was founded as early as 1720. It was The Water Club of the Harbour of Cork, in Ireland, renamed The Royal Cork Yacht Club in 1828.

Boating as a popular pastime (which it is today almost all over the world), is, however, a phenomenon of the 20th century, although pleasure-sailing had already begun to reach a wider public by the end of the 19th century. To a large extent Britain led the way in the spreading of pleasure-boating as a pastime for the man in the street, but already in the 1880s in the United States there were some very interesting exceptions to the rule that sailing for fun was an occupation for the royal and the rich.

One of these exceptions was the "sandbagger" of New York, Long Island, and New Jersey. It was a cheap, wide-beamed sailing machine with an enormous rigging, the weight of which was balanced by a ballast of sand in bags weighing from 50 to 100 pounds (25–50 kg). The crew of between 10 and 12 worked frenetically at shifting the sandbags from one side to the other, as the boat tacked.

The "Log Canoe" of Chesapeake Bay was another exception to the above rule. It was a popular craft with a narrow beam and large sails. Two of its crew of three had to act as counter-weights on the end of a movable plank that projected over the windward side. This counter-weight plank is still used on sailing canoes and dinghies, such as the English "Hornet". Modern types of the "Log Canoe" are still built.

According to early statistical figures, in 1904 there were 15,000 pleasure-boats in the United States, the world's leading boating country. At that time the number was slightly larger in Great Britain. At the beginning of the 1960s, the number of boats had risen to well over 8 million in the United States, with motorboats dominating. Today the figure is being doubled.

In Scandinavia, which has often been in the forefront when it comes to quality in pleasure-boat building, the number of boat owners has risen steadily. There are over 3,000 sailing boats built every year in Sweden, whose oldest sailing club, the Royal Swedish Sailing Society, was founded in 1830.

Most sailing boats made today are type-boats, which means that they are built in series without having to be identical in all details, or are one-design boats where all the boats have to be exactly the same. The one-design class, the "Starboat", was constructed three years before the outbreak of World War I, by the American Francis Sweisguth. The class was Olympic until 1972. In 1913 the Swedish "Stjärnbåten" was drawn by J. Jacobsson as a junior-boat for Gothenburg Royal Sailing Society (GKSS).

In the beginning of the century the dinghy for everyday use was re-shaped for massproduction and racing as a result of British and American ideas. It was soon accepted as a cheap pleasure-boat. In 1914 a clinker-built, loggert-rigged 12-foot dinghy with a centre-board was constructed. It was the first one-design dinghy to be internationally acknowledged, and it was sailed by twenty nations in the Amsterdam Olympics in 1928.

The first International Measuring-rule, or Rating Rule, which was intended to permit more efficient and fairer sailing competitions, was created in 1907, the same year as the International Yacht Racing Union was founded. After several revisions, the rule became the basis for the development of the many "R-boats" that were built between the wars. Local rating rules date as far back as the 1880s.

In 1929 the International "5-meter-rule" was created. It was intended to make way for cheaper sailing boats. The same intention led to the shaping of the "5.5 meter" class which was created twenty years later. Unfortunately the boats that were designed according to these rules did not turn out as cheap as intended, but they were extremely fast racers. The "5.5" was an Olympic class between 1952 (Helsinki) and 1968 (Mexico). In Kiel, in 1972, it was succeeded by the "Soling", designed by the Norwegian Jan H. Linge.

Modern dinghy-racing started in Britain in 1927 when a group of enthusiasts introduced the 14-foot dinghy. It had a two-layer moulded hull with a U- or V-shaped bottom and was thus one of the first really modern dinghy designs. The first dinghy, however, to fulfill the demand for one-design, a reasonable price and speed, and a construction simple enough for amateurs, was the "Snipe", designed in 1931 by the American William Crosby. It is today an international class consisting of over 20,000 boats. Another remarkable sailing dinghy is the "Finn-dinghy", which got its name after the Olympic Games where it made its first appearance, in Helsinki in 1952. It is one of Richard Sarby's designs.

The reasons for the immense popularity of sailing-dinghies the world over are not hard to find. Many of the boats can be built by amateurs and they are easy to transport and stow. They are not overwhelmingly expensive, and they are often suitable for beginners as well as for advanced racing-competitors. The more sophisticated dinghy-types have few equals as racing-machines. The world's largest one-design dinghy class was, in 1973, the American "Sunfish", a typical example of a boat for both sailing-practice and hard competition. Other well-known classes are the child-dinghy "Optimist", by Clark Mills of Florida, 1948, the junior-dinghy "Jolly Scott", designed by Peter Lawner, and van Essen's Olympic "Flying Dutchman" of 1951 and his "Flying Junior" of 1958.

In 1956 Knud Olsen designed a smaller "sister" to the Finn-dinghy. The new boat was intended for home-building in plywood and was called the "OK-Dinghy". Today it is sailed all over the world. The same applies to Christian Maury's French "420", drawn in 1959. Four fast racing machines are John Westell's "5-0-5" of 1954, Milne's "Fireball", designed in 1962, the Danish master-designer Paul Elfström's "Trapetz-dinghy" of 1965 and the American "Laser-dinghy" which was built by Bruce Kirby right before the Olympics 1972 as a simple one-design boat without unnecessary extra equipment. Three years after its introduction, over 22,000 "Lasers" were being sailed, all over the world.

Two important sailing boat classes have yet not been mentioned. The oldest one emanates from the drawing-board of the well-known Norwegian designer Johan Anker, as a result of an order placed by the GKSS of Sweden in 1928. The "Dragon" was from the beginning a cheap one-design boat, built for both family cruising and hard racing. In 1929 it could be bought for 3,000 Swedish Crowns (about £ 600 or $ 2,400 in today's money). After the "energy-crisis" in 1974 a fiberglass "Dragon" costs almost twenty times that amount. The class entered the Olympics in 1948 and continued as an Olympic boat until 1972. Unlike the "Dragon", the 6.7-meter "Tempest" is not meant for family sailing. It is designed by the famous British boat- and rigging-engineer, Ian Proctor, as an exclusive racing machine only for advanced competition. The "Tempest" first appeared as an Olympic class in the Mexico Games in 1968.

In 1941 the Swedish Sailing Association announced a competition, the aim of which was to produce a cheap and well-sailing cruising- and racing sailing boat. From the suggestions and drawings entered in the competition, Tord Sundén designed the "Nordic Folkboat", today widely spread throughout Europe, especially in Scandinavia, Germany, Holland and Switzerland. In 1967 Sundén designed a larger fiberglass version of the same boat, named the "International Folkboat" or "IF-boat", and in 1974 another, but larger, boat of the same family, the 9.5-meter family-cruiser the "Marieholm 32" left his drawingboard.

A name-combination, known to every reader of boating-magazines, is "Sparkman & Stevens". The magnificent designs of these two Americans have won prizes in most of the world's sail-racing arenas. Their boats are built not only in the United States, but also in Japan, Germany, Denmark (Sagitta 35), Sweden (IW 31), and Finland. In the latter country Nautor AB in Jacobstad builds the famous Swanboats, the first of which, the "Swan 43", was designed in New York in 1968. Another boat designer, whose name cannot be left out, is the Dutchman E.G. van der Stadt, the father of the famous "Stormvogel". Among his designs are such classes as "Varianta", "Splinter", "Harmony" and "Optima", the latter a fast family-cruiser designed in 1970.

The Frenchman Michel Dufour has produced some very interesting boat-designs with many unorthodox detail-solutions. "Arpège", "Safari", "Sylphe", and the 1974-construction "Dufour 34" are some of his boats. Well-known are also the large series of inexpensive "Hurley-boats" by another interesting designer, the Englishman Ian Anderson.

Other successful designers are the Canadian George Hinterhoeller, who in 1958 drew and built the first "Shark 24", today a very popular class, the Englishman Laurent Giles, father of among others the "Westerly Longbow", and the earlier mentioned Danish Olympic sailor Paul Elfström, who in 1975 built the first sailing boat with a bulb-bow.

Catamarans and trimarans today exist in large classes and great numbers. Catamaran-dinghies and other smaller multi-hull craft are being sailed in most boating countries. Bigger family- and cruising-craft are well represented only in the United States and Great Britain.

Of great importance for the development of the modern multi-hull craft have been the America's Cup boat designer Nathanael Herreshoff, the Russian Victor Tchetchet, and the English brothers Roland and Francis Prout from Essex. Nathanael Herreshoff designed and built six experimental catamarans in the 1870s, before he started to construct boats for the America's Cup. The first of his catamarans, *Amaryllis,* won an easy victory at New York Yacht Club's anniversary regatta in 1876.

Victor Tchetchet drew his first catamaran in Russia, and won the Spring Race of the Imperial Yacht Club in Kiev with it in 1908. The "obscure" craft was disqualified and the type was banned by the Russian Sailing Association. In 1945 Tchetchet, who had moved to the United States at the time of the Russian revolution, sailed the first trimaran in the western world. Two years later seven trimarans competed in the country. Today their number exceeds 200,000. The best-known classes are "Telstar 26" and the "Cross 42", which can be amateur-built.

The prototype of the "Shearwater-catamaran" was built by the Prout brothers in 1954. The following year the "Shearwater III" was on sale in Great Britain. It is now a racing class in more than ten countries.

Another Englishman, Rodney March, designed the "Tornado-catamaran" in 1967. His catamaran is probably the fastest serial-produced racing sailing boat in the world. It is sailed with a trapeze and has been logged in speeds exceeding 30 knots. The "Tornado" is the first multi-hull boat that has been approved as a racing class for the Olympic Games, where it started for the first time in 1976 together with the new dinghy "470", designed by the Frenchman André Corneau.

MODERN PLEASURE-BOATING

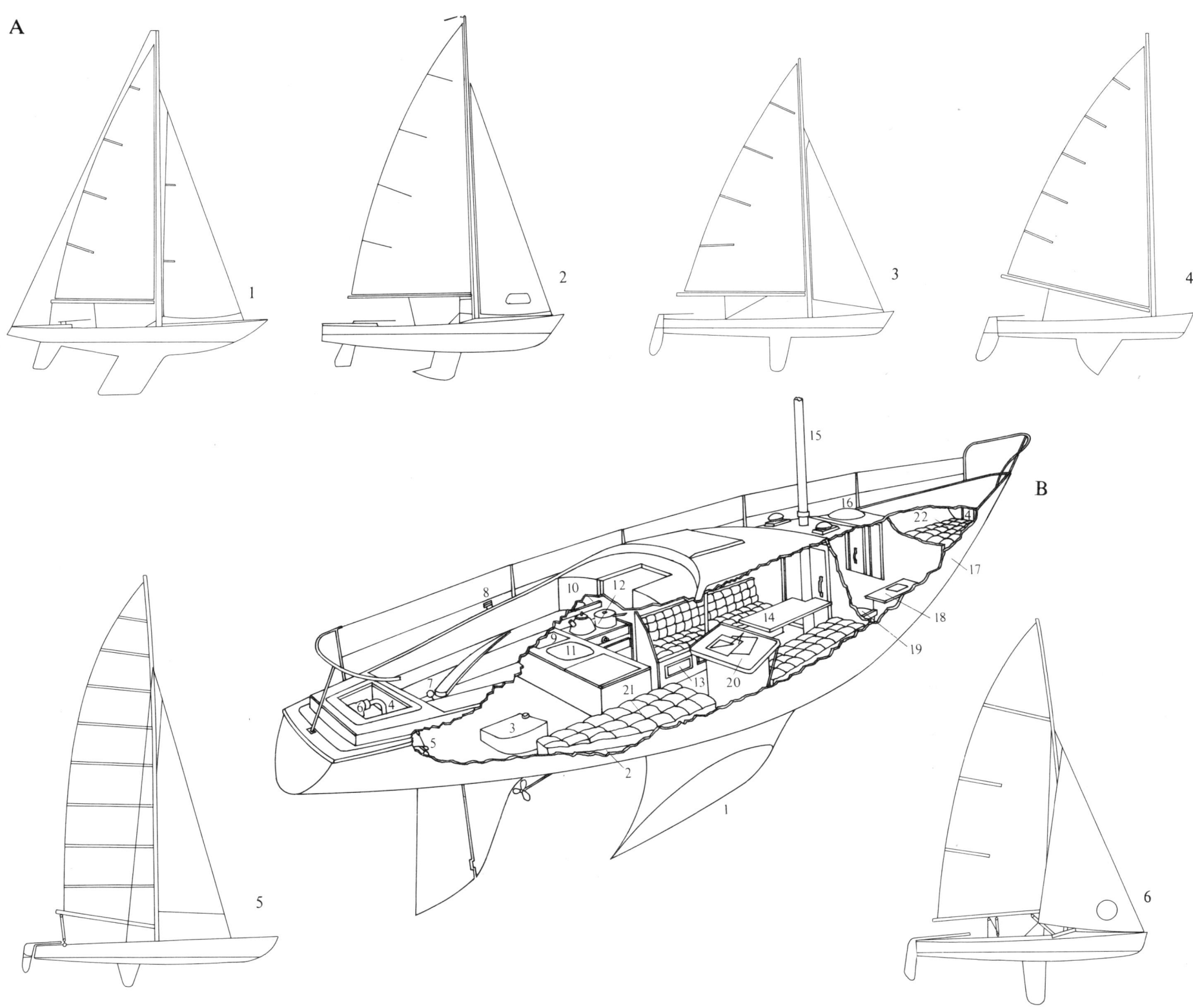

YACHT FITTINGS

A *The Olympic Classes (Year of debut)*
1 Soling (1972)
2 Tempest (1972)
3 Flying Dutchman (1960)
4 Finn-dinghy (1952)
5 Tornado-catamaran (1976)
6 470-dinghy (1976)

B *Cutaway through ocean-racing family cruiser. IW 31, designed by Sparkman & Stevens, built from fiberglass-strengthened plastic. Sail area 36 m², displacement 3.6 tons, length 9.3 m (30 ft), breadth 2.7 m (8.5 ft), draught 1.6 m (5.2 ft), five berths*
1 Fin keel
2 Motor
3 Fuel tank
4 Stowage space
5 Drainage pump
6 Diesel-powered heating unit
7 Motor control lever
8 Sheet-winch
9 Icebox
10 Plate-shelf
11 Washing-up bowl. Freshwater tap with foot-pump.
12 Galley with two-flame stove
13 Lockers beneath berths
14 Folding table
15 Mast
16 Fo'c'sle hatch with window
17 Water tank (150 liters, 33 gallons)
18 Movable washing-basin with foot pump
19 Marine-lavatory
20 Adjustable navigation-table
21 Berth projecting under cockpit
22 Fo'c'sle with two berths

191

SAILING YACHTS

MODERN SAILING YACHTS

1. Star
2. Snipe
3. Westerly Longbow
4. Tumlaren
5. Moth (British)
6. Moth (American)
7. International canoe
8. 8 ft. register class
9. 12 sq. m. class
10. 14 ft. dinghy
11. Flying Fifteen
12. 12 ft. class
13. Merlin/Rocket class
14. Firefly
15. Swallow
16. International 12-meter yacht *(Weatherly)*
17. International 6-meter yacht
18. Vega
19. Y W Cadet
20. Ketch
21. J.O.G.
22. Dufour 34
23. International 5.5-meter yacht
24. Yawl

192

SAILING YACHTS

A SELECTION OF ONE-DESIGN YACHTS

1. Blue Jay
2. Comet
3. Dyer Dhow
4. 5 O 5
5. Lightning
6. 420-dinghy
7. H-boat
8. Flying Junior
9. Minette
10. Triton
11. Sunfish
12. Folkboat
13. Laser-dinghy
14. Wood Pussy
15. Knarr
16. OK-dinghy
17. Pirate dinghy
18. 30 sq. m. Danish double-ender
19. Swedish double-ender (not one-design)
20. Korsar
21. Oslo-dinghy
22. 30 sq. m. skärgårdskryssare
23. Einheitselbjolle
24. Killingen
25. 7 m Sperrholzjollenkreuzer (plywood cruiser)
26. 6.5 KR-Seekreuzer (not one-design)

193

RACING

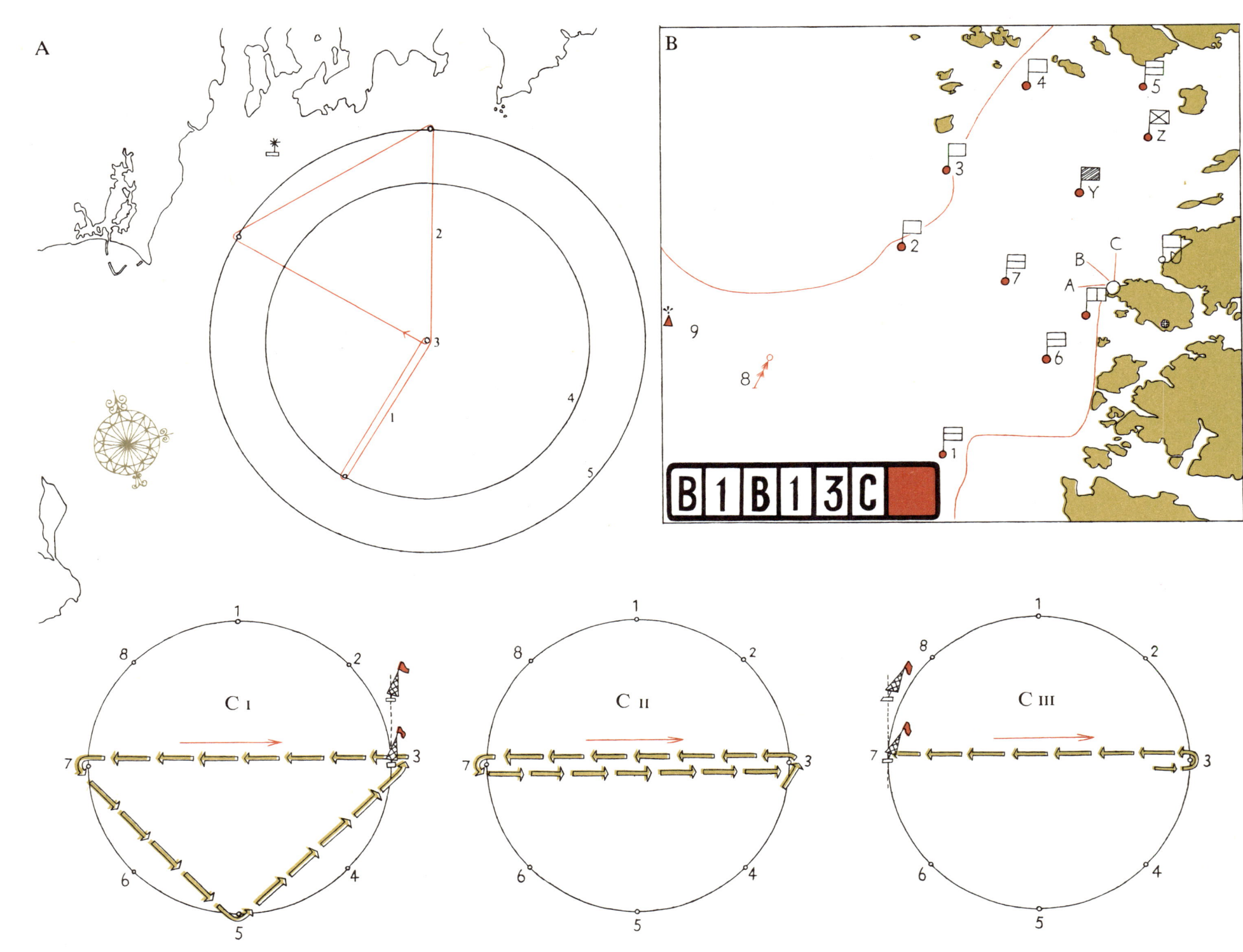

YACHT RACING

A *The course of the America's Cup*
1. First, this course is sailed windward and leeward twice
2. Then, the triangular course is sailed once
3. Start and finish. The direction of the wind is supposed to be southwest.
4. 6-mile circle
5. 8-mile circle

B *A common type of racing course*
A, B, or C is start- and finishing-line. 1—9 and U, Y, and Z are rounding buoys. The red lines give the boundary of the courses. The inset signboard with letters and figures is the courseboard, which is placed at the starting center. The signboard shows the following course: After the start over the B line the following buoys are to be rounded: 1, the buoy B of the starting line, 1 and 3, after which C is used for a finishing line. A red or blue field to the right indicates whether the buoys are to be taken on the port or on the starboard side of the boat. (This example shows the racing courses at Marstrand, Sweden.)

C *The courses of the Olympic Games*
At the Olympic Races 8 buoys are laid out in a circle with a radius of 1 nautical mile. In this arrangement the starting place and the rounding buoys may be varied, depending upon the direction of the wind. In the diagrams the wind blows from the west, so the boats start at buoy No. 3. At first, a triangular course is sailed, 3—7—5—3 (CI), and then a windward and leeward course, 3—7—3 (CII), and finally a windward course from 3 to the finish at 7 (CIII).

RACING

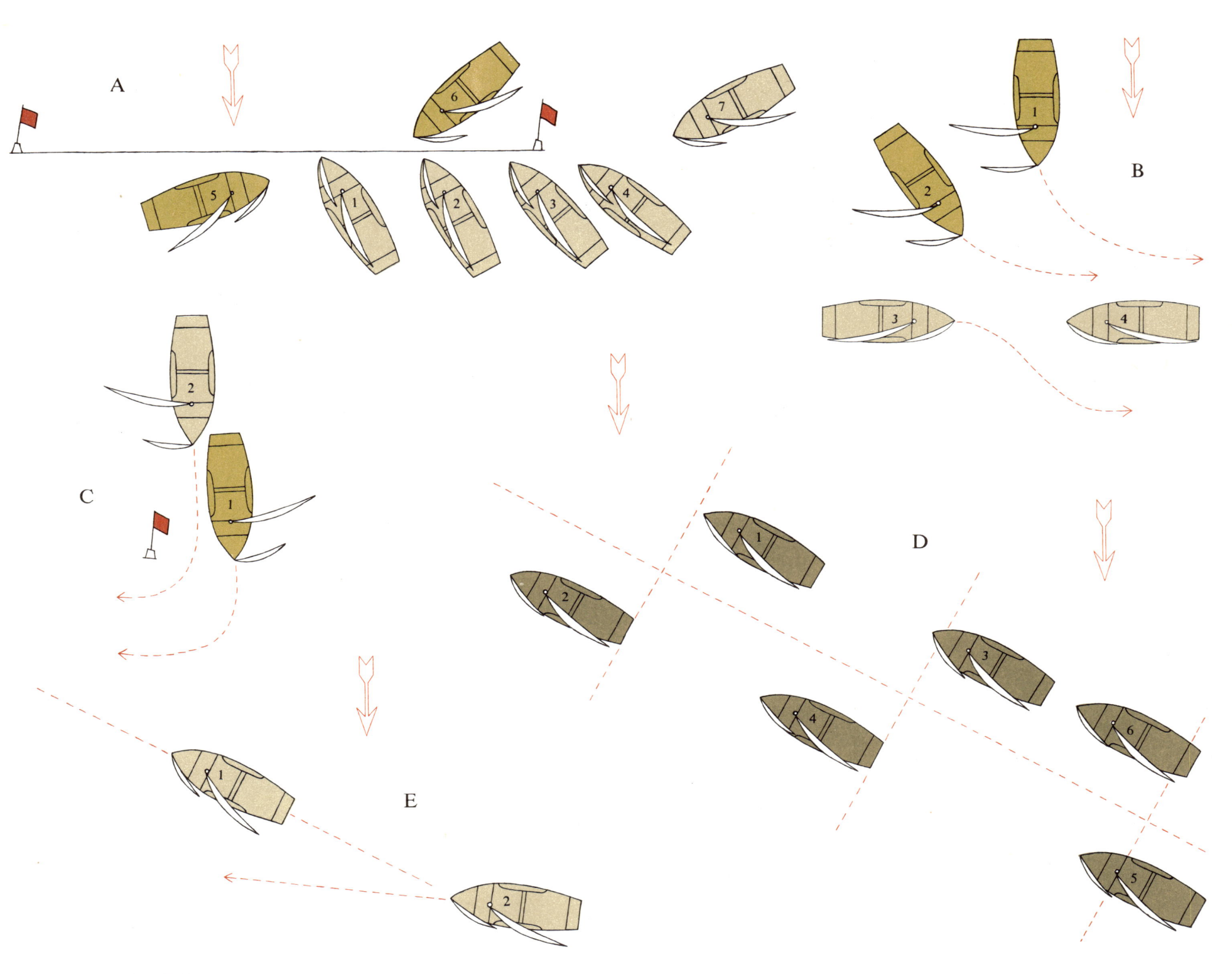

RULES OF YACHT RACING

A *Starting boat should lie on the wind or, when starting, in fair wind steering for the first buoy*

1, 2, and 3 are starting correctly
At the start 3 is allowed to force 4 outside the buoy (See C)
5 is sailing on the port tack and has to give way to 1, 2, 3, and 4
6 has to give way to the others
7. Not a permitted course at the start

B *If two boats are sailing on different tacks the one which has the wind on the port side has to give way to the other*
1, 2, and 3 should give way to 4

C *Exception from B*
When rounding a buoy 1 has to give way to 2, if the stem of the overtaking boat has passed athwart of the stern of the leading boat
Exception: at start (See A)

D *Some definitions*
1 is astern of 2
The stem of 3 has passed the athwartship line of the stern of 4 and 3 should give way to 4 except when they are rounding a buoy (See C) By hauling her wind, 4 is allowed to block 3's hawse. When the mast of 5 is abeam the helmsman of 6, 5 must not luff any more but should bear up (toward the buoy)

E *If the distance between the boats is less than 3 boat lengths 1 must not restrain 2 from trying to pass to leeward*

195

YACHT FITTINGS

YACHT FITTINGS AND DETAILS, CATAMARAN AND LJUNGSTRÖM YACHT

A *Catamaran of Cougar Class*
B *Yachting blocks of stainless steel*
C *Forged turnbuckle*
D *Flattop deck winch*
E *Windlass*
F *Light metal fitting on masthead for shrouds and spreader*
G *Elastic gasket with wood toggle*
H *Log register*
I *Yacht of the Ljungström type*
This type of boat often had a streamlined hull and a rotating mast without stays, around which the sails were rolled when they were taken in. The sail was double and had no boom. When the wind was right aft it was carried wing and wing, as shown in the diagram.
J *Rubber fender*
K *Yacht blocks of plastic laminate and stainless steel*
L *Steering gear of a big racing yacht*

YACHT FITTINGS

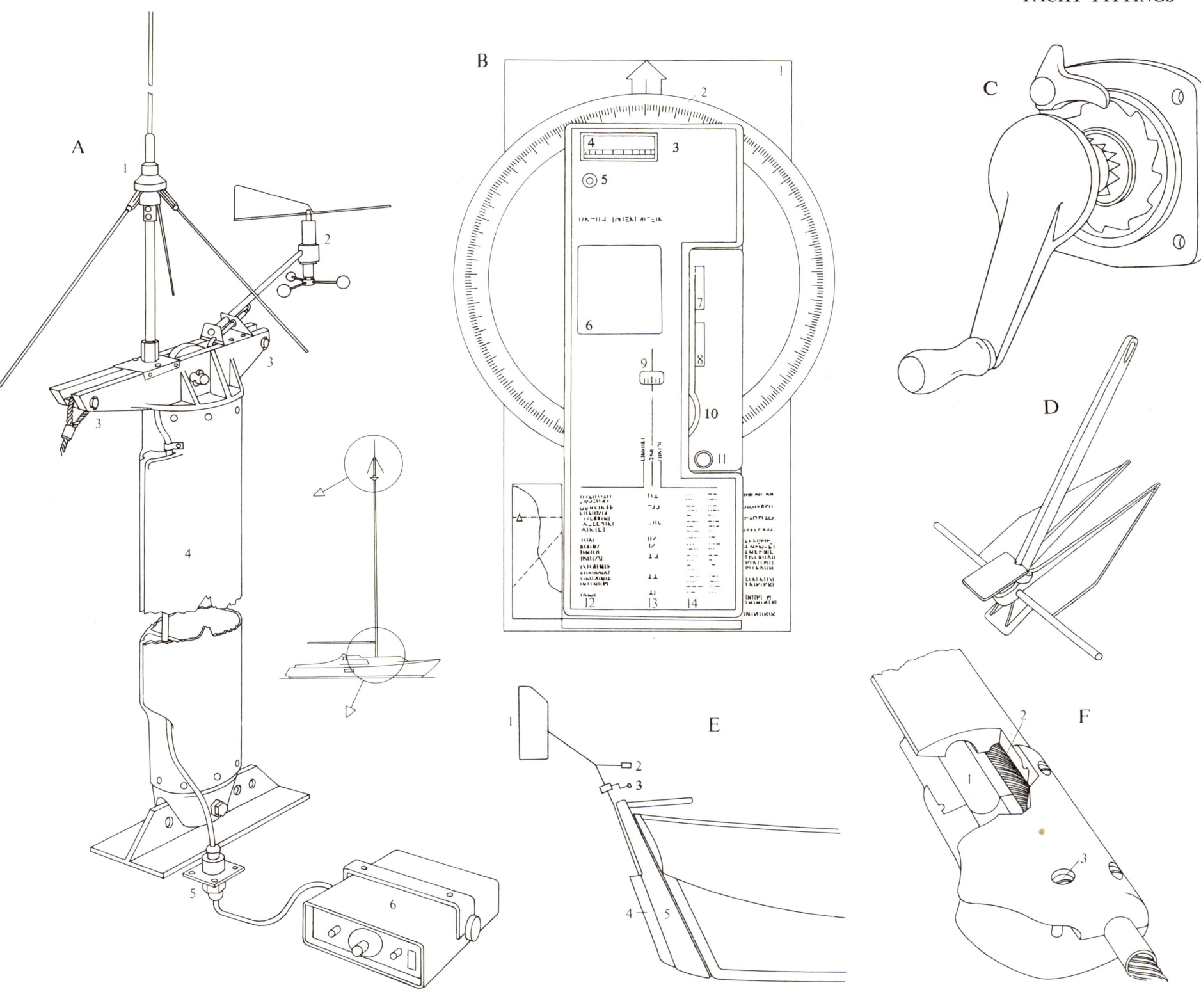

A *Masthead aerial for sailing boats*
1 Aerial with short aluminum antennas, protected by plastic covers
2 Anemometer
3 Masthead fitting
4 Aluminum mast
5 Deck contact
6 Radio unit

B *Battery powered electronic direction finder*
1 Base plate
2 Degree card
3 Receiver
4 Instrument for the measuring of signal strength
5 Earphone
6 Loudspeaker
7 Noise suppressor
8 Volume
9 K H Z-frequency scale
10 K H Z-frequency wheel
11 Battery check
12 Radio beacon
13 Radio beacon frequencies
14 Radio beacon morse signals

C *Halliard winch, as fitted on mast*

D *Danforth anchor*

E *Wind helm with trimming helm, the area of which is about 10% of that of the main rudder. The trimming helm is connected to the vane which influences the Flettner-rudder which in its turn acts on the main rudder.*
1 Vane
2 Counterweight
3 To-and-from lever
4 Main rudder
5 Flettner-rudder

F *Head-foil, which is mounted on the fore-stay. The fore-leech fits in a tunnel in the foil when the sail is set. The head-foil gives improved aerodynamic performance to the sail and allows the boat to come closer to the wind*
1 Luff tunnel
2 Fore-stay
3 Tensioning screw adjusts funnel to different sail-dimensions

CRUISING YACHT

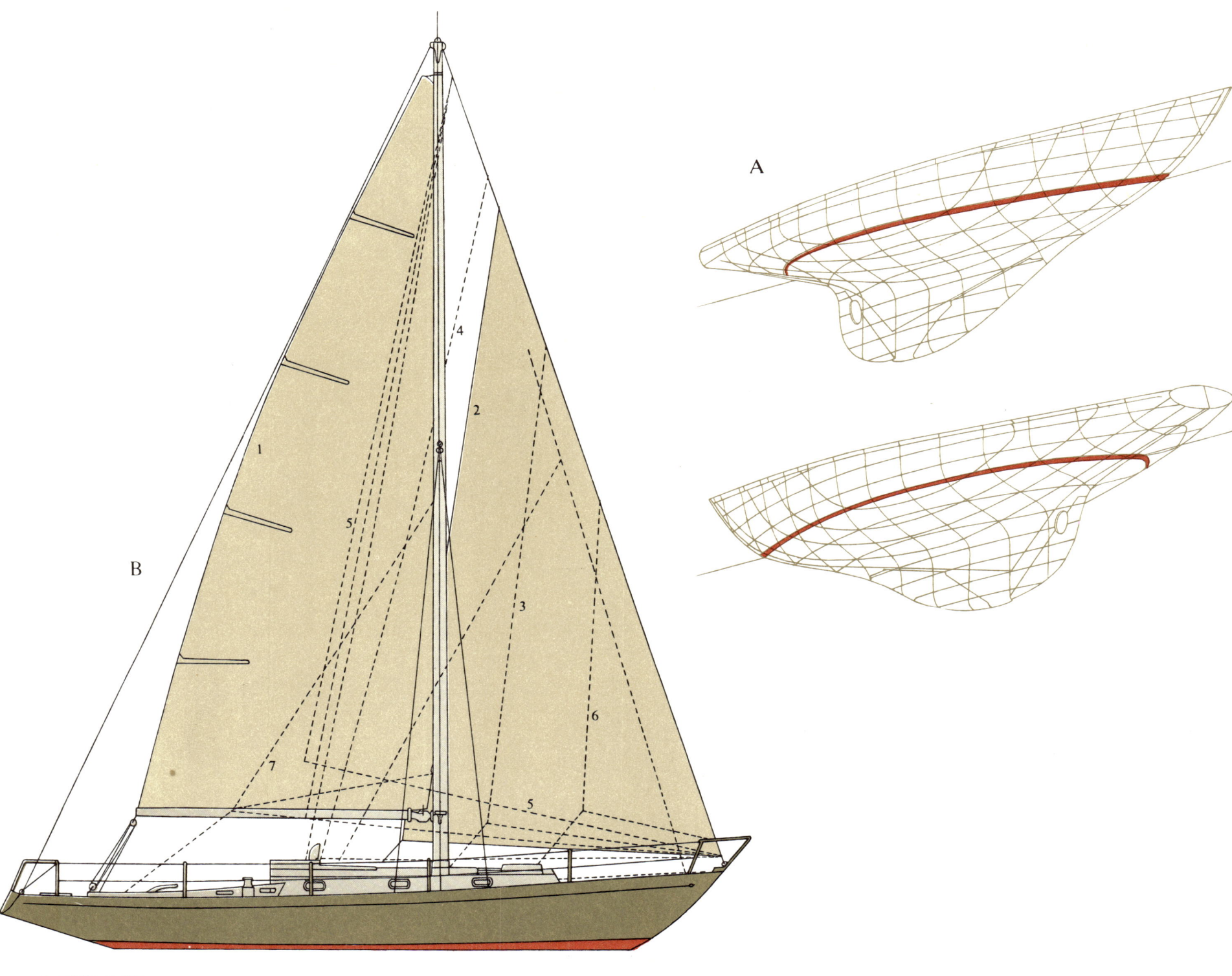

CRUISING YACHT

Cruising yacht designed by Sparkman & Stephens and built for a French owner, total length 40 ft., length on water line 29 ft., breadth 10 ft., draft 6½ ft., displacement 7.69 tons, lead keel 3.37 tons

A Perspective drawing of of hull as seen from below from the starboard bow and from the port quarter

B Sail plan, area of sails 533 square feet (according to international rules)

1 Main sail, 258 square feet
2 Jib No. 1, 237 square feet
3 Jib No. 2, 135 square feet
4 Genoa No. 1, 327 square feet
5 Genoa No. 2, 381 square feet
6 Storm staysail
7 Storm trysail

Engine, 25 hp at 4,800 r.p.m., 1.71:1 reduction gear

CRUISING YACHT

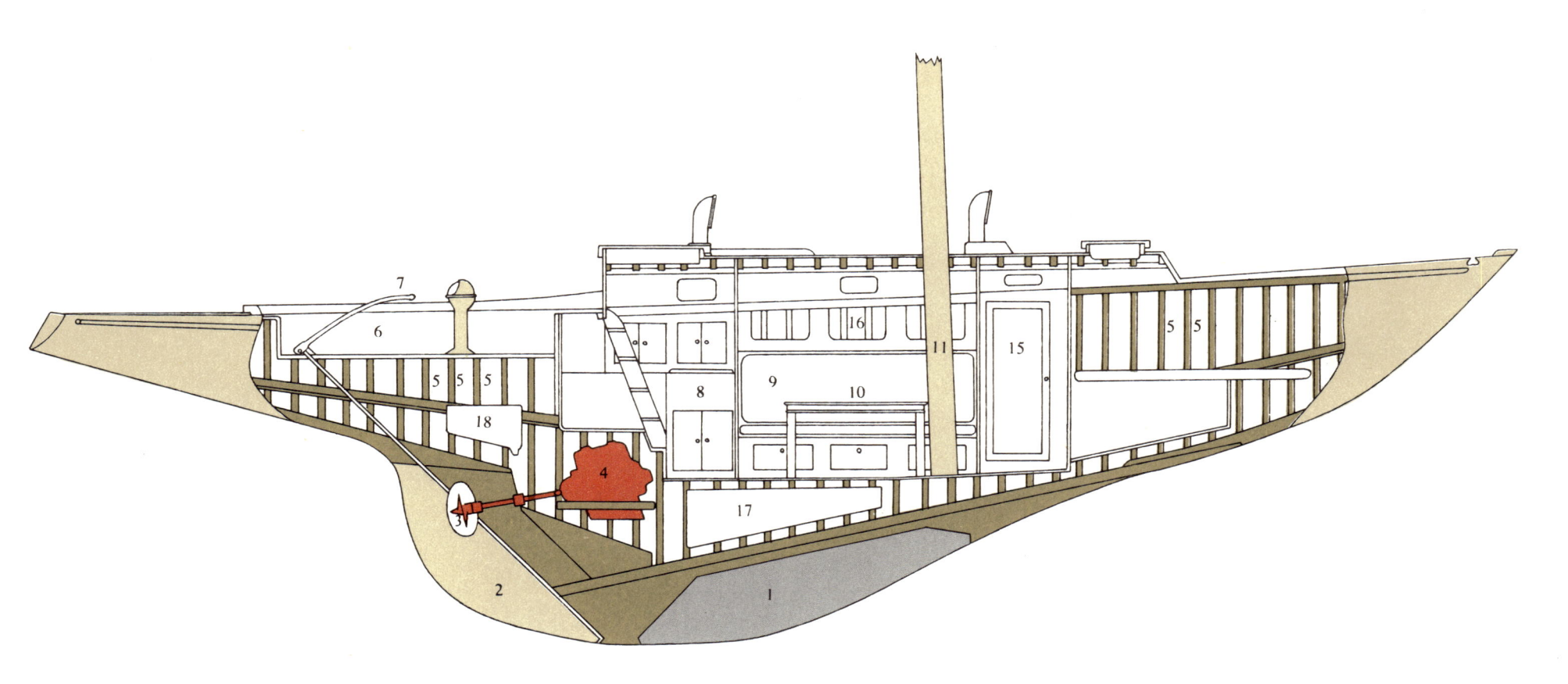

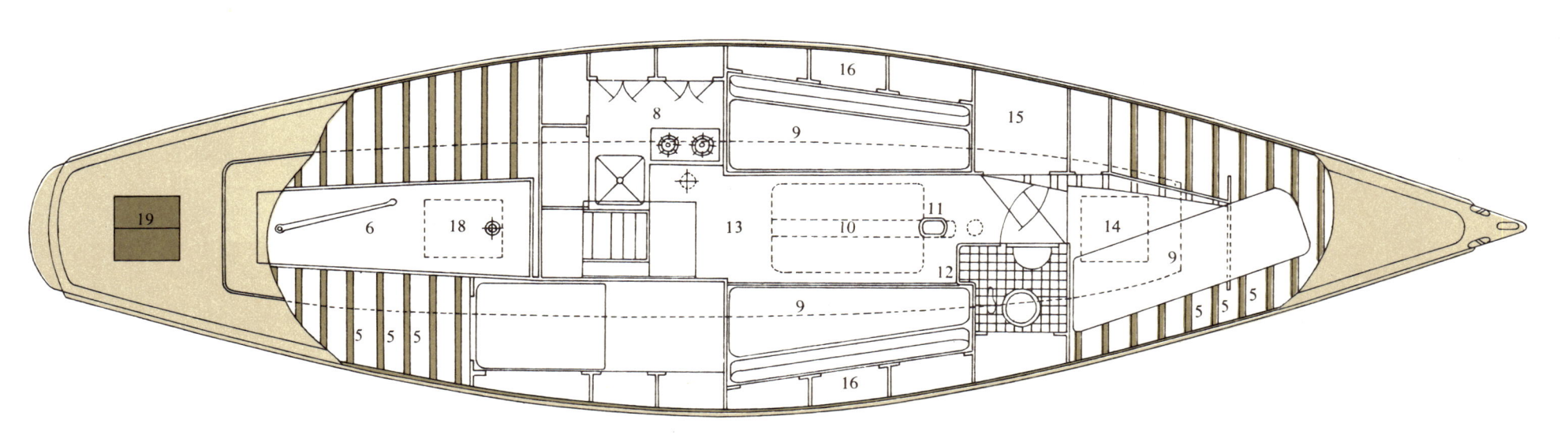

CRUISING YACHT

1 Lead keel
2 Rudder
3 Propeller
4 Engine
5 Frames
6 Cockpit with binnacle
7 Tiller
8 Galley
9 Berth
10 Table
11 Mast
12 Lavatory
13 Saloon
14 Fo'c'sle
15 Wardrobe
16 Lockers
17 Fresh water
18 Fuel
19 Hatch to sail locker

199

MOTORBOATS

MOTORBOAT TYPES

1. Small wooden boat with inboard motor
2. Undecked laminated fiberglass plastic boat
3. Small outboard fiberglass boat
4. Outboard fiberglass racing boat
5. Wooden cabin boat with outboard motor
6. 36 ft. motor cruiser
7. Fifty-fifty cruiser
8. 66 ft. motor cruiser
9. 25 ft. inboard cabin boat
10. 120 ft. motor cruiser
11. Sport fisherman
12. 30 ft. cruiser with two inboard motors
13. Outboard racer
14. 20 ft. plywood boat
15. Inboard racer
16. Houseboat

MOTORBOAT DETAILS

A *Outside view of modern outboard motor*

B *Inside view of outboard motor*
1. Starting wire
2. Flywheel
3. Crankcase
4. Cylinders
5. Spark plugs
6. Strut
7. Cooling pipe
8. Exhaust
9. Propeller shaft
10. Fin
11. Ahead pinion
12. Reverse pinion
13. Gear housing
14. Shaft
15. Reverse pawl
16. Angular setting
17. Securing clamps
18. Tiller

C *Safety ski flag* Approved by American Water Ski Association; signifies that the boat is pulling water skier

D *Inboard-outboard engine*

E *Depth-distance indicator* This indicator shows both soundings and horizontal distances

F *Radar for small craft*

G *Variable-pitch propeller*

H *Aerosol-powered foghorn*

A detail from an etching illustrating the battle on the Sound on October 29, 1658, appropriately introduces the chapter on gunnery. The etching was obtained from Histoire de Charles X by Pufendorf.

WARSHIPS AND GUNNERY

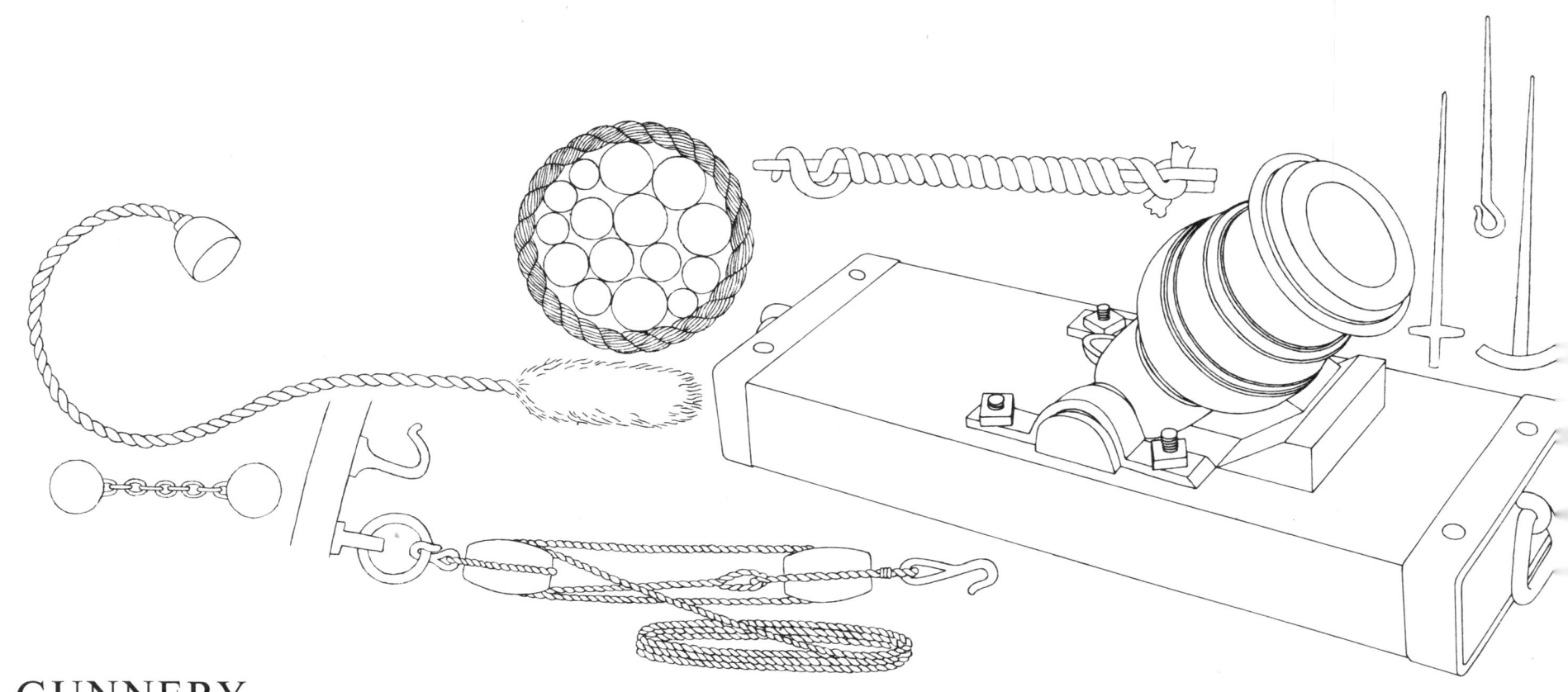

GUNNERY

BY ALAN W. H. PEARSALL

Sea warfare was at first carried on with the same weapons used on land: arrows, darts, javelins, swords, and lances; and the combatants wore the customary armor to protect themselves against their opponents' attacks. Sea warfare was largely fought by soldiers, who employed military methods and tactics.

From the 14th century onward the gun became the weapon most in use. Early guns were made of iron bars forged together and lashed by metal strapping. They were usually breech loaders, and were mounted on wooden fulcrums. They fired round stone shot. Such guns were used on the bows of galleys, and to some extent along the broadside of the newly developed North European fighting ship.

By the 16th century methods of manufacture had improved so that gun barrels could be cast in one piece; and from the 17th century the bore was hollowed out after casting. These guns were muzzle-loading, to give added strength; and, with more effective gunpowder, had a much greater range. In experienced hands, these guns could be fired almost once every minute. They fired solid round shot, usually made of iron, but other destructive types of ammunition were used as well. Still, the manufacture of such guns was not sufficiently precise for great accuracy of aim. These guns were the chief armament of ships for nearly three hundred years. They used a carriage of two vertical brackets connected by suitable crosspieces, the whole mounted on four wheels. Many such guns, like the classic cannon, survived into the next era. They were then primarily used as broadside guns.

Special types of ordnance were used for particular purposes. Short guns, called mortars, fired at an elevation of about forty-five degrees. They threw shells into towns or ports and were fitted on especially protected ships. These shells were hollow round shot, filled with powder and fired by a time fuse. Howitzers fired shells, too, but from ordinary carriages at a lower elevation. About 1779 carronades were introduced. These were cannon which had a short barrel, thus lightening the weight of the artillery while allowing heavy shot to be fired. However, this was accomplished at the expense of length of range. Small swivel guns were also used to fire at an enemy's decks; these guns had a stock and butt like a musket, and pivoted on a swivel fitted into sockets in the bulwarks.

The 19th century brought revolutionary developments in arms at sea. Smooth-bore guns were increasingly used for firing shells and, with an increase in the size of guns, came the introduction of armored ships. Thus began a long race between gun and armor. Rifling was the first of these important changes. With its aid, accuracy increased and a more thorough use of the propulsive power of powder was made. To get the most out of both accuracy and power breech-loading was adopted, so that longer barrels, which were built up of coils, and a very tight fit of the projectile in the barrel were possible. Various types of breech were tried, and despite some difficulties, breech-loading guns were in use by all navies by 1880.

Gun carriages showed parallel developments. The old wooden type gave way to a pivot-slide carriage, and this was now made of iron to take the weight of increasingly larger guns. But the carriages were cumbersome, and a suitable substitute had to be found. This was the turret and its variants, by which guns were mounted inside an armored structure which turned on ball bearings. Such mountings revolutionized the design of ships, which had already begun a period of transformation with the introduction of armor and the increasing size of guns. The larger guns led naturally to a reduction in the number of guns needed. These same factors made it necessary for designers to use machinery for elevating, training, and loading the guns.

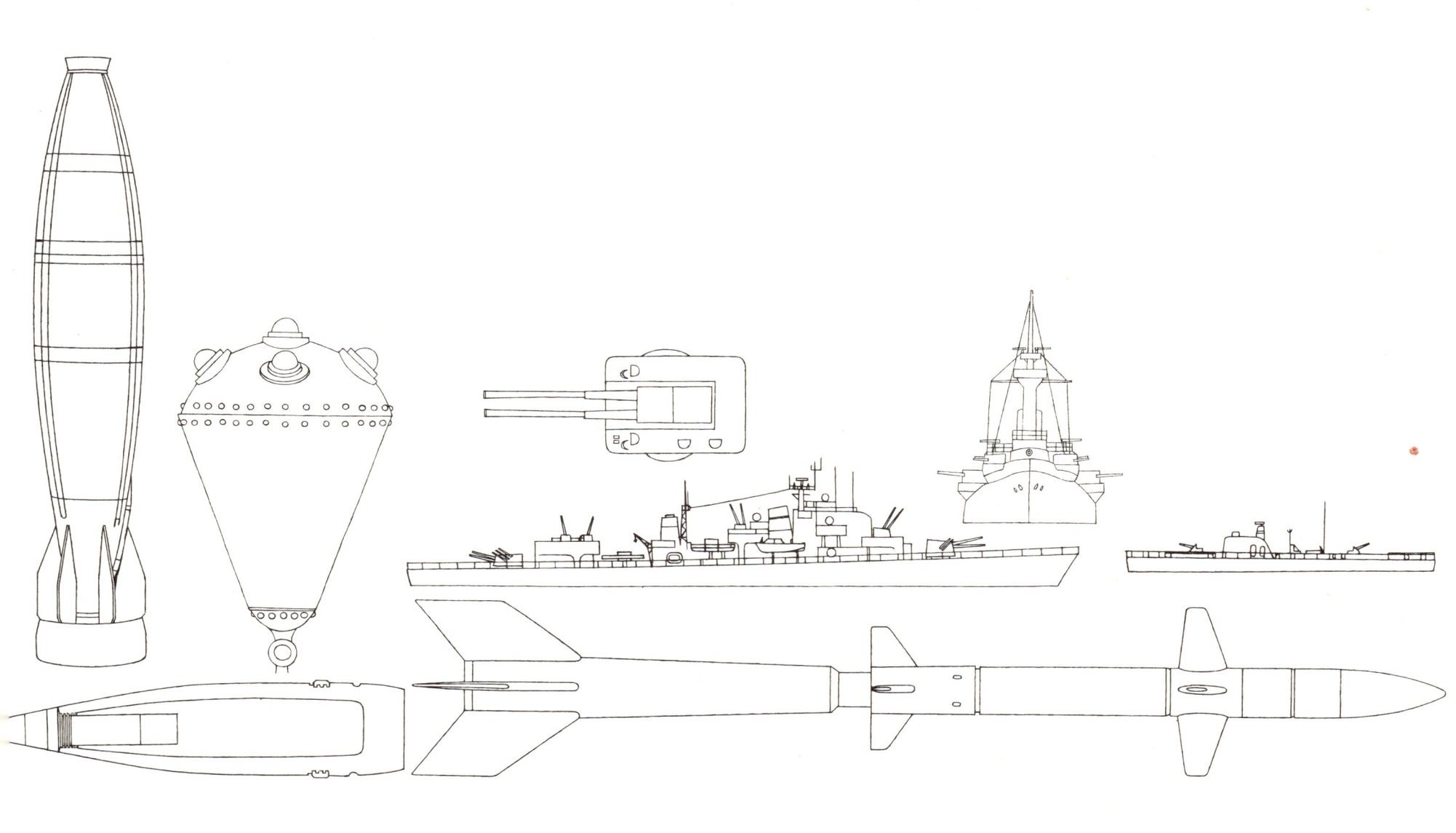

At the end of the 19th century, there was a trend toward the use of small rapid-firing guns. This kind of gun used a cartridge which contained an explosive charge and the projectile to be fired, both in a brass case. Previously, the charge of powder in a silk bag had been loaded separately from the shot. Also in this period many types of machine gun appeared, such as the Nordenfeldt, Gardner, Gatling, and Maxim. Many of these pieces had several barrels.

Projectiles changed enormously. Round shot was replaced by long cylindrical shells with pointed noses. The explosive power of these shells was vastly greater in destructive force; some were made with re-inforced noses so as to pierce armor, others contained bullets for use against personnel, and the fuses by which they were exploded became more complicated.

The introduction of improvements in powder brought important changes, one being a smokeless powder which kept the battle area fairly clear.

The war of 1914—1918 represented the culmination of this era. From this time on, the gun was the center of a system, as all its artillery functions were worked by mechanical means; the individual gun was now directed by increasingly complex fire-control systems. Further improvements were made in the construction and mechanism of the modern gun so that it had a vastly greater accuracy.

Other important branches of armament were carried in ships. In the 18th century carcasses, or floating explosive charges, were sometimes used, as were also fire and explosion ships. In the early 19th century rockets were first employed in this more brutal kind of warfare. Mines, then called torpedoes, were used in the American Civil War and subsequently refined in various ways, some being controlled from shore, others depending on contact with or later still a mere proximity to a ship. The actuating machinery of these mines varied. A crude form of the torpedo proper was also used in the American Civil War. Various other types were subsequently tried, such as towing and spar torpedoes. However, the invention of the locomotive torpedo, which gave greater range and caused less danger to the attacker, rapidly gained predominance. It was also developed so as to increase its speed, range, and accuracy, and with a variety of firing mechanisms so that modern torpedoes are able to "home" on their target.

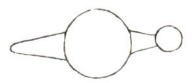

205

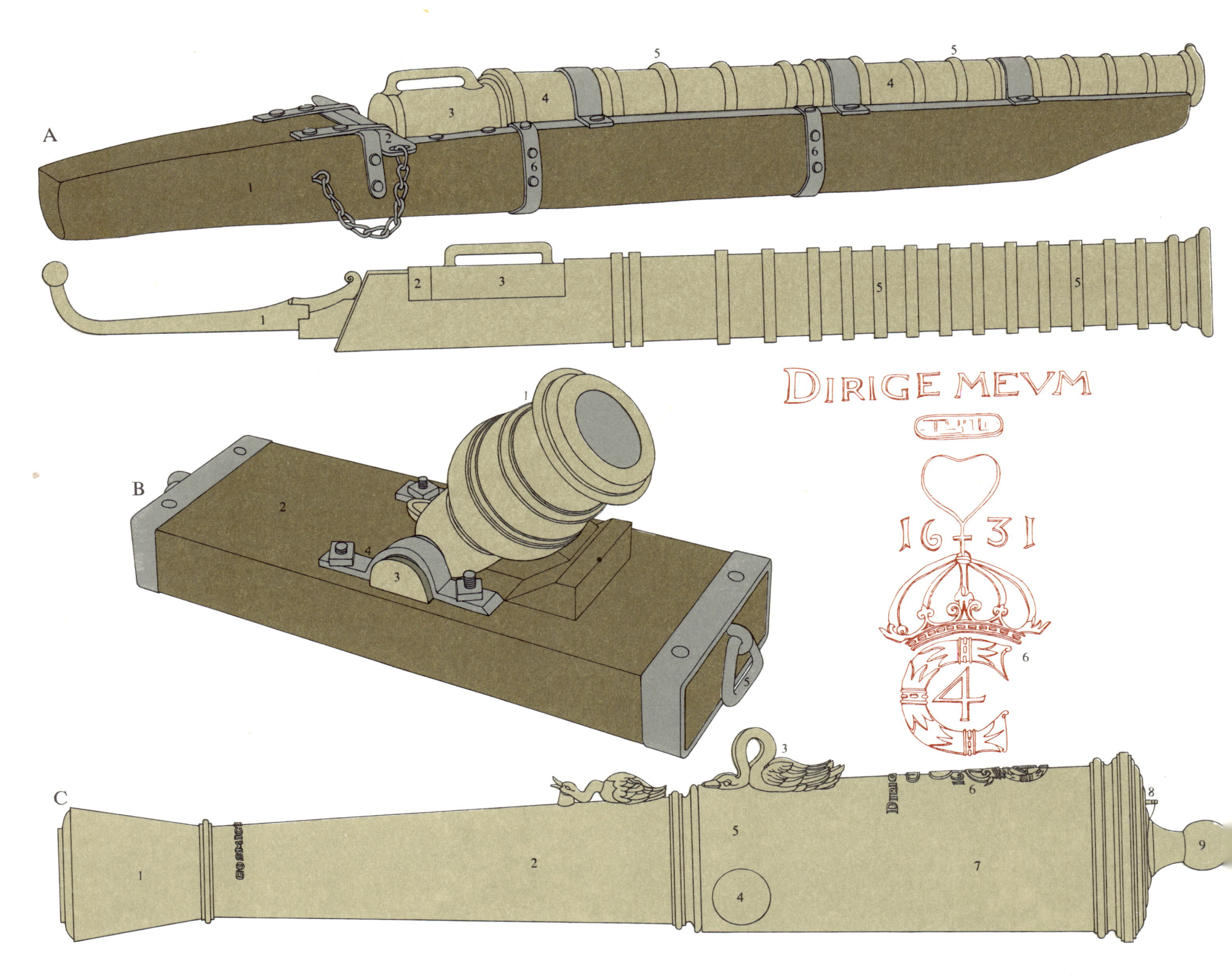

OLD GUNS

A *Guns from the 15th century*
1. Stock
2. Lock wedge
3. Chambered breech block
4. Barrel
5. Iron hoops
6. Bands

B *64-pounder mortar*
1. Mortar
2. Wooden bed
3. Trunnion
4. Trunnion keeper
5. Hoisting and lashing ringbolt

C *Danish 24-pounder bronze gun cast in 1631*
1. Muzzle swell
2. Chase
3. Dolphin
4. Trunnion
5. Second reinforce
6. The crowned monogram of King Christian IV of Denmark
7. First reinforce
8. Touch-hole
9. Cascabel

OLD GUN

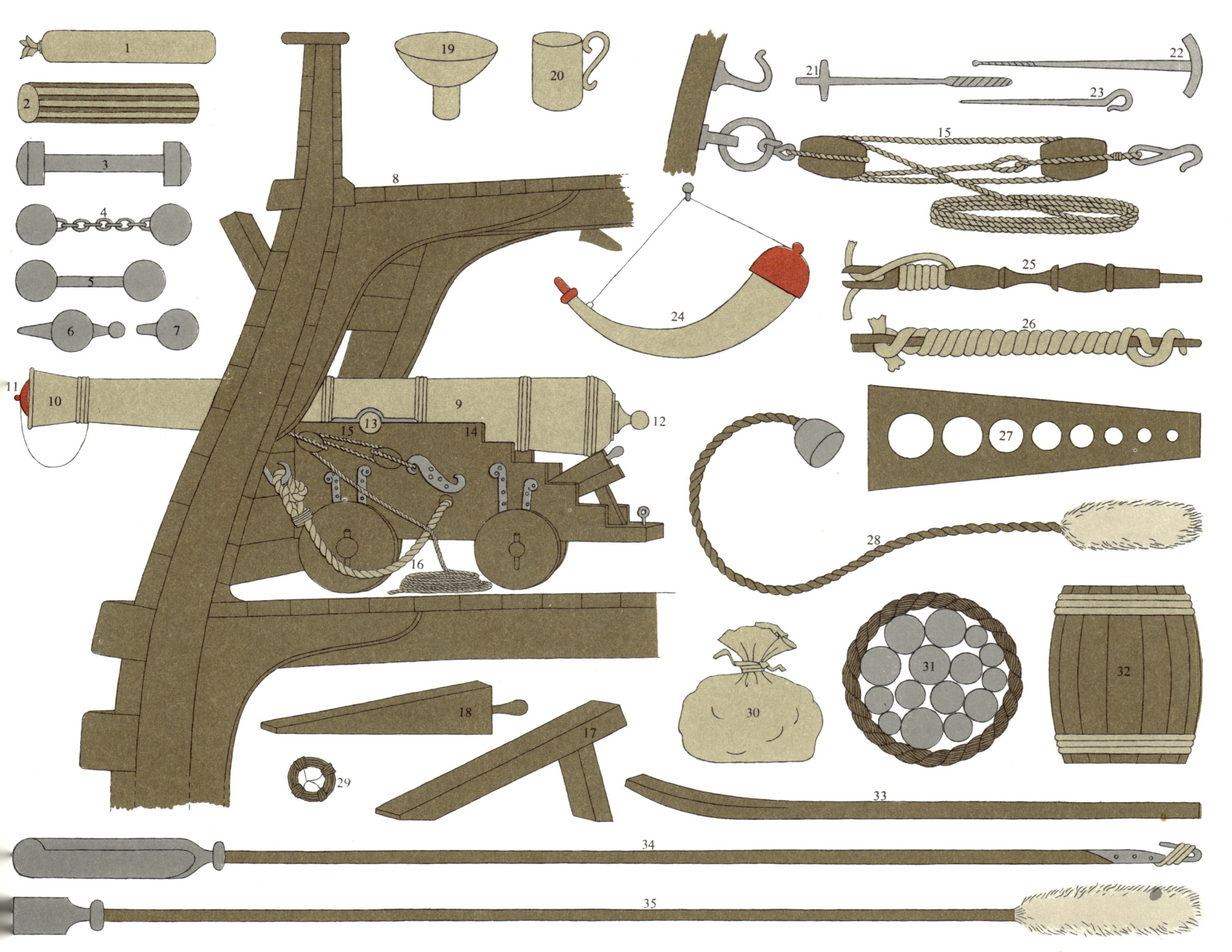

GUN WITH ACCESSORIES, 1691 (FROM Å.C. RÅLAMB)

1 Cartridge	5 Bar-shot	11 Tompion	18 Quoin	24 Powder horn	30 Musket ball bag
2 Case-shot	6 Peak shot	12 Cascabel	19 Funnel	25 Lint stock	31 Shot grommet
3 Bar-shot	7 Hand grenade	13 Trunnions	20 Powder measure	26 Lint stock of iron	32 Powder keg
4 Chain-shot	8 Section of ship's side	14 Gun carriage	21 Vent bit	27 Shot gauge	33 Hand spike
	9 Gun	15 Train tackles	22 Vent auger	28 Rammer and sponge	34 Gun ladle
	10 Muzzle	16 Breeching	23 Priming wire, reamer	29 Fire grommet	35 Rammer and sponge
		17 Bed			

207

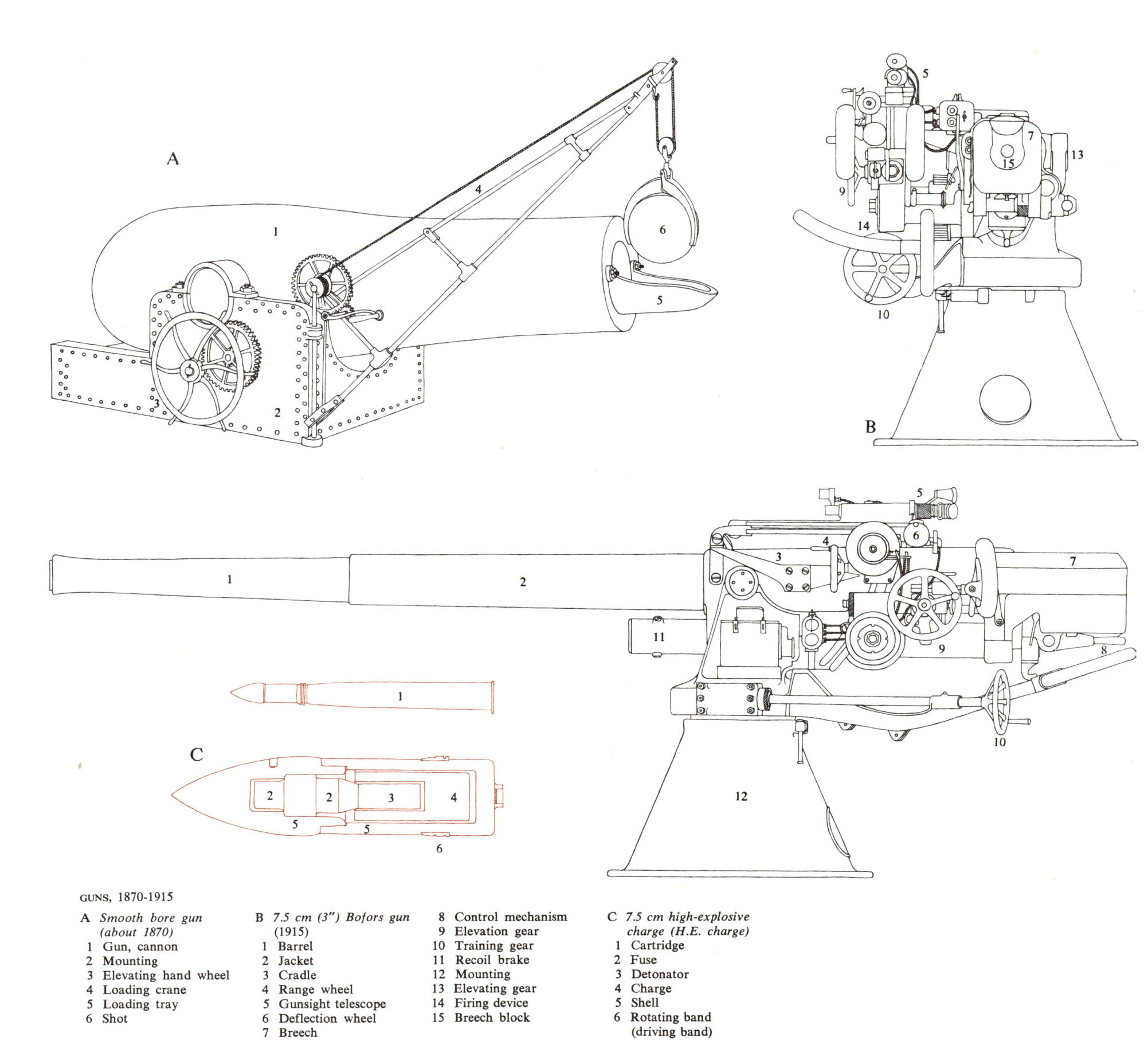

OLD GUNS

GUNS, 1870-1915

A *Smooth bore gun (about 1870)*
1. Gun, cannon
2. Mounting
3. Elevating hand wheel
4. Loading crane
5. Loading tray
6. Shot

B *7.5 cm (3") Bofors gun (1915)*
1. Barrel
2. Jacket
3. Cradle
4. Range wheel
5. Gunsight telescope
6. Deflection wheel
7. Breech
8. Control mechanism
9. Elevation gear
10. Training gear
11. Recoil brake
12. Mounting
13. Elevating gear
14. Firing device
15. Breech block

C *7.5 cm high-explosive charge (H.E. charge)*
1. Cartridge
2. Fuse
3. Detonator
4. Charge
5. Shell
6. Rotating band (driving band)

AUTOMATIC GUN

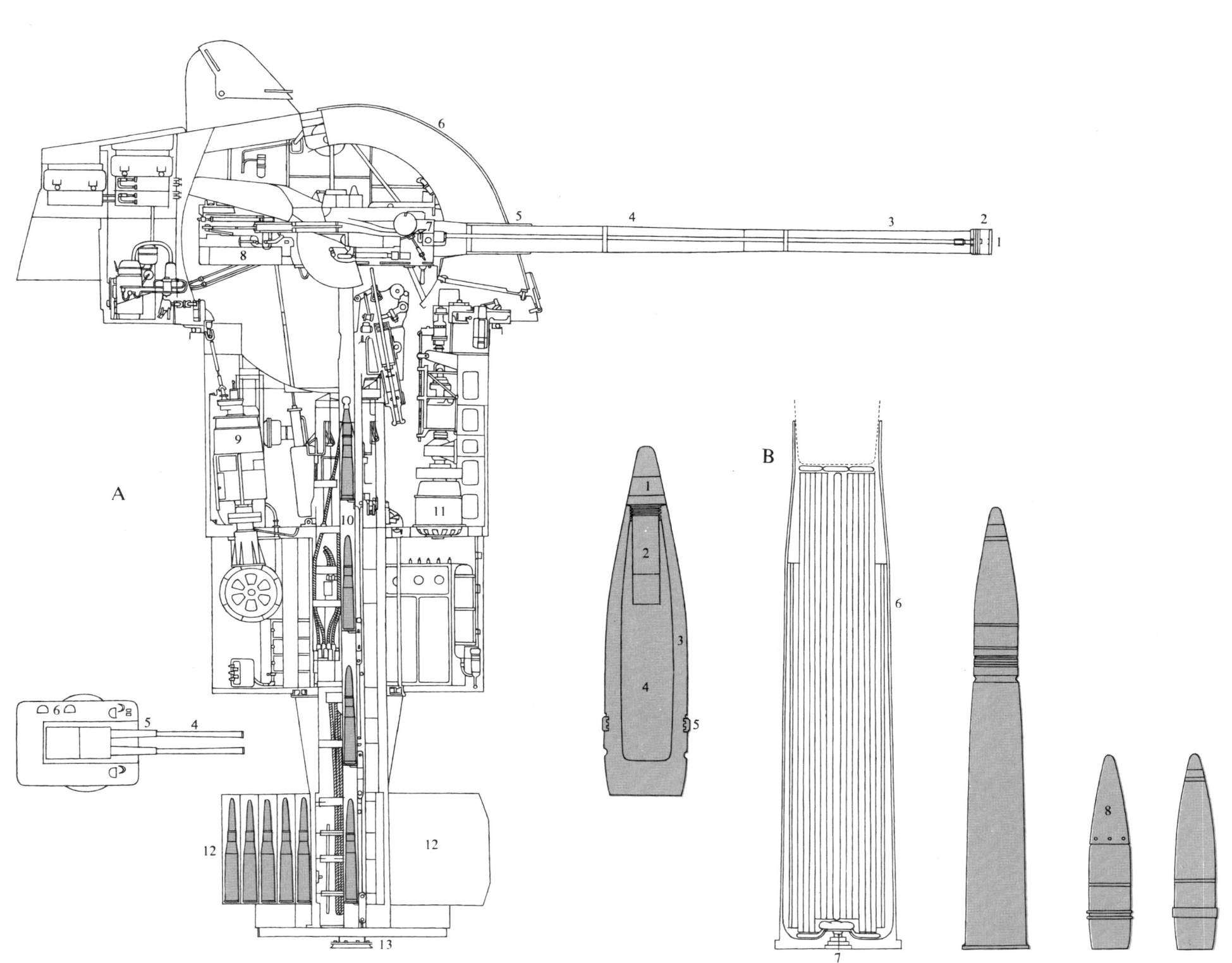

A *Automatic gun in twin mounting* (12 cm)
1. Axis of bore
2. Muzzle
3. Barrel
4. Twin guns
5. Cradle
6. Turret
7. Breech
8. Recoil brake
9. Ammunition hoist motor
10. Ammunition hoist
11. Training motor
12. Magazine
13. Pivot

B *Ammunition*
1. Nose fuse
2. Detonator
3. Shell
4. Charge
5. Rotating band (driving band)
6. Propellant charge
7. Primer
8. Ballistic cap

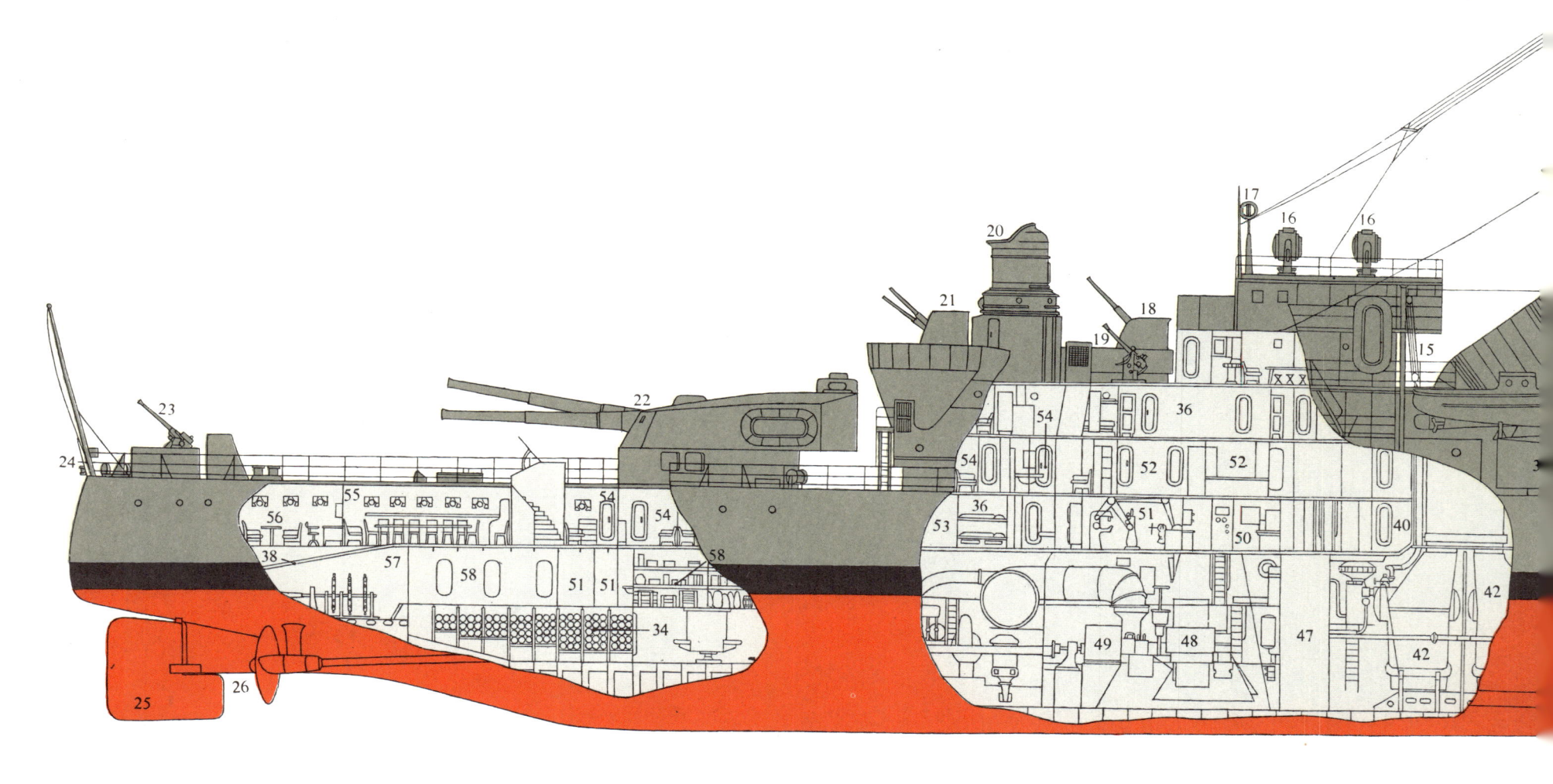

COAST DEFENCE SHIP

210

COAST DEFENCE SHIP

COAST DEFENCE SHIP, 1922

Swedish coast defense battleship Gustaf V, displacement, 7275 tons, from a drawing by Gösta Kaudern in Svenska Flottans Historia

1. Forecastle deck
2. Windlass
3. Twin gun turret (11 inches)
4. Rangefinder
5. Anti-aircraft gun
6. Pilot bridge
7. Rangefinder
8. Conning tower (pilot turret)
9. Rangefinder
10. Signal bridge
11. Director control tower with rangefinder
12. Radio antenna
13. Stack
14. Motorboat
15. Boat davits
16. Searchlight
17. Radio direction finder
18. 75 mm anti-aircraft gun
19. 20 mm anti-aircraft gun
20. Director control tower for anti-aircraft gun
21. 75 mm anti-aircraft gun
22. Twin gun turret (11 inches)
23. 40 mm anti-aircraft gun
24. Smoke screen maker
25. Rudder
26. Propeller
27. Bilge keel
28. Paravane holder
29. Icebreaking stem
30. 6 inch guns
31. Ammunition hoist
32. Barbette
33. Shell magazine
34. Powder magazine
35. Combat information center
36. Crew's quarters
37. Warrant officers' accommodation
38. Protective deck
39. Chain locker
40. Washroom
41. Pilot room
42. Boiler
43. Galley
44. Sick bay
45. Magazine
46. Generator
47. Coal bunker
48. Turbine
49. Reduction gearing
50. Radio office
51. Workroom
52. Operating rooms
53. Engineer's office
54. Officers' quarters
55. Wardroom
56. Cabin for the Admiral of the Fleet
57. Hand-steering room
58. Storerooms

ANTI-AIRCRAFT GUN

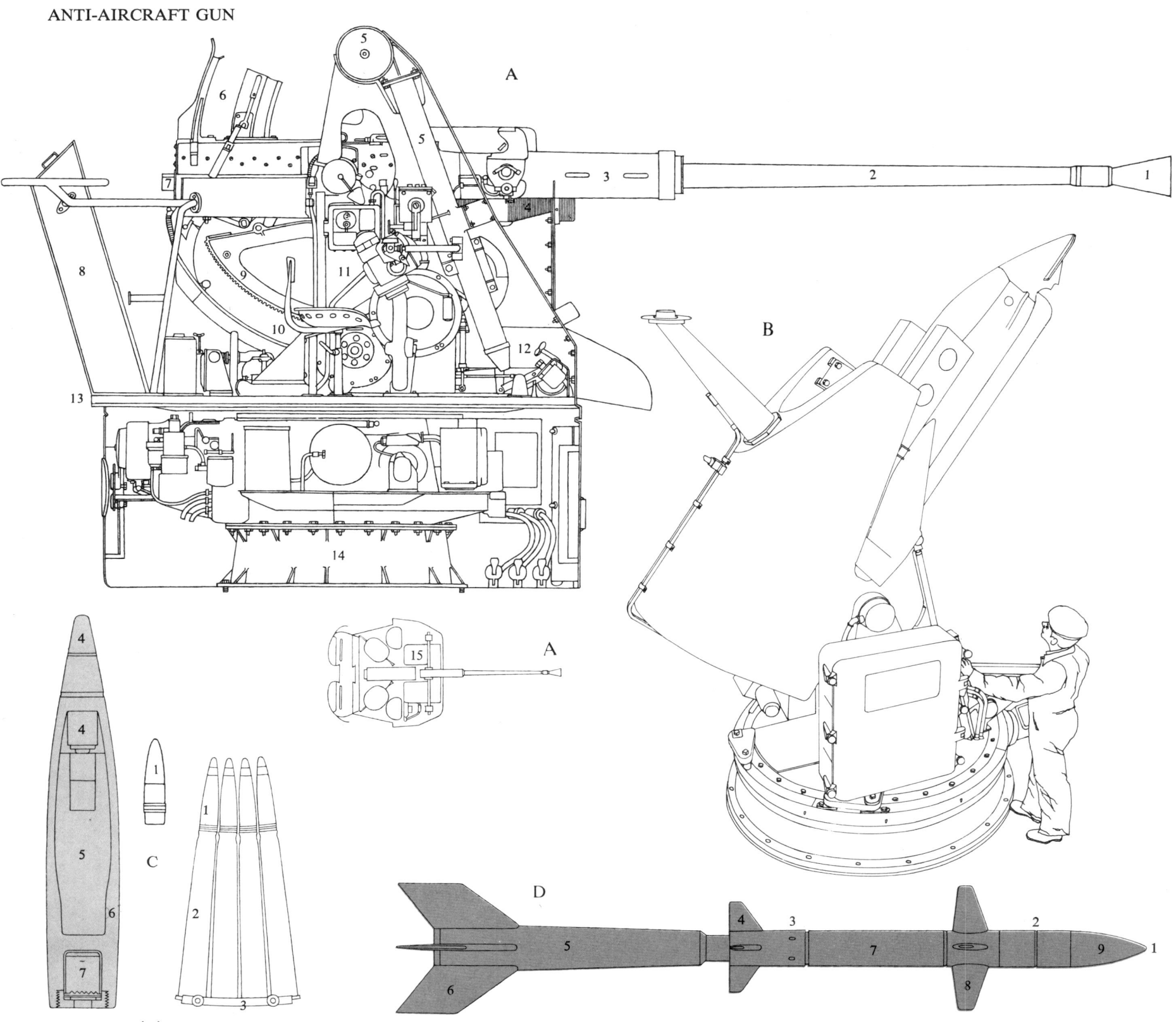

ANTI-AIRCRAFT (AA) GUN AND MISSILE

A *Anti-aircraft gun (Automatic)*
 (Bofors 40 mm mod/48)
1. Flash reducer
2. Barrel
3. Cradle
4. Recoil brake
5. Gun balancing gear
6. Automatic loader
7. Rammer
8. Magazine
9. Elevating arc
10. Seat
11. Training and elevation gear
12. Firing device
13. Platform
14. Mounting
15. Shield

B *Long range missile on launching platform*

C *Anti-aircraft ammunition*
1. Projectile
2. Cartridge case, cartridge
1+2 Round (complete)
3. Loading clips
4. Percussion fuse, nose fuse
5. Charge
6. Shell
7. Flare

D *Guided Missile*
1. Proximity fuse
2-3. Guidance and control sections
4. Missile tail fins
5. Booster
6. Booster fins
7. Sustainer motor with container for fuel
8. Missile wings
9. Warhead

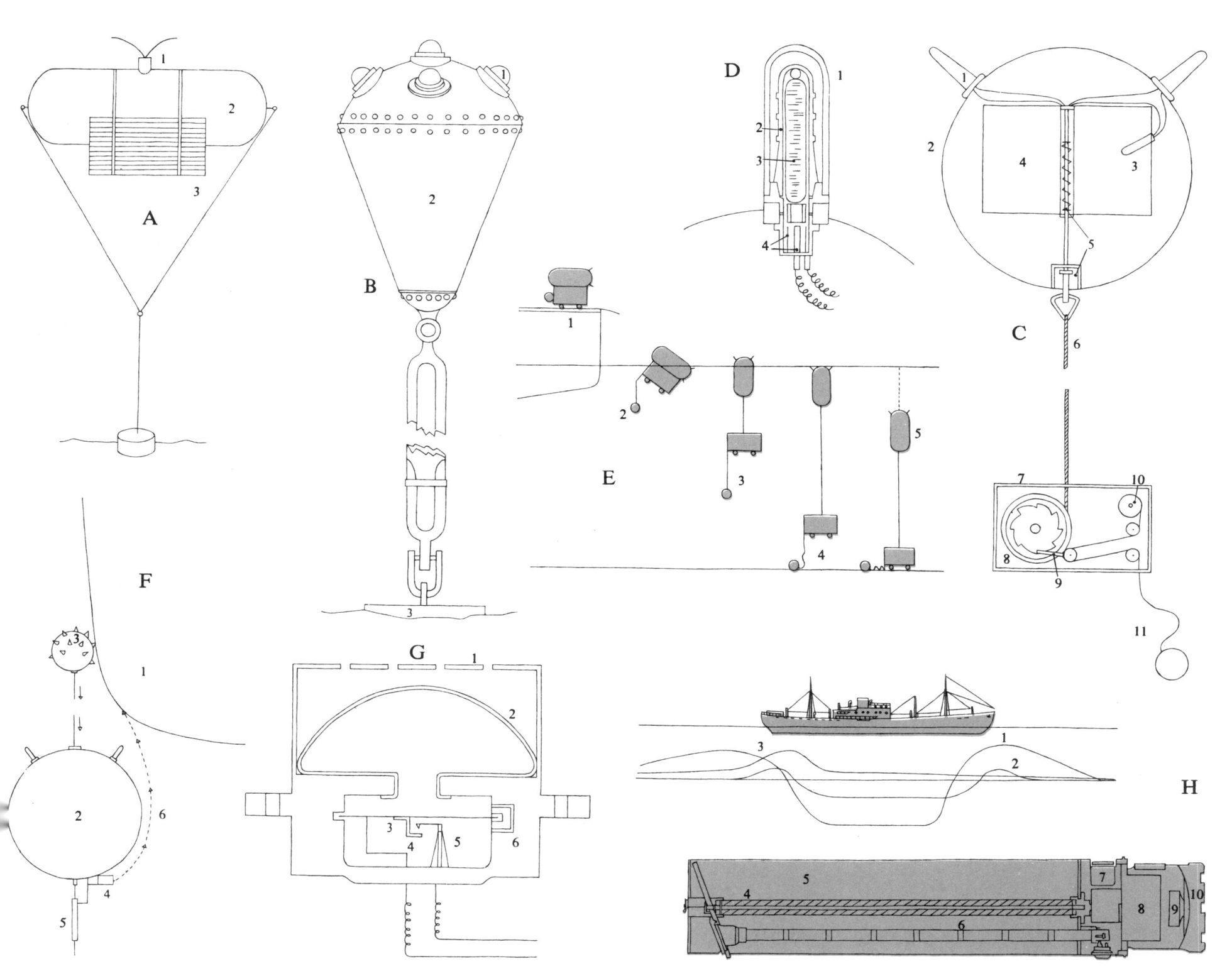

MINES

A *Fulton's mine, the first moored mine*
1. Mechanical firing mechanism
2. Charge container
3. Wooden box

B *Mechanical mine* (about 1830)
1. Contact horn or button
2. Shell of mine
3. Anchor

C *Modern noncontrolled set-depth contact mine*
1. Mine horn
2. Shell of mine
3. Primer
4. Charge
5. Automatic disposal arrangement
6. Mooring cable (rope)
7. Anchor
8. Mooring cable drum
9. Pawling mechanism
10. Plummet wire drum
11. Plummet wire and plummet

D *Herz horn*
1. Horn cover
2. Lead horn
3. Electrolyte container
4. Electrodes

E *Depth-setting arrangement*
1. Mine before laying
2. Plummet falling
3. Length of plummet wire = set depth
4. Plummet bottoms, pawling locks cable drum
5. Moored mine

F *Antenna mine*
1. Ship's hull
2. Mine
3. Antenna buoy with copper points
4. Electrode
5. Lower antenna
6. Sea water acting as electrolyte

G *Pressure mine ("Oyster" mine), firing device*
1. Casing
2. Rubber bag
3. Diaphragm
4. Diaphragm contact
5. Adjustable contact
6. Leak hole

H *Magnetic (magnetic-acoustic) mine*
1. Variation of earth's magnetic field underneath ship with permanent magnetism
2. Variation of earth's magnetic field underneath degaussed ship
3. Variation of sound pressure
4. Induction coil
5. Charge
6. Primer with detonator
7. Safety device
8. Instrument box (with relay, ship counter, etc.)
9. Acoustic device
10. Parachute container

213

MINESWEEPING

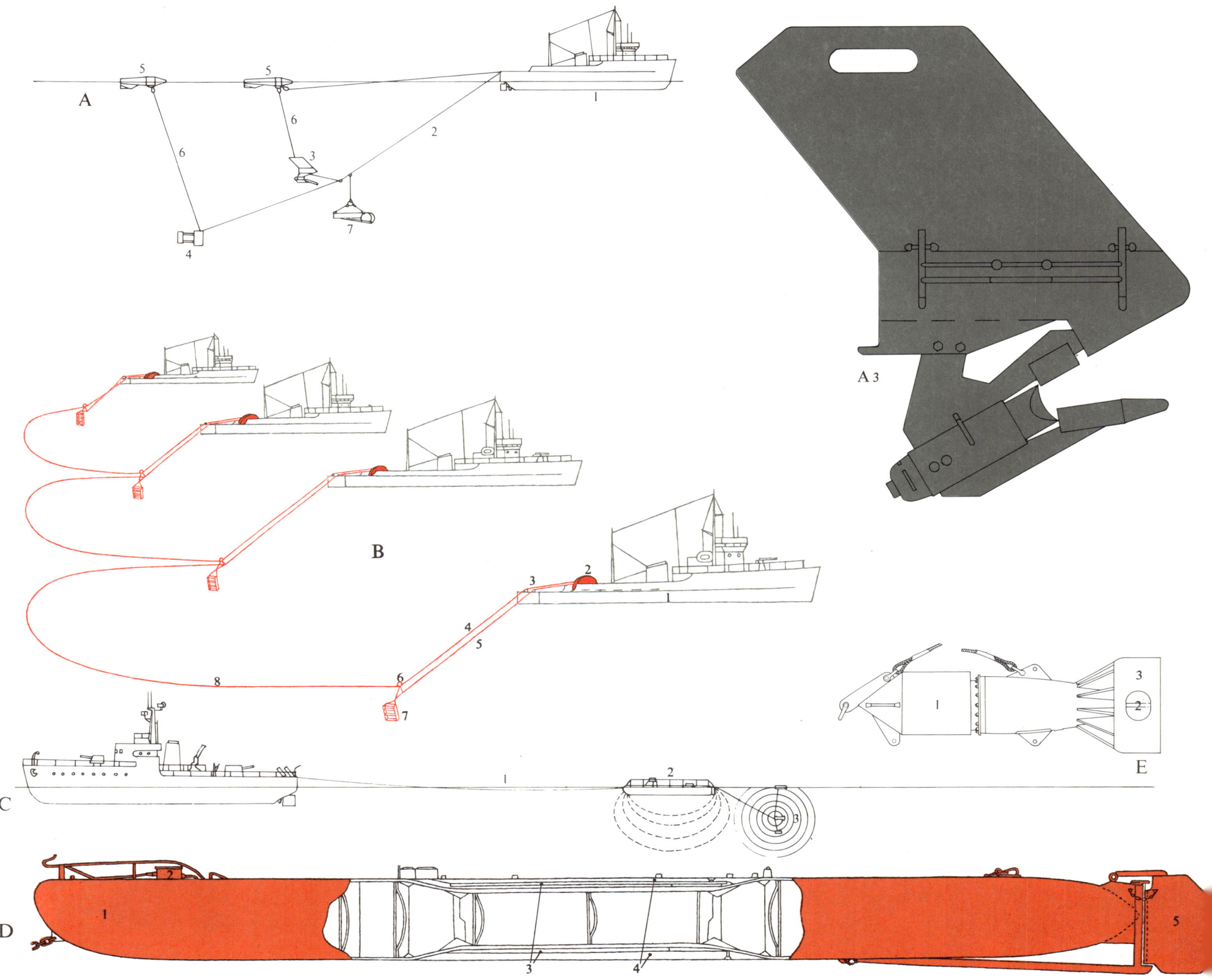

MINESWEEPING

A *Mechanical one-boat sweep, consisting of steel wires towed through the water in arrow formation in order to cut the mooring-cables of the mines.*

1. Mine sweeper
2. Sweep wire towing line
3. Detonator-gripper with charge that blows off the mine-mooring, or with powder-charge that works a cutting-chisel
4. Kite
5. Buoyancy buoys
6. Buoyancy cable
7. Cutting-plane

B *Wire sweep*
1. Minesweeper
2. Winch
3. Stern chock
4. Sweep wire
5. Kite wire
6. Snatch block
7. Kite, depressor
8. Serrated wire

C *Solenoid-acoustic sweep*
1. Towing line and feeding cable
2. Solenoid casing
3. Acoustic hammer box

D *Floating solenoid casing*
1. Bow of casing
2. Cable connection box
3. Space for cable coil
4. Wooden sheathing
5. Rudder

E *Acoustic hammer buoy*
1. Hammer box
2. Sternpiece
3. Power-generating propeller

214

# TORPEDO

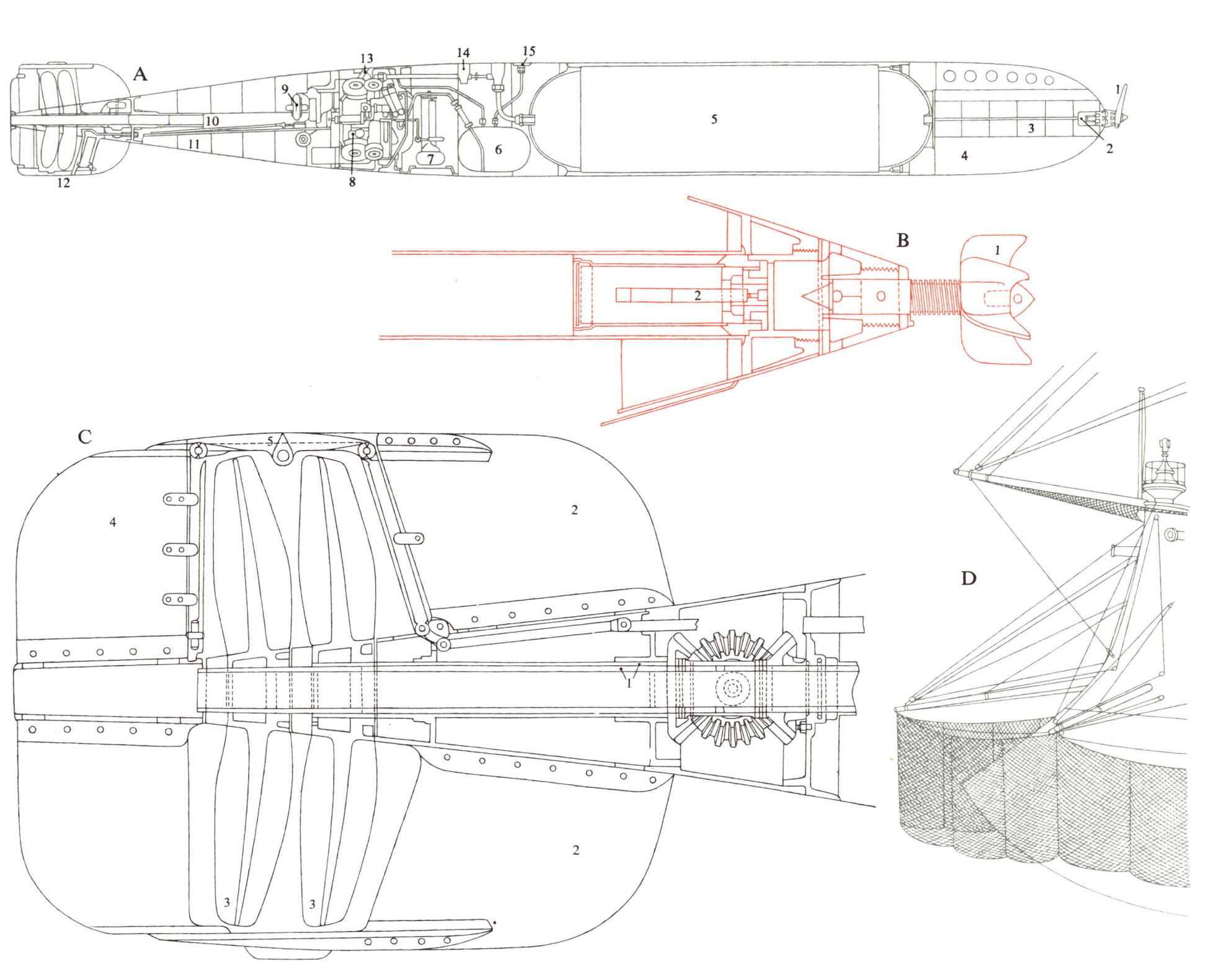

THE TORPEDO

A *Torpedo*
1 Horn
2 Primer
3 Explosive charge
4 Warhead
5 Air flask, air vessel
6 Fuel or water tank, destroyer torpedo: alcohol; submarine torpedo: water
7 Depth gear
8 Steam engine
9 Gyro-servomotor
10 Propeller shafts
11 Afterbody
12 Tail section
13 Air lever
14 Air charging valve
15 Fuel (water) charging valve

B *Pistol*
1 Safety propeller
2 Primer

C *Tail section*
1 Propeller shafts
2 Fins
3 Propellers
4 Steering rudder
5 Depth rudder

D *Torpedo net*
1 Swinging boom
2 Torpedo net

The torpedo net was an attempt to prevent damage from torpedo attacks

215

ANTI-SUBMARINE WEAPONS

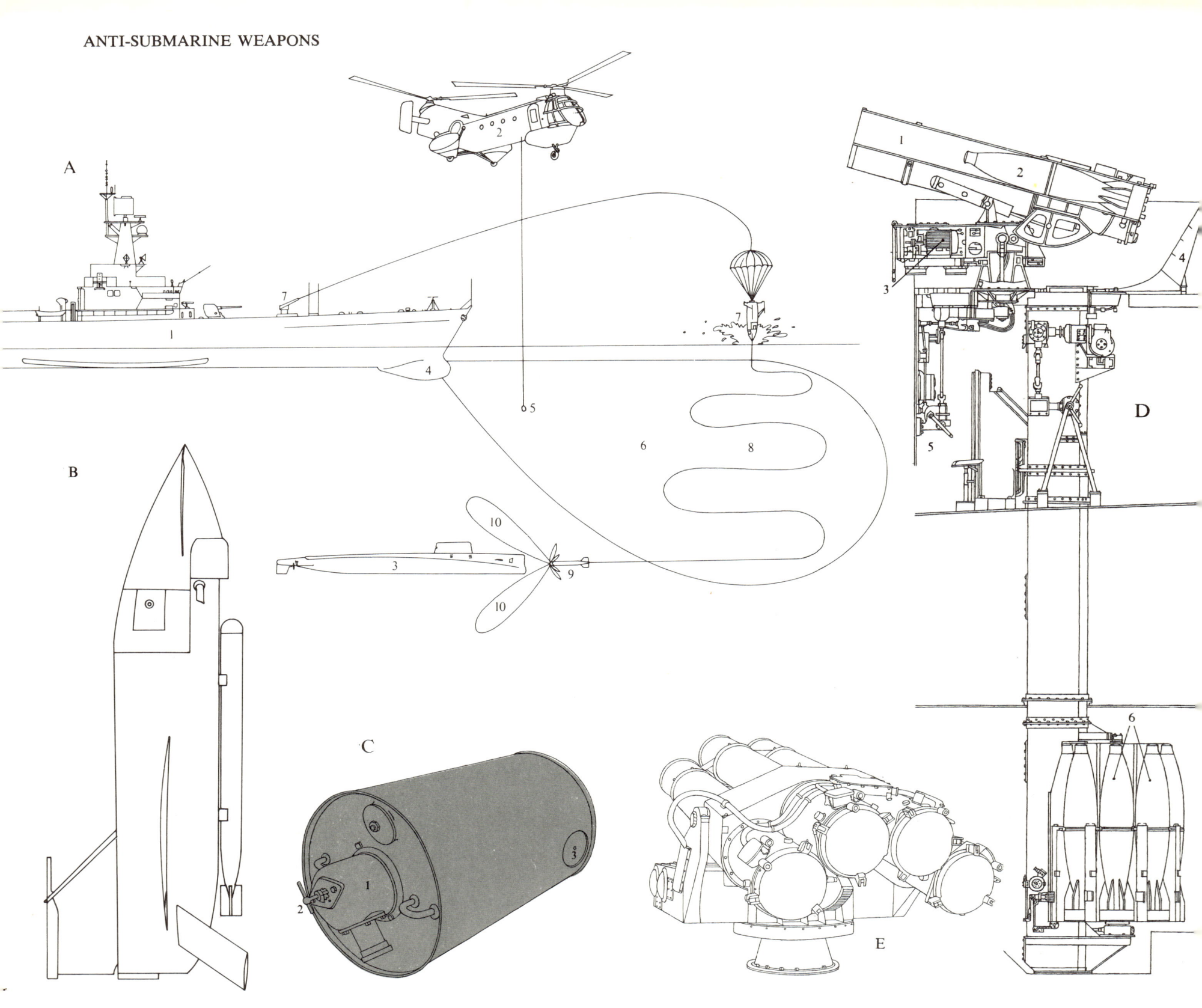

ANTI-SUBMARINE WEAPONS

A *Submarine-hunting situation*
1. Frigate
2. Anti-submarine helicopter
3. Submarine
4. Sonar dome
5. Helicopter's hydrophone (dipping asdic)
6. Frigate's sonar lobe (asdic beam)
7. An anti-submarine missile is fired into the sector where the submarine has been detected. On reaching the surface the missile releases an anti-submarine torpedo with a pre-set searching scheme and an active sonar that traces the target
8. Anti-submarine torpedo's course scheme
9. Anti-submarine torpedo
10. Torpedo's sonar beams

B *Anti-submarine* IKARA *missile. The missile is launched from a surface vessel. When it reaches the target sector a parachute is released and the missile descends while "homing" on the target-submarine*

C *Depth Charge (D/C)*
1. Depth regulator
2. Depth setting key
3. Safety device

D *Anti-submarine (AS) rocket launcher*
1. Barrel
2. AS-rocket
3. Training motor
4. Flash shield
5. Training gear
6. Magazine

E *Same as D (Four-tube launcher)*

WEAPON CONTROL SYSTEMS

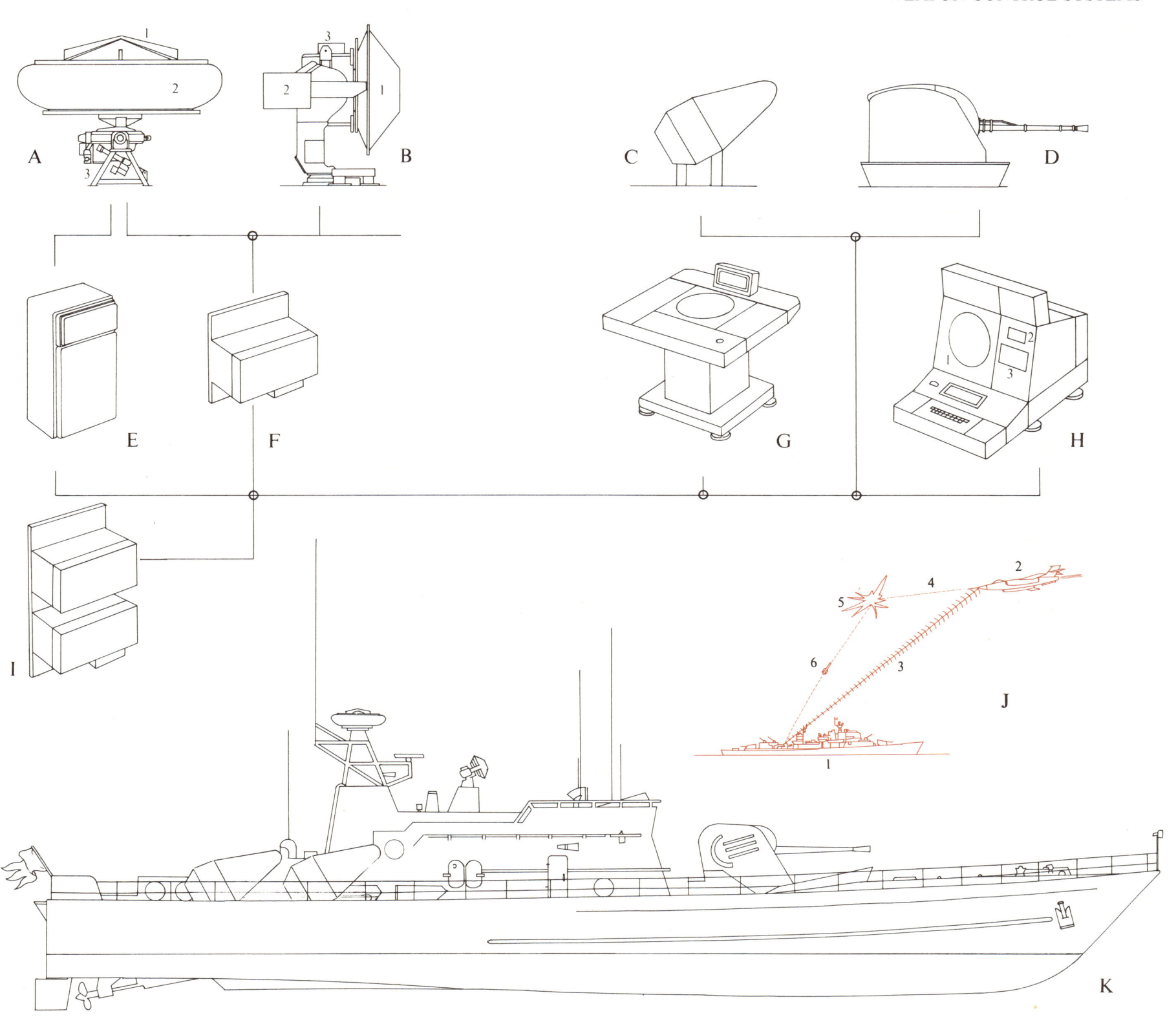

DIGITAL WEAPON CONTROL SYSTEM

Development
Weapon control system materials have, since World War II, improved from mechanical analogue computers with manual adjustment of input values and manual reading of computing results for the control of guns and other weapons to integrated systems where measured values from different information sensors are combined and computed, and the weapons are automatically directed towards their targets

Fire Control
The picture from the surveyance radar is shown on a PPI (display unit). When the operator discovers a target-echo, he marks it with a symbol and orders the director to move to the indicated sector and search for the target with its radar at the given distance. The director finds the target and the given distance. The director radar finds the target and "locks" the director to it, whereupon the target is continually followed. The measured target values, together with values on the movements of the hunting ship, and data for gun, ammunition etc., are used by the computer to calculate a future impact point towards which the gun is pointed and the projectiles are fired.

A Surveyance antenna
 1 Feeder
 2 Reflector
 3 Platform (turntable)

B Director
 1 Radar antenna
 2 Television camera
 3 Radar unit

C Sea-to-sea missile

D Multi-purpose gun

E Tracking radar

F Amplifier unit

G Combat information indicator

H Artillery indicator
 1 PPI
 2 A-scope
 3 TV-monitor

I Computer unit

J Combat situation
 1 Hunting ship
 2 Target
 3 Target distance
 4 Target speed vector
 5 Future impact point
 6 Missile (projectile) trajectory

K Torpedo boat

217

WARSHIPS

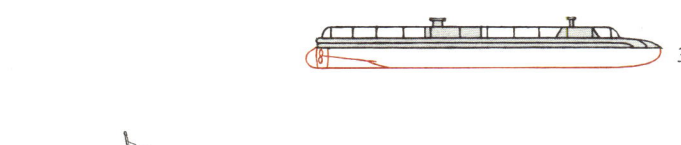

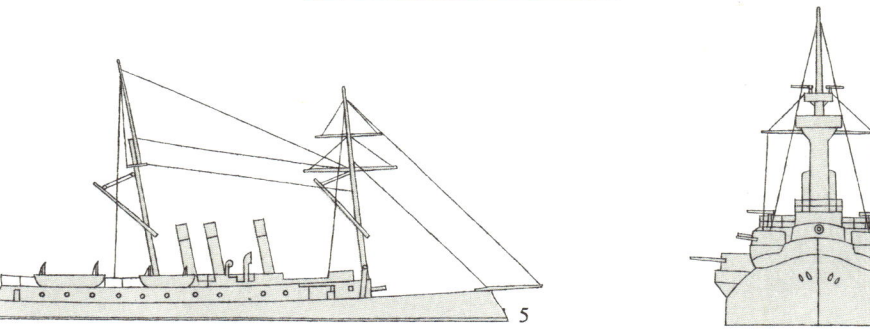

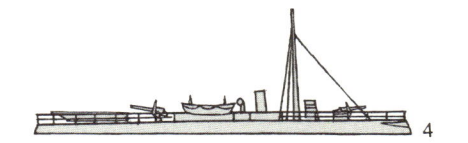

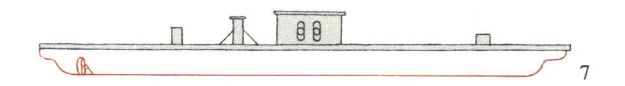

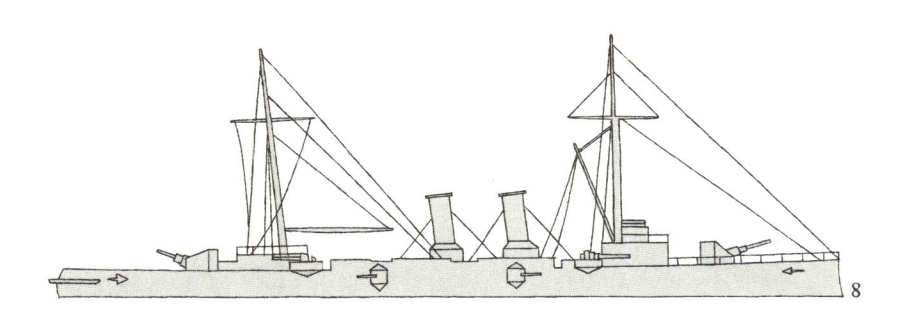

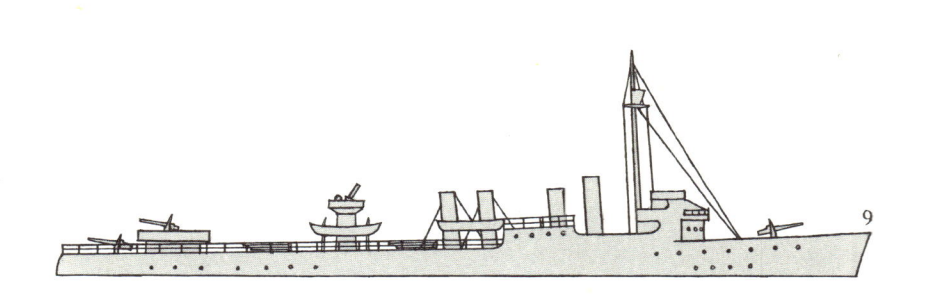

WARSHIPS

1. Nelson's flagship at Trafalgar, *Victory,* built as early as 1765
2. American frigate, about 1800
3. French submarine, 1863
4. French torpedo boat, 1890
5. Swedish gunboat, 1870
6. French ironclad, *Jauréguiberry,* end of the 19th century
7. John Ericsson's *Monitor,* 1864
8. The British protected cruiser, *Edgar,* end of the 19th century
9. American destroyer, 1917

WARSHIPS

WARSHIPS

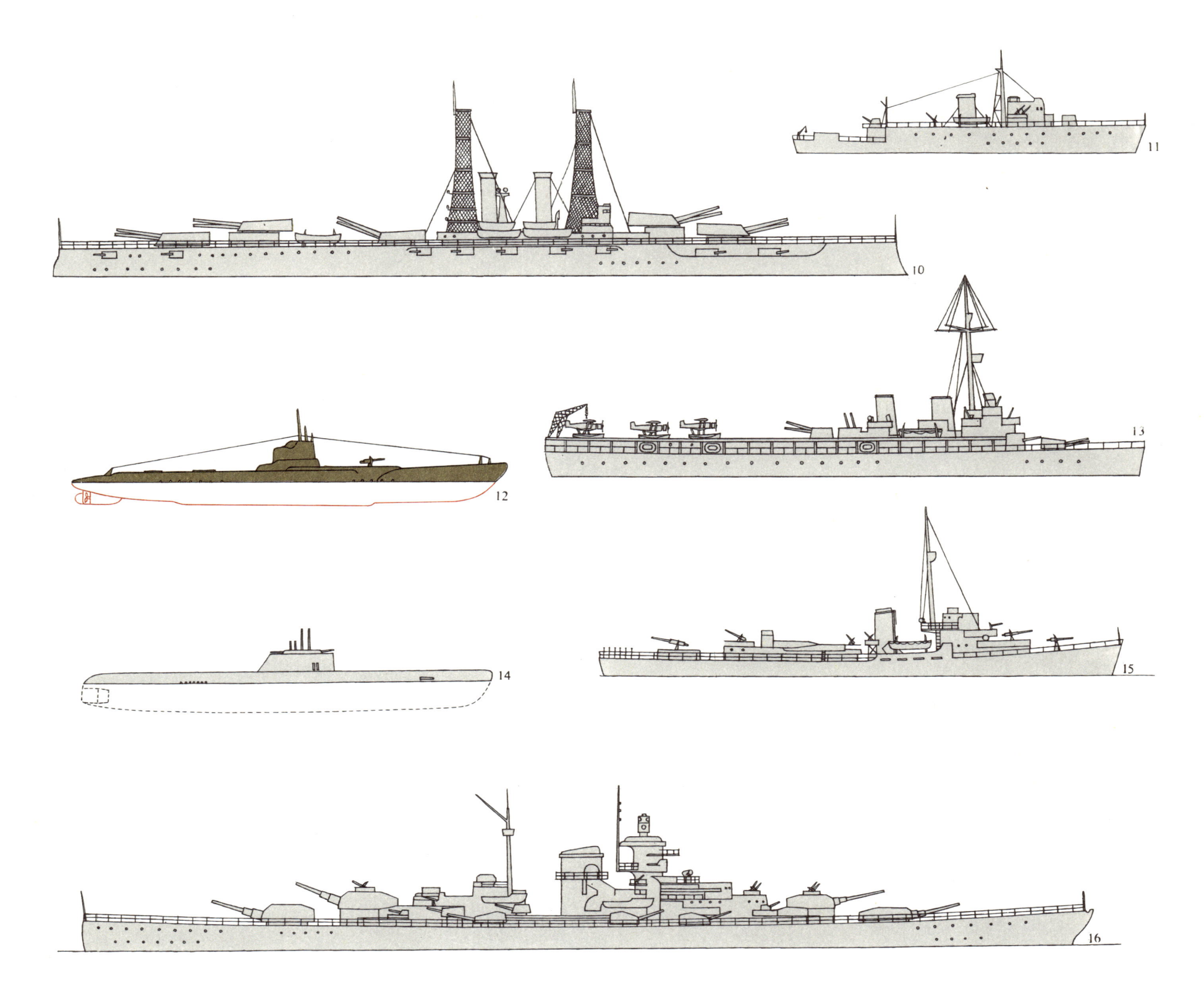

10 American battleship, *Texas,* 1912
11 British minesweeper, end of W.W.II
12 German submarine, W.W.I
13 Swedish aircraft-carrying cruiser, *Gotland,* 1934
14 German snorkel-fitted submarine, W.W.II. The snorkel is a watertight telescopic air intake, which makes it possible for the submarine to use its diesel engines when submerged
15 American escort vessel (frigate), W.W.II
16 German battleship, *Bismarck,* launched 1939

WARSHIPS

WARSHIPS

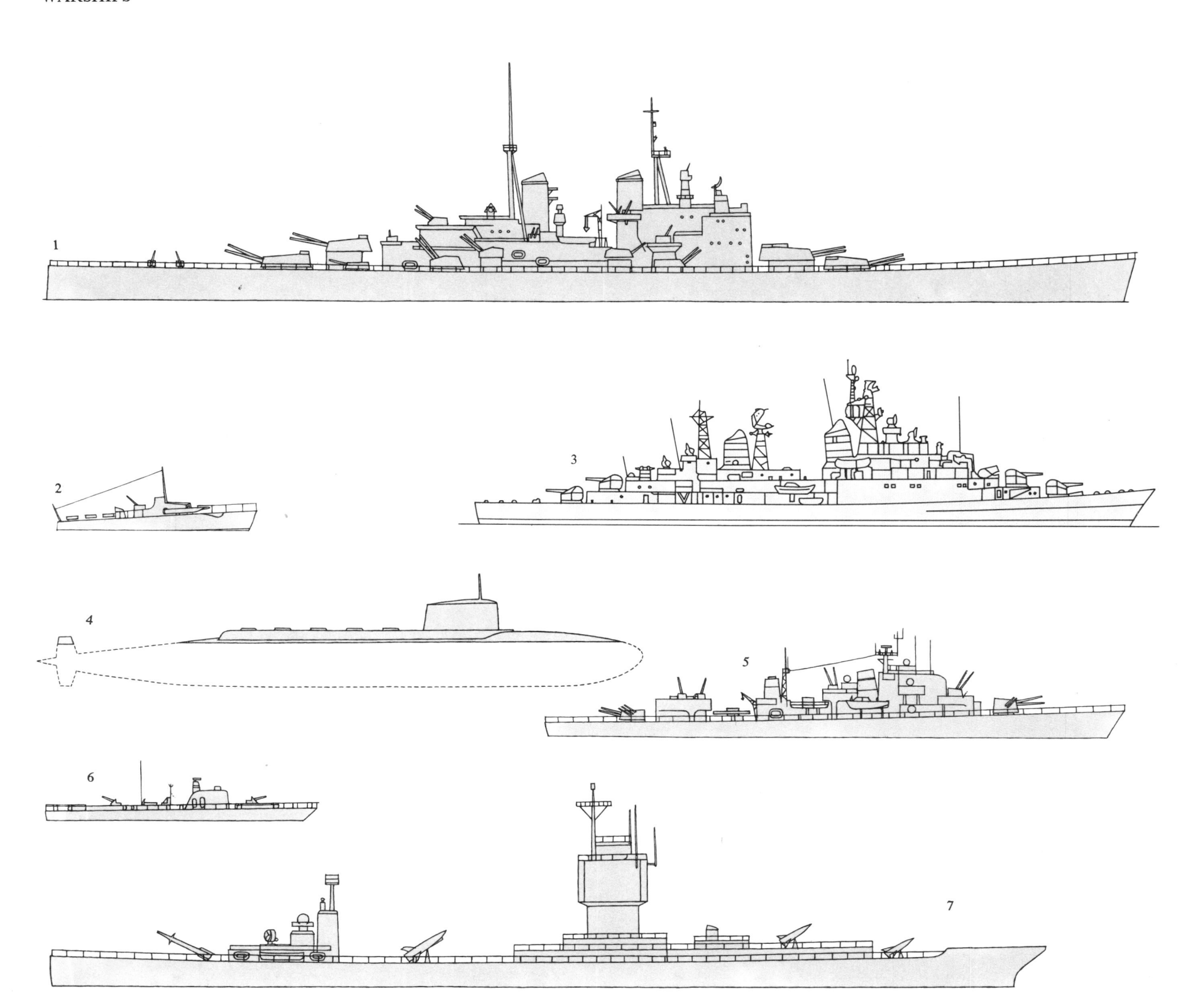

1 British battleship *Vanguard*, 1946. She was the Royal Navy's last capital ship

2 British motor torpedo boat (MTB), beginning of W.W.II

3 German destroyer *Hessen*, launched 1968, displacement 4,400 tons, length 128 m (420 ft), breadth 13.4 m (44 ft), draught 5.2 m (17 ft), 4–10 cm (3.9 in) dual purpose guns, 36 knots

4 American nuclear-powered submarine with 16 Polaris missiles

5 Swedish destroyer *Östergötland*, launched 1956, displacement 2,600 tons, length 112 m (367.5 ft), breadth 11.2 m (36.8 ft), draught 3.7 m (12 ft), 4–12 cm (4.7 in.) rapid fire guns, 1 quadruple Seacat surface-to-air missile launcher, 36 knots

6 Swedish motor torpedo boat *Rigel*, launched 1959, displacement 170 tons, length 45 m (148 ft), breadth 5.8 m (19 ft), draught 1.6 m (5.2 ft), speed 40 knots

7 American nuclear-powered missile-cruiser *Long Beach*, launched 1959, displacement 17,350 tons, length 220 m (721 ft), breadth 22.3 m (73 ft), draught 8.8 m (29 ft), 1 twin Talos surface-to-air missile launcher, 2 twin Terrier surface-to-air launchers, 2–12.7 cm (5 in) guns, 1 ASROC 8-tube launcher, 35 knots

WARSHIPS

WARSHIPS

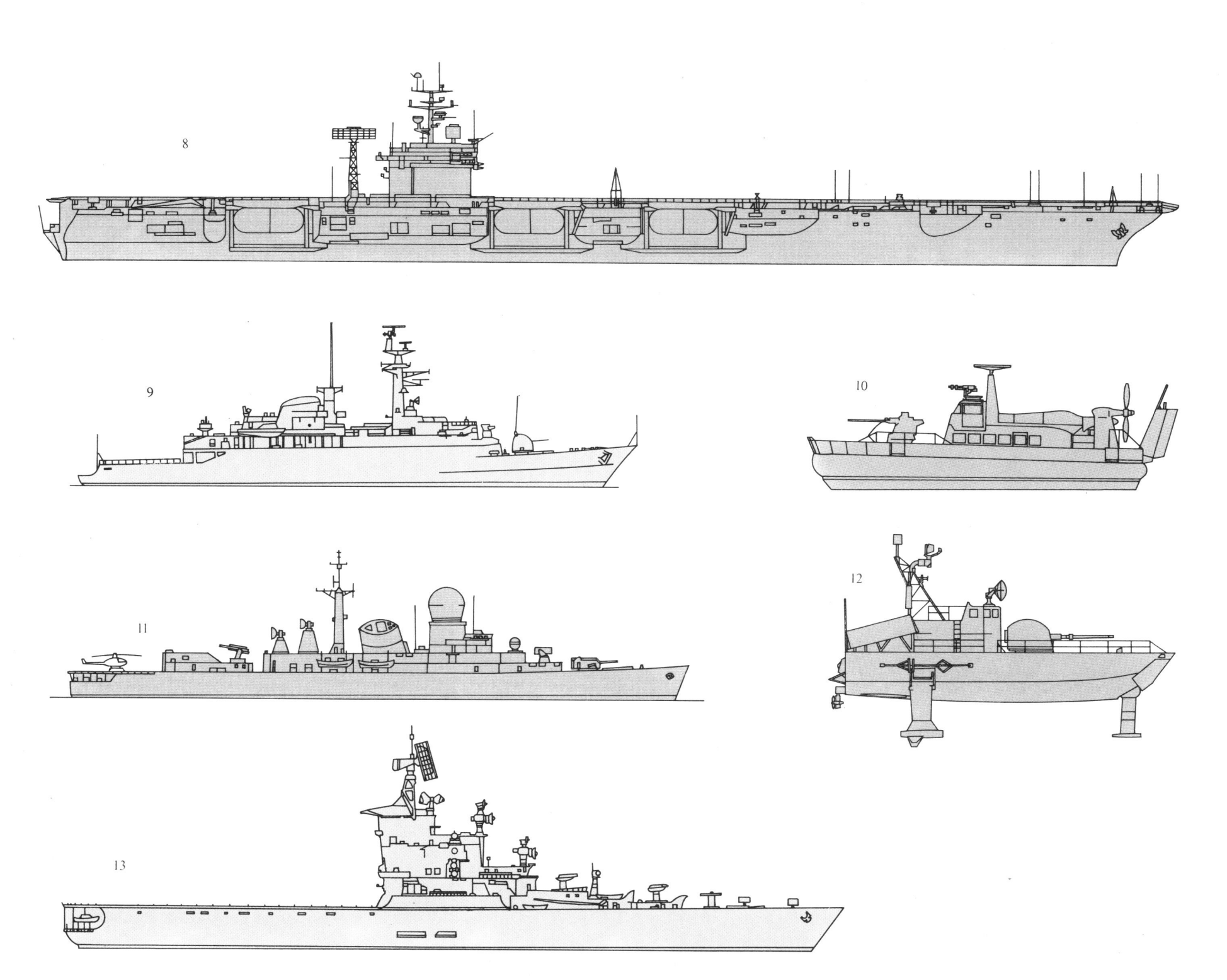

8 American nuclear-powered attack aircraft carrier *Dwight D. Eisenhower,* launched 1974, displacement 91,400 tons, length 317 m (1,040 ft), breadth 40.8 m (134 ft), draught 11.3 m (37 ft), approx. 100 aircraft, crew including air wing personnel 6,100, 3 Basic Point Defence Missile System launchers with Sea Sparrow missiles, over 30 knots

9 British frigate *Active,* launched 1972, displacement 2,500 tons, length 109.7 m (360 ft), breadth 12.7 m (42 ft), draught 3.7 m (12 ft), 1 Lynx anti-submarine helicopter, 1 quadruple Seacat surface-to-air missile launcher, 1–11.5 cm (4.5 in) gun, 34 knots

10 British fast interceptor Hovercraft SR.N6 Mk 6A, length 17.7 m (58 ft), breadth 7 m (23 ft), 1-twin barrel 30 mm cannon, one 7.62 mm machine gun, max. speed 53 knots

11 Netherlands destroyer *De Ruyter,* launched 1973, displacement 5,400 tons, length 131 m (430 ft), breadth 14.8 m (49 ft), draught 4.6 m (15 ft), 2–12 cm (4.7 in) guns, 1 helicopter, Tartar and Sea Sparrow Point Defence Missile Systems, 30 knots

12 Italian missile-carrying hydrofoil gunboat *Swordfish,* launched 1974, speed 45–50 knots

13 Russian helicopter-cruiser *Leningrad,* completed 1969, displacement 15,000 tons, length 190.5 m (625 ft), breadth 23 m (76 ft), draught 7.6 m (25 ft), 18 Hormone A helicopters, 2 SAN-3 missiles, 30 knots

An old engraving shows Magellan during his trip around the world, 1519—1522. Magellan was never able to complete this first circumnavigation of the globe himself, and of the original five vessels, with 265 men in the crew, only one ship, the VICTORIA; *and eighteen men returned. The engraving introduces the chapter on navigation and ship-handling.*

NAVIGATION AND SHIP-HANDLING

NAVIGATION AND SHIP-HANDLING

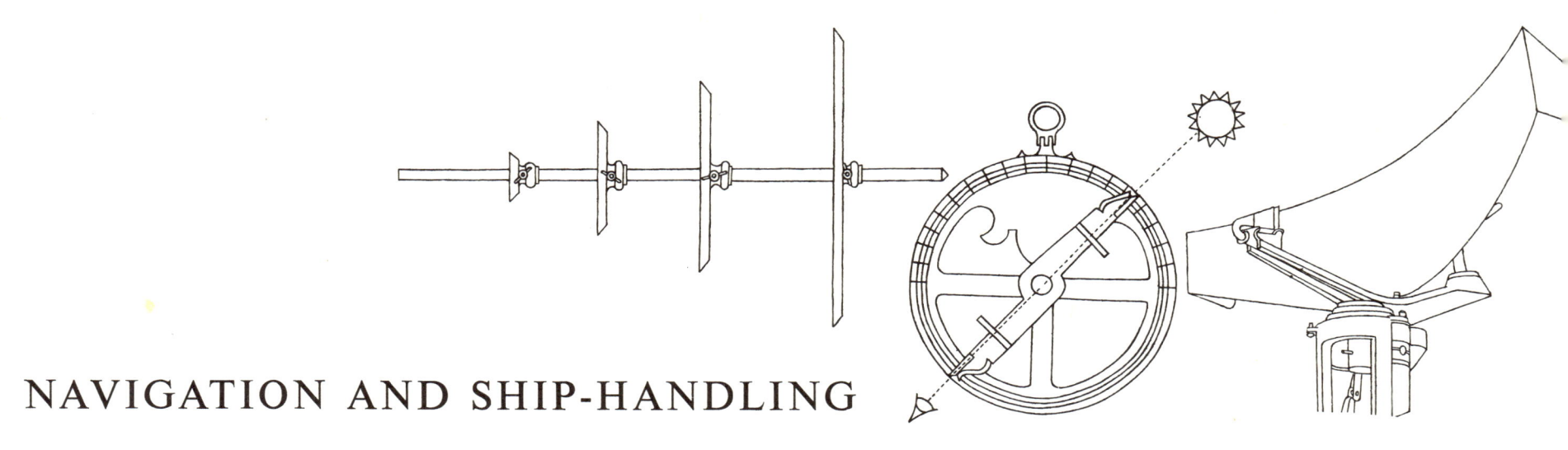

BY ROLF SCHEEN

The term navigation for this science is of comparatively recent date when compared with man's own hundreds-of-thousand-year history. Nobody knows when the first boat or the first ship was launched, but it is evident that the first man could not go very far from his original home without being stopped by water when he went out to look for something to eat. That water had to be spanned; the primitive craft is very, very old in the history of mankind. The first primitive navigation took place without an intended place of destination. The object was just to get over, to cross or pass a river, a bay, or a small lake. Of these first navigators, no man had ever been on the other side of a body of water. He only moved over the globe without knowing or thinking of a destination. Food was the only thing he thought of. He went in search of food; he crossed the water in order to get food. Only later, having left places where food was good and plentiful, he wanted to return, to find the same places once more. Then the question was to find one's way. Man learned to find out where he was. His primitive navigation must now be considered an art. The peoples of the Stone Age and of the Bronze Age might have been marvelously clever in many ways. But even if astronomy was considered a science in Babylon 3,800 years before our era and even if the Chinese were able to compute the advent of solar eclipses more than 4,000 years ago they were not able to transfer the results of astronomy to practical navigation at that time.

Rivers and coastal waters can be so turbid that even with a small boat it is impossible to see the bottom, if you have enough water to float the keel. Therefore, man from the oldest times has been forced to measure the depth of the water he was going to use. On ancient pictures of Egyptian riverboats a man can be seen in the fore part of the boat using a pole to determine depth and the advisability of continuing navigation. Very early, sailors or fishermen also learned to use lead and line to measure the depth when a pole could no longer be made use of. The lead was used on board the ship that was to take the Apostle Paul to Rome, the ship that foundered in the year 62. The lead was then so developed that it was already marked in fathoms. The main object of the lead was to save the ship from going aground. If the position of a shoal or bank had already been determined, other means were used to avoid it. Much used were (and are) the so-called landmarks. It is unnecessary to know all the ground, if you are to determine your position through landmarks and can follow a safe way through or past the dangerous places.

Very early, people who had learned to write were recording necessary information mostly, perhaps, for their own benefit. Greeks and Phoenicians collected what they could in so-called *peripli,* covering whole territories. Others misused this information. Herodotus (ca. 450 B.C.) relates that King Darius I of Persia about 490 B.C. hired Phoenician ships to spy upon the Greek coast in order to procure information about this country. Later on, sea charts became still more important than sailing directions. They could not be truly useful before the invention of the compass and they could never satisfy modern requirements until hydrographic offices had been established by the different nations to organize the work of surveying, sounding, etc.; but the chief of the famous library of Alexandria, Eratosthenes (276—196 B.C.) had already produced a map of the world with the first primitive framework of parallels and meridians.

A good chart should enable its user to draw the course (the compass direction) between two places. The charts on Mercator's projection were easily satisfactory in this respect. Gerard Mercator made the degrees of longitude parallel. As a result, he could draw a correct course line between two places on his chart, but the scale of the chart varied from the Equator toward the poles, so that at 60 degrees North, for instance, one nautical mile on the chart had twice the length of the mile at the Equator. In the neighborhood of the poles, the method could not be used at all.

As is well known, the distance from the Equator to the poles of the earth is divided in 90 degrees of latitude (north or south) for the purpose of ascertaining the position of a ship, for use on charts, for observations, etc. The Equator itself has been divided into 360 degrees of longitude, with verticals called meridians up to the poles. No 0-meridian being standard, different countries have used varius 0-meridians. At sea it was better to have a common 0-meridian for ships of all nations; consequently, many countries followed King Louis XIII's orders to place the 0-meridian through the Isle of Ferro. Ferro was thought to be the westernmost point of the Old World. From the year 1884, the 0-meridian through the Greenwich Observatory in England (founded 1675) may be considered international.

A great deal of courage was needed in ancient times to sail far out from the coast, losing all sight of land. No compass, no reliable charts existed. Good weather, the spirit of adventure, the feeling of having a good boat certainly tempted many to continue their explorations when prudence ought to have kept them back. As daring sea expeditions, the adventures of the old Norsemen through the mists of the North Atlantic to Iceland, Greenland, and North America must be said to rank high, but it must be presumed that they had quite a good knowledge of the celestial bodies and their movements in order to find their way to such distant countries and back again. Next to the sun, the Pole Star and perhaps still more the Little Dipper have helped navigators. For the Norsemen the brightest summer nights and also the Midnight Sun played a great part in their seamanship. Their ancient astronomical terms have been preserved, but their meaning has been difficult to explain, even in modern times. (For instance: *Eyktarstad)*

It has long been possible to determine latitude with a fair amount of certainty. But longitude was an almost insoluble problem so long as no instrument capable of measuring time with the necessary accuracy for use at sea had been invented. A chronometer was needed. Prizes were offered to anybody who could find the means of discovering the longitude. In 1714 the English Parliament granted 20,000 pounds for this purpose. Astronomers were able to determine the longitude by the help of lunar distances and other observations, but their methods were too impractical to be used at sea. At last, after working a whole lifetime, a Yorkshireman, John Harrison, in 1774, was given the prize for his invention. With Harrison, a revolution in the history of navigation had taken place; from now on the longitude of a ship's position at sea could be determined.

The most important innovation, however, was much older; this was the invention of the compass. No one knows who the inventor was. The Chinese Emperor Hoang-Ti is said to have used magnets on his chariot to find his way south as early as the third millennium B.C. But the earliest date for the use of a compass on board a ship occurs in Chinese literature in A.D. 1111, and it is possible that China had gotten the compass from India. According to Are Frode, the Norsemen are said to have used the *leidarstein* (loadstone or lodestone) for a primitive compass during a voyage to Iceland as early as in the year A.D. 868. Considering the huge quantities of magnetite to be found in Norway, it is not at all unreasonable to suppose that Norwegians very early conceived the idea of using magnetism on board their ships as they used it during their lives on shore. Their ability to find their way across the seas if they had no form of compass is almost incomprehensible.

Celestial navigation is based upon the measurement of the altitude of celestial bodies and the determination of their direction. All ships measuring the same celestial body at the same time and at the same altitude will be placed on the same astronomical position line. This can be determined according to principles first laid down by the American naval officer Thomas H. Summer in 1837, and further amplified by Marc St. Hilaire around 1875. Many different instruments have, in the course of time, been constructed for the measurement of the altitude of celestial bodies; the quadrant is said to have been invented by the Greek astronomer Hipparchos as early as the year 150 B.C. Levi ben Gerson from Catalonia discovered the Jacob's staff or the cross-staff in 1342; John Hadley constructed the Hadley quadrant in 1731; the British naval officer Campbell made the sextant in 1757.

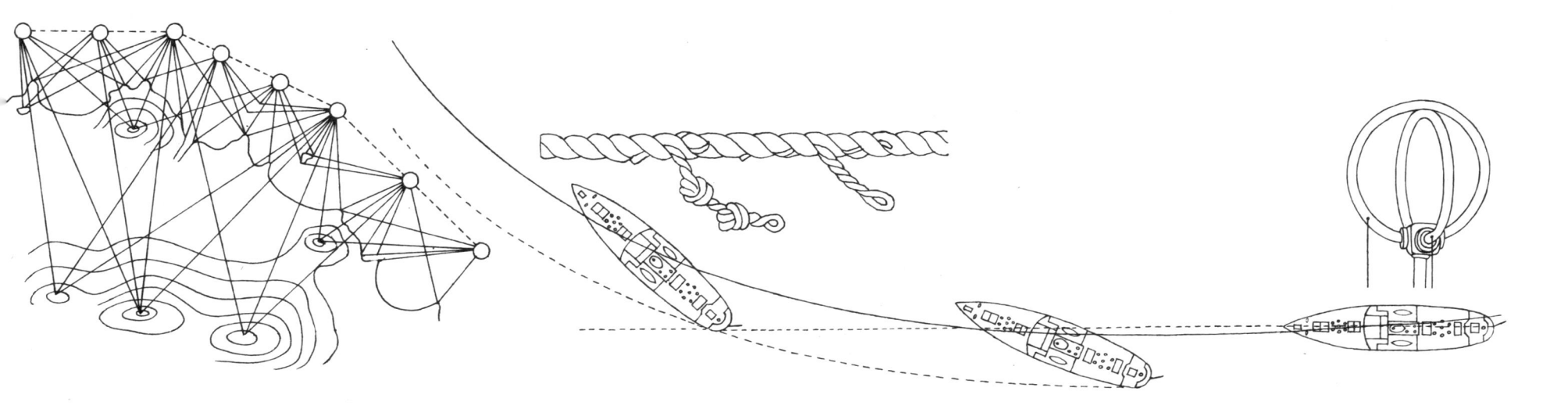

To use celestial navigation it is necessary to have a number of tables computed in advance. Regimontanus Real published his *Ephemerides Astronomica* in 1475. Thomas Mayer at Göttingen edited the tables to be used in finding Greenwich time in 1755. The British Nautical Almanac, founded by the royal astronomer Nevil Maskeleyne and officially published since 1767, has proved its great value for the seafaring man using celestial navigation.

In modern times, especially after the Second World War, electronic navigation has become more and more important. Radio bearings were being experimentally used at the very beginning of the wireless era, in the 20th century. At present there are long-range radio navigational aids of the type called *Sonne* in German and *Consol* in English.

The Loran system, with the use of the so-called hyperbolic position line net systems, is based upon radio range finding instead of radio direction finding. The Decca system has much in common with the Loran, but transmits radio waves continually, not in interrupted signals as the Loran does. The position of a ship is determined by the phase difference between three waves received from three co-operating transmitters, which is measured and utilized together with a special Decca chart.

The simplest way of finding a course is naturally to steer directly to a goal, but that can only rarely be done. Sailing on the ocean, the course must be computed according to the latitude and the longitude and the longitude of the place of departure and of the destination. The magnetic compass has for many hundreds of years been used as the most convenient aid for finding one's way over the sea, but notice must be taken of the variation caused by the difference in position of the geographical North Pole from the magnetic North Pole. Consideration must also be taken of the amount of iron in the ship and her machinery, which will cause a deviation on the compass that will change with different courses and with different latitudes. This deviation is caused by magnetic forces on board the ship added to the magnetism of the earth.

In the 20th century magnetic compasses are more and more being replaced by gyrocompasses which are independent of magnetism and which, after a few small corrections, will point directly toward the geographical North Pole. These gyrocompasses can easily be combined with gyrodials for taking bearings. They can also be combined with gyropilots for automatic steering of the ship.

Before the advent of charts, which give exact distances, it was, of course, very difficult to determine how far the ship had gone in a certain span of time. On rowing vessels some nations used to reckon the distance according to the time the rowers had been active (watches). Real distance, given in leagues, miles, etc., is, of course, much more exact. During the sailing ship era, the hand log and hourglass were used, but they could only give the speed at the time of logging. Nothing was recorded directly by the log as to the distance run. Later on, various kinds of patent logs were constructed to give the distance. They were towed after the ship and a special mechanism counted the number of miles run, which could be read directly on a dial on board the ship.

Thousands and thousands of foundered ships bear silent witness of the dangers of a vessel on her way from one port to another. Here, a very short summary will be given.

Invisible shoals. They are marked on the chart, if known. They are marked by beacons or lights, but these can be sunk or stray from their station, while the shoals represent permanent dangers. Darkness. Before lighthouses or lights were built along the coasts it was hardly possible to navigate at night. Even now, coastal navigation has its dangers; the coastal waters are perilous for a sailing ship or a powered vessel not under control, either of which could be thrown on a lee shore in a storm at any time of day. Lanterns are meant to help ships that pass at night, but too often they have been out of order.

Collisions. These happen too frequently. International rules of the road help to avoid them. Go slow, when necessary! Don't be afraid to stop! In modern times radar can be a help.

During wartime, mines, torpedoes, and other dangers are added to the usual perils of the sea. Degaussing or deperming will help against some mines. Convoys, camouflage, etc., have saved many ships from torpedoes.

A tragedy can come at any hour: fire, shipwreck, etc. Lifeboats and all kinds of lifesaving equipment must always be kept in perfect order, and all on board must know how to handle it. The use of distress signals must also be learned, so that you are always ready to tackle dangerous situations.

Engines have made maneuvering easier. Modern ships may have several rudders; and even a rudder in the fore part of the vessel; submarines must have horizontal rudders, called hydroplanes, for steering in the depths. The hull is shaped so that the ship can turn very quickly. Engines can shift their vast power from one direction to another in seconds. However, wind, current, or breakdowns can destroy all these advantages. At the critical moment it is again man who must take over. He must do the real job; and he must know how to do it whether he is on a small picket boat or the commander of the mightiest ship in the world.

The term navigation, in modern times, is also used with airplanes. We talk about aerial navigation. Many of the problems for the ship and for the airplane are the same, but the far greater speed in the air and the height of the plane make navigation in the sky very different from navigation in the sea. That is still more so with the rocket. Rocket navigation, perhaps, uses the science of ballistics more than navigation, and it apparently has nothing to do with the old-time ship's navigation. After all, that may not be so correct. Ship navigation is so old and offers so much experience through the ages that it is difficult to think of anything really new that could happen in the art.

The revolution has come already, starting with a new base: electronic navigation. That revolution will continue, dictated by the needs of ships, airplanes, and rockets. Technical discoveries will also continue, as we strive for perfection.

The danger is that quick development will go beyond the conception of the ordinary human mind, until at last no one will be able to control our navigation.

For the sake of safety at sea, on land, and in the air, we must hope that man, the well-intentioned, thinking man, will always have the lead, will always be the controlling factor.

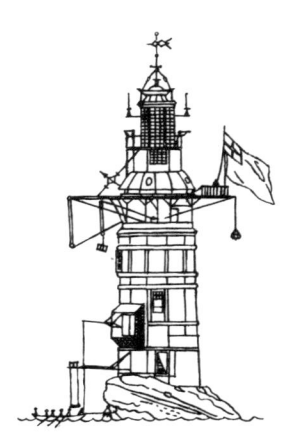

LEAD

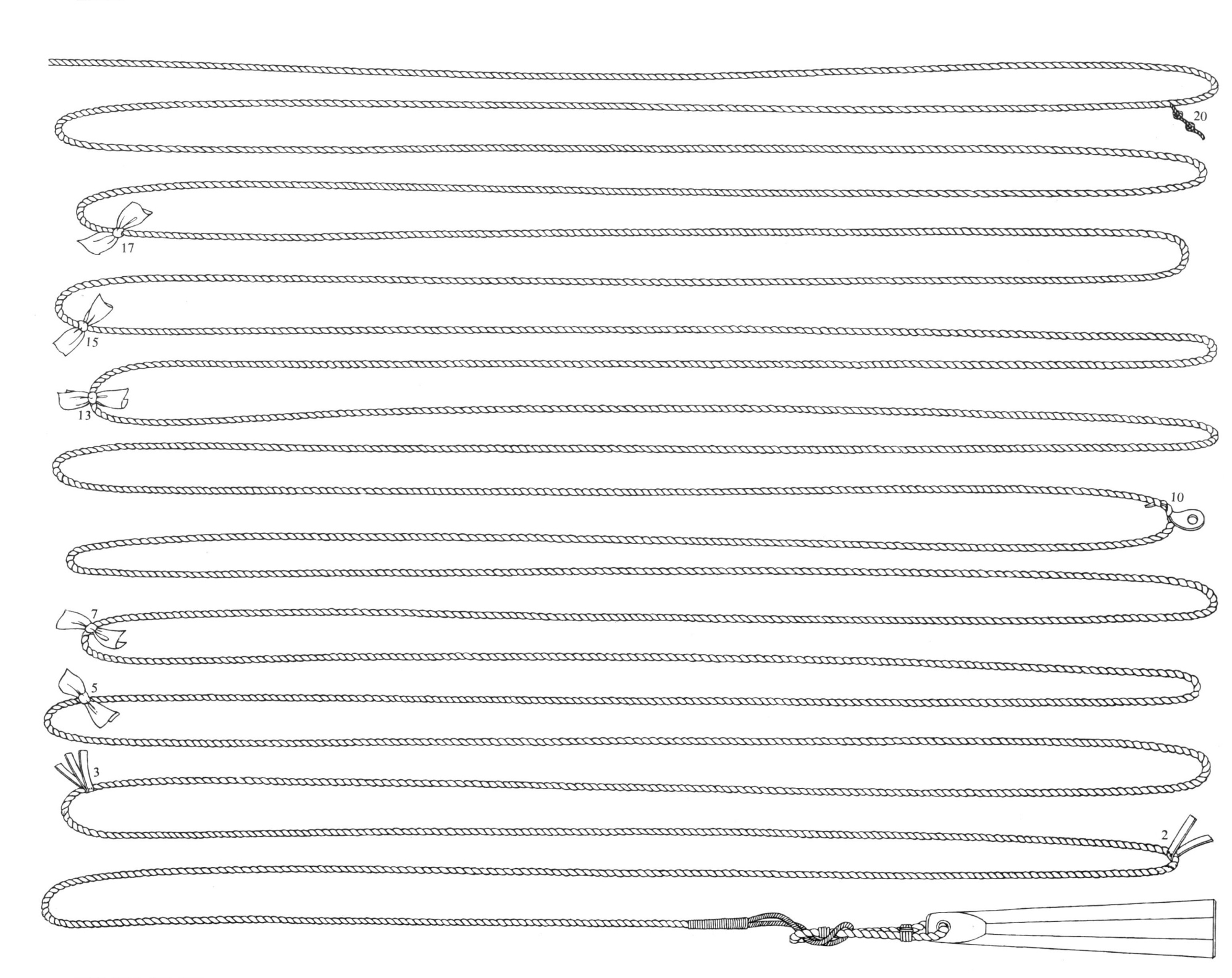

HAND LEAD AND LINE

The lead is the sailor's oldest navigational instrument, known even in ancient Egypt. It consists of a lead weight and a measured line, which is used to determine the depth of water. For different depths, leads of different weights were used, but today the deep-sea lead is replaced by sounding machines or echo sounders. The hand lead is still used occasionally in shallow water. The line used to be 20 fathoms long, and in the Royal British Navy it is marked in the following way:

- 2 fathoms: two strips of leather
- 3 fathoms: three strips of leather
- 5 fathoms: a piece of white duck
- 7 fathoms: a piece of red bunting
- 10 fathoms: a piece of leather with a hole in it
- 13 fathoms: a piece of blue serge
- 15 fathoms: a piece of white duck
- 17 fathoms: a piece of red bunting
- 20 fathoms: a piece of house line with two knots

LEAD

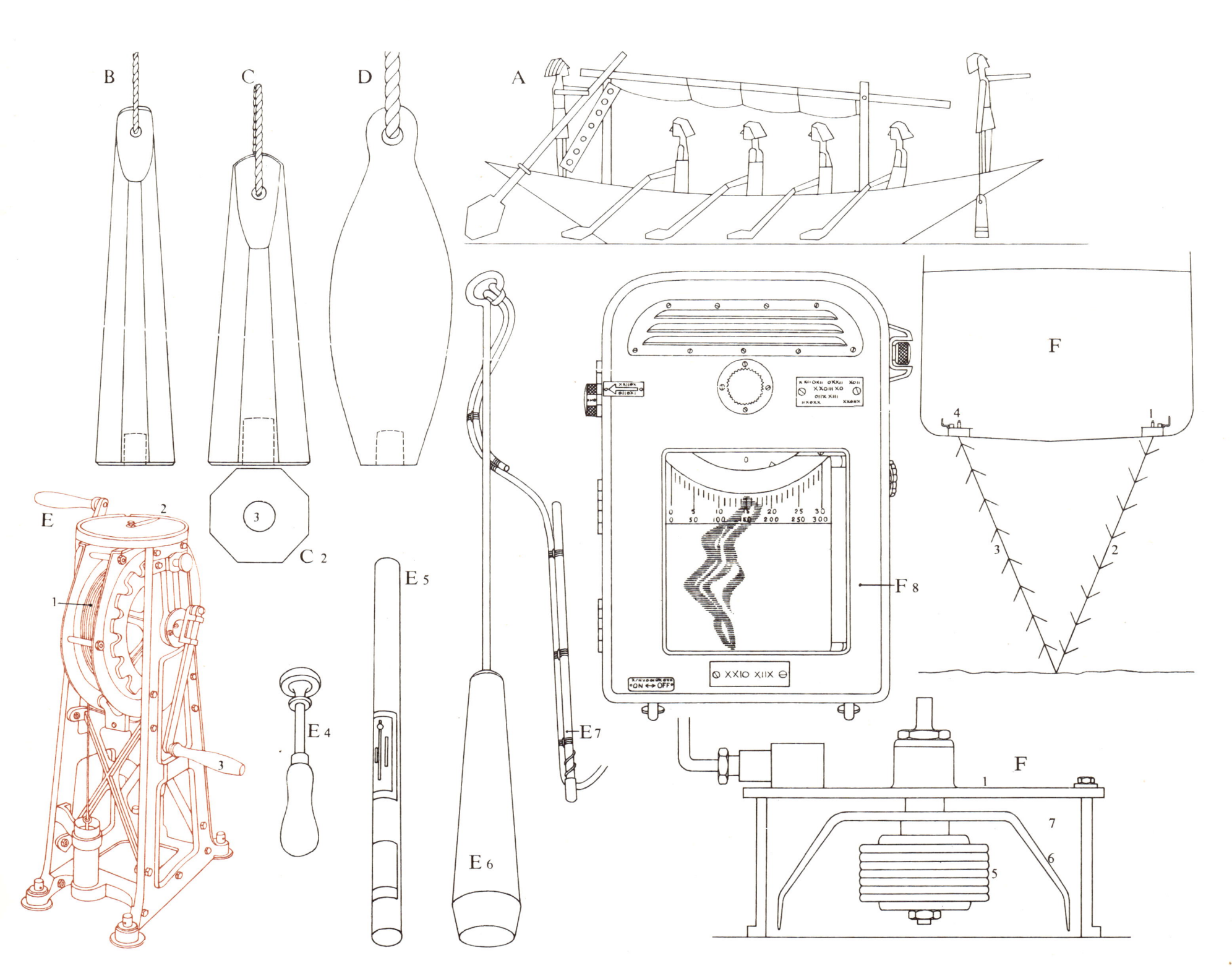

THE LEAD

A *Egyptian boat model with oarsmen, helmsman, and leadsman (from a grave sediment, 2060-1730 B.C.)*

B, C *Deep-sea lead 16 to 20 lbs. The lower end of the lead, C2, is hollowed out, 3, to receive an arming of tallow on which samples of the sea bed are brought up for examination.*

D *Deep-sea lead of cast iron*

E *Sounding machine To make soundings possible without reducing the speed of the ship a sounding machine with a thin wire must be used*

1. Wire drum
2. Dial and pointer, indicating how many fathoms of wire have run out
3. Handle, to wind in the lead and also to act as a brake on the drum
4. Feeler which indicates when the lead has reached the bottom
5. Cylinder with glass sounding tubes
6. Sinker
7. Glass tube in brass guard. The tube is sealed at the upper end. The water entering the tube from the lower end compresses the air corresponding to the depth of water. By discoloring a mercury salt in the tube the water leaves a mark at the line of greatest compression and by this the depth of water is known.

F *Sound travels at a known speed through the water, and the echo sounder measures the time it takes for a transmitted sound to travel from the ship to the sea bed and return to the ship as an echo.*

1. Transmitter
2. Separate sound transmissions
3. Echoes of transmissions
4. Receiver
5. Oscillator in transmitter, 1
6. Reflector
7. Fresh water tank, welded to bottom plating
8. Recording unit

LOG

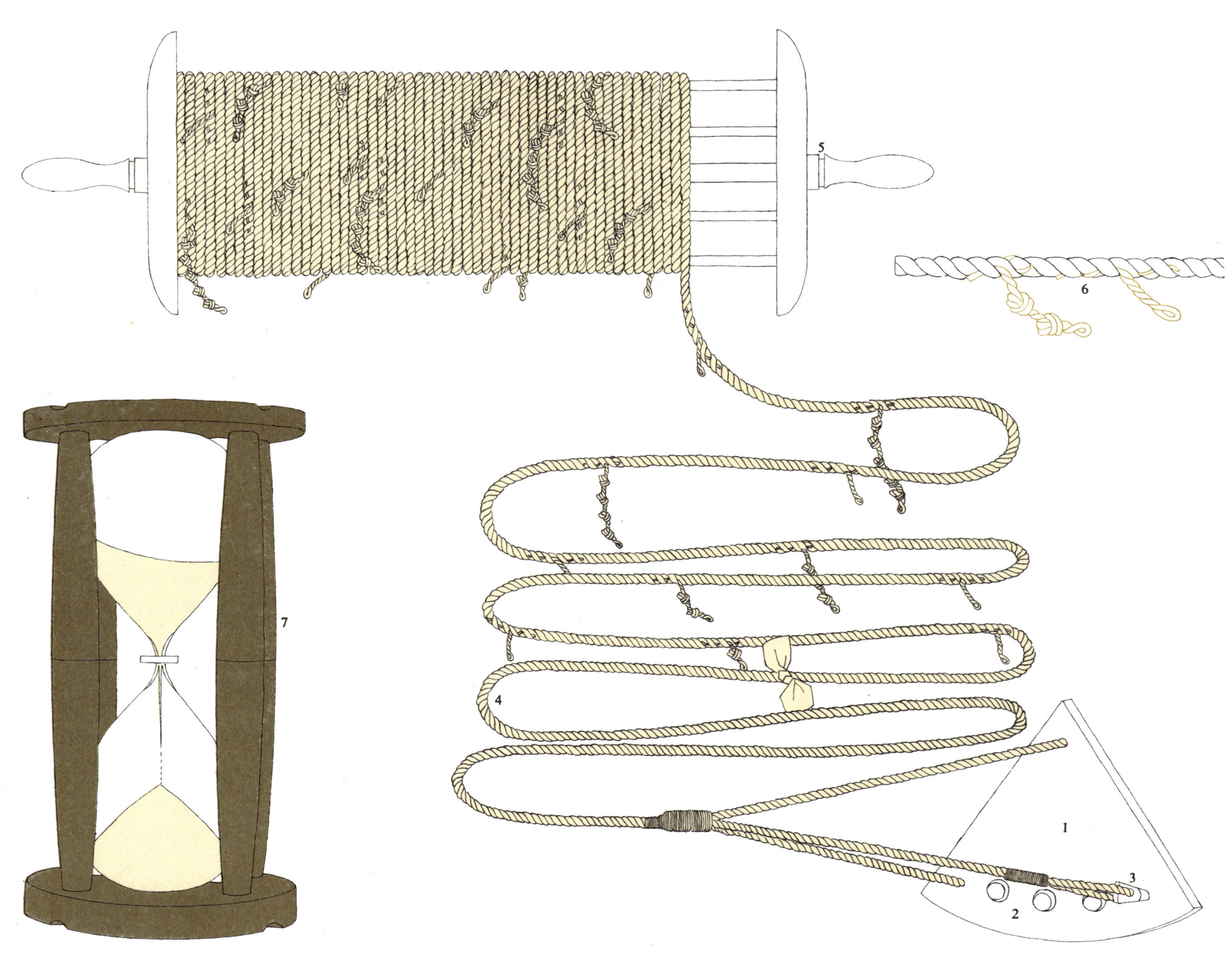

THE OLD LOG WITH A LINE AND GLASS

The chip log is an old instrument for measuring the speed of a ship. It consists of a flat piece of wood formed as a sector of a circle and weighted to enable it to float upright, secured to a line so as to make it float square. When thrown overboard it will remain stationary in the water and, as the ship sails away, the measured line will reel off at a corresponding rate. An hourglass determines the fixed interval of time, and the length of line run out will measure the speed of the ship. A quick pull on the line will detach the peg in the log chip, making it float flat so it can be hauled in.

1. The log, known as the wood float or chip
2. Lead pellets holding the chip vertically in the water
3. Wooden peg, which allows the chip to float flat when it is pulled out
4. Log-line measured off in "knots," having a similar relation to a nautical mile as the trickle of sand in the hourglass has to one hour
5. Log reel
6. Mark for two knots and a plain mark for half a knot
7. Hourglass, log glass, running for 28 seconds. A 14-second glass is used for speeds over 8 knots

LOG

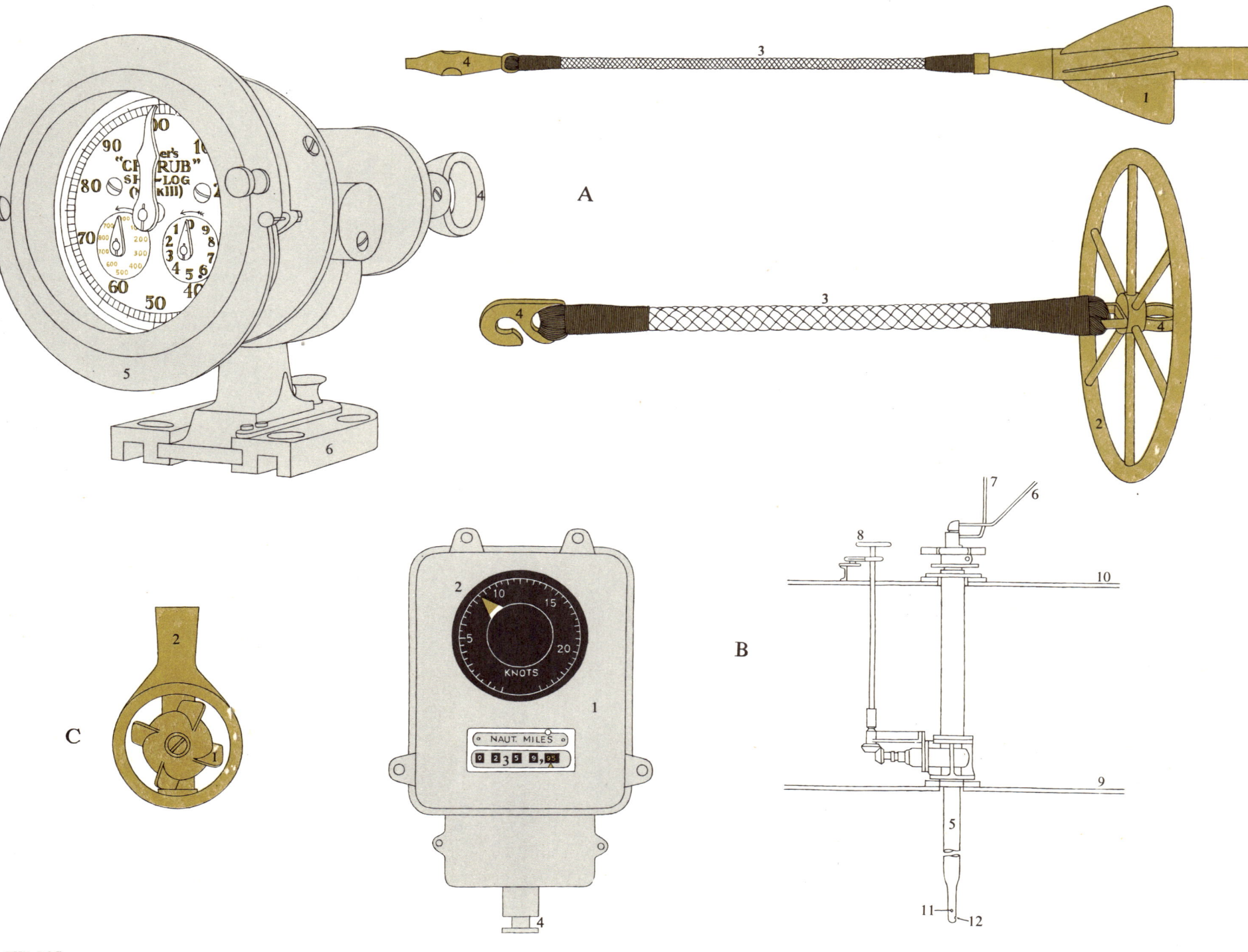

THE LOG

A *Patent or taffrail log*
1. Rotator
2. Governor
3. Connecting log line
4. Fish and hook-and-eye fastenings
5. Register
6. Base plate

B *Pitometer log*
1. Indicator
2. Speedometer
3. Counter
4. Connection to log
5. Pitot tube
6. Low pressure tube to log
7. High pressure tube to log
8. Operating hand wheel for Pitot tube
9. Bottom plating
10. Top of double bottom
11. Static orifice
12. Dynamic orifice

C *Details of Chernikeeff log*
This is similar to the Pitometer log, but has a small fan called the impeller in the tube which extends from the ship's bottom. The rotation is electrically registered.
1. Impeller
2. Tube

COMPASS CARDS

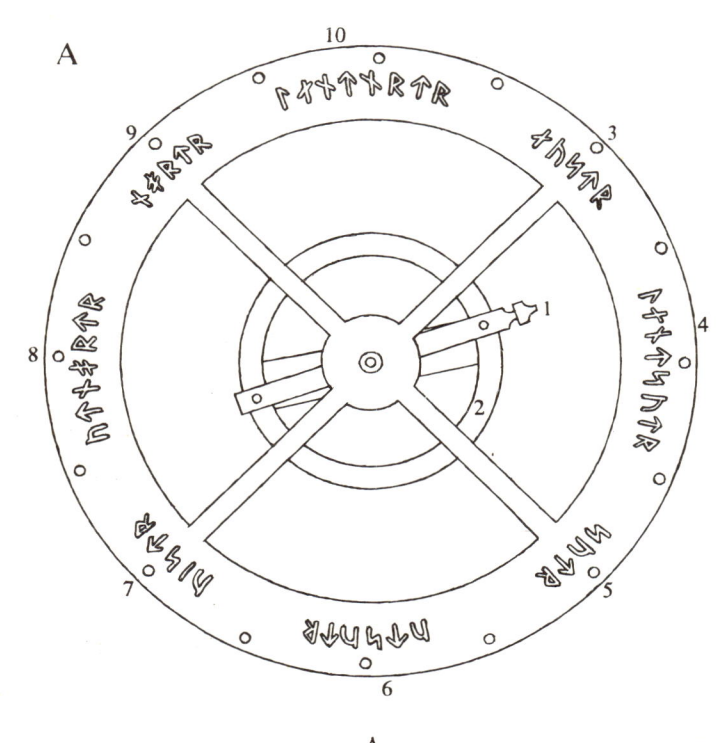

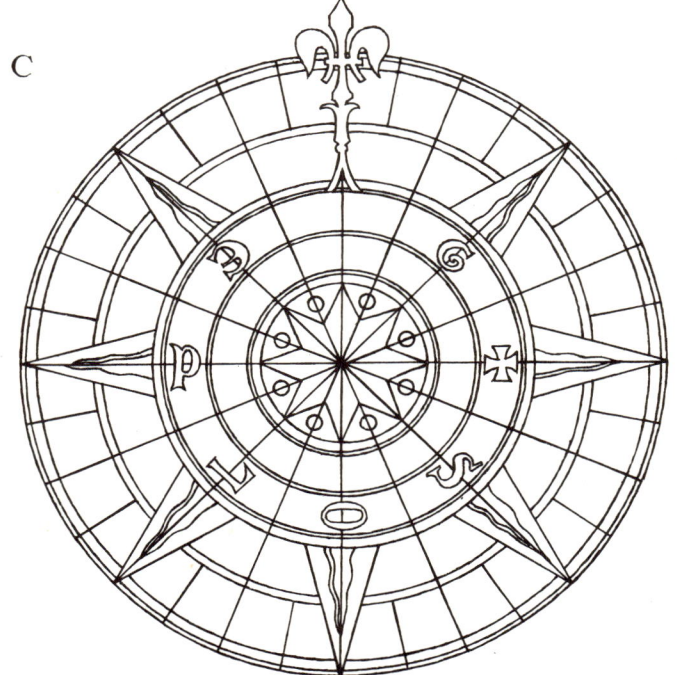

OLD COMPASS CARDS

A *Compass, 13th century Reconstruction of a Scandinavian compass (leidarstein) with a bronze bowl and a wooden float, with a lodestone to point the compass*

1. Lid forming a cross with a center hole controlling the float
2. Float with lodestone
3. AUSTR, east
4. LANDSUDR, southeast
5. SUDR, south
6. UTSUDR, southwest
7. VESTR, west
8. UTNORDR, northwest
9. NORDR, north
10. LANDNORDR, northeast

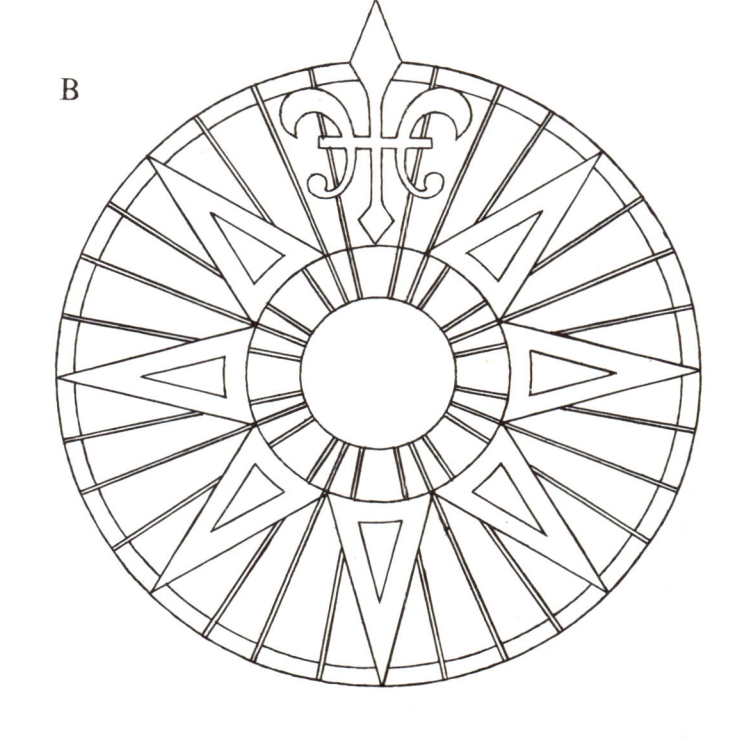

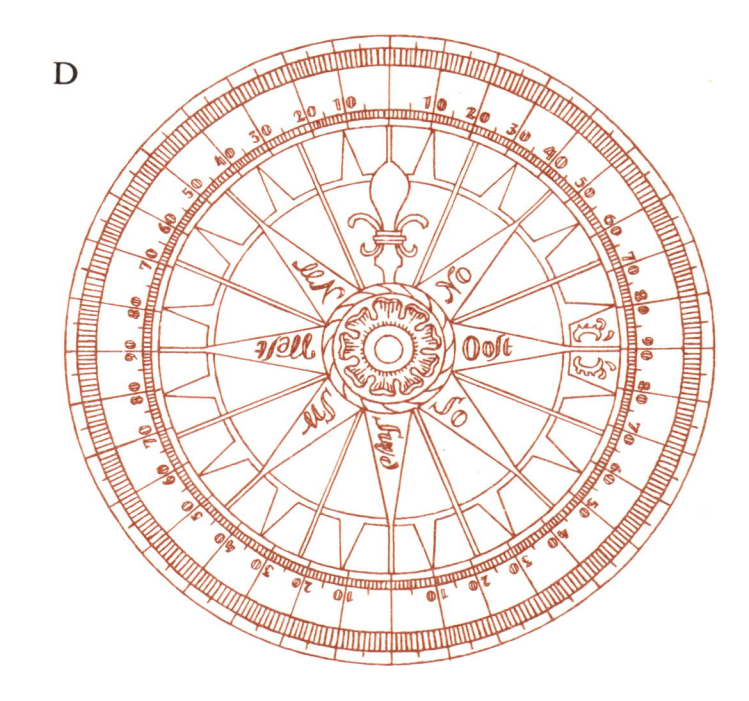

B *Compass card, 1345*

C *Compass card, 1545*

D *Compass card, end of the 18th century*

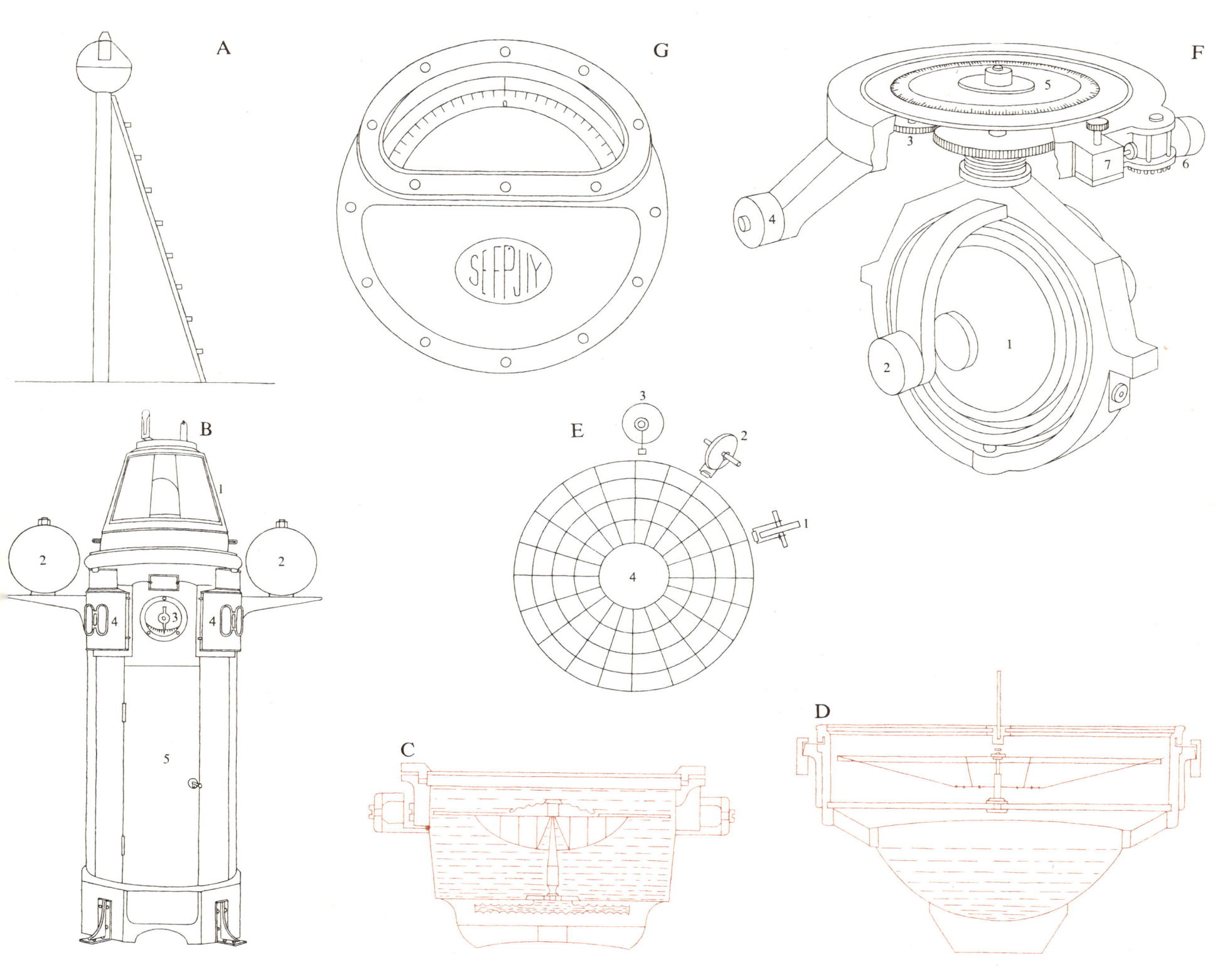

COMPASSES

A *Pole compass*
The laws of deviation were not fully understood in the early iron vessels; one way to get the compass out of the influence of the iron was to place the compass on a pole — often on a level so high that a ladder was needed to reach it

B *Compensating binnacle*
Later, this deviation was compensated for by soft iron and permanent magnets in a binnacle
1. Protecting hood with a pelorus mounted on top
2. Quadrantal correctors
3. Clinometer
4. Paraffin oil lamps for emergency lighting
5. Locker for permanent magnets

C *Liquid compass, sectional drawing*
In most ship's compasses the compass card is immersed in a liquid which moderates its motion

D *Dry compass, sectional drawing*

E *The gyrocompass principle*
1, 2, 3 A pendulous gyro always adjusts its axis toward the North Pole
3. A gyro axis pointing north
4. The North Pole

F *Inside view of a gyrocompass*
A gyrocompass is not influenced by deviation, but shows true north
1. Rotor case
2. Compensating weights
3. Motor
4. Bearings
5. Compass card
6. Repeater transmitter
7. Correcter for speed and latitude

G *Gyro-repeater compass*

231

NAVIGATIONAL INSTRUMENTS

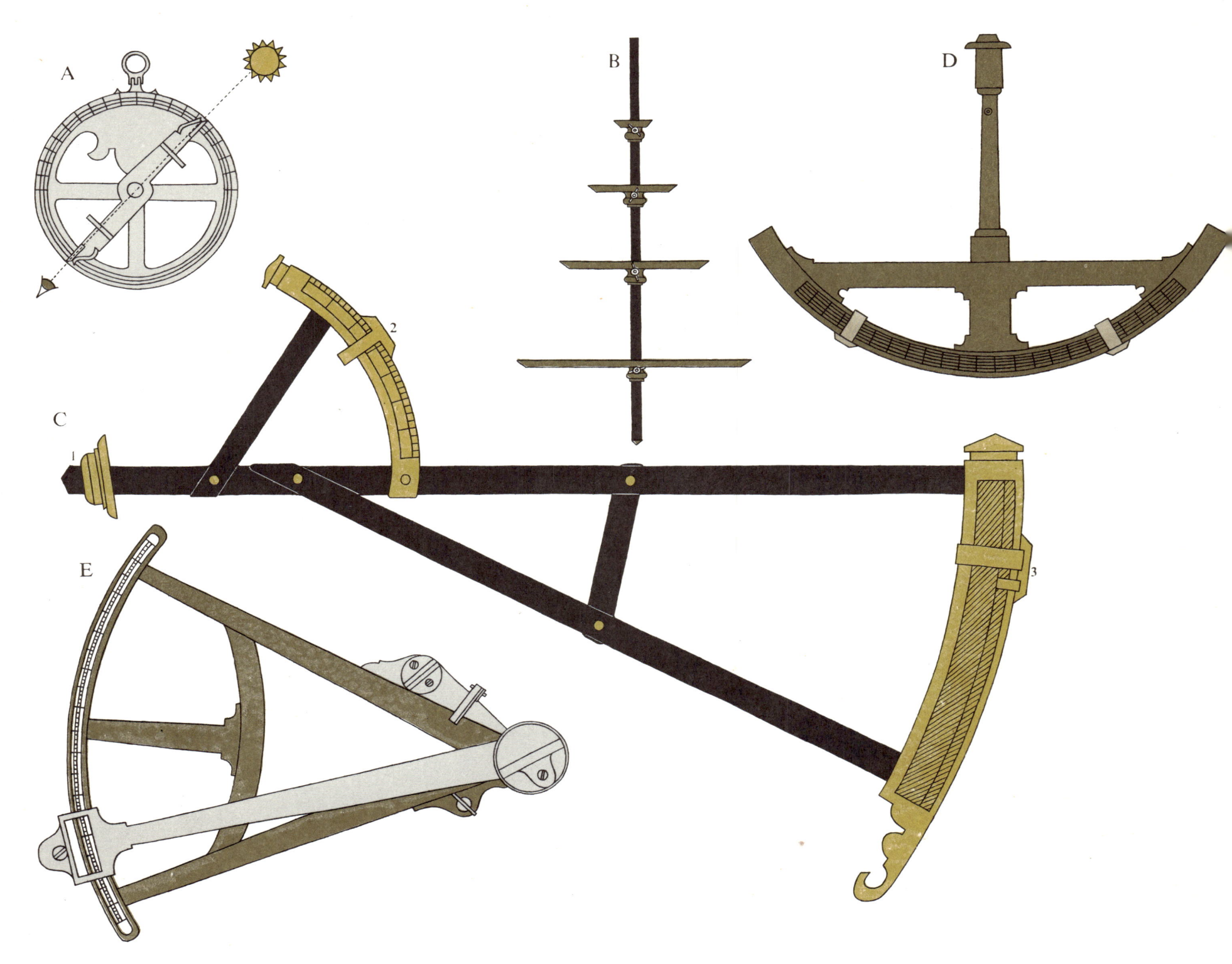

OLD NAVIGATIONAL INSTRUMENTS

A Astrolabe, constructed by the Arabs in the 10th century, and used, mostly by the Spaniards and Portuguese, up to the 17th century. It consists of a freely suspended graduated ring with a diametrical ruler holding two sight vanes through which the sun or a star may be observed, the altitude being read off on the circle.

B The fore staff is composed of a square staff and three vanes of different lengths. The sides of the staff have different scales, each corresponding to one of the vanes. When observing the altitude of the sun (star) only one vane is used. Holding one end of the staff to his eye, the observer moves the vane until he sees its lower end level with the horizon and the upper end in one with the sun. The altitude is read off where the vane cuts the staff.

C Davis' quadrant is composed of two arcs of a circle having the same center and three vanes: the horizon vane (1) with a slot, the shade vane (2), and the sight vane (3) with a sight hole. The horizon vane is fixed at the center, the other two vanes run upon the arcs. The quadrant is used with the observer's back to the sun. The shade vane is set at a suitable number of degrees, and the observer moves the sight vane until he observes the sun's shadow in one with the horizon, as seen through the slot in the horizon vane.

D Gunter's quadrant is made on the same principles as the Davis' quadrant, and it is used with the observer's back to the sun.

E Hadley's octant, invented in 1731, and a forerunner of the sextant. The octant brought the art of measuring altitudes at sea to theoretical perfection, and later improvements are due to better methods of manufacturing only.

SEXTANT

A MODERN SEXTANT

The sextant is an improvement on Hadley's octant, which is said to have been invented in 1731. The sextant is a portable, reflecting astronomical instrument for measuring angles. When used, it can be held in the hand without a stand, which is essential on board ships at sea. The instrument consists of a sector-shaped frame with a graduated arc of a circle. Pivoted at the center of the arc is a radius bar, which swings across the surface of the graduated arc. The principal parts of a sextant are:

1. The frame
2. The arc, known as the limb
3. The index bar
4. Clamping mechanism
5. Micrometer screw
6. Index mirror
7. Horizon glass
8. Telescope
9. Index shades
10. Horizon shades
11. Measured angle
12. Reading of measured angle, here 45° 0'

BEARINGS

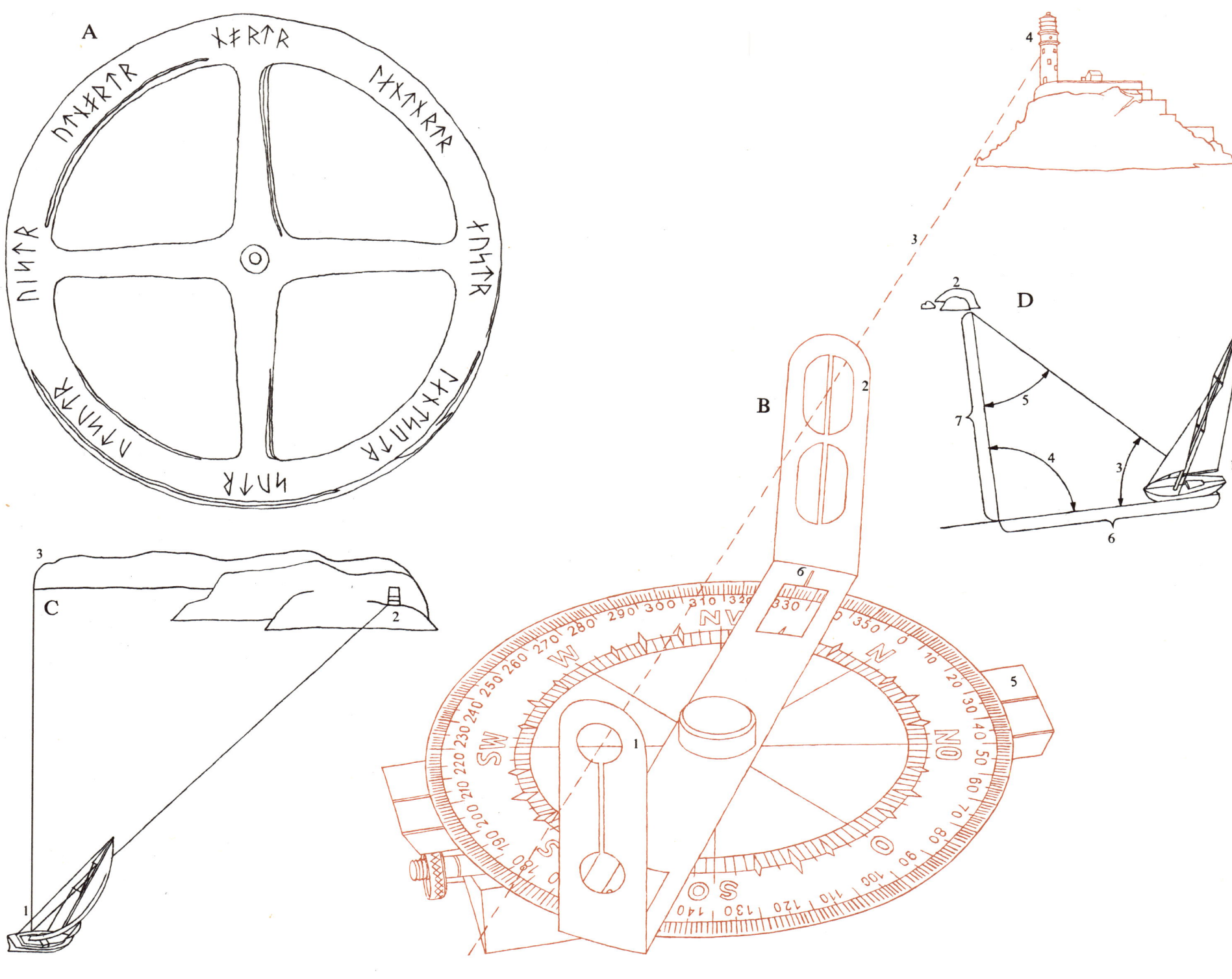

BEARINGS

A *Reconstruction of a compass card from the Viking Age*

B *Pelorus*
1, 2 Sight vanes
3 Position line
4 Object
5 Fore-and-aft mark to which the ship's course on the pelorus is clamped
6 Compass bearing

C *Cross bearing*
The exact position of the ship (1) will be known if bearings of two objects (2 and 3) are taken at the same time

D *Distance by four-point bearing*
When a fixed object (2) is bearing 45 degrees on the bow (3) note the time or log. Then the same course is steered until the object bears on the beam, or 90 degrees from the course (4). The distance (6) run by the ship (1) in the interval is the distance (7) of the object when abeam. This is clear from the fact that the ship's course and the two bearings form an isosceles triangle (3, 4, 5), where the two sides (6, 7) are equal.

WIRELESS DIRECTION FINDER

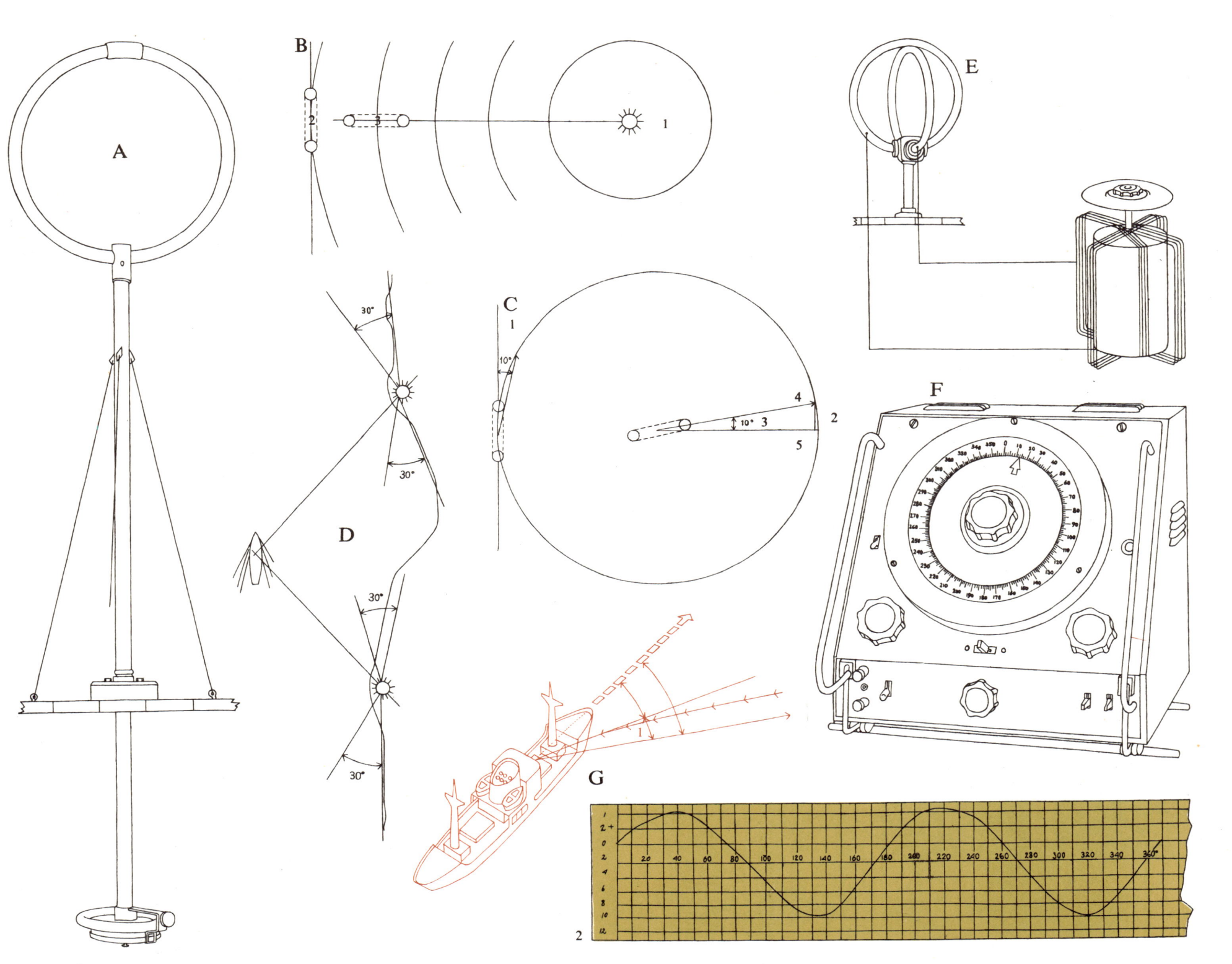

WIRELESS DIRECTION FINDER

A *With the aid of a rotatable aerial in the form of a loop or frame the bearing to a radio station may be fixed*

B *The theory*
1 Radio station sending
2 When the frame aerial is facing the direction of the station the incoming signal is not audible
3 When the frame aerial is edge on to the direction of the transmitting station, the signal strength is reaching its maximum

C *How to take a bearing*
With the loop aerial in the position of B 2, there is a well-defined silence arc of a few degrees on each side of the required direction. By rotating the frame either way the signal rises to audibility, and by reading off on the scale the two points limiting the arc of silence the midpoint between gives the direction of the transmitting station. If the frame is at B 3 and is turned 10 degrees, it makes no difference in the sound. Graphically it is as radius 4 projected on radius 5 to radius 5, or as Cos 10° to 1. In the position B 2 the difference in sound is quite audible, like the line C 2 compared with 0 or utter silence.

D *Cross bearing*
The wireless bearings are generally taken as cross bearings in the same manner as optical bearings. Sectors of 30° near the coastline should be avoided, as the bearings are unreliable in that zone.

E *Fixed loops*
Modern installations may have two fixed loops at right angles to one another. By a system of coils the same result is obtained as when a turnable frame aerial is used.

F *Direction finder operating panel*

G *Because of the deviation influence of the hull, the incoming radio wave will deviate from the true direction (1). A table of radio deviation may look like G 2. The deviation is relative to the ship's head only.*

235

RADIO NAVIGATION

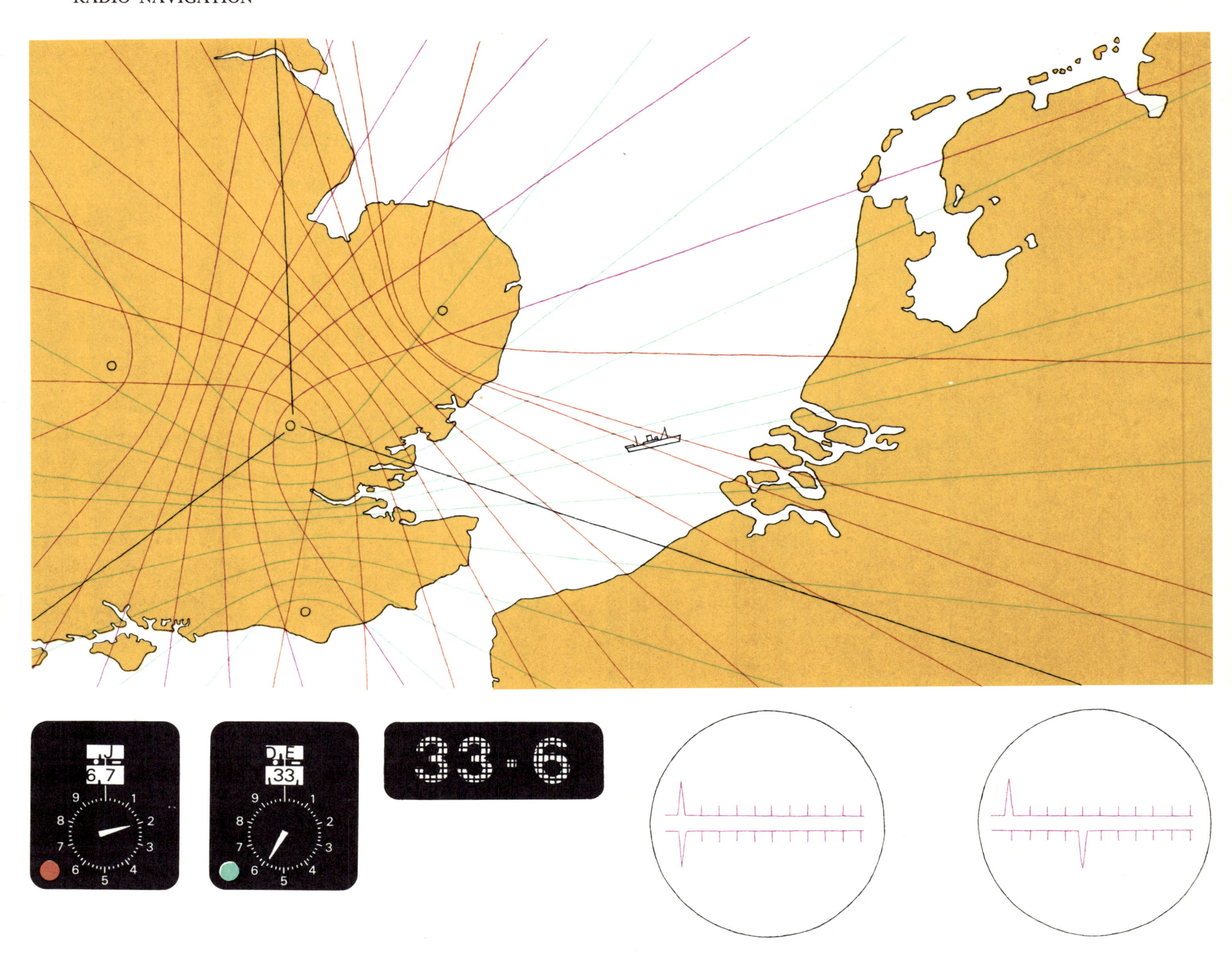

RADIO NAVIGATION: DECCA, LORAN, ETC.

By sending radio waves at exactly the same moment from two stations and by measuring the intervals between their arrival at a ship it is possible to fix a line on which the ship must be located. If the two pulses arrive at the same time, this line is the normal median line between the two stations. But if there is a difference in time, the line is a hyperbola. By measuring the difference in time between two pairs of stations, each pair giving a hyperbola, the ship must be on their intersection.

Special charts with these hyperbolas printed in red, green, and purple are used with the Decca system. The receiving unit registers the difference in time automatically and shows it as hyperbola numbers on three dials. Each Decca chain consists of one master station which together with three slave stations forms three pairs of senders. Each pair is represented in the Decca chart by a system of hyperbolas of its own color. On the red and green dials in the figure above it is possible to determine on which hyperbola the ship is positioned at the moment of observation.

In the Loran system the difference in time between the two sending stations is shown on a cathode ray tube, as illustrated to the right in the figure above. The left circle shows no difference between the pulses, and so the ship must be on the normal median line between the two stations. The right-hand picture indicates a difference in time, which means that the ship is on a hyperbola which is then determined in the same way as in the Decca system.

RADAR (page 237)

A *Principles of radar*
A scanner (1) sends out high-frequency radio pulses in a beam (2), which is very narrow in the horizontal plane. The beam sweeps around the horizon through the rotation of the scanner. The radio pulses are fed to the scanner through a wave guide (3). The target (4), which is hit by the beam, reflects part of it (5) back to the scanner, and through the wave guide the echo signal goes to the T.R. unit (6). Here, the signal is transformed so that the P.P.I. (7), which is the Plan Position Indicator, can give a picture

Continued

RADAR

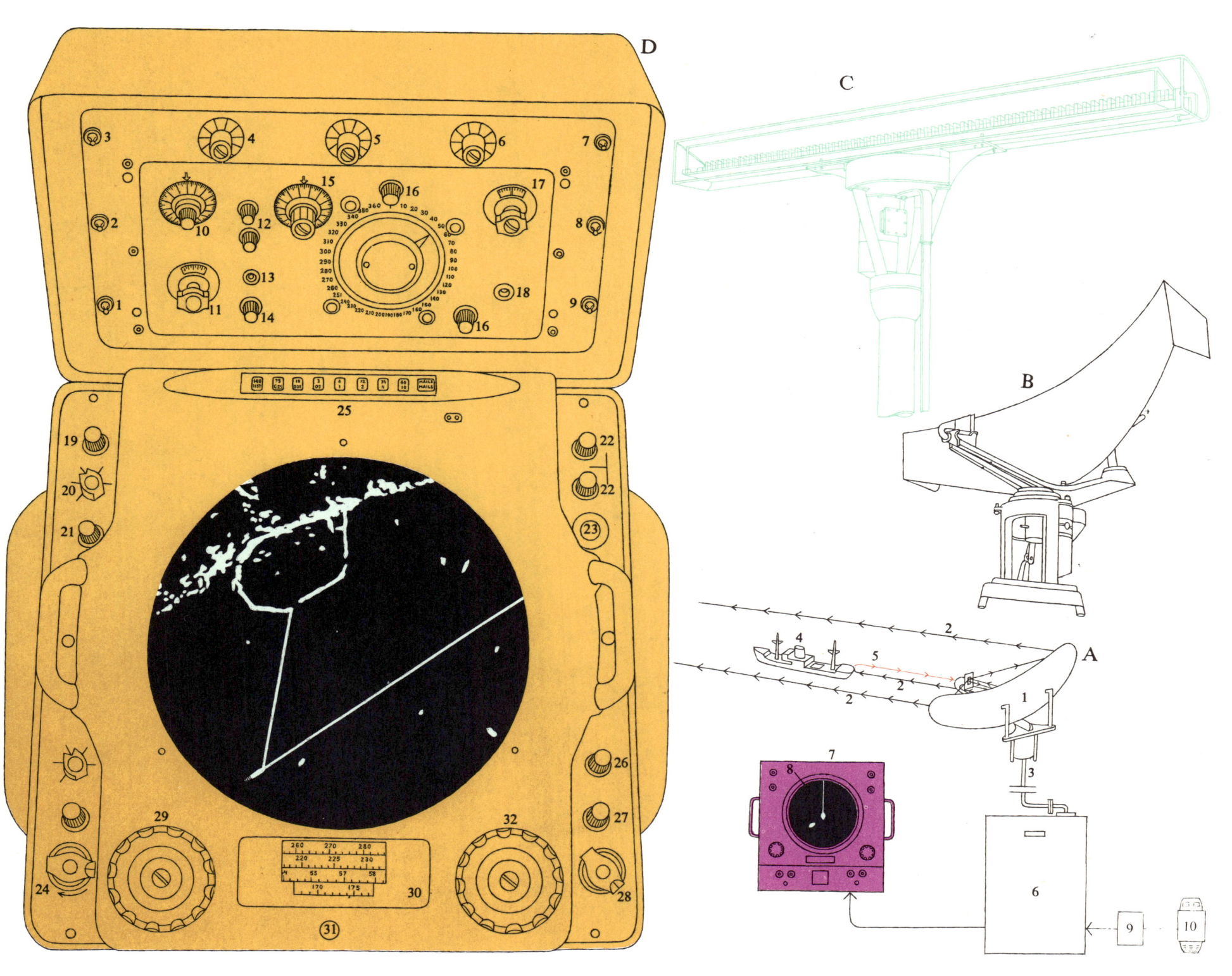

signal. On the P.P.I. tube's screen (8) a line appears at the center signal. On the P.P.I. tube's screen (8) a line to the edge of the tube and in the same direction as that in which the scanner is pointing. The light intensity on the line is strengthened by the target's echo signal, and in this way marks the target on the screen. The bearing is given by the direction of the line from the center of the screen, and the target's range by the distance of the echo from the center of the screen.

- 9 Voltage regulator or stabilizer
- 10 Motor generator
- B 6-foot scanner
- C Slotted wave guide scanner
- D True motion radar
- 1 Radar on/off
- 2 Scanner on/off
- 3 Standby/transmit
- 4 Tuning
- 5 Gain
- 6 Anti-clutter sea
- 7 Tx/Rx monitor
- 8 Power monitor on/off
- 9 Pulse length
- 10 Hand speed control
- 11 Speed input selection
- 12 N/S and E/W re-sets
- 13 Re-set
- 14 Log flasher
- 15 Course-made-good control
- 16 Compass repeater
- 17 Presentation switch
- 18 Relative motion warning
- 19 Focus
- 20 Tube brilliance
- 21 Anti-clutter rain control (variable F.T.C or differentiation)
- 22 Shift control
- 23 Illumination dimmers
- 24 Range scale switch
- 25 Range scale and range ring interval indicator
- 26 Range ring brilliance control
- 27 Range marker brilliance control
- 28 Interscan and variable range marker range scale
- 29 Bearing cursor control
- 30 Bearing and range measurement scales
- 31 Heading marker control
- 32 Coarse and fine ranging controls

237

LIGHTHOUSES

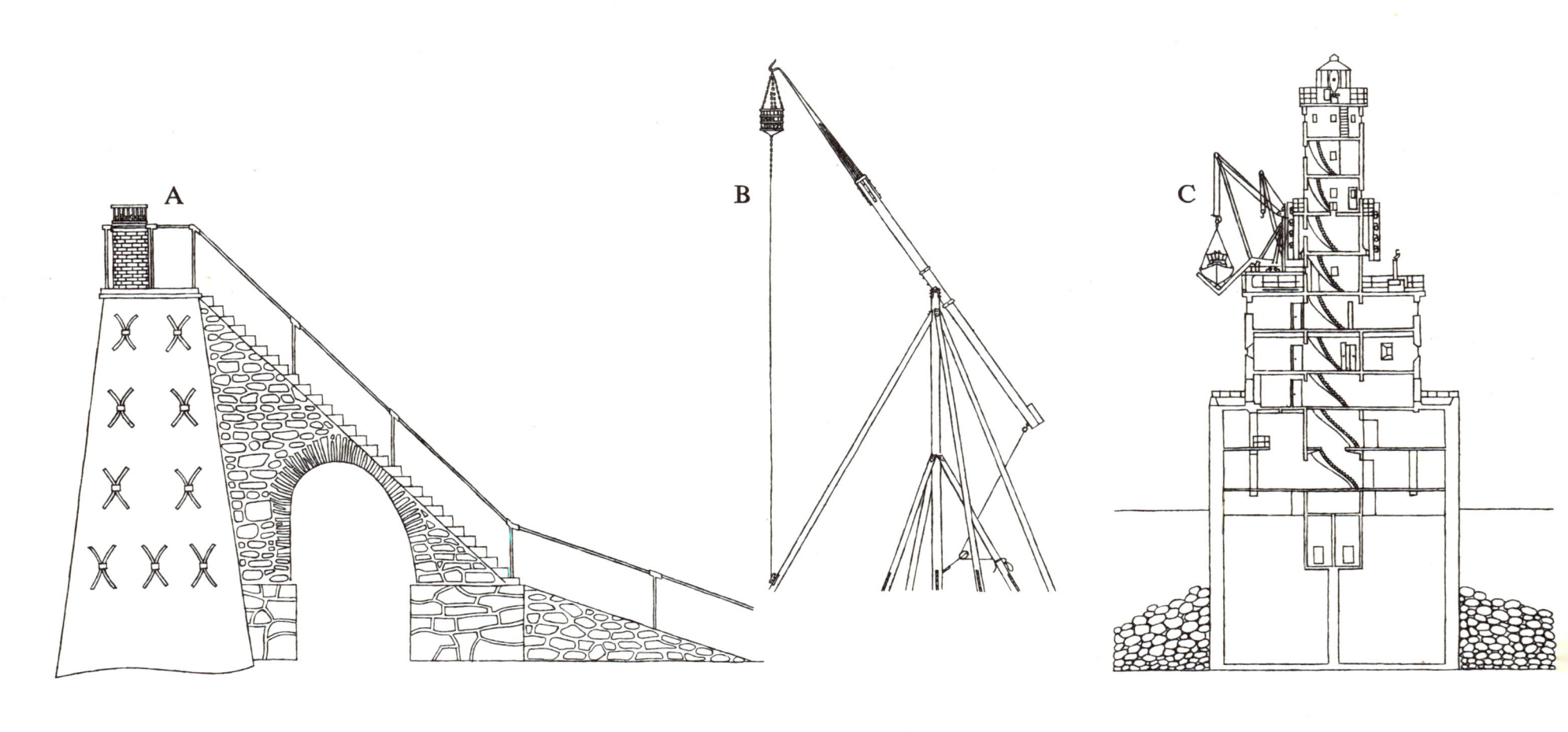

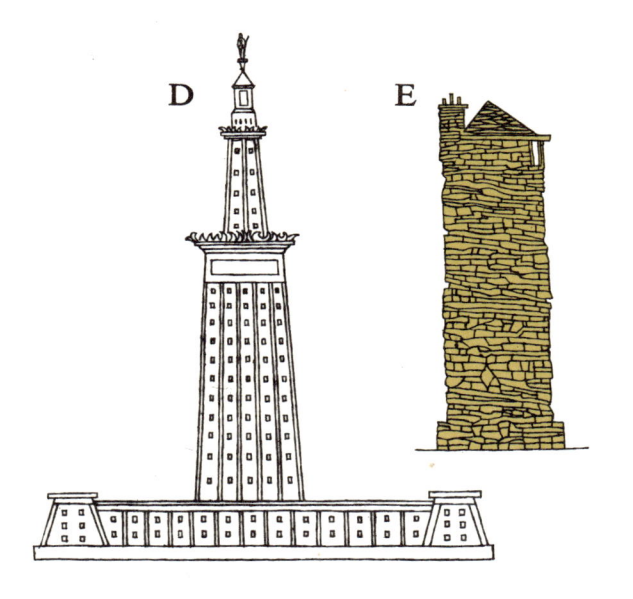

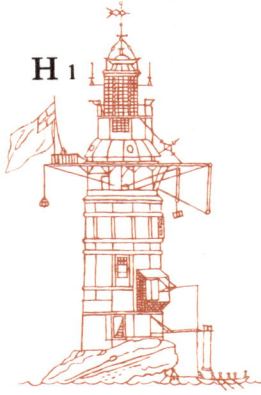

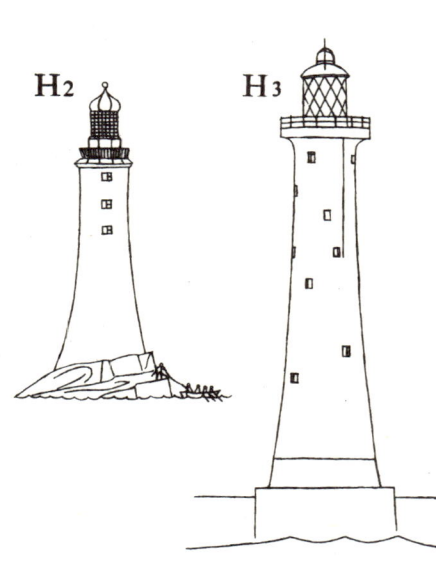

LIGHTHOUSES

- A Open coal fire at Djursten, Sweden, 1765
- B Fire on tilting spar, 1635
- C Modern caisson lighthouse, built of concrete on shore, launched, and towed to its station and there sunk
- D Pharos at Alexandria, 300 B.C.
- E Torre de Herculum at Coruna, at the time of Christ
- F Tour d'Ordre at Boulogne, A.D. 40
- G Cordouan at the mouth of Girande estuary in France, 1610
- H Eddystone light in the Channel
  - 1 1698 (at low water)
  - 2 1759 (at low water)
  - 3 1882 (at high water)

LIGHTHOUSE LAMPS

LIGHTHOUSE LAMPS

A *Lighthouse lamp for paraffin oil with 4 wicks, 1880's*

B *Lens arrangement with Fresnel's lenses and prisms, about 6 feet diameter; 500,000 Heffner lights*

C *Light buoy*
1 Lamp burning acetylene gas
2 Sun valve, which puts the light out in daytime and thus reduces the consumption of gas by 50%
(1 and 2 are shown in detail in D)

3 Radar reflector
4 Whistle
5 Mooring chain
6 Anti-rotating fin
7 Ballast

D *Lamp and sun valve*
1 Sun valve
2 Fresnel lens

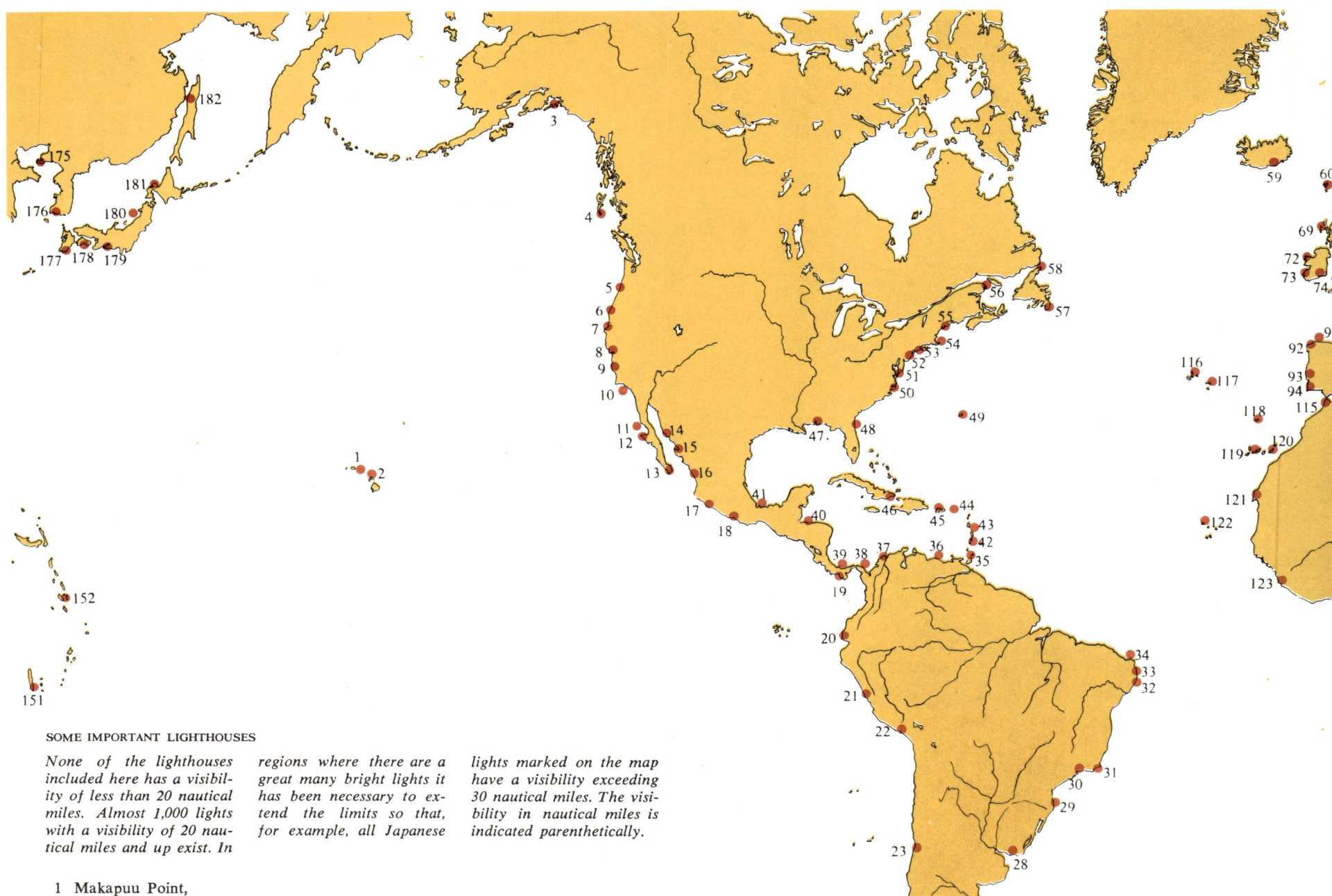

LIGHTHOUSES

SOME IMPORTANT LIGHTHOUSES

None of the lighthouses included here has a visibility of less than 20 nautical miles. Almost 1,000 lights with a visibility of 20 nautical miles and up exist. In regions where there are a great many bright lights it has been necessary to extend the limits so that, for example, all Japanese lights marked on the map have a visibility exceeding 30 nautical miles. The visibility in nautical miles is indicated parenthetically.

1 Makapuu Point, Oahu (27)
2 Molokai (28)
3 Cape Hinchinbrook (22)
4 Cape St. James, Queen Charlotte Islands (24)
5 Main Channel (22)
6 Cape Blanco (22)
7 Cape Mendocino (28)
8 Farallon, San Francisco (26)
9 Point Sur (23)
10 Anacapa Island (23)
11 West Benito Island (28)
12 Natividad Island (26)
13 Cape Tosco (23)
14 Guaymas, Cape Haro (24)
15 Cerro Partido (24)
16 Mazatlán (30)
17 Punta de Campos (26)
18 Acapulco, Grifo Island (26)
19 Golfito (24)
20 Santa Elena Point (25)
21 Callao (25)
22 Atico Point (21)
23 Curaumilla Point (24)
24 Guafo Island (28)
25 New Year's Islands, Staten Island (20)
26 Cape Virgins (21)
27 Leones Isle (23)
28 Montevideo (29)
29 Arvoredo Islet (24)
30 Castelhanos Point (27)
31 Cape Frio (28)
32 Cape Agostinho (24)
33 Olinda Point (24)
34 Mel Point (24)
35 Chacachacare Islet, Trinidad (30)
36 El Roque (23)
37 Cartagena (26)
38 Manzanillo Point (24)
39 Bocas del Toro (23)
40 Port Cortez (23)
41 Roca Partida (23)
42 Cape Moul à Chique, St. Lucia (35)
43 La Trinité Bay, Martinique (27)
44 Hams Bluff, St. Croix (27)
45 Cape Borinquén (24)
46 Guantánamo (26)
47 Pensacola (20)
48 St. Augustine (20)
49 Gibb's Hill, Bermuda (26)
50 Cape Hatteras (20)
51 Cape Charles (20)
52 Chapel Hill Beacon (21)
53 Staten Island (21)
54 Cape Cod (20)
55 Seguin Island (20)
56 Cape Gaspé (26)
57 Cape Pine (40)
58 Belle Isle (28)
59 Dyrholaey (27)
60 Myggenaes (22)
61 Sumburgh Head, Shetland Islands (24)
62 Dunnet Head (24)
63 Whitby (22)
64 South Foreland (26)
65 Lizard (21)
66 Great Ormes Head (24)
67 St. Bees (25)
68 Mull of Galloway (25)
69 Barra Head (33)
70 Flannan Islands, Hebrides (24)
71 Cape Wrath (27)
72 Clare Islands (25)
73 Bull Rock (23)
74 Mine Head (23)
75 Cape Stolbiovo (20)
76 Kharlov Island (27)
77 Vardöy (22)
78 Udsire (22)
79 Kullen (24)
80 Hogland (26)
81 Dager Ort, Kopu (25)
82 Dornbusch (24)
83 Stevns Klint (21)
84 Hirtshals (20)
85 Helgoland (24)
86 Hook of Schouwen (41)
87 Cape Gris-Nez (21)
88 Cape La Heve (27)
89 Ouessant (20)
90 Biarritz (22)
91 Hercules Tower, Coruña (25)
92 Cape Finisterre (29)
93 Cape Roca (30)
94 Cape St. Vincent (22)
95 Mesa de Roldán (31)
96 Cape Nao (27)
97 Cape Formentor, Mallorca (30)
98 Cape San Sebastián (31)
99 Cape Camarat (28)
100 Punta del Faro (27)
101 Cape Pertusato (25)
102 Cape Sandalo (28)
103 Imperatore Point, Ischia (31)
104 Milazzo (24)
105 Cape Santa Maria di Leuca (25)
106 Sapientza (25)

LIGHTHOUSES

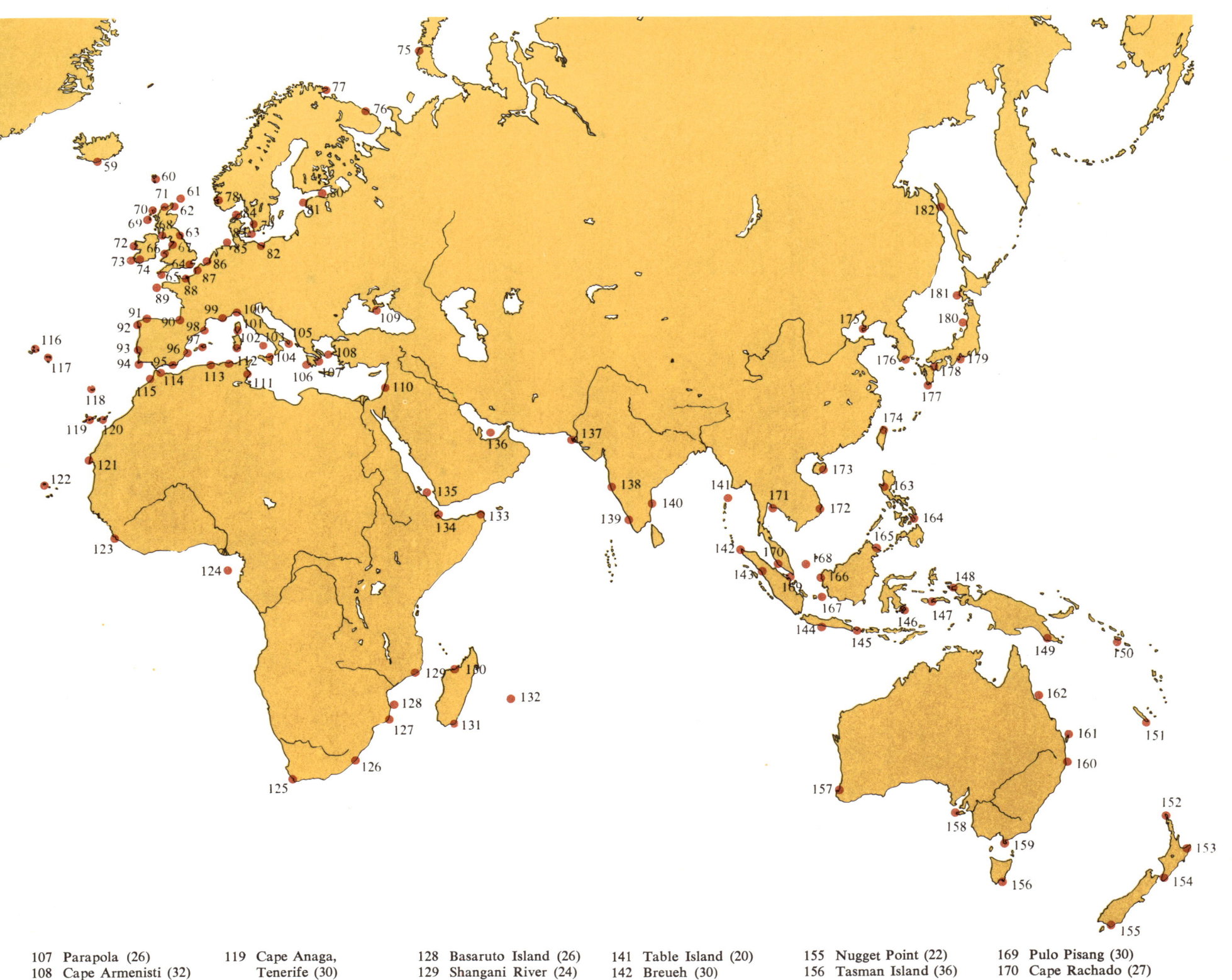

107 Parapola (26)	119 Cape Anaga, Tenerife (30)	128 Basaruto Island (26)	141 Table Island (20)	155 Nugget Point (22)	169 Pulo Pisang (30)
108 Cape Armenisti (32)	120 Isleta Point, Grand Canary (30)	129 Shangani River (24)	142 Breueh (30)	156 Tasman Island (36)	170 Cape Rachado (27)
109 Cape Meganom (25)	121 Cape Verde (26)	130 Katsepe Head (27)	143 Batu Mandi (30)	157 Cape Naturaliste (29)	171 Koh Pai (30)
110 Mount Carmel (30)	122 Fontes Pereira de Melo, Cape Verde Islands (27)	131 Taperina Point (24)	144 Chilachap (30)	158 Cape Borda (30)	172 Cape Padaran (30)
111 Cape Carthage (29)	123 Ponta Quicombo (28)	132 Flat Island, Mauritius (25)	145 Kelapa Islet (30)	159 Deal Island (40)	173 False Tinhosa (30)
112 Cape de Garde (30)	124 Ilha das Cabras, Sao Thome (25)	133 Cape Guardafui (Ras Asir) (35)	146 Wangi Wangi (29)	160 Cape Byron (26)	174 Agincourt Island, Hoka sho (30)
113 Cape Carbon (29)	125 Cape of Good Hope (23)	134 Ras-al-Bir (22)	147 Ambon Island (24)	161 Sandy Cape (27)	175 Gyoku San (41)
114 Ceuta (29)	126 Copper (28)	135 Jebel Teir (30)	148 Batanta (22)	162 Fitzroy Island (29)	176 Shashi To (24)
115 Cape Spartel (24)	127 Barra Falsa (27)	136 Jaziat Halul (21)	149 Port Moresby (24)	163 Cape Bolinao (24)	177 Toi Misaki (38)
116 Ribeirinha Point, Fayal (28)		137 Drigh Road (23)	150 Guadalcanal Island (20)	164 Suluan Island (28)	178 Okino-Shima (32)
117 Ferraria Point, San Miguel (25)		138 Aguada, Goa (23)	151 Port Noumea (22)	165 Sandakan (33)	179 Ko Shima (75)
118 Pargo Point, Madeira (35)		139 Kadalur Point (20)	152 Cape Reinga (31)	166 Great Sambas River (53)	180 Awo Shima (39)
		140 Madras (20)	153 East Cape (30)	167 Serutu Island (30)	181 Motsuta Misaki (40)
			154 Cape Palliser (23)	168 Anamba Islands (33)	182 Cape Lazareva (38)

241

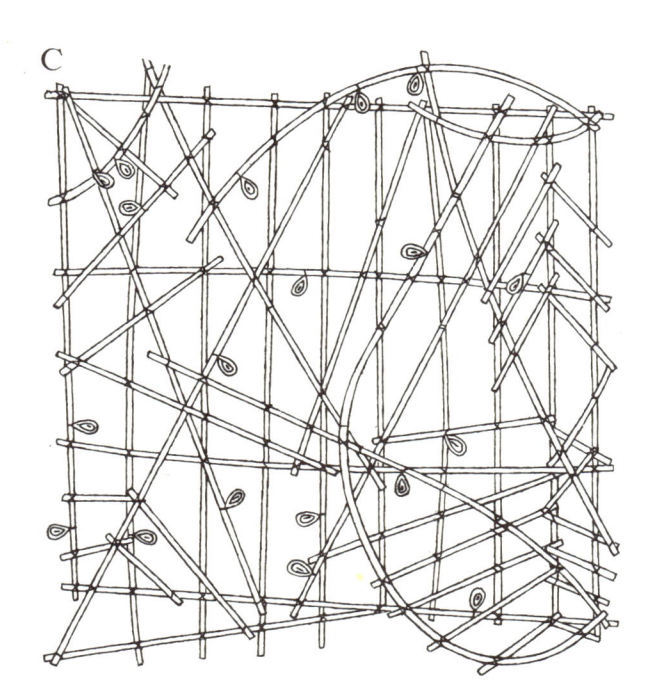

CHARTS

CHARTS

Verbal descriptions have probably existed as long as man has sailed. The oldest written "pilots" are the Greek Periples which gave distances and courses (about 300 B.C.). These were the origins of the Roman Portulanes. In the 15th and 16th centuries "pilots" were published in most West European countries.

A The depths off the Norwegian coast are described by Olaus Magnus, in 1555, as being bottomless.

B The title page of the Dutch "Het Leeskaartboek van Wisboy" (the "Chart book" from Visby), first published in 1551. Several editions followed in Dutch as well as in German. The book also contained woodcut shore views. This figure is from the edition of 1561.

C Native chart of the Marshall Islands consisting of a framework of palmleaf veins with shells or coral pieces indicating the different islands and their relative positions. The distances between the islands were not always known, but most important were the directions.

D Shore view showing transit marks, etc., on a modern chart or in a pilot.

CHARTS

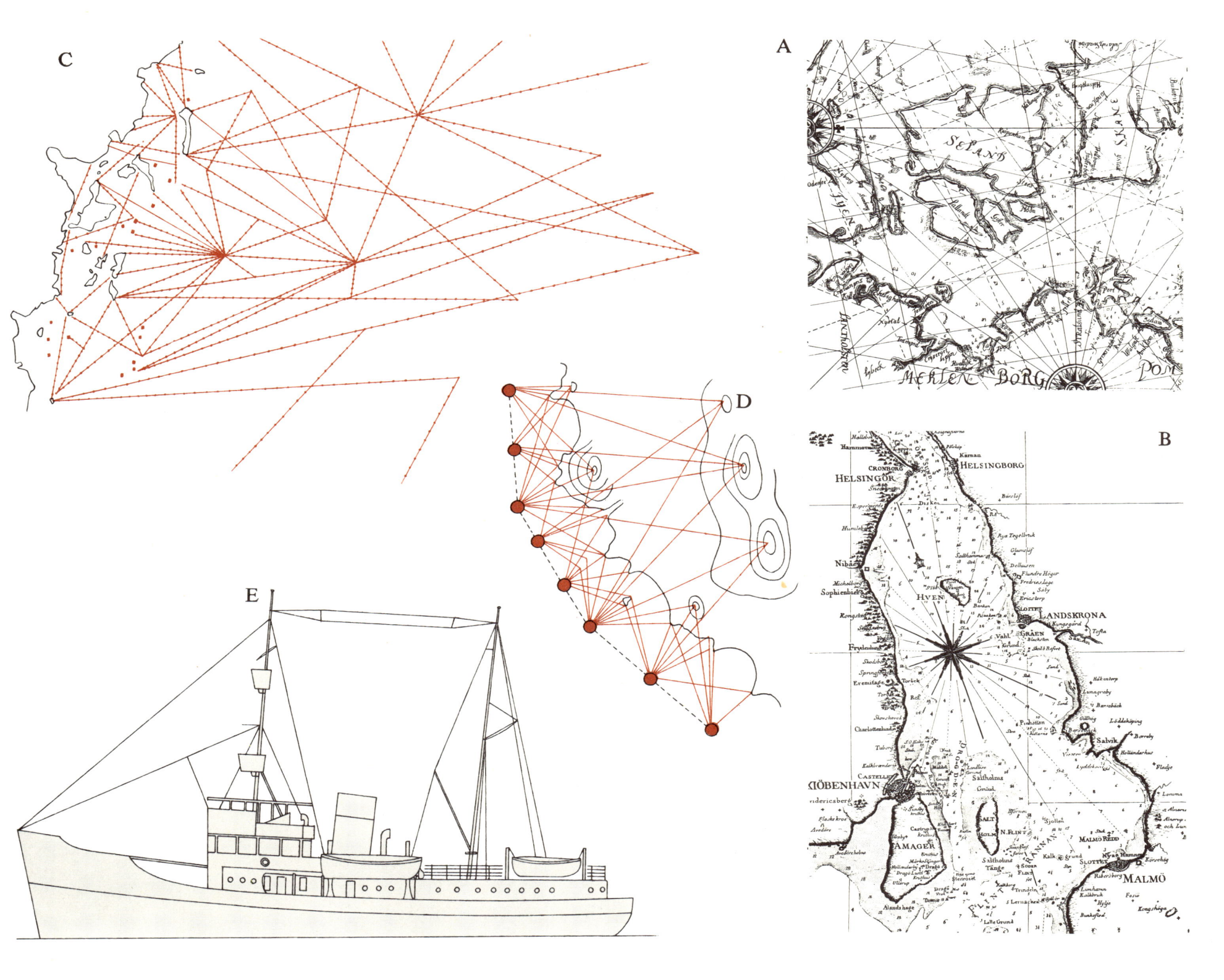

CHARTS AND SURVEYING

A *Detail from a Swedish chart of the Baltic, 1645*

B *A Swedish chart of the Sound, 1819; the same region is shown in the upper part of A*

C *Coast survey chart, beginning of the 19th century*

D *"Running survey," a common British method to plot the shore line*

E *Swedish surveying vessel, Gustaf af Klint*

THEORY OF SAILING

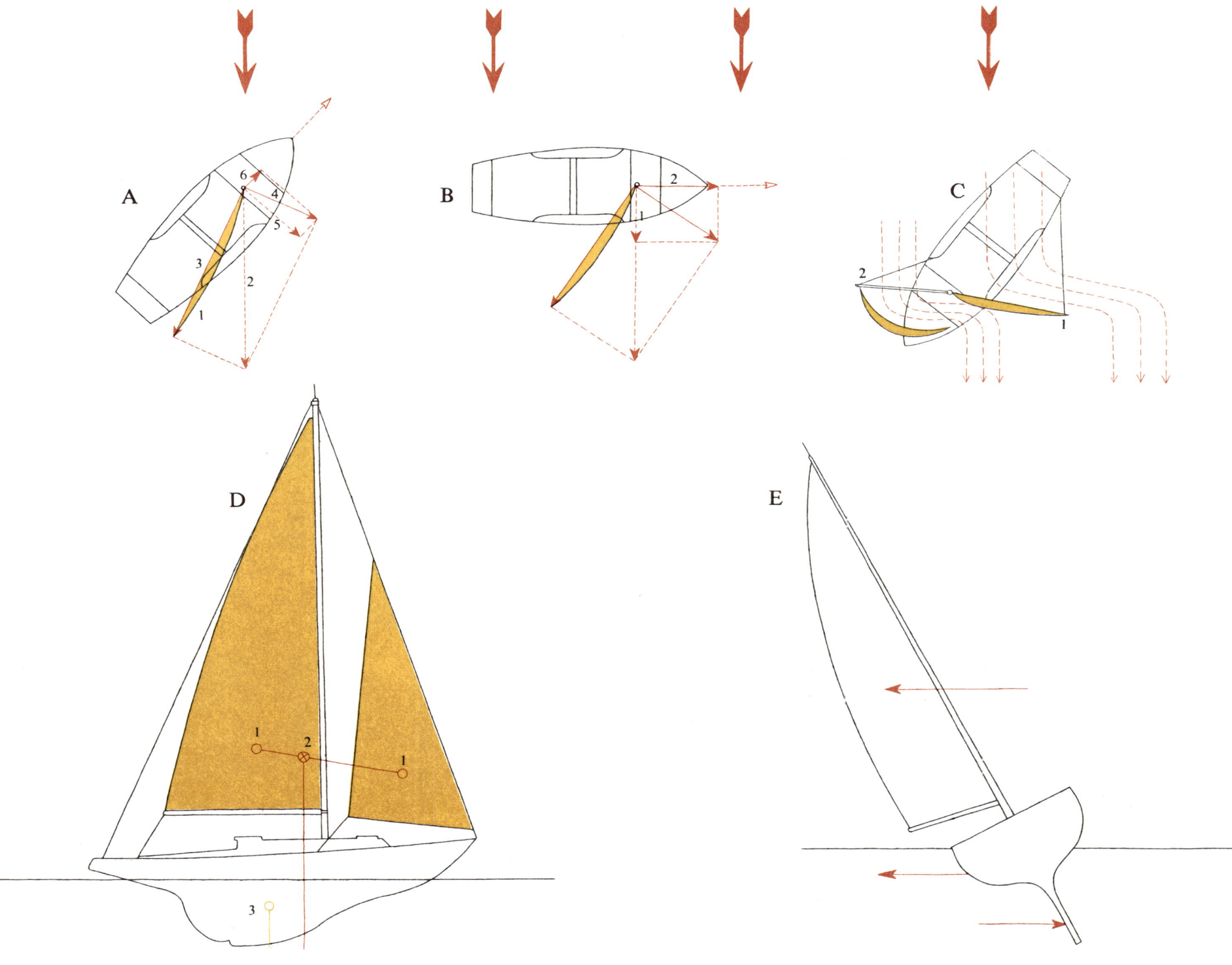

THEORY OF SAILING

A *A boat beating to windward*
1. Sail
2. The force and direction of the wind, which can be resolved into the two components, 3 and 4
3. This force blowing parallel to the sail may be disregarded
4. This force can be resolved into two components, 5 and 6
5. This force works abeam and tends to heel the boat and to drive it to leeward. This tendency, however, is largely overcome by the lateral resistance of the water on the boat's hull and keel.
6. Of the original wind force, it is this component only that carries the boat ahead

B *Reaching; the wind abeam*
1. When the wind is abeam the lateral component (1) is reduced and the fore and aft component (2) is increased. The boat moves faster than when beating to windward (A).

C *Running*
When running, the sails must not be at right angles to the direction of the wind
1. Mainsail
2. Spinnaker

D *Center of effort*
Every sail has a center of effort (1). The center of effort of the total sail area (2) is obtained by combining the centers of each sail. Theoretically, if the center of effort is ahead of the center of lateral resistance (3), the boat will tend to pay off from the wind. If 2 is abaft 3, the boat will tend to come up into the wind.
In reality, the boat, when sailing, is heeling to leeward and the force of the wind will be applied at the center of effort on the lee side of the boat and cause her to luff. To counteract this, the center of effort of the sails is always placed forward of the center of lateral resistance, as shown above.

E *A fact which is not familiar to everyone is that a drop keel under special circumstances may have a dangerous capsizing effect, for instance, if the boat when running suddenly broaches to.*

SET OF SAILS

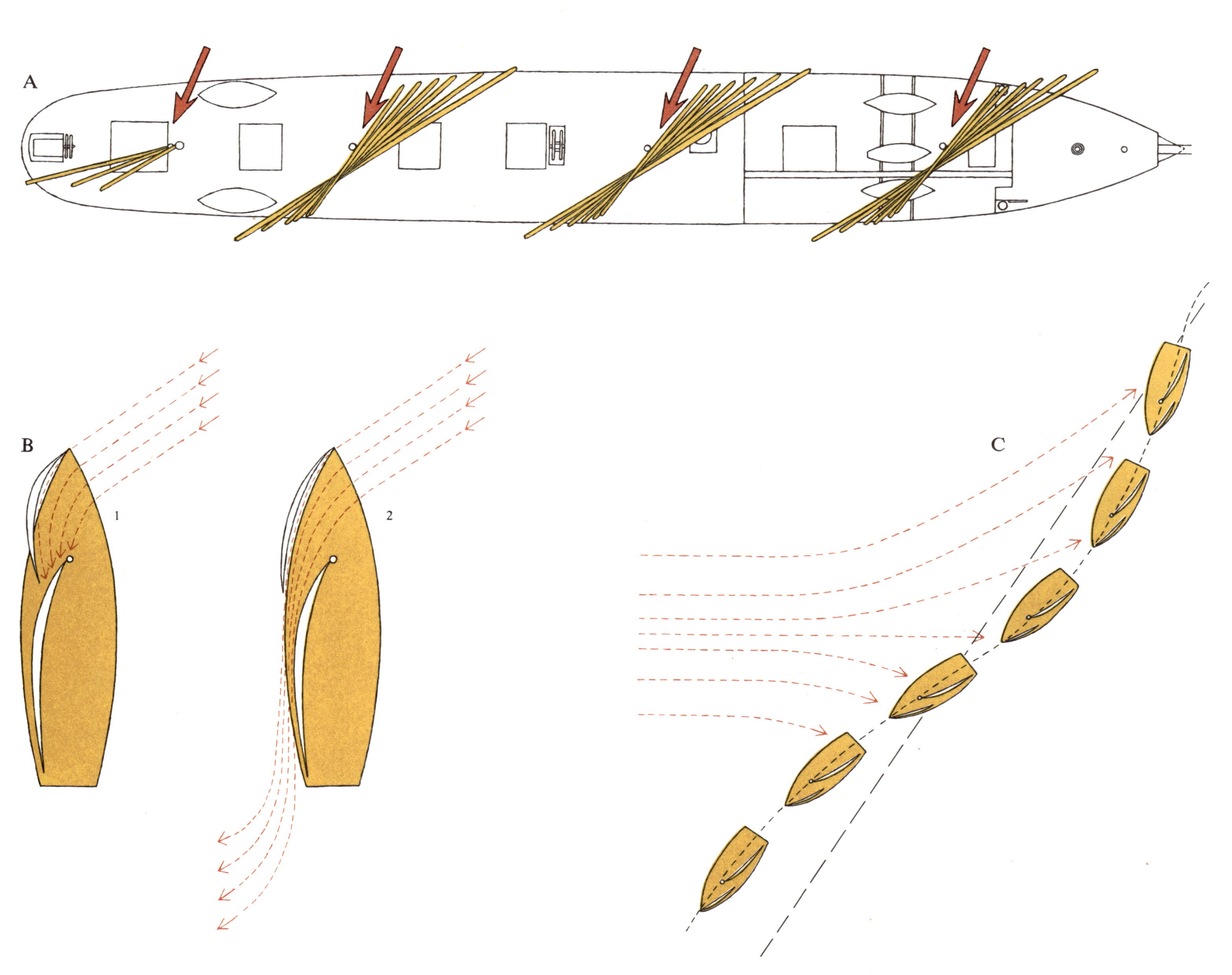

THE SET OF SAILS

A *A square-rigged vessel beating to windward*
In a square-rigger sailing on the wind the lower yards are always braced up more than the upper yards. The reason for this is that the lower sails cannot be set as flat as the upper sails, and thus require a broader wind to fill them than the small sails. Again, should the wind shift and the ship be caught aback, the upper sails will back first and warn the ship in time so that she can be paid off.

B *The lead of the fore staysail sheet*
1 There must be sufficient gap between the fore staysail and the mainsail, otherwise (as in the figure) the driving force of the mainsail will be reduced

2 A fore staysail which is correctly sheeted increases the suction on the lee side of the mainsail and thus increases its power

C *Unsteady wind*
A squall generally blows in a fan-shaped pattern. In spite of paying-off at the beginning and then luffing, the squall may be used to bring the boat to windward of her first track.

245

DIFFERENT COURSES

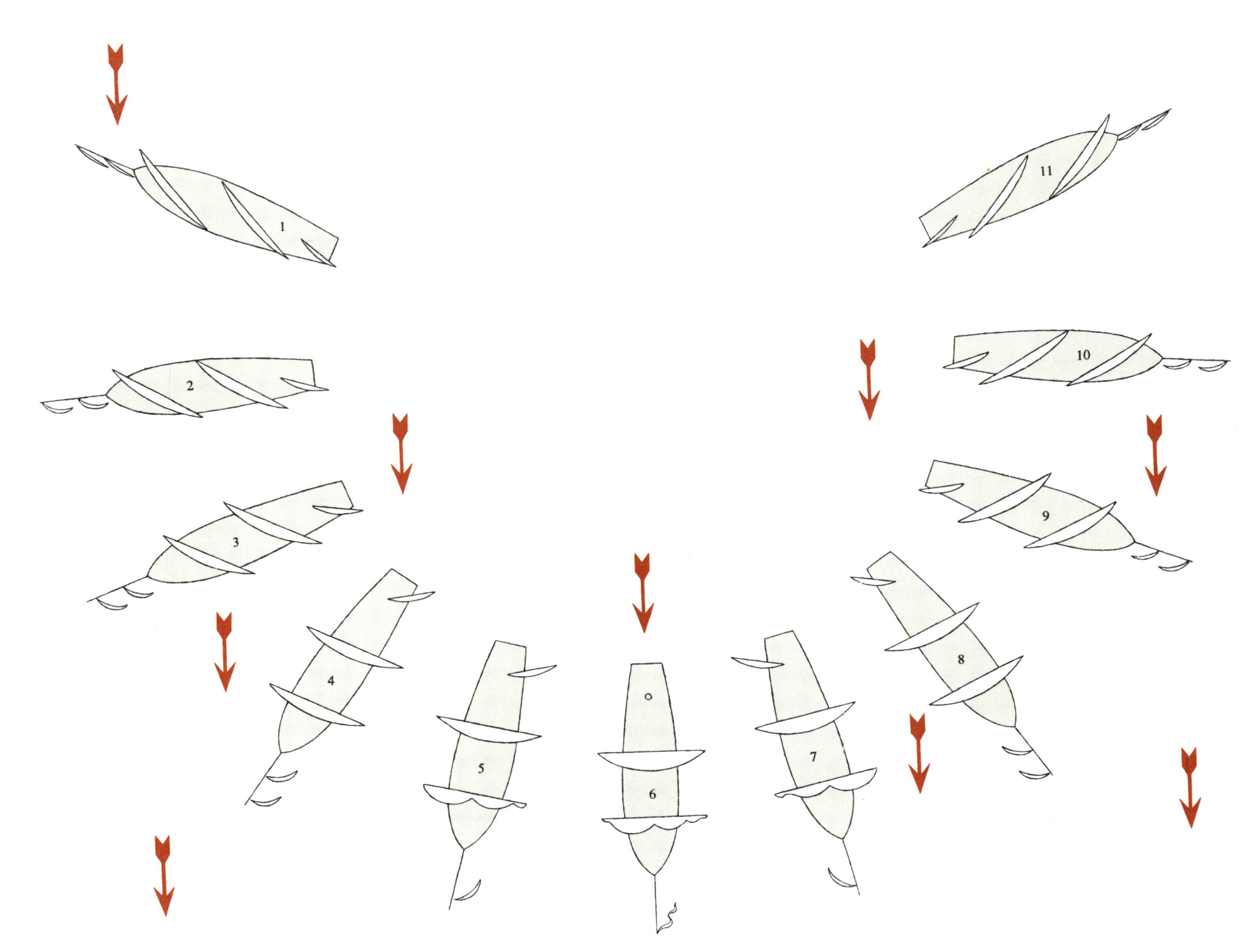

A BARK SAILING ON DIFFERENT COURSES

1. Bark sailing on the wind on the starboard tack
2. Sailing, reaching with wind abeam on the starboard side
3. Going large with the wind abaft the beam on the starboard side
4. Running free with the wind on the starboard quarter
5. Running before the wind; the wind is on the starboard side; headsails are partly blanketed, some staysails are furled
6. Running dead before the wind, scudding in a gale; spanker is furled, staysails not drawing, the headsails are blanketed
7. Running before the wind; wind is on the port side. Headsails are partly blanketed, some staysails are furled
8. Running free with the wind on the port quarter
9. Going large, sailing with a fair wind, with the wind abaft the beam on the port side
10. Sailing, reaching with the wind abeam on the port side
11. Sailing on the wind on the port tack

SMALL BOAT HANDLING

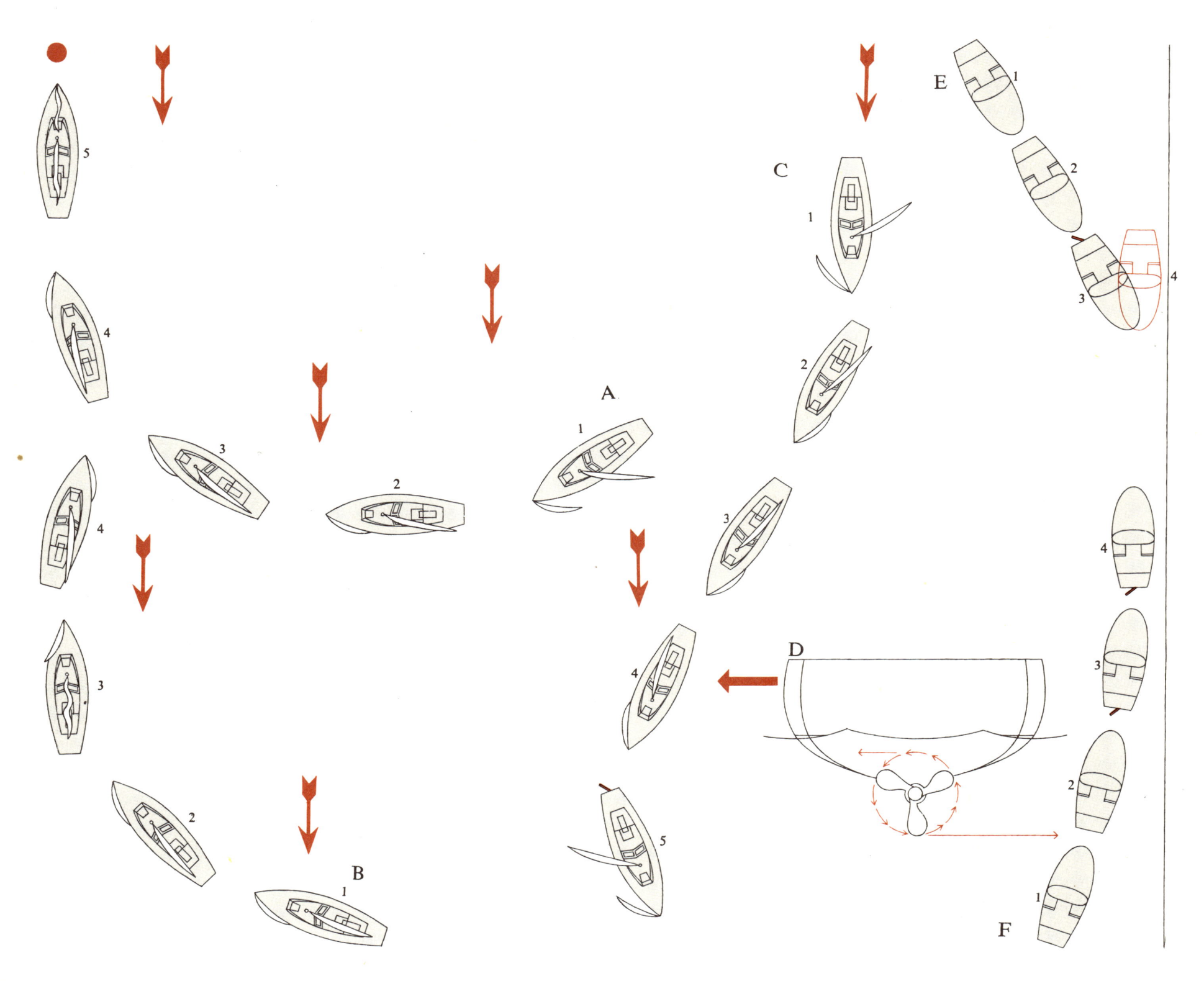

SMALL BOAT HANDLING

A *To fetch a buoy*
1. Sails set to the wind
2. Luff and trim sails to the wind
3. Luff and flatten in the sails
4. Luff as much as possible and spill the wind from the foresail and mainsail
5. Steer close to windward of the buoy and carefully judge the speed of approach

B *Going about*
1. Keep her full and by
2. "Helm's alee"
3. Flatten the foresail (applicable to dull-turning boats only)
4. Haul the foresail over and trim sheets by the wind on the new tack

C *Jibing*
1. Boat steering before the wind; you want to take the wind on the port quarter
2. Luff a little and shorten your sheets
3. By ready to jibe
4. Up helm; jibe easily and let the sheets run
5. Meet her and trim yaw sails

D *Yawing influence of right-hand propeller going astern;* the blades of the screw have a better grip in the water at the deepest part of the rotation, and work the stern to port

E *Going alongside, port side to the quay*
1. Approach the quay at a broad angle
2. Stop
3. Full astern
4. Stop

F *Starboard side to the quay*
1. Small angle to pier; stop
2. Slow astern
3. Port helm
4. Stop

247

WEARING

A SQUARE-RIGGED VESSEL, A THREE-MASTED BARK, WEARING

1. The bark is sailing on the wind on the starboard tack.
2. "Ready to wear ship!" The mainsail is clewed up and the braces are coiled down for running.
3. The spanker is furled. "Up helm!" "Square in the mainyard!" The wheel is put to port and the mainyard is squared.
4. Without sail aft the vessel is paying off.
5. The bark is before the wind. "Round forward!" The headsails are braced around and the jibs sheeted over to starboard.
6. When she is coming up on the new tack the headsails will meet her. The after yards are braced up.
7. The spanker is set and all sails are trimmed by the wind.
8. The bark is kept on the wind on the port tack. The main sail is set and the deck cleared up.

248

TACKING

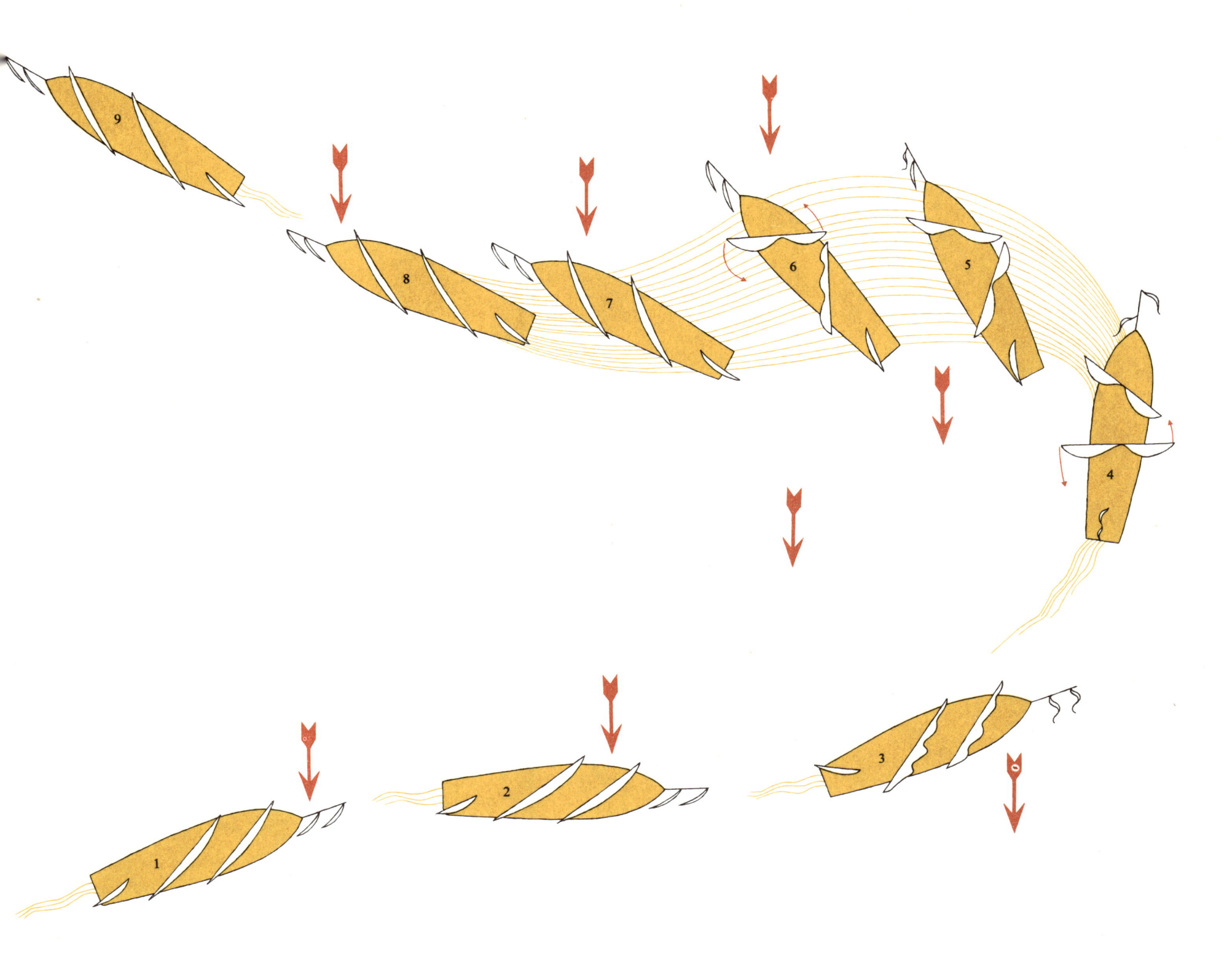

A SQUARE-RIGGED VESSEL, A THREE-MASTED BARK, TACKING

1. The bark is sailing on the wind on the port tack. "Ready about!"
2. She is kept off a little to make all sails draw better to increase the speed.
3. "Helm's alee!" The wheel is put down, the headsheets are let go to make the jibs spill the wind; the spanker is hauled aweather to assist the luffing.
4. The bark is nearly into the wind. Now "Mainsail haul!" The mainyards are braced around, the jibs are hauled over and sheeted home, while the vessel is head in the wind.
5. The movement ahead is decreasing. With the headsails aback the bark is forced over to port.
6. When the sails of the mainmast begin to fill, the order is, "Let go and haul!" and the headsails are hauled around.
7. The vessel is paying off until the sails are filling. All sails are trimmed by the wind.
8. The bark is going ahead, the wake is becoming normal.
9. She is kept on the wind on the starboard tack; the running gear is coiled down.

BACKING AND FILLING

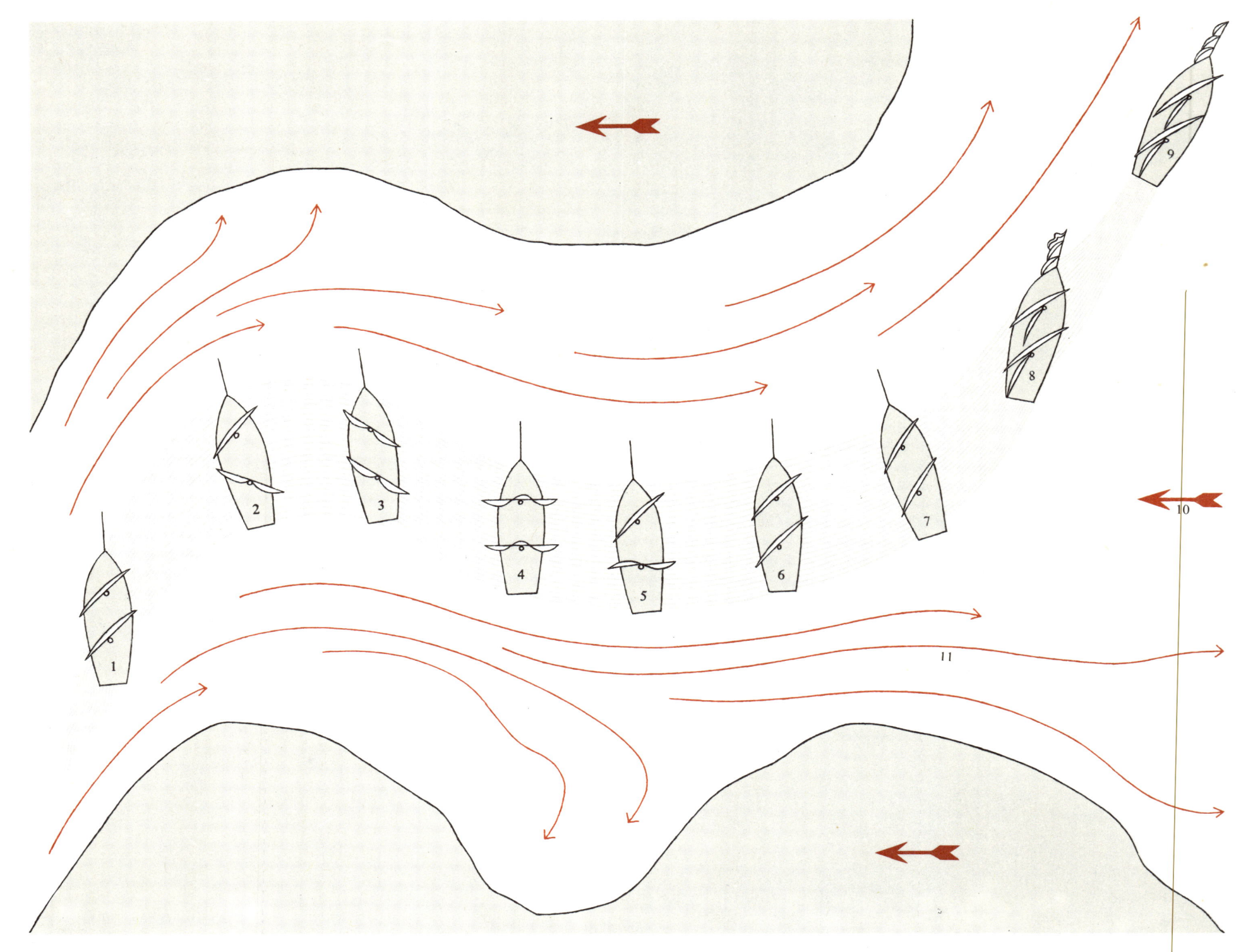

A SAILING VESSEL, A BRIG, BACKING AND FILLING DOWN A RIVER WITH THE EBB TIDE, AGAINST A HEADWIND. SHE HAS ONLY THE TOPSAILS SET.

1. The brig is filling both topsails to make her move ahead to keep her in the fairway
2. Backing the mainyard stops her progress and makes her drift broadside downriver
3. Backing all makes her take a stern board
4. By pointing the yards into the wind she is made to stand still and drift with the ebb tide
5. Filling the fore topsail makes her draw ahead
6. Filling all makes her go ahead more
7. She is kept off a little to increase her movement through the water
8. She is making sail, and trims them by the wind
9. She is clear of the river and stands to sea under all sail on the starboard tack
10. Wind direction
11. The ebb tide

TO HEAVE TO

TO HEAVE TO AND TO GOOSE-WING A SAIL

When a sailing ship was in a contrary gale of wind the order to heave to meant that most of the sails were taken in and the helm was put down. This kept the ship's head to the wind, and, with the sea on the bow, she would ride well enough as long as some sail could be carried. This full-rigged ship has the fore topmast staysail, the mizzen staysail and the goose-winged main lower topsail set. To furl the weather half of a lower topsail was the last resource to shorten sail without having to furl all and drift under bare poles. The large scale drawing shows a part of the main mast with the goose-winged lower topsail. The numbers indicate:

1. Main mast
2. Heel of topmast
3. Mainyard with mainsail furled
4. Upper topsail yard with topsail furled
5. Lower topsail yard
6. Goose-winged lower topsail
7. Heavy lashing on sail, parceled to protect sail from chafe
8. Size of lower topsail when set
9. Lower topsail buntlines
10. Lower topsail clewlines

251

MANEUVERING

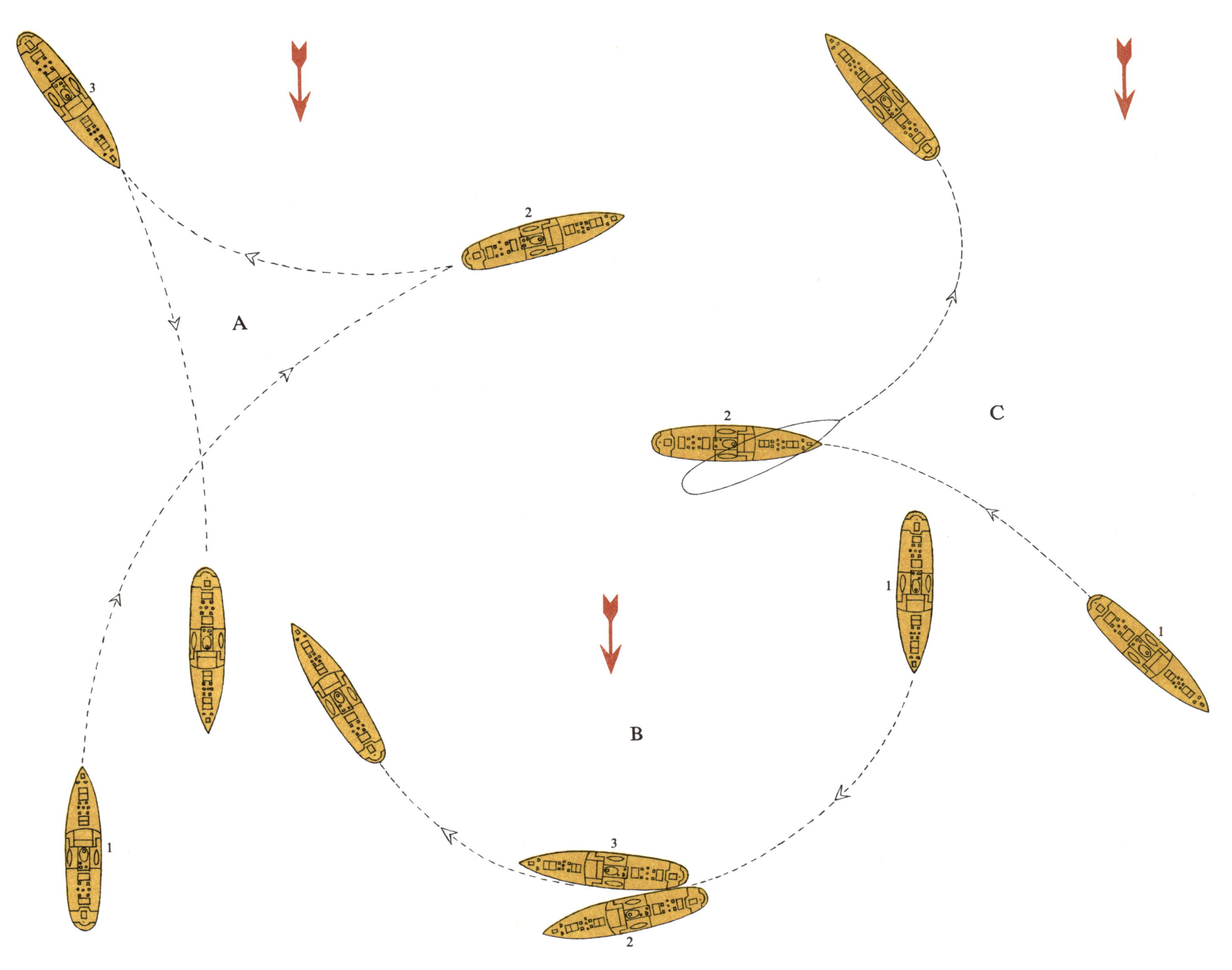

MANEUVERING A POWERED SHIP WITH A RIGHT-HANDED SINGLE SCREW *(Page 253)*

A *Turning with the wind ahead*
1. Ahead with the rudder hard astarboard
2. Full astern with the rudder hard aport
3. Ahead with starboard rudder
4. Steady the helm on the new course

B *Turning with the wind astern*
1. Ahead with the rudder astarboard
2. Full astern with starboard rudder
3. Before getting sternway: Full ahead with starboard rudder and the screw effect will help swing the ship
4. Steady on the new course

C *Turning with the wind on the quarter*
1. Astern with the rudder hard astarboard
2. Full ahead with port rudder; steady the helm on the new course

A *The effect of the rudder*
1. When turning, the power of the rudder may be dissolved into two components: one braking the ship and one forcing the stern aside
2. When the ship starts turning, a resistance arises on the bow which co-operates with the rudder
3. Only after several ship's lengths will the stern pass the original track

B *Heeling during a turn*
1. At first, the ship is heeled inward. This depends upon the fact that the rudder component and the lateral resistance work on different levels. Then, the centrifugal power applied at the center of gravity makes the ship list outward.

252

MANEUVERING

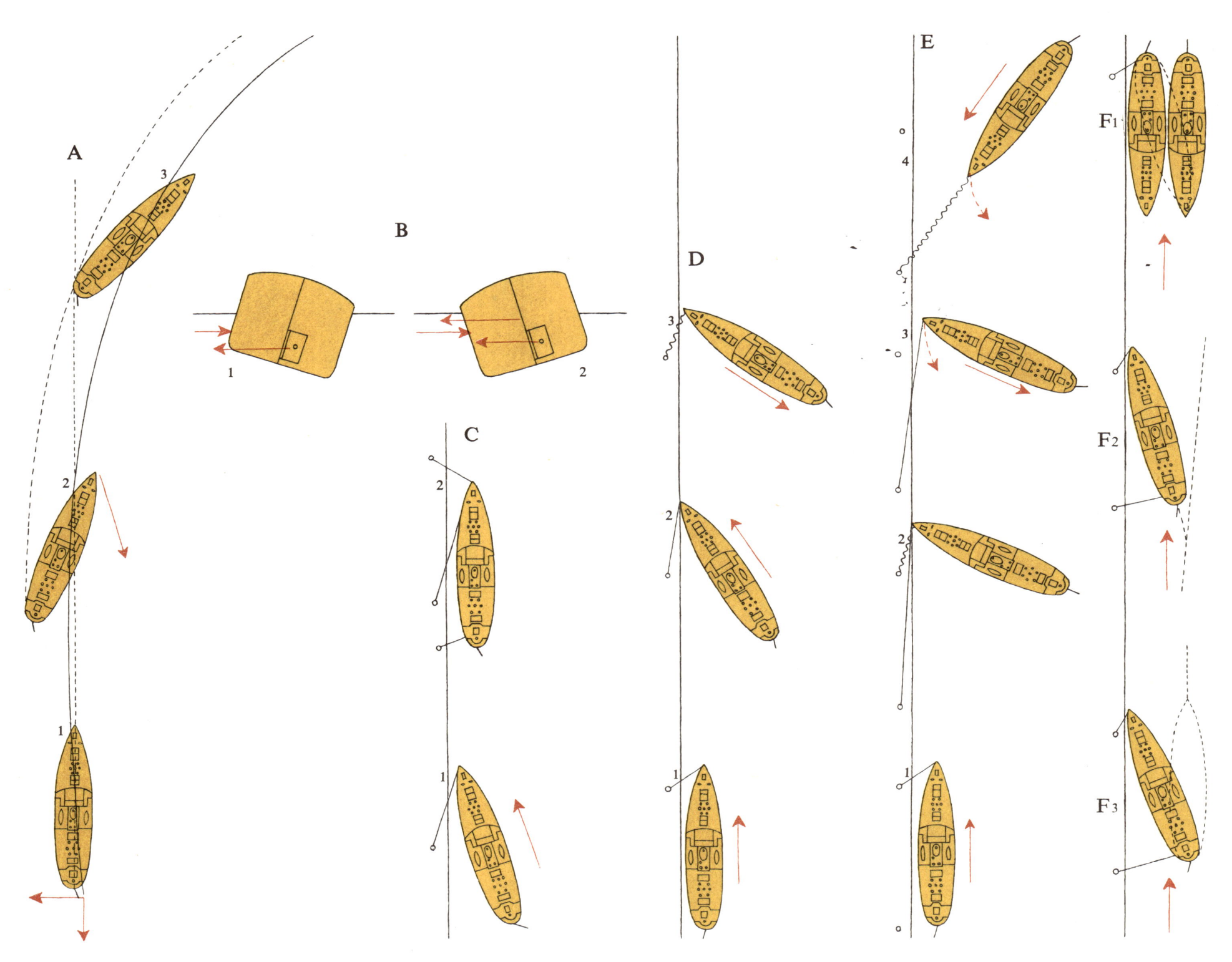

MANEUVERING A POWERED SHIP

C *Going alongside*
1 Put a spring ashore, slow ahead, starboard the rudder
2 When in position, tie her up, finish with engines

D *Leaving the quay*
1, 2 Keep a spring ashore, go slow ahead, and port your rudder
3 Let go the spring, slow astern, rudder amidships

E *Leaving the quay turning*
1 Keep a spring ashore, go slow ahead, and port your rudder
2 Stop engine, rudder amidships, shift the spring, further astern
3 Heave away the spring, go slow astern, starboard rudder
4 Let go the spring, go slow ahead, port your rudder

F *Leaving the quay under different current circumstances*
1 The ship has the current from ahead and the starboard side to the quay. Hold on to the spring aft and ease off the forward breast rope. The vessel is held parallel with the quay by engine and rudder.
2 The ship has the port side to the quay and the tidal stream aft (right-handed screw), the forward spring is held on and she is eased off by the breast rope aft. When all clear, slow astern and let go the shore lines.
3 If the ship has the current aft port side to quay, and left-handed propeller (or starboard side to quay, right-handed propeller), the forward spring is held on, and the aft breast rope is eased off. Then the breast rope is held on while the engine is put slow astern, with the rudder to port (starboard).

253

MOORING

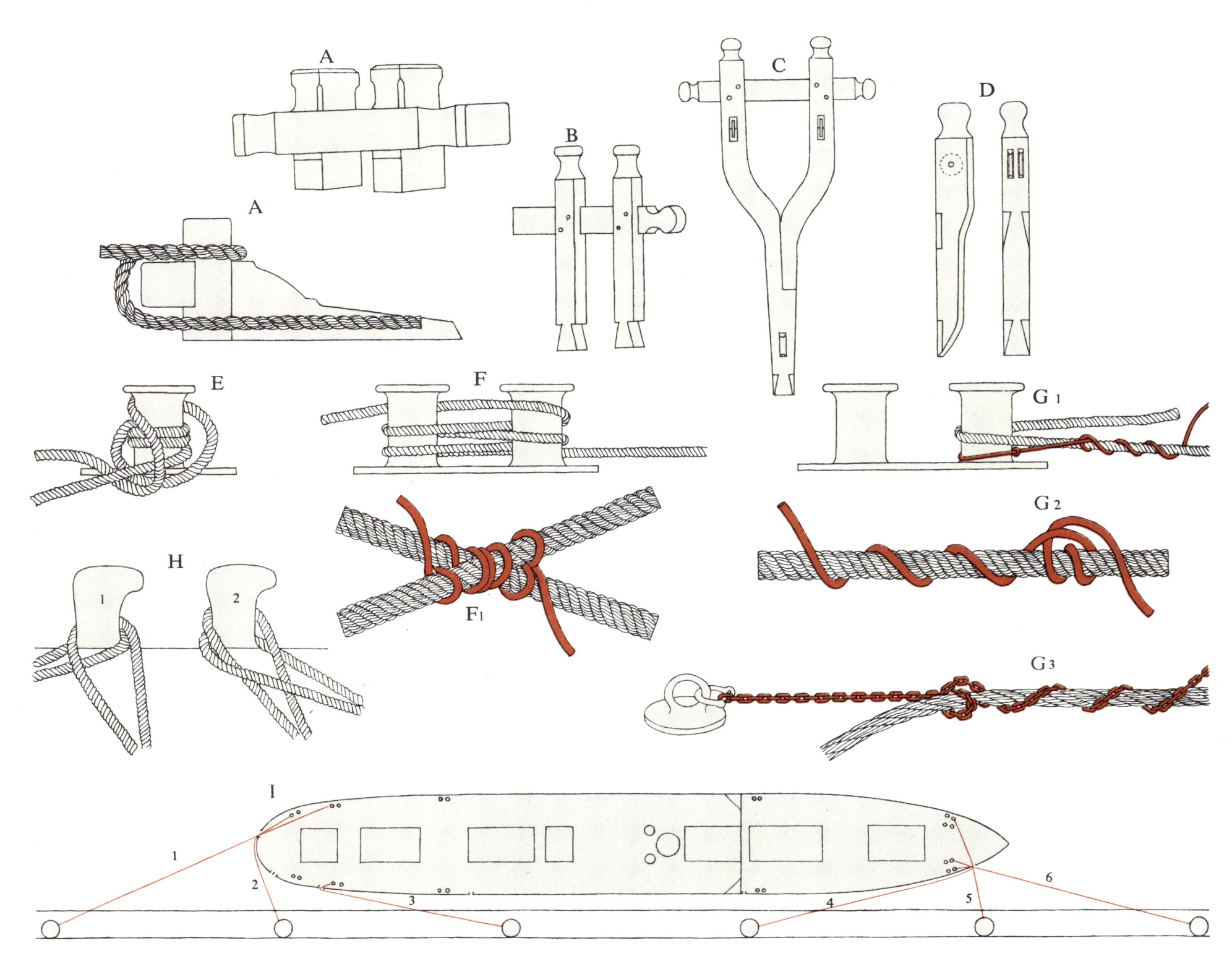

MOORING AND BELAYING

A *Bitts*
B *Knightheads*
C *Bitts on the forecastle head*
D *Knighthead*
A–D are from a book on ship building by Å.C. Rålamb (1691)
E *Belaying to a single bollard*
F *Belaying to twin bollards*
 1 Racked turns
G *Stoppering a rope*
Stoppers are used when hawsers are to be moved from the winch to the bollards, chain stoppers are used on wires
H *Two berthing hawsers on the same bollard on shore*
 1 Wrong way, the second hawser will block the first one
 2 Right way, either of the hawsers can be removed from the bollard independently of the other
I *Berthing hawsers*
 1 Stern rope
 2 After breast rope
 3 After back spring
 4 Fore back spring
 5 Fore breast rope
 6 Head rope

AUXILIARY VESSELS

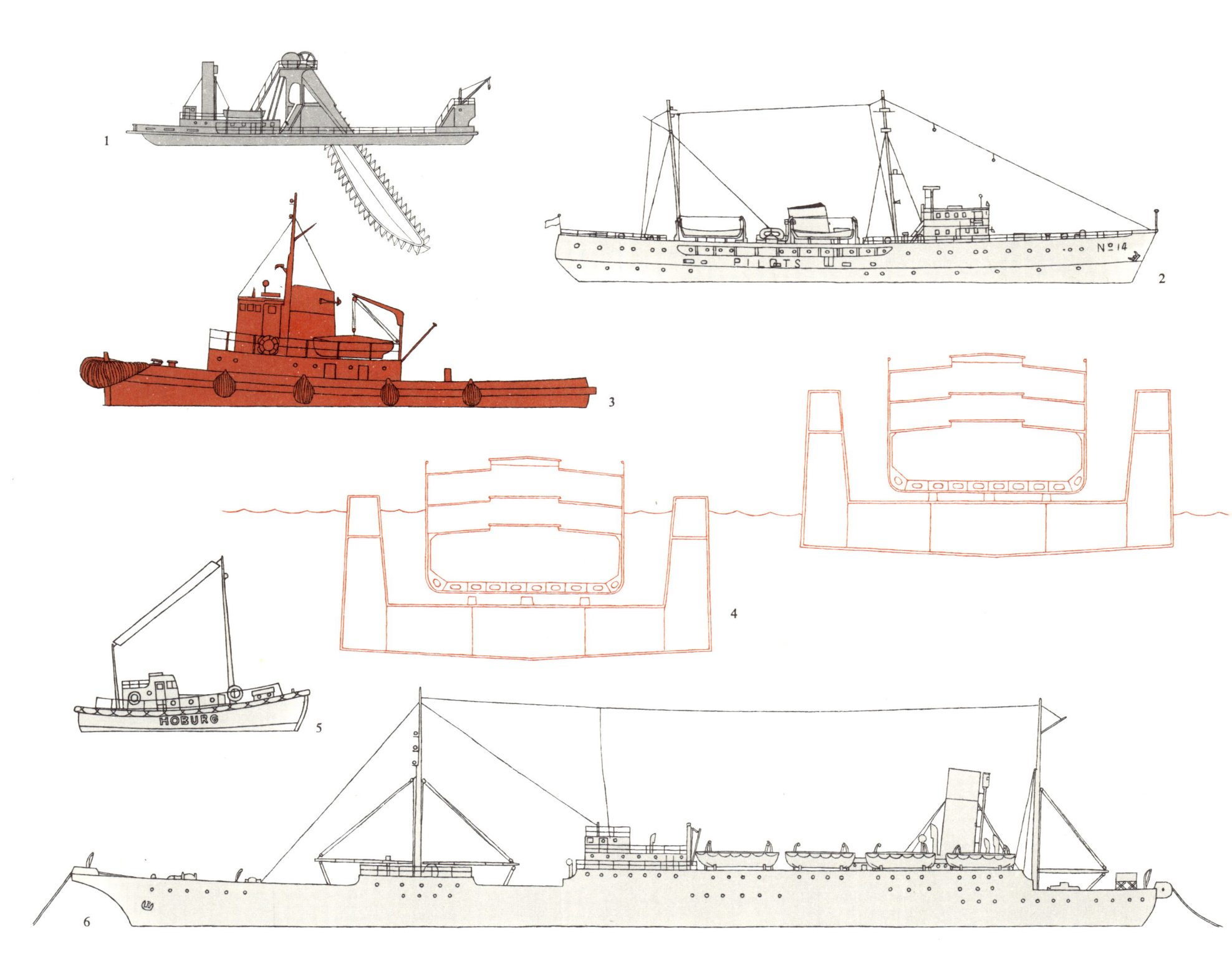

AUXILIARY VESSELS

1 Bucket dredger
2 Pilot vessel
3 Harbor tug
4 Floating drydock
5 Swedish cruising lifeboat
6 **Cable ship**

255

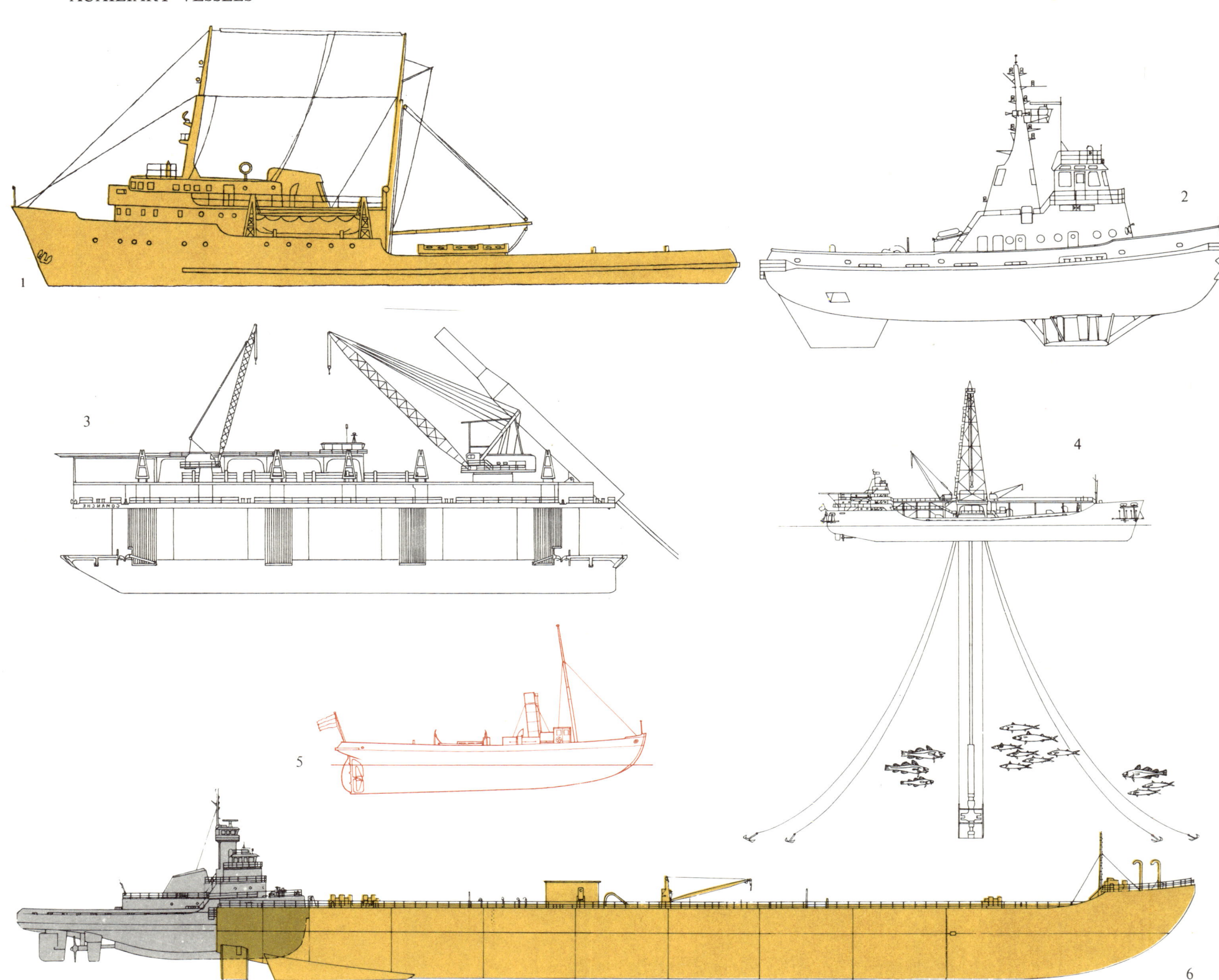

AUXILIARY VESSELS

1 Ocean-going tug
2 The tug *Mercur*, delivered in 1972
3 Pipe laying vessel. Lengths of pipe are welded together on the inclined ramp and then released into the water
4 The oil drilling ship *Grand Isle*, with turret mooring which allows the ship to head into prevailing winds and currents while positioned over the well
5 *Eisbrecher*. The world's first ice breaker solely built for this purpose. Launched in Hamburg in 1871
6 The tugboat *Exxon Sunshine State* whose prow fits in a notch in the stern of the barge it pushes. The system is called a push-tow
7 The U.S. Coast Guard ice breaker *Polar Star*, completed in 1975. Length 121.9 m (400 ft), breadth 25.4 m (83 ft), draught 9.1 m (30 ft), displacement 12,000 tons. She is the first ice breaker in the world to have direct-coupled gas-turbine engines and c.p. propellers
8 Schematic diagram of the *Polar Star's* machinery arrangement
  1 Gas-turbine
  2 Main diesels
  3 A.C. generators
  4 Reduction gearing
  5 Rectifier
  6 Clutch
  7 D-C. main motor
9 Cutaway through an ice breaker of the ATLE-URHO-class. *Atle* was delivered in 1974 and is the first ice breaker intended for year-round service in the Gulf of Bothnia

AUXILIARY VESSELS

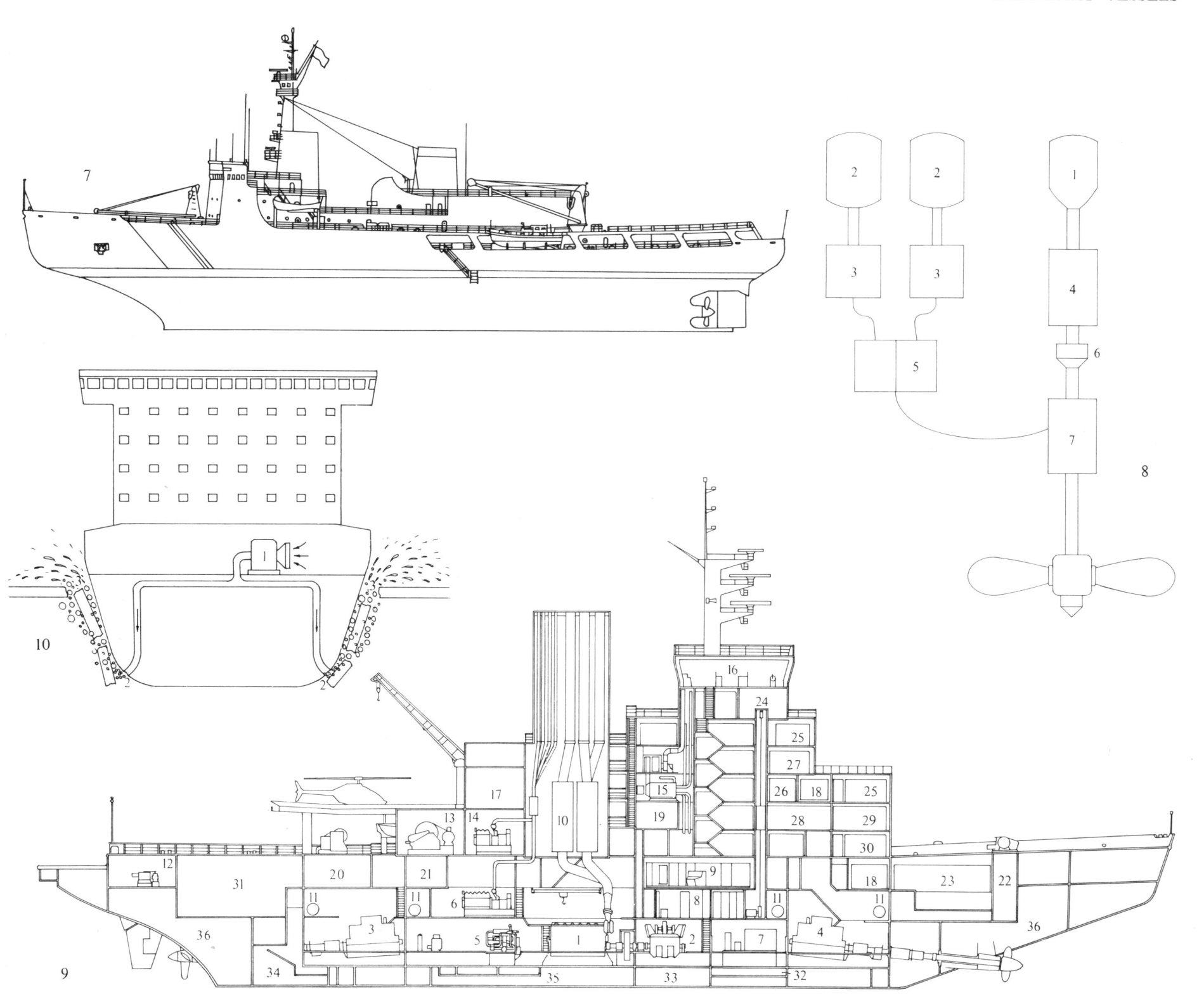

1 Main diesel engine
2 Main generator
3 Aft propeller motor
4 Bow propeller motor
5 Pumps and coolers
6 Auxiliary diesel generator
7 Sewage treatment tank
8 Apparatus room
9 Machinery control room
10 Silencer room
11 Heeling pipe
12 Steering gear
13 Towing winch
14 Emergency generator
15 Air conditioning room
16 Navigation centre
17 Helicopter equipment
18 Sauna
19 Air intake for the machinery
20 Cargo hold
21 Oil and chemical store
22 Chain locker
23 Gymnasium
24 Sea cabin
25 Officers' cabins
26 Hall
27 Saloon
28 Pantry
29 Crew's mess
30 Crew
31 Fuel oil
32 Sludge
33 Overflow oil
34 Sea water inlet
35 Lubricating oil
36 Ballast water

10 Principal functions of the Wärtsilä ice clearing air-bubbling-system designed for ice breakers and icegoing cargo liners. The system blows highly compressed air through a row of openings in the ship's sides and creates an upflow of water that reduces friction when the ship works its way through snow-covered ice or ice-barriers.

1 Air compressor
2 Nozzles
3 Airflow that lifts the water along the ship's sides and reduces ice-friction

257

SAILOR'S OUTFIT

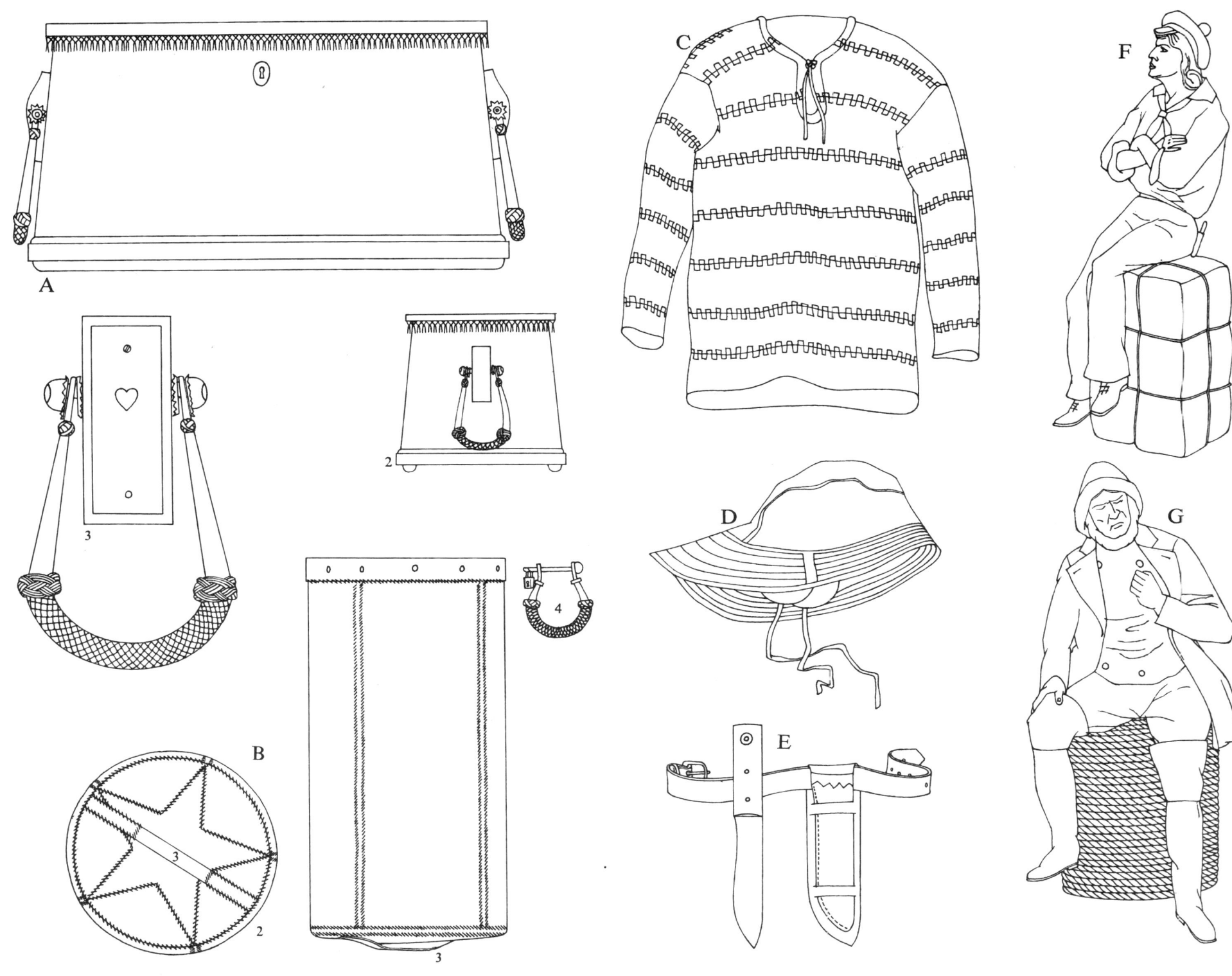

SAILOR'S OUTFIT

A   Seaman's chest with tassel work on its canvas-covered lid
   2 End view of chest
   3 Fancy handle

B   Sailor's canvas bag (3 ft. high), made of five half cloths
   2 The bottom of the bag with its canvas handle, 3
   4 The shackle of the bag with bolt and lock

C   Shetland wool jersey
D   Sou'wester

E   Sailor's sheath knife, carried in the middle of the back where it was available to both hands

F   A young sailor from the 1860's

G   An old sailor from the 1860's

EQUIPMENT

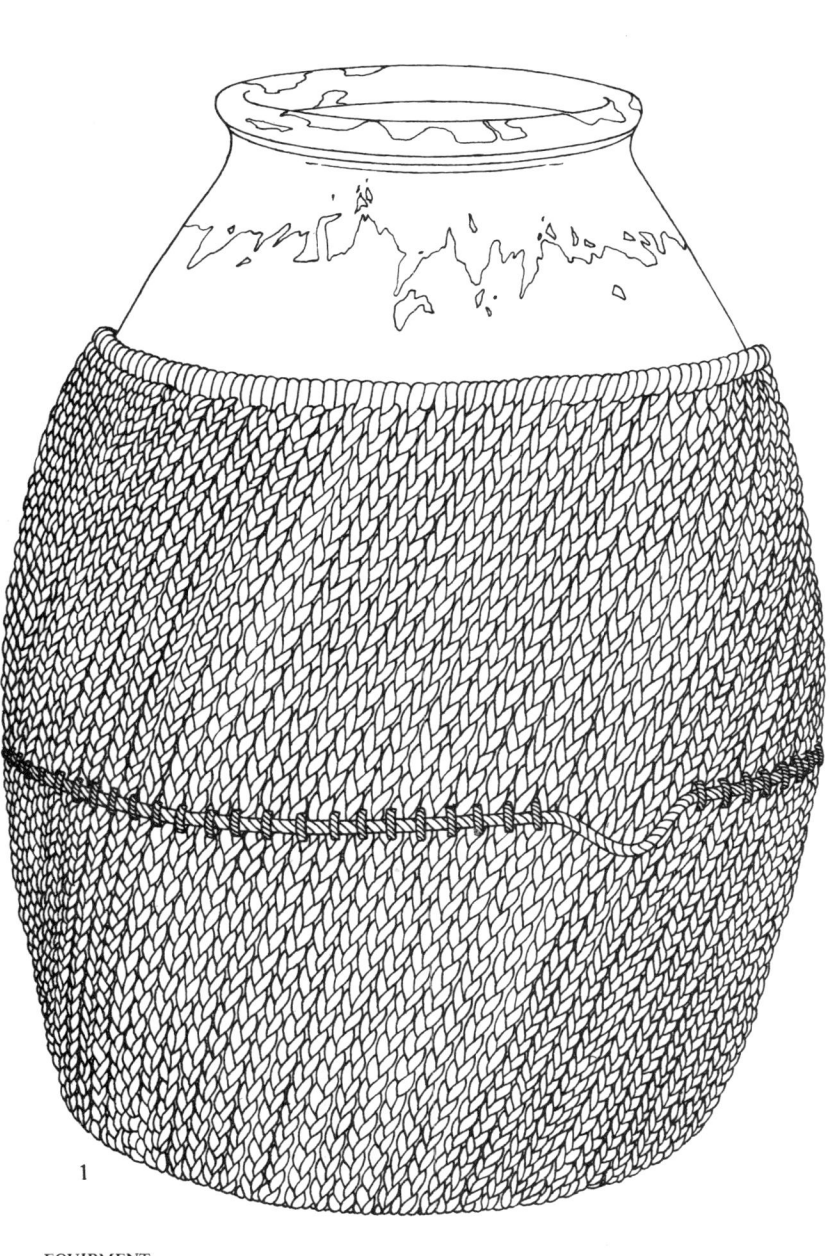

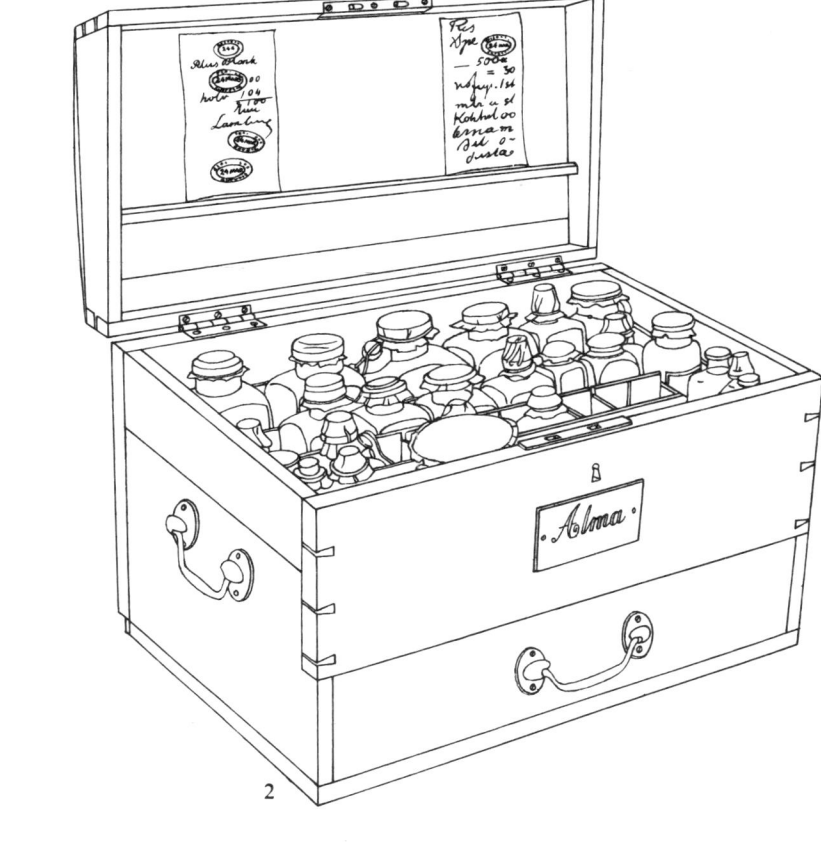

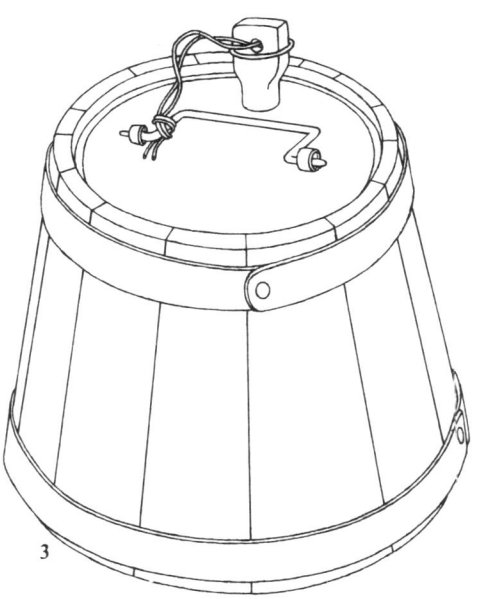

EQUIPMENT

1. Water jar (4 ft. high), from a Swedish East Indiaman, 18th century
2. Medicine chest, 19th century
3. Rum keg
4. Earthenware jug for wine or vinegar

259

PROVISIONS

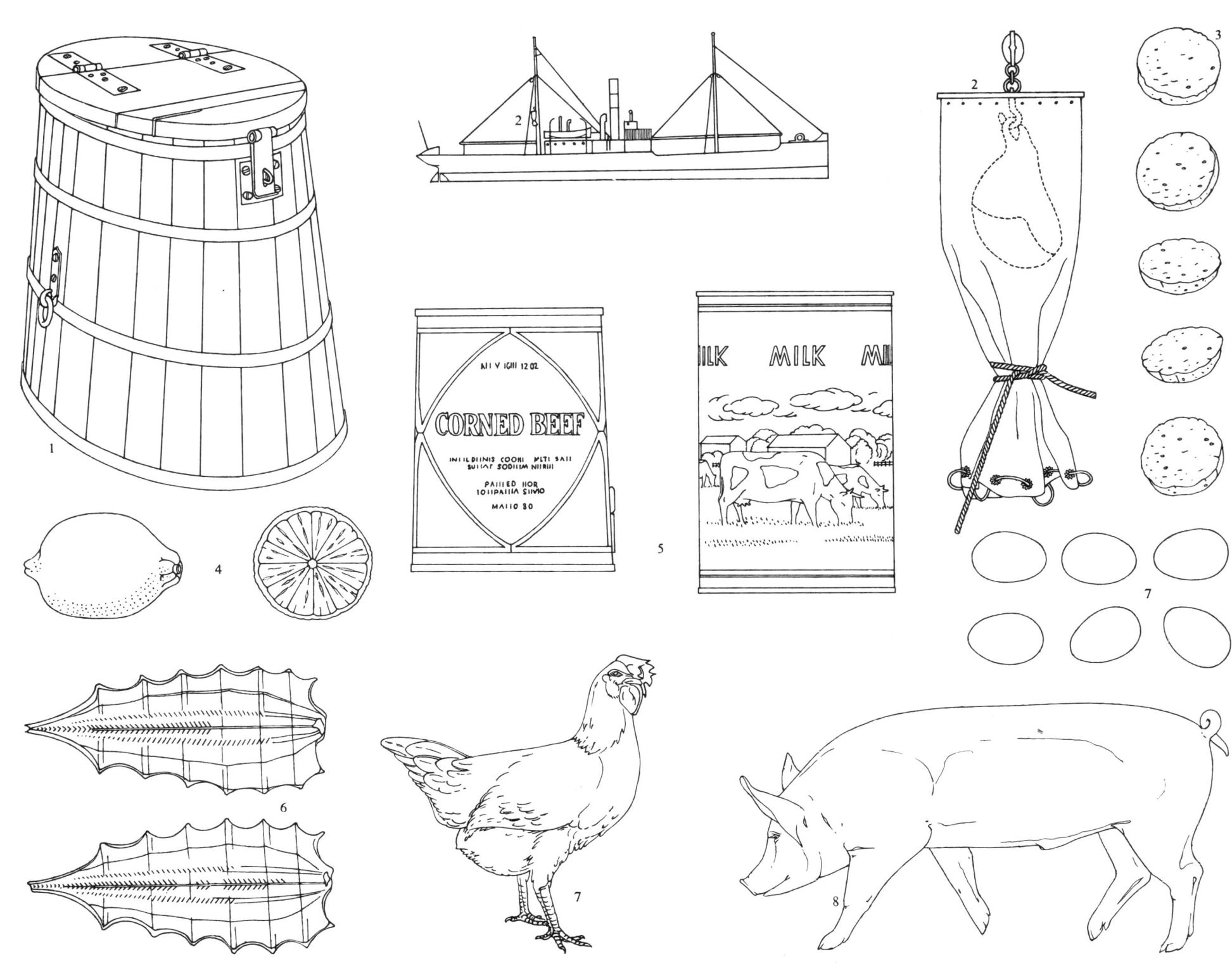

PROVISIONS

Today, food on board ships is the same as that on shore. By freezing and other methods of preservation it is possible to keep fresh food even on long voyages. Formerly, however, things were different. Preserved food was scarce and voyages took a longer time.

1 Harness cask for salted beef and pork
2 A canvas bag used to hang meat in the rigging may be seen even in our day
3 Ship biscuits
4 To prevent scurvy, lime juice was used
5 When the Frenchman F. Appert invented the canning method in 1804 the problem of food supply on board ships began to be solved. The most common canned products on board were corned beef and condensed milk.
6 Dried fish, a common food on board
7, 8. On long voyages sailing ships carried some livestock for fresh provisions. In good weather, chickens would thrive and lay eggs for the cabin table. Pigs could stand all kinds of weather at sea, and a few were always carried on deep-water voyages.

SAILOR'S HOBBIES

SAILOR'S HOBBIES

1. Ship model in bottle
2. Circular mat, plaited of three parts
3. Three-stranded Turk's head
4. Cross made on board, and used as cabin-altar during W.W. II
5. Bottle engraved with a nail by two Danish sailors on board the sloop *3 Bröder* (3 Brothers)
6. Carved wooden box
7. Tool bag of canvas with strap of sennit
8. Plaited cot strap

261

This picture of a rope-yard is taken from the classic nautical volume Allgemeines Wörterbuch der Marine *by J.H. Röding, published in 1798.*

INDEX

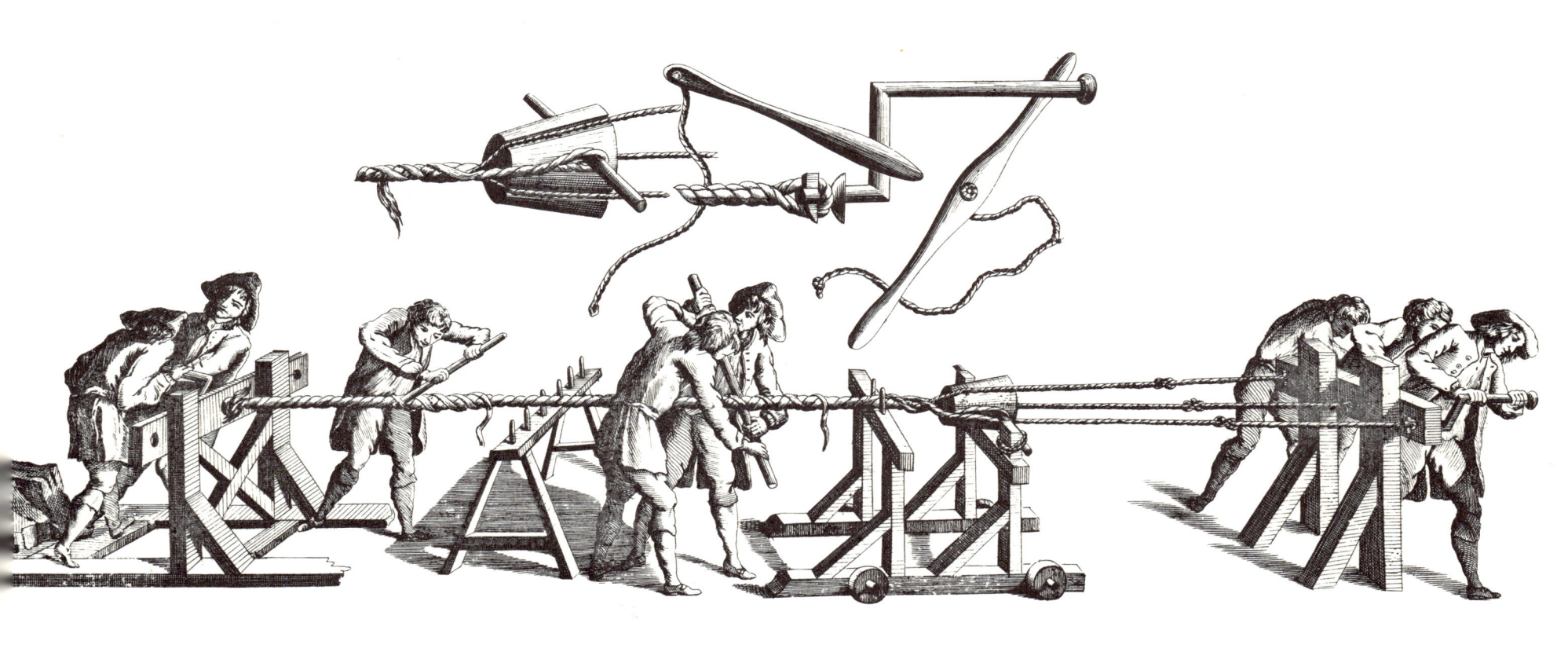

A

A (signal flag) 138
AA gun 212
Acacia 18
Acapulco 240
Accessories, gun with 207
Accident (signal flag) 139
Accommodations 210, 211
Acetylene gas 239
A.C. generator 257
Acoustic hammer box 214
Acoustic mine 213
Action information organization 217
Active 221
Adze 18, 34, 35
Aerial 197
Aerial loop 235
Aerosol-powered foghorn 201
After back spring 254
Afterbody 22, 23, 40, 41, 215
After breast rope 254
After castle 18
After deadwood 41
After end of an all-welded cargo ship 45
Aft end cylinder 166
After peak bulkhead 44
After peak tank 44, 45
After perpendicular 24
After steaming light 65
After yard 248
Aft oil pan 166
Aft turbocharger 166
Agincourt Island 241
Aguada 214
Ahead pinion 201
Air casing of funnel 154
Air charging valve 215
Air cock 62
Air compressor 257
Air compressor intake 166
Air conditioning room 257
Air cushion 19
Air flask 215
Air intake 159, 167, 220, 221, 257
Air intake duct 159
Air lever 215
Air receiver 167
Air receiver access 166
Air search radar 217
Air warning radar 217
Aircraft carrier 220, 221
Aircraft-carrying cruiser 218, 219
Åland Islands, ketch from 129
Alaska Packers Association 136
Albacore 180
Alexandria (lighthouse) 238
Algerian chebec 127
Alleyway 60, 154
All-welded cargo ship 45
Alphabetical flags 138

Ambon Island 241
America 188
American Bank schooner 173
American dragger 174
American Export Lines, Inc. 49
American five-masted fore-and-aft schooner 76, 77
American President Line 137
American seiner 174
American troller 174
American tuna clipper 175
American Water Ski Association 201
America's Cup 188, 194
Amerikaland 162
Ammunition 209, 212
Ammunition hoist 209, 210, 211
Ammunition hoist motor 209
Amoy 129
Amplifier unit 217
Anacapa Island 214
Anamba Islands 241
Anchor 54, 55, 178, 196, 213
Anchor arm 54
Anchor buoy 177
Anchor chain 239
Anchor crane 92
Anchor gear 55
Anchor ring 54
Anchor stock 54
Anemometer 197
Angle bar 39
Angle clip 36
Angler 180
Angular setting 201
Anker, Johan 186
Antenna 210, 211, 217
Antenna buoy 213
Antenna mine 213
Anti-aircraft gun 210, 211, 212
Anti-aircraft missile 212
Anti-rotating fin 239
Anti submarine (a.s.) missile 216
Anti-submarine rocket 216
Anti-submarine rocket launcher 216
A.s. torpedo 216
Anti-submarine weapon 216
Apparatus room 257
Appert, F. 260
Apron 29, 32, 33
Arabian dhow 128, 129
Arc 18, 212, 233
Arcs of ship's lights 65
Archibald Russell 116
Arctic Buccaneer 175
Arctic Steamship line 49
Argentina 134
Arm with brace 62
Armament 19, 217
Artillery indicator 217
Arvoredo Islet 240

Asashio 165
A-scope 217
Asdic 216
Asdic beam 216
Ash pit 152, 154, 156
Ash pit door 156
AS-rocket 216
Assistance (signal flag) 139
Astern turbine element 157
Astronomical instruments 233
Atico Point 240
Atle-Urho class 257
Atomic fission 159
Atomic nucleus 159
Auger 34, 35, 207
Aurella 165
Austr 230
Australia 135
Automatic aircraft gun 212
Automatic disposal arrangement 213
Automatic gun, 5 inches 209
Automatic loader 212
Automatic mooring winch 58
Automatic steering 47
Auto-pilot 47
Auxiliary coaster 66
Auxiliary engine 167
Auxiliary sailing vessels 133
Awning-decked vessel 53
Awo Shima 214
Axe 34, 35
Axis of bore 209

B

B (signal flag) 138
Bacat I 164
Back 178
Backing and filling 250
Back piece 42
Back plate 152
Backrope 86, 88, 89
Back spring 254
Backstay 80, 81, 83, 85
Back tube plate 152
Bait 172
Bait holder 172
Balance 150
Balance cylinder 154
Balance reef band 114
Balanced rudder 43
Balanced rudder in a twin-screw ship 43
Balcony 42
Ballast 40, 154, 257
Ballast iron 239
Ballistic cap 209
Ballistic data handling 217
Balsa wood 148
Baltic 18, 243
Baltic sloop 133
Baltimore clipper 19, 127
Band 105, 111, 206

Band brake 57
Bangladesh Shipping Corp. 49
Bank schooner 173
Barb 176
Barbette 210, 211
Barge 66, 128, 129
Bar holes 56
Bark 41, 72, 73, 74, 76, 77, 100, 101, 108, 113, 116, 119, 121, 127, 130, 131, 175, 246, 248, 249
Bar keel 36, 44
Barkentine 50, 74, 75, 109, 129, 130, 131, 173
Barometric pressure 217
Barra Falsa 241
Barra Head 240, 241
Barracuda 180, 181
Barrel 46, 56, 57, 109, 206, 209, 212, 216
Bar shot 207
Basaruto Island 241
Base line 24
Base plate 229
Basic fire control principle 217
Basket 18
Batanta 241
Batten 27, 31, 84, 115
Batten cleat 63
Batten wedge 63
Battery-operated buoyant light 67
Battle cruiser 218, 219
Battleship 210, 211, 220, 221
Batu Mandi 241
Beakhead 18
Beam 27, 29, 30, 31, 32, 33, 37, 40, 41, 44, 45, 63, 179, 216, 237
Beam engine 153
Beam trawl 179
Bearding line 41
Bearer boiler 152
Bearers 67
Bearing 44, 45, 58, 62, 150, 154, 155, 157, 166, 167, 231, 235, 237
Bearing box 62
Bearing cap 57
Bearing foundation 45
Bearing plate 234
Bearings 234
Beatas 121
Beating 121
Beating to windward 244, 245
Becket 109, 122, 123
Bed 207
Bed plate 46, 57, 58, 154, 155, 156, 167
Beef 260
Bees 86
Before the wind 247, 248
Beer cask 40
Belaying 254
Belaying pin 107, 109

Belgium 134
Belfry 59
Bell 59
Bell whistle 59
Belle Isle 240
Belly (fishing net) 179
Bends 27, 55, 142
Benito Island, West 240
Bergylt 180
Bermuda 19, 240, 241
Bermuda rig 133
Bermuda sail 99
Bermuda-type trysail 92
Berth 60, 199
Bevel 34, 35
Biarritz 240, 241
Bilancella 129
Bilge 30
Bilge keel 31, 154, 210, 211
Bilge keelson 27, 30
Bilge plate 27
Bilge pump 62, 107
Bilge.rail 67
Bilge strake 30, 31
Bilge stringer 27, 30
Bill, anchor 54
Binnacle 40, 199, 231
Bireme 148
Biscuit 260
Bismarck 220
Bit 34, 35, 88, 89, 204
Bitt 32, 254
Black Ball Line, the 136
Blackwall hitch 84, 142
Blade 42, 44, 148, 149, 247
Blade wheel 157
Blading 157
Block 66, 82, 83, 88, 89, 93, 109, 122, 123, 124, 196, 197
Blowing nozzles 48
Blow off valve unit 159
Bluefish 180
Blue Funnel Line 49
Blue Peter 136, 138
Blue Star Line 137
Board 20, 21, 27, 63, 179
Boat chock 66
Boat deck 45, 167
Boat davits 210, 211
Boat fall 66
Boatswain's call 59
Bobstay 80, 86, 87, 88, 89
Bobstay piece 32
Bocas del Toro 240
Body plan 22, 23, 24
Boeier 126
Bofors 40 mm 212
Boiler 150, 154, 156, 157, 159, 167, 210, 211
Boiler bearer 152, 154
Boiler casing 156, 157
Boiler exhaust 167
Boiler exhaust pipe 167
Boiler generating tube 157
Boiler room 154
Boiler stay 152

Boiler tube 152
Boilers, types of older 152
Bollard 33, 66, 254
Bolt 27, 28, 29, 44, 56, 112, 191
Bolt for tack cringle 191
Bolt rope 105, 115
Bolt with cotter pin 141
Bone gorges 172
Bone hook 172
Bonito boat 174
Bonnet 87, 112, 120
Boom 25, 92, 93, 115, 191, 215
Boom band 93
Boom end 115
Boom foresail 92
Boom foresail sheet 92
Boom guy 93
Boom head 93
Boom head eye plate 93
Boom topping lift 92
Booster 212
Booster fin 212
Bore 209
Boss 44
Bosun's store 32
Bottom 19, 227
Bottom cooling water pipe 167
Bottom floor 45
Bottom frame 36
Bottom longitudinal 31
Bottom planking 20, 21, 27
Bottom plating 36, 45, 151, 154, 229
Bottom shell 31
Bottom strake 30
Boulogne (lighthouse) 238
Bovo 129
Bow 29, 51, 253
Bow light 190
Bowline 87, 90, 121, 142
Bowline bridle 121
Bowline cringle 121
Bowline on the bight 142
Bow net, cod 176
Bow pole 176
Bowsprit 18, 20, 21, 33, 60, 72, 73, 86, 87, 88, 89
Bowsprit bee 86
Bowsprit cap 86
Bowsprit shroud 86, 88, 89
Bow-thruster 43
Bow tunnel 43
Box boiler 152
Box keelson 38
Brace 30, 34, 35, 42, 62, 83, 87, 90, 92, 104, 106, 107, 108, 110, 112, 245, 248, 249
Brace pendant 106
Brace runner 106
Brace winch 108, 109
Bracket 31, 36, 44, 57, 154
Bracket end 27
Brail 114

265

Brake 57, 58, 62, 209, 212, 227
Brake handle 57
Brazil 129, 134
Breadth, half 24
Bream, Ray's 180
Breasthook 29, 32, 33, 36
Breasthook bolt 29
Breast rope 253, 254
Breech 209
Breechblock 206
Breeching 207
Breueh 241
Brick fireplace 61
Bridge 25, 47, 158, 210, 211
Bridge deck 25, 167
Bridge house 154
Bridge telegraph 158
Bridle bowline 121
Brig 74, 102, 130, 131, 250
Brigantine 51, 74, 130, 131
Brill 181
Britannia 188, 189
British India Co. 137
British motor trawler 174
British Navy 139
British sailing trawler 174
British seiner 174
British steam drifter 174
British steam trawler 173
British Tankers Co., Ltd. 137
Broach to 244
Broadside 250
Bronze gun 206
Bronze wires tiller rope 141
Bucket dredger 255
Bulb angle 39, 63
Bulb angle bar 39
Bulb plate 39
Bulkhead 30, 31, 36, 44, 45
Bulkhead longitudinal 31
Bulkhead stiffener 45
Bulldog grips 141
Bullock's horn 59
Bull Rock 240, 241
Bulwark 20, 21, 41, 44
Bulwark brace 30
Bulwark cap 30
Bulwark planking 27
Bulwark plating 30
Bulwark stanchion 27, 44
Bull's eye 104, 105
Bumpkin 87
Bunk 60
Bunker 155, 210, 211
Bunker stay 154
Bunt 113
Bunting 226
Buntline 83, 104, 106, 107, 108, 113, 251
Buntline blocks 104
Buntline hitch 104
Buoy 176, 177, 278, 195, 239, 247
Buoyancy 67
Buoyancy buoys 214

Buoyancy cable 214
Buoyancy tank 67
Buoyancy tube 67
Buoyant light 66
Buoy line 176, 178
Buoy rope 178
Burbot 181
Burner 159
Burton 84
Butt 62
Buttocks 22, 23, 24
Button chorn 213
Button point 38
Butt strap 30
Butt weld 39
By-pass valve 157
By the wind 121

C

C (signal flag) 137, 138
C-2 standard vessel 163
Cabin 22, 23, 40, 60
Cabin altar 261
Cabin boat 200
Cabin house 41
Cabin house accommodation 60
Cabin, Admiral of the Fleet 210, 211
Cable 32, 55, 56, 140, 214
Cable coil 214
Cable compressor 60
Cable connection 214
Cable drum 213
Cable-laid rope 140
Cable-laying vessel 65
Cable reliever 57
Cable ship 65, 255
Cable tier 32
Cadet 192
Caique (Turkish) 128
Caisson lighthouse 238
Caligula, Emperor 54
Callao 240
Cam roller 166, 167
Cam segment 167
Camshaft 157, 166, 167
Canada 134
Canada Steam Ship Lines, Ltd. 49
Canadian Pacific Railways Co. 137
Canning 260
Canoe 18, 128, 129, 192
Cant frame 44
Cant timber 28
Canton 135
Canvas 106, 258
Canvas handle 258
Cap 30, 44, 78, 79, 81, 86, 88, 89, 91, 110, 115, 209
Cap backstay 80, 81, 83
Cape Agostinho 240
Cape Anaga 240, 241
Cape Armenisti 241
Cape Blanco 240
Cape Bolinao 241
Cape Borda 241

Cape Boriquen 240
Cape Byron 241
Cape Camarat 241
Cape Carbon 241
Cape Carthage 241
Cape Charles 241
Cape Cod 240
Cape de Garde 241
Cape Faro 241
Cape Finisterre 240, 241
Cape Formentor 241
Cape Frio Island 240
Cape Gaspé 240
Cape of Good Hope 241
Cape Gris-Nez 241
Cape Guardafui 241
Cape Haro 240
Cape Hatteras 240
Cape Hinchinbrook 240
Cape La Heve 241
Cape Lazareva 240, 241
Cape Meganom 241
Cape Mendocino 240
Cape Moul à Chique 240
Cape Nao 241
Cape Naturaliste 241
Cape Padaran 241
Cape Palliser 241
Cape Pertusato 241
Cape Pine 240
Cape Rachado 241
Cape Reinga 241
Cape Roca 240, 241
Cape St. James 240
Cape St. Vincent 240, 241
Cape Sandalo 241
Cape San Sebastian 241
Cape Santa Maria di Leuca 241
Cape Spartel 241
Cape Stolbiovo 241
Cape Tosco 240
Cape Verde 240, 241
Cape Verde Islands 240, 241
Cape Virgins 240
Cape Wrath 241
Capsizing effect 244
Capstan 32, 40, 56, 57, 88, 89
Capstan bar 56
Capstan partner 57
Captain's cabin 60
Captain class 218, 219
Caravel 18, 126
Car ferry 165
Cargo batten 27
Cargo fall 93
Cargo fall heel blocks 93
Cargo hoist block 93
Cargo hold 257
Cargo hook 93
Cargo liner 164
Cargo ship 31, 37, 45
Cargo ship rigging 93
Cargo vessel with deck cranes 93
Cargo winch 58, 93
Carley life float 66
Carling 29, 31
Carpenter's hatchet 34, 35
Carpenter's tools 34, 35
Carrack 18, 126

Carriage 207
Carrick bitt 33, 56
Carrier 177
Carrying capacity 19
Carrying rope 42
Cartagena 240
Cartridge 207
Cartridge case 212
Carvel 18
Carvel-built 39
Cascabel 206, 207
Case shot 207
Casing 47, 57, 58, 62, 157, 167, 213
Cask 40
Castelhanos Point 240
Castle 18
Catamaran 196
Cathead 20, 21, 32, 33, 55, 56, 88, 89
Cathead stopper 55
Cathode ray tube 236
Catug 256
Caulking iron 34, 35
Caulking mallet 34, 35
Caulking seam 38
Ceiling 27, 33, 41
Ceiling plank 29
Celebes Paduakan 129
Cement filling 36, 44, 45
Center girder 31, 36
Center keelson 36
Center of effort 244
Center of gravity 253
Center of lateral resistance 244
Centerboard 196
Centerline 24, 37
Centerline deck stringer 30
Centerline keelson 27, 30
Centrifugal power 253
Centrifugal pump 62
Cerro Partido 240
Ceuta 241
Chacachacare Islet 240
Chafing spar, to protect the sail when reefed 112
Chain 46, 47, 93, 110, 236
Chain bolt 27
Chain cable 55
Chain locker 36, 60, 210, 211, 257
Chain locker bulkhead 36
Chain pipe 57
Chain plate 20, 21, 27, 84, 85, 124
Chain shot 207
Chain span 109
Chain swivel 55
Chain transmission casing 166
Chain transmission stretcher 166
Chain wheel 107
Chalk line 34, 35
Chambered breech block 206
Channel 27, 39, 163, 238
Channel bar 39
Chapel Hill Beacon 240

Chapman, af 188
Charge 209, 212, 213, 215, 216
Charge container 213
Charging valve 215
Charlotte Dundas 160
Charlotte Islands 240
Charts 236, 242, 243
Chase 206
Chasse marée 173
Chebec (Algerian) 127
Cheek 78, 79, 115
Cheek block 112
Cheek of windlass bitt 56
Chemicals 19
Chernikeef log 229
Chesapeake Bay 19
Chest, sea 258
Chilachap 214
Chile 134
Chilled cargo 25
Chime whistle 59
China 19, 129, 134
China Merchant Nav. Co. 137
Chinese junk 51
Chip log 228
Chisel 34, 35
Chock 29, 32, 57, 66, 214
Chopping axe 34, 35
Christian IV, Denmark 206
Church pennant 137
Cie Générale Transatlantique 49
Circulating-pump discharge pipe 154
Circulating tank 167
Circular water line 48
Clamp 27, 201
Clamping mechanism 233
Clare Islands 240, 241
Classifying Society 52
Claw hammer 34, 35
Cleat 63, 82, 122
Clermont 150, 160
Clew 104, 105, 106, 113, 114, 115, 117, 118, 120, 248
Clew cringle 114
Clewgarnet 83, 87, 90, 91, 104, 105, 107, 108, 113
Clewgarnet block 122
Clewline 83, 87, 90, 106, 107, 108, 110, 117, 251
Clew ring 118
Clew shackle 115
Clinker-built 26, 39
Clinker planking 18
Clinometer 231
Clip hooks 122
Clipper 19, 76, 77, 121, 127, 175
Clips 30, 36, 190, 212
Closed shelter-decked vessel 53
Clove hitch 84, 142
Clutch 257
Clutch lever 58
Coal bunker 154, 210, 211

Coal fire 238
Coalfish 181
Coaming 29, 31, 33, 63
Coaming stanchion 63
Coarse dial (range receiver) 217
Coastal tanker 163
Coast defence ship 210, 211
Coaster 61, 66, 128, 163
Coast survey chart 243
Cockpit 199
Cocks (air and drain) 62
Cod 181
Cod bow net 176
Cod end 176, 179
Code 137, 139
Code flag 136
Code signals 138
Coil 213, 214, 248
Colin Archer 67
Collar 30, 42
Collier 162
Colling's & Pinkney's patent 92, 112
Colombia 134
Column (pump) 62
Combat information center 210, 211
Combat information indicator 217
Combat situation, weapon control 217
Combustion chamber 152, 159, 167
Combustion chamber casing 159
Comet 160
Comet 193
Come up into the wind 244
Commander's flag 136
Commercial code 139
"Commonwealth Star" 135
Communication 138
Companion hood 40
Compass 19, 34, 35, 60, 92, 197, 230, 231
Compass bearing 234
Compass card 230, 231, 234
Compass saw 34, 35
Compensating binnacle 231
Compensating weight 231
Competition rowing 149
Composite vessel 19, 27
Compound engine 153
Compression chamber 167
Compression stroke 167
Compressor air delivery unit 159
Compressor, cable 60
Compressor rotor blades 159
Compressor turbine shaft 159
Computer unit 217
Condenser 150, 151, 154, 155, 156, 159
Condenser head 154, 156

Conger eel 180
Connecting arm 167
Connecting rod 46, 58, 150, 151, 155, 166, 167
Connecting rod bearing 166
Connecting rod lubricating pipe 166
Connecting strap 44
Conning tower 210, 211
Constant-tension mooring winch 58
Constructional details of wooden ship 28
Contact horn 213
Contact mine 213
Container for fuel 212
Contra-guide rudder 43
Controllable pitch propeller (c.p.propeller) 158, 159
Control panel 61
Control rod 159
Control section 212
Control tower 210, 211, 217
Convention for Safety of Life at Sea 67
Coolant 159
Cooler 167
Cooling air supply pipe for compressor turbine 159
Cooling oil drain 166
Cooling oil entrance 166
Cooling oil main pipe 167
Cooling oil return pipe 167
Cooling oil telescopic pipe 167
Cooling pipe 201
Cooling water outlet 151
Cooling water pipe 166, 167
Copper (lighthouse) 241
Core (rope) 141
Cordage 140, 143
Cordouan (lighthouse) 238
Cork float 176
Cork line 177
Corpen 137
Correcter (compass) 231
Coruña 238, 240, 241
Costa Rica 134
Cot strap 261
Cotter pin 141
Cougar class 196
Counter 20, 21, 213, 229
Counter sunk point 38
Counterweight 48, 197
Counterweight water 48
Coupling 57, 157
Coupling box 58
Coupling flange 45, 155
Coupling handle 58
Coupling rod 46
Course 27, 30, 100, 101, 110, 113, 120, 121, 139, 194, 217, 246
Course changing 47
Course clewgarnet 83

Course setting unit 47
Cover (hatch) 31, 63
Covering board 20, 21, 27
Coxswain 149
Crab 181
Crab iron 34, 35
Cradle 66, 209, 212
Crane 92, 93, 167
Crane jib 93
Crane post 93
Crank 66
Crankcase 167, 201
Crankcase access door 166
Crank disc 46
Crank end bearing 167
Crank pin 58, 156, 167
Crank pin bearing 166
Crankshaft 62, 151, 154, 155, 156, 167
Crankshaft journal and main bearing 166
Crank web 155, 156, 166
Crayon 34, 35
Creel 172
Crew's lavatory 60
Crew's quarters 210, 211
Cringle 105, 114, 115, 118, 121
Cross bearing 234, 235
Cross box 156
Crosshead 46, 47, 56, 57, 58, 156, 167
Crosshead bearing 166, 167
Crosshead bracket 57
Crosshead connection 62
Crosshead guide 155, 167
Crosshead guide plate 156
Crosshead pin 166, 167
Crosshead shoe 166, 167
Crossjack 72, 73, 100, 101, 102, 113
Crossjack brace 108
Crossjack buntline 107, 108
Crossjack clewgarnet 107, 108
Crossjack lift 107
Crossjack sheet 108
Crossjack tack 108
Crossjack yard 72, 73, 75, 77
Cross of St. Andrew 135
Cross of St. George 135
Cross of St. Patrick 135
Cross section of diesel engine 167
Cross tie 31
Crosstree 78, 79, 83, 106, 107, 110
Crowbar 34, 35
Crown anchor 54
Crown of donkey boiler 152
Crow's nest 93
Cruiser 200, 218, 219, 220, 221
Cruiser stern 45
Cruising lifeboat 255

Cruising yacht 192, 198, 199
Cruising Yacht Club of Australia 197
Crusades 18
Crutches 40, 41
Cunard Steamship Co. 137
Cunningham's patent reefing gear 112
Curaumilla Point 240
Curtis (velocity stage) 157
Cutter 117, 128, 129, 132, 133, 214, 255
Cutting plane 214
Cutwater piece (gripe) 33
Cycloidal propeller 158
Cylinder 46, 47, 57, 58, 62, 150, 154, 155, 156, 166, 201
Cylinder bow 37
Cylinder column 154, 155
Cylinder cover 154, 155, 156, 166, 167
Cylinder in position for scavenging 166
Cylinder liner 166, 167
Cylinder lubricator 62, 166
Cylinder valve 48
Cylindrical boiler (Scotch type) 152

D

D (signal flag) 137, 138
Dager Ort 240, 241
Daily use fuel tank 167
Danforth anchor 197
Danger (signal flag) 138
Danish double-ender, 30 sq.m. 193
Danish motor fishing boat 174
Dannebrogen 189
Davits 66, 210, 211
Day Morse lamp 65
Day watch 59
D-boiler 157
Dead block 121
Deadeye 27, 84, 122, 124
Deadwood 33, 40, 41
Deal Island 241
Decca system 236
Deck 29, 31, 37, 44, 45, 107, 167, 248
Deck beam 18, 29, 32, 36, 37, 40, 41, 44, 45, 63, 154
Deck cargo 52
Deck crane 25, 93
Deck girder 45
Deck hook 29
Deck hook bolt 29
Deckhouse 22, 23, 25
Deck line 52
Deck longitudinal 31, 45
Deck pillar 36, 44
Deck plan 22, 23
Deck planking 29, 57
Deck plating 63
Deck scraper 34, 35
Deck stanchion 29

Deck stores 60
Deck transverse 31
Deck web 45
Deck winch 196
Decoration 50, 51
Deep floor 36, 44, 45
Deep-sea lead 227
Defence ship 210, 211
Deflection 217
Degaussed ship 213
Denmark 135, 162
Denmark 133
Depressor (kite) 214
Depth of water (charted) 242
Depth charge (D/C) 216
Depth-distance indicator 201
Depth gear, torpedo 215
Depth regulator, depth charge 216
Depth rudder 215
Depth setting arrangement, mine 213
Depth setting key, depth charge 216
Derrick 93
De Ruyter 221
Design 19
Destroyer 216, 218, 219, 220, 221
Destroyer torpedo 215
Detonator 209, 213
Detonator gripper 214
Deutschland 161
Deviation 231, 235
Devitt & Moore 136
Dhow (Arabian) 129
Diagonal 24, 33
Diagonal deck beam hanging knee 41
Diagonal engine 153
Diagonal, lines plan 22, 23, 24
Diaphragm turbine 157
Diaphragm contact, mine 213
Diesel electric 257
Diesel engine, 2-stroke 167
Diesel engine, 4-stroke 167
Diesel engine cross section 167
Diesel engine, main 257
Diesel generator, auxiliary 257
Diesel oil tank 167
Digital weapon control system 217
Dimmer control, steering gear 47
Dinghies 192, 193
Dipping Asdic 216
Dipping lugsail 133
Direct-acting pump 62
Direct drive, diesel engine 166
Direct-drive steam engine 150
Direction finder 235
Direction control tower (DCT) 210, 211
Director radar 217
Disabled (signal flag) 138

Discharge flange, pump 62
Discharge valve box, pump 62
Displacement 24
Disposal arrangement, mine 213
Distance indicator 201
Distance line 115
Djursten (lighthouse) 238
Dogfish 180
Dolphin 206
Dolphin striker 86, 88, 89
Don't pass ahead 138
Donkey boiler 152
Donkey funnel 152
Door to crosshead guide 166
Dory 178
Dornbusch 240, 241
Double-bar link, paddle engine 151
Double-bar link, quadruple expansion engine 156
Double Blackwall hitch 84
Double block 122, 123
Double bottom 154, 229
Double bottom tank 167
Double continuous weld 39
Double-ended boiler 152
Double-ender, Swedish 193
Double purchase 123
Double-reduction gear 157
Double-riveted butt strap 38
Double sheet bend 142
Double strop 122
Double topsails 76, 77, 110, 121
Double wall knot 84
Dowel 18
Downhaul 83, 87, 88, 89, 106, 107, 112, 119
Downhaul tackle 112
Dragger 174
Drag link 150
Dragon class 186, 187
Drainage pump 191
Drain tube, life raft 67
Drake, Sir Francis 64
Draft marks 52
Draw knife 34, 35
Dress ship 137
Dried fish 260
Drift 250
Drifter (net) 178
Drigh Road 241
Drili 34, 35
Drilling machine 167
Drive tail, pump 62
Driver mast 74
Driving band, shell 209
Driving motor, winch 58
Driving wheel, windlass 57
Dromedarus 50
Drop keel 244
Drott 189
Drumhead, capstan 57

Dry compass 231
Dry dock 256
Ducts, air 167
Dufour 34, 192
Dunnet Head 240, 241
Duplex-type, direct-acting pump 62
Dutch barge 128, 129
Dutch cap 79
Dutch fleut 42, 126
Dutch koff 128, 129
Dutch motor coaster 163
Dutch motor fishing boat 174
Dutch pilot cutter 133
Dutch pinnace 127
Dutch yacht 188
Dwight D Eisenhower 221
Dyer Dhow 193
Dyrholaey 240, 241

E

E (signal flag) 138
Earing 105, 115, 120
Early machinery 19
Early ship types 18
Earthenware jug 259
Ease off 247
East Asiatic Co., Ltd. 49
East Cape 241
East India Company 136
East Indiaman 127, 259
East Indies 19
East Pakistani boat 128
Ebb tide 250
Eccentric rods 151, 154, 155, 156
Eccentric straps 150, 151, 155
Echo signal, radar 237
Echo sounder 227
Economizer, fuel 156
Eddystone (lighthouse) 238
Edgar (cruiser) 219
Edge to edge, planking 18
Edinburgh Cup 186, 187
Edward VII, England 188
Eel 172, 180
Effect of rudder 253
Egypt 226
Egyptian boat model 227
Egyptian markab 129
Egyptian paddle 148
Egyptian sea-going ship 126
8 (signal flag) 137
Einheitselbjolle 193
Eire 134
Eisbrecher 256
Eking 29
Elastic gasket 196
Elder Dempster Lines, Ltd. 49
Electrical services junction box 159
Electric control panel 61
Electric coupling box 58
Electric deck crane 93
Electric driving motor 58
Electric equipment platform 93
Electric generator 167

267

Electric light 93
Electric motor 57
Electric turning motor 166
Electric welding 19
Electric windlass 57
Electric stove 61
Electric telegraph 158
Electrode 213
Electrolyte container, mines 213
Electronic direction finder 197
Elevating arc 212
Elevation gear 212
Elevator 61
Ellen 50
Ellerman Lines, Ltd. 49
El Roque 240
Emergency (signal flag) 137
Emergency lighting 231
Emergency tiller 46
Empresa Nacional 49
Encased valve spring, diesel engine 166
End lap of plating 38
End-seizing 124
Engine 150, 151, 153, 154, 155, 156, 167, 199, 215
Engine frame 156
Engine operating room, *Gustav V* 210, 211
Engine room arrangement (gas turbine vessel) 159
(motor ship) 167
(icebreaker) 257
Engine room telegraph 158, 166
English sailing lifeboat 255
Enoch Train White Diamond Line 136
Ensign 137, 197
Ensign gaff 136
Ensign staff 137
Equal angle bar 39
Equipment, sailor's 259
Equipment platform, (deck crane) 93
Erikson, Gustaf 136
Ermak 257
Escape valve 154, 155
Escort vessel 220, 221
Eskimo paddle 148
Ethnographical boat types 128, 129
Evaporator 167
Exchanger, heat 159
Exhaust 159, 201
Exhaust annulus 159
Exhaust boiler 167
Exhaust boiler by-pass 167
Exhaust boiler outlet 167
Exhaust casing entrance 167
Exhaust gas boiler 167
Exhaust gas pipe 166
Exhaust gas valve 166, 167
Exhaust gas valve yoke 166, 167
Exhaust manifold 167

Exhaust pipe 58, 151, 154, 167
Exhaust pipe casing 167
Exhaust receiver 167
Exhaust stroke 167
Exhaust valve cam segment 166, 167
Exhaust valve lever 166, 167
Exhaust valve pull rod 167
Expansion chamber 159
Explosive charge, torpedo 215
Explosives, flag 138
Extended bridge 53
External bouyancy lifeboat 67
Extraction steam port, steam engine 156
Exxon Sunshine State 256
Eye bolt 123, 191
Eye bolt for tack 191
Eye plate 93
Eye splice 143
Eyelet 121
Eyelet hole 115, 121

F

F (signal flag) 138
Factory ship 175
Fairleader 83
Falls 66, 107, 109, 122
False keel 20, 21, 27, 33, 41
False Tinhosa (lighthouse) 241
Fan 167, 229
Farallon (lighthouse) 240
Fastnet Race 188
Fast-sailing vessel 19
Fathom 226, 227
Fayal (lighthouse) 240, 241
Feed pipe 152
Feed-water pipe 156
Feed-water pump 159
Feeler (sounding machine) 227
Felucca 173
Fender 196
Ferraria Point (lighthouse) 240, 241
Ferry 165
Fiber (rope) 140
Fiberglass boat 200
Fiberglass lifeboat 67
Fids 125
Fiddle block 122, 124
Fidley 154
Fidley grating 154
Fidley top 154
Fife rail 107
Fifty-fifty cruiser 200
Figure of eight knot 142
Figurehead 19, 20, 21, 51
Fillet weld 39
Filling chock 32
Fin 201, 212, 215, 216, 239

Finder range 210, 211, 217
Fine control radar 217
Fine dial (range receiver) 217
Fin keel 191
Finland 129, 134
Finn 191
Fins 216
Finska Ångfartygs AB 49
Fire control radar 217
Firefly 192
Fire grommet 207
Fireplace 61
Fire-proofed lifeboat 67
Firing data 217
Firing device 212, 213
Firing mechanism 213
First IP-connecting rod 156
First IP-cylinder 156
First reef band 114
First reinforce 206
First tube bank 156
First Substitute (signal flag) 137
First watch 59
Fish 180, 181, 229
Fisherman's bend 142
Fishing an anchor 55
Fishing boats 173, 174, 175, 178
Fishing implements 172
Fishing methods 176, 177, 178, 179
Fishing smack 176
Fishing tackle 55
Fission, nuclear 159
Fittings, yacht 190, 191, 197
Fitzroy Island 241
5 (signal flag) 137
Five bladed propeller 158
5 0 5 (one-design yacht) 193
5.5-meter yacht 192
Five-masted bark 74, 116, 130, 121
Five-masted barkentine 130, 131
Five-masted fore-and-aft schooner 74, 132, 133
Five-masted full-rigged ship 74, 76, 77, 130, 131
Five-masted two-topsail schooner 130, 131
Fixed-keel boat (Dragon) 186, 187
Fixed loop aerial 235
Flagpole 75, 77, 78, 92, 137
Flags 134, 135, 136, 137, 138, 139, 176, 197, 201
Flame tube 159
Flannan Islands 241
Flare 212
Flash reducer 212
Flash shield 216
Flask 215
Flat, watertight 37
Flat-floored 19
Flat Island 241
Flat plate keel 38, 39, 154

Flat seam 106
Flemish knot 142
Flettner rudder 197
Flexible framework 18
Float 172, 177, 178, 230
Floating capacity, lifeboats 67
Floating drydock 255
Floating link, steering gear 47
Floating trawl 179
Floor 26, 27, 30, 31, 32, 33, 36, 38, 40, 44, 45, 151, 154
Floor ceiling 27
Flooring 26, 167
Flush-decked 19
Flush-decked ship 53
Flute, Dutch 127
Flying Clipper 189
Flying Dutchman 191
Flying jib 88, 89, 100, 101, 102, 103, 119
Flying jib boom 86, 87, 88, 89
Flying jib boom guy 86, 87, 88, 89
Flying jib downhaul 88, 89, 119
Flying jib halliard 119
Flying jib sheet 87, 88, 89, 119
Flying jib stay 86, 87
Flying jib tack 88, 89
Flying Junior 193
Flywheels 58, 109, 150, 201
Fo'c'sle 18, 22, 23, 25, 53, 199
Fo'c'sle and poop, vessel with 53
Fo'c'sle deck 36, 210, 211
Fo'c'sle hatch 191
Fo'c'sle head 25, 254
Fog horn 59, 201
Folding hatch cover 63
Folding rule 34, 35
Folding table 191
Folkboat 193
Fontes Pereira de Melo (lighthouse) 240, 241
Food 260
Food tank 67
Foot 20, 21, 106, 114, 115, 120, 178
Foot of sail 120, 191
Footrope 86, 88, 89, 90, 91, 106, 107, 110, 114, 118, 176, 177, 178, 179
Fore-and-aft component 244
Fore-and-aft jib sheet block 123
Fore-and-aft mark 234
Fore-and-aft rigged topmast 75, 77
Fore-and-aft schooner 50, 74, 75, 76, 77, 102, 116, 132, 133, 189

Fore-and-aft topsail 117
Fore and after 29
Fore back spring 254
Flettner rudder 197
Forebody 22, 23, 32, 33
Forebody of OBO-ship 37
Fore bonnet 120
Fore boom 92
Fore boom topping lift 92
Fore brace 92, 108
Fore breast rope 254
Fore buntline 108
Fore cant timber 29
Fore cap backstay 80
Forecastle, *see* fo'c'sle
Fore clewgarnet 87, 108
Fore course (sail) 100, 101
Fore end cylinder 166
Fore end of crankshaft 166
Fore floor 33
Forefoot 20, 21, 32
Fore gaff 92
Fore gaff topsail 102
Fore hatch 60
Fore hatch coaming 33
Fore lower mast 72, 73, 80
Fore lower topgallant brace 108
Fore lower topgallant buntline 108
Fore lower topgallant clewline 108
Fore lower topgallant sail 100, 101, 103
Fore lower topgallant sheet 108
Fore lower topgallant yard 72, 73
Fore lower topsail 100, 101, 102, 103
Fore lower topsail brace 108
Fore lower topsail buntline 108
Fore lower topsail clewline 108
Fore lower topsail sheet 108
Fore lower topsail yard 72, 73
Foremast 20, 21, 25, 32, 33, 74, 75, 77, 80, 81, 87, 92, 93, 110, 115
Foremast head 115
Forenede Dampskibsel-skab, Det 137
Fore peak 115, 116
Fore peak bulkhead 36
Fore peak halliard 115, 116
Fore peak hatch 60
Fore peak roof 37
Fore peak tank 36
Fore rigging 80, 87
Fore royal 100, 101, 102
Fore royal backstay 80
Fore royal brace 108
Fore royal buntline 108
Fore royal clewline 108
Fore royal mast 72, 73, 80

Fore royal pole 72, 73
Fore royal sheet 108
Fore royal stay 80, 86, 88, 89
Fore royal staysail 119
Fore royal staysail downhaul 119
Fore royal staysail halliard 119
Fore royal staysail sheet 119
Fore royal yard 72, 73
Fore sail 87, 92, 100, 101, 102, 103, 110, 120, 198, 247
Fore sail sheet 92
Fore sheet 87, 108, 116
Fore shroud 80
Forestay 80, 86, 87, 88, 89, 92, 115, 197
Forestay lanyard 87
Fore staysail 92, 102, 103, 115, 245
Fore staysail halliard 115
Fore staysail sheet 118
Fore steaming light 65
Fore tack 87, 108
Fore tack bumpkin 87
Fore throat 115, 116
Fore throat halliard 115, 116
Fore top 72, 73
Fore topgallant backstay 80
Fore topgallant bowline 87
Fore topgallant mast 72, 73, 80, 92
Fore topgallant rigging 80
Fore topgallant sail 102
Fore topgallant stay 80, 86, 87, 88, 89
Fore topping lift 116
Fore topmast 72, 73, 80, 92
Fore topmast backstay 80
Fore topmast cap backstay 80
Fore topmast crosstree 72, 73
Fore topmast preventer stay 86
Fore topmast rigging 80
Fore topmast stay 80, 86, 87, 88, 89, 92
Fore topmast staysail 88, 89, 92, 100, 101, 102, 103, 119, 251
Fore topmast staysail downhaul 87, 88, 89, 119
Fore topmast staysail halliard 119
Fore topmast staysail sheet 88, 89, 119
Fore topmast staysail tack 86, 88, 89
Fore topsail 87, 102
Fore topsail bowline 86, 87
Fore topsail brace 90
Fore trysail 103
Fore upper topgallant brace 108
Fore upper topgallant buntline 108

Fore upper topgallant downhaul 108
Fore upper topgallant sail 100, 101
Fore upper topgallant sheet 108
Fore upper topgallant yard 72, 73
Fore upper topsail 100, 101, 102, 103
Fore upper topsail brace 108
Fore upper topsail buntline 108
Fore upper topsail downhaul 108
Fore upper topsail sheet 108
Fore upper topsail yard 72, 73
Fore vang 92
Fore yard 72, 73, 75, 77, 87, 92, 110
Forward bitt 33
Form 19
Formosa 134
Forward director control tower 217
Forward elevation 36
Forward oil pan 166
Forward perpendicular 24
Forward turbocharger 166
Foundation 58, 151, 157
4 (signal flag) 137
Four-by-three tackle 123
Four-fold tackle 123
Four-letter signal 139
Four-masted bark 72, 73, 74, 76, 77, 80, 100, 101, 108, 116, 130, 131
Four-masted barkentine 103, 130, 131
Four-masted fore-and-aft schooner 74, 102, 132, 133
Four-masted full-rigged ship 74
Four masted jackass bark 130, 131
Four-masted ship 102, 130, 131
Four-masted topsail schooner 130, 131
Four-point bearing 234
470-dinghy 191
Fourth Substitute (signal flag) 137
Four-tube launcher 216
420-dinghy 193
Frame 26, 27, 28, 30, 36, 38, 39, 44, 45, 199, 233, 235
Frameless double-ender 18
Frame lines 22, 23
Framework 18
Framing 18, 31, 37, 45
France, flag 134
France 164
Frapping ring 63

Freeboard 53
Freighter 164
French Grand Bank schooner 173
French lugger 173
French motor trawler 173
French tunny yawl 175
Fresh water pump 107
Fresh water summer loadline 52
Fresh water summer timber loadline 52
Fresh water tank 227
Fresh water tropical loadline 52
Fresh water tropical timber loadline 52
Fresnel lens 64, 239
Frigate 32, 40, 86, 216, 218, 219, 220, 221
Front header, boiler 156
Front plate, boiler 152
Front tube plate, boiler 154
Fruit carrier 164
Fuel charging valve 215
Fuel drain unit 159
Fuel injection pump 166, 167
Fuel oil tank 167, 257
Fuel pipe 167
Fuel pump 167
Fuel tank 191, 215
Fuel valve 166, 167
Full astern 247
Full line 19
Full-rigged four-masted ship 102
Full-rigged ship 74, 76, 77, 102, 251, 257
Full speed astern 138
Full dimensioned ship 53
Fulton, Robert 150, 160
Fulton's mine 213
Funnel 49, 61, 150, 152, 154, 167, 207
Funnel cape 154
Furl 248, 251
Furnace 152, 156, 157
Furnace bar 152, 156
Furnace bridge 152, 156
Furnace door 152, 156
Furnace front 152
Furnace grate 156
Furnace peephole 157
Furnace tube 157
Furness Lines 49
Futtock 26, 27
Futtock rigging 81
Futtock shrouds 81, 83, 90, 91, 110
Fuse 209, 212, 216

G

G (signal flag) 138
Gaff 72, 73, 92, 114, 115, 116, 117, 136
Gaff band 123
Gaff-rigged cutter 132, 133
Gaff sail 99, 114, 115, 116, 117

Gaff topsail 92, 100, 101, 103, 117
Gaff topsail 92, 100, 101, 103, 117
Galleass 18
Galleon 18, 126
Galley 18, 22, 23, 32, 61, 148, 191, 199, 210, 211
Galley funnel 61
Galley oar 148
Galley stove 61
Galley wood 32
Galliot 18
Gallows 26
Galvanized-steel strand 141
Gammoning 86, 87
Garboard strake 20, 21, 27, 30, 154
Garnet 107
Gas boiler 167
Gasket 86, 104, 113, 191
Gas-turbine 159, 257
Gas turbine outlet to boiler, diesel engine 166
Gauge board, diesel engine 166
Gauge glass 152
Gävle 139
Gear 47, 55, 106, 109, 119, 150, 157, 159, 167, 196, 212, 215, 216
Gear housing 58, 201
Gearing, reduction 210, 211
Generator 167, 210, 211, 237, 257
Genoa (jib sail) 198
German heur boat 173
German motor trawler 174
German North Sea ketch 173
Gibb's Hill (lighthouse) 240
Gig 132, 133
Ginblock 106
Gipsy head 58
Girder 19, 30, 36, 37, 45, 93
Gironde estuary (lighthouse) 238
Girth band 118
Gland sealing 62
Glass fiber 19
Gloriana 188
Glued 19
Glückauf 161
Goa (lighthouse) 241
Goal-post mast 93
Go(ing) about 247
Going alongside 253
Going large 246
Gokstad ship 18, 26, 42
Golden Hind 64
Golfito (lighthouse) 240
Gooseneck bolt 82
Gooseneck fitting 93
Goose-winged sail 251
Gorge (bone bait holder) 172

Gouge 34, 35
Governor 229
Grab rope 67
Grand Banks 173
Grand Canary Island (lighthouse) 214
Grand Isle 256
Grapnel 55
Grasshopper engine 153
Gravity davit 66
Great barracuda 180
Great Britain, flag 135
Great cabin 40
Great Eastern 160
Great Harry 64
Great Ormes Head (lighthouse) 240, 241
Great Sambas River 241
Great Western 160
Greece 134
Greek boats 18
Greek fishing boat 173
Greek Periples 242
Greek warship 148
Greenland whale 180
Grenade 207
Grifo Island (lighthouse) 240
Grinnell, Ninturn & Co. 136
Grip oar 149
Grip rope 141
Gripe 20, 21, 32, 33, 66
Grommet 207
Ground line 178
Grängesberg-Oxelösund, Trafik AB 49
Guadalcanal Island (lighthouse) 241
Guafo Island (lighthouse) 240
Guantánamo (lighthouse) 240
Guard ring propeller 155
Guaymas 240
Gudgeon 44, 45
Gudgeon strap 42, 43
Guided missile 212, 220, 221
Guide pulley 46
Gun 60, 206, 210, 211, 212
Gun balancing gear 212
Gunboat 207
Gun carriage 207
Gun deck beam 32, 40
Gun elevation 217
Gun ladle 207
Gunport 40
Gunport lid 51
Gun tackle 123
Gunter rig 99, 132, 133
Gun with accessories 207
Gustaf af Klint 243
Gustav V 210, 211
Gustavus III, Sweden 188
Guy 86, 87, 88, 89, 93
Guy lead block 88, 89
Gyoku San 241
Gyrocompass 47, 231
Gyrohydraulic steering control 47
Gyroservomotor 315

Gyroscope 48
Göta River boat 128

H

H (signal flag) 138
Haddock 181
Hadley, John 233
Hake 181
Half beams 29
Half-breadth plan 24
Half-hitch 142
Halibut 178, 181
Halliard 72, 73, 83, 107, 109, 110, 112, 115, 116, 117, 119, 124
Halliard block 115
Halliard spanner 106
Halliard tackle 106
Halliard winch 109, 197
Hall's anchor 55
Hamburg American Line 137
Hamburger Paquet 160
Hammer 34, 35
Hams Bluff (lighthouse) 240
Hand grenade 207
Hand hole plates, boiler 156
Handle 34, 35, 57, 62, 67, 109, 227, 258
Hand lead 226
Hand line 172
Hand rail 154
Hand saw 34, 35
Hand spike 207
Hand-steering room 210, 211
Hand-steering wheel 46
Hand wheel 166
Hanging knee 41
Hanks 118
Hansa, Deutsche Dampschiffahrts-Gesellschaft 49
Hanseatic League 126, 136
Harbor tug 255
Hardie, John & Co. 136
Harness cask 260
Harpoon 172, 176
Hatch 22, 23, 25, 36, 60, 63, 199
Hatch beam 63
Hatch beam support 63
Hatch board 63
Hatch coaming 63
Hatch cover 29, 63
Hatch end beam 29
Hatch end pillar 45
Hatch girder 31
Hatchet 34, 35
Hatchway 20, 63
Hatchway beam 29
Hatchway carling 29
Hatchway coaming 29
Haul over 247
Hawse pipe 36, 60
Hawser 140, 141
Hawser bend 55
Hawse timber 29
H-boat 193

Head 29, 42, 57, 66, 83, 105, 114, 115, 117, 118, 178
Head cringle 118
Head earing 105, 115
Header boiler 156
Head foil 197
Head ledge 29
Headline 176, 177, 178, 179
Headpiece 20, 21
Head rail 32
Headrope 114, 254
Headsail 246, 248
Headsheet 249
Head timbers 32
Heart thimble 85
Heat exchanger 159
Heating unit, diesel powered 191
Heaving anchor 56
Heave to 251
Heavy boom 93
Heavy boom heel 93
Heavy lashing 251
Hebrides (lighthouse) 240, 241
Heel block 93
Heeling 253
Heeling pipe 257
Heel of keel 43
Heel of mast 79
Heel of rudder post 45
Heel of topmat 91, 251
Heel pintle 43
Heel rope 86
Heffner light 239
Height-finding radar 217
Helgoland (lighthouse) 240, 241
Helicopter 216
Helicopter equipment 257
Helm alee 247, 249
Helm follow-up 47
Helm indicator 47
Helmsman 42
Hemp 141
Hemp-clad wire rope 141
Hemp stay 118
Hemp string 141
Hemp strop 124
Hercules Tower (lighthouse) 240, 241
Herlofsen & Co., Sigurd 49
Hermaphrodite brig 130, 131
Herreshoff, Nathaniel 188
Herring 172, 181
Herriot Cup 187
Herz horn 213
Herzogin Cecilie 100, 101
"Het Leeskaartboek van Wisboy" 242
Hessen 220
Heur boat 173
H.F. Eimskipafélag Island 49
High frequency radio pulses 236, 237
High-pressure connecting rod 154
High-pressure cylinder 154

269

High-pressure tube 229
High speed neutron 159
Hinge 63
Hinge pin 63
Hitch 84, 104, 142
Hirtshals 240, 241
Hogland (lighthouse) 240, 241
Hoist, ammunition 210, 211
Hoisting motor 93
Hoisting ringbolt 206
Hoisting rope 93
Hoisting wire 141
Hoka sho 241
Hold 25, 27, 163
Holder, paravane 210, 211
Hold pillar 27, 30
Hold stanchion 27
Hole, limber 38, 44
Hollow water line 19
Honduras 134
Hood 40, 46
Hook 33, 36, 66, 93, 172
Hooker 127
Hooker of Schouwen 240, 241
Hoop 34, 35, 54, 82, 107, 112, 115, 117, 179, 206
Horizon glass 233
Horizon shade 233
Horizontal bulkhead stiffener 36
Horizontal engine 153
Horizontal planes 22, 23
Horn 213, 215
Horn cover 213
Horn windows 64
Horn with tallow to hold needles 125
Horse 106, 107, 118, 122
Horse iron 34, 35
Hourglass 59, 228
Houseboat 200
House flags 136, 137
House line 226
House marks 136
Housing 201
Housing of topmast 75, 77
HP-connecting rod 156
HP-cylinder 151, 156
HP-turbine 157
Hulk 18
Hull 18, 22, 23, 53
Humber keel (Yorkshire) 128
Hydraulic telemotor pressure gauge 47
Hydroplane 48
Hyperbola 236

I

I (signal flag) 138
I-beam 39
Ice boat 197
Ice breaker 257
Icebreaking stem 210, 211
Ida 50
Ikara missile 216
Ilha das Cabras (lighthouse) 241
Impact point 217
Impeller 62, 229
Imperatore Point (lighthouse) 240, 241
Implements, fishing 172, 176
Impulse turbine 157
Inboard motor 200
Inboard-outboard engine 201
Inboard racer 200
Index bar, sextant 233
Index glass, sextant 233
Index shade, sextant 233
India, flag 134
Indiaman, East 127
Indian paddle 148
Indicator valve 166
Induction coil 213
Inflatable life-raft 67
Information center 210, 211
Inglefield's anchor 55
Inglefield clips 190
Injection pump 167
Inlet manifold 167
Inlet steampipe 58
Inlet valve 167
Inner bobstay 86
Inner bottom center line strake 38
Inner buntline 104
Inner crossjack buntline 107
Inner jib 88, 89, 100, 101, 102, 103, 115, 119
Inner jib boom guy 88, 89
Inner jib downhaul 88, 89, 119
Inner jib halliard 115, 119
Inner jib sheet 88, 89, 119
Inner jib stay 80, 88, 89, 115
Inner jib tack 88, 89
Inner lower studding sail halliard 110
Inner martingale stay 88, 89
Inner post 40, 41
Inside strake 30, 38
Instrument box, magnetic acoustic mine 213
Intake, engine room air 167
Intake stroke, diesel engine 167
Intercostal keelson 30
Intercostal vertical keel 37
Intermediate cylinder 154
Intermediate-pressure connecting rod 154
Intermittent fillet weld 39
Internal gear rings 159
International buoyance, lifeboats 67
International canoe 192
International Dragon class 186, 187
International Dragon Gold Cup 187
International 5.5-meter yacht 192
International signal code 138, 139
International 6-meter yacht 192
International 12-meter yacht 192
International Yacht Racing Union 186
Into the wind 249
Inverted vertical reciprocating compound engine 153
IP-cylinder 156
Ironclad 218
Iron drum end of rolling spar 112
Iron hoops 206
Iron knee 19
Iron Monarch 164
Iron rudder 43
Iron sheer strake 27
Iron ship 19, 231
Iron steamer 44
Iron-stocked anchor 55
Iron yard 82
Isleta Point (lighthouse) 240, 241
Ischia (lighthouse) 240, 241
Israel, flag 134
Italia, Società Per Azoni di Navigazione 49
Italian fishing craft 128, 129
Italy, flag 134
IW-31 191

J

J (signal flag) 138
Jacht 128
Jack 136
Jackass bark 130, 131
Jackstaff 87, 137
Jack stay 104, 105, 106, 115, 121
Jackyard 117
Jackyard topsail 117
Japan, flag 134
Japanese bonito boat 174
Japan Mail S.S. Co., Ltd. 137
Jarvis, J.C., Captain 109
Jauréguiberry 218
Jaziat Halul (lighthouse) 241
Jebel Teir (lighthouse) 241
Jeer, main 91
Jeer capstan 31
Jet thrust, spinnaker 190
Jib 88, 89, 93, 100, 101, 103, 115, 119, 248, 249
Jib boom 86, 87, 88, 89
Jib boom gammoning 86
Jib boom guy 86, 87, 88, 89
Jib boom heel rope 86
Jib boom horse footrope 86
Jib-headed gaff topsail 117
Jib-headed spanker 103
Jib outhaul 86
Jib sheet 87, 88, 89
Jib sheet block 123
Jibstay 80, 86, 87, 115
Jib topsail 103
Jigger 72, 73, 80, 102, 103, 107, 116
Jigger gaff topsail 102, 103
Jigger lower mast 72, 73, 80
Jigger lower topsail 102
Jigger mast 74, 75, 77, 80, 108
Jigger pole 72, 73
Jigger rigging 80
Jigger royal 102
Jigger shroud 80
Jigger stay 80
Jigger staysail 100, 101, 110
Jigger staysail downhaul 119
Jigger staysail halliard 119
Jigger staysail sheet 119
Jigger top 72, 73
Jigger topgallant mast 80
Jigger topgallant stay 80
Jigger topgallant staysail 100, 101, 119
Jigger topgallant staysail downhaul 107, 119
Jigger topgallant staysail halliard 119
Jigger topgallant staysail sheet 119
Jigger topmast 72, 73, 80
Jigger topmast rigging 80
Jigger topmast stay 80
Jigger topmast staysail 100, 101, 103, 119
Jigger topmast staysail downhaul 107, 119
Jigger topmast staysail halliard 119
Jigger topmast staysail sheet 119
Jigger upper topsail 102
Jigger yard 75, 77
J.O.G. sailing yacht 192
Joggle plank 28
Joggling 39
Johnson Line 137
Joint 18, 19, 39
Jolie Brise 188
Jouffrouy d'Abbans, Claude de, Marquis 160
Jullanar 188
Junction box 37, 47
Junk 51, 129
Junk ring 155
Junk ring bolt 155

K

K (signal flag) 138
Kadalur Point (lighthouse) 241
KaMeWa propeller 158
Katsepe Head (lighthouse) 241
Keel 20, 21, 26, 27, 28, 30, 31, 32, 33, 36, 37, 38, 39, 40, 41, 44, 154, 210, 211
Keel boat 186, 187
Keel breadth 19
Keel length 19
Keel plate 27
Keel scarf 33, 41
Keel strake 31
Keelson 26, 27, 30, 32, 33, 36, 38, 40, 41, 78
Keelson scarf 41
Keep clear (signal flag) 138
Kelapa Inlet (lighthouse) 241
Ketch 74, 75, 103, 129, 132, 133, 173, 192
Kevels 32
Kevel head 33
Keypiece 18
Keystone Shipping Co. 49
Keyway 155
Kharlov Island (lighthouse) 240, 241
Killingen 193
Kimari (India) boat 128
King rod 150
Kirsten-Boeing propeller 158
Kite, depressor 214
Klavenes & Co. A.F. 49
Knarr 193
Knee 27, 29, 31, 33, 40, 41, 56
Knight head 29, 32, 254
Knots 42, 142, 228
Knutsen, AS Knut 49
Koff (Dutch) 129
Koh Pai (lighthouse) 241
Koninklijke Nederlandsche Stoomboot Maatschappij 49
Kopu (lighthouse) 240, 241
Korea, flag 134
Korsar 193
Ko Shima (lighthouse) 241
Koster boat 128
Kravel 126
Krayer 127
Kullen (lighthouse) 240, 241

L

L (signal flag) 138
Lace piece 33
Lacing 18, 115, 118, 120
Ladder 167
Laeisz, Ferdinand 136
Laeisz mast 75, 77
Laeisz yard 75, 77
Lamina brake 58
Lamp 64, 176, 239
Lamp locker 22, 23, 41
Landnordr 230
Landsudr 230
Lantern 40, 64, 65, 178
Lanyard 84, 86, 87, 124
Lap joint 39
Laser dinghy 193
Lashed-on planking 18
Lashing 42
Lashing boom 93
Lashing ringbolt 206
Lateen mizzen 120
Lateen rig 18
Lateen sail 99
Lateen topsail 117
Lateral component 244
Lateral resistance 244, 253
Lathe 167
Latitude 231
La Trinité Bay (lighthouse) 240
Launch 133
Launcher rocket 216
Lauritzen, J. 137
Laval nozzle 157
Law, Thomas & Co. 136
Lawson, Thomas W. 74
Lazyjacks 116
Lead 226, 227
Lead block 88, 89, 106
Lead horn 213
Leading block 66, 83, 106
Leading block for topgallant sheet 112
Leading net 176
Lead keel 199
Leadline 177, 226
Lead of the sheet 245
Lead sinker 176
Leadsman 227
Leak hole 213
Leech 105, 106, 114, 118, 120, 121
Leech line 104, 113
Leech rope 114, 118, 120
Lee side 117
Left-handeded twisted strand 141
Left-hand lay 140
Leidarstein 230
Leningrad 221
Lens 239
Leones Isle (lighthouse) 240
Liberia, flag 134
Liberty standard vessel 162
Lifeboat 66, 67
Lifeboat davits 66
Life float 66
Life line 66
Life raft 66
Lift 90, 72, 73, 83, 87, 90, 91, 92, 104, 105, 106, 107, 110, 113, 116, 122, 124

Lights 64, 65, 67
Light buoy 239
Lighthouse 60, 65, 238, 240, 241
Lighthouse lamps 239
Light metal 19
Lighting (yacht) 193
Lightship 257
Lignum vitae rollers 112
Limb 150, 233
Limber board 27
Limber hole 30, 44
Limber strake 27
Line 30, 172, 177, 178, 226, 228
Line fishing boat 173
Liner 167
Line shaft bearing 45
Line shaft flange 157
Line shaft section 45
Lines of a modern cargo ship 24
Lines of a wooden sailing ship 22, 23
Ling 181
Link 47, 55, 58
Link operating bar 151
Lint stock 207
Lipton, Sir Thomas 188
Liquid compass 231
Liverpool 139
Lizard 240, 241
Ljungström type yacht 196
Lloyd Brasileiro 49
Lloyd's Register 25, 52
Lloyd Triestina, Società Per Azioni di Navigazione 49
Loader, automatic gun 212
Loadline disc 52
Loadlines 52
Loading clip 212
Load water line 22, 23, 24
Lobster 181
Local stabilizer 217
Locker 32, 37, 40, 60, 210, 211
Lodestone 230
Lodging knee 29
Log 18, 228, 229, 234
Log canoe 18
Log glass 228
Log line 229
Log reel 46, 228
Log register 196
Long Beach 220
Long bridle 121
Longitudinal bulkhead 31, 45
Longitudinal deck girder 45
Longitudinal material 19
Longitudinal middle line 22, 23
Longitudinal section 32, 33, 40, 41, 44
Longitudinal section through engine room 167
Long range missile 212
Long ship 18, 126
Loom 149
Loran system 236

Low-pressure connecting rod 154
Low-pressure cylinder 154
Low-pressure tube 229
Low-pressure connecting rod 156
Lower cap 78, 79
Lower cap backstay 83
Lower deadeye 84
Lower deck 27, 44, 167
Lower deck beam 30, 154
Lower deck clamp 27
Lower deck hanging knee 27
Lower deck planking 27
Lower deck shelf 27
Lower deck stringer plate 27, 30
Lower deck tie plate 27, 30
Lower deck waterway 27
Lower hold ceiling 33
Lower lift 122, 124
Lower mast 72, 73, 75, 77, 78, 79, 80, 106, 107, 110, 113
Lower masthead 79, 91
Lower platform 167
Lower rigging 81, 83, 110
Lower sail 104, 120
Lower sheet 107
Lower shroud 81
Lower spanker 100, 101, 116
Lower spanker gaff 72, 73
Lower square sail 113
Lower stay 83
Lower studding sail 110
Lower studding sail yard 110
Lower topgallant brace 108
Lower topgallant buntline 108
Lower topgallant clewline 108
Lower topgallant sail 100, 101, 103
Lower topgallant sheet 108
Lower topgallant tie 83
Lower topgallant truss 83
Lower topgallant yard 72, 73, 75, 77, 83
Lower topsail 100, 101, 103, 110, 113
Lower topsail brace 108, 110
Lower topsail buntline 107, 108, 251
Lower topsail clewline 108, 110, 251
Lower topsail lift 110
Lower topsail sheet 107, 108, 110, 113
Lower topsail yard 72, 73, 75, 77, 83, 107, 110, 251
Lower yard 83, 104, 105, 107, 110, 113, 245

Lower yardarm 124
Lower yard footrope 110
Low pressure cylinder 151, 156
Low pressure cylinder steam inlet 151
Low pressure turbine 157
Lubricating oil pipe 167
Lubricating oil main pipe 167
Lubricating oil circulating tank 167
Lubricating oil cooler 167
Lubricating oil pump 167
Lubricating oil return pipe 167
Lubricator 62
Luff 114, 115, 118, 195, 244, 245, 247, 249
Luff rope 114, 118
Luff tackle 123
Luff tunnel 197
Luff upon luff, shroud 84
Lug 18, 63
Lug sail 99, 132, 133
Lübeck 136

M

M (signal flag) 138
Machinery 19
Machinery control room 257
Machinery plan 167
Mackerel 172, 176, 178, 180, 181
Madeira (lighthouse) 241
Madras (lighthouse) 241
Magazine 209, 210, 211, 212, 216
Magnet 231
Magnetic field 213
Magnetic mine 213
Magnetism 213
Magnus, Olaus 242
Mail flag 136
Main and 'tween deck diagonal hanging knees 33
Main bearing 154, 155, 156
Main-bearing lubricating oil pipe 167
Main bonnet 120
Main boom 92
Main boom topping lift 92
Main brace 90, 108
Main buntline 108
Main cap 91
Main capstan 40
Main Channel (lighthouse) 240
Main clewgarnet 90, 91, 108
Main course 100
Main deck 25, 36, 44, 45, 53, 167
Main deck beam 30, 33, 41

Main deck diagonal hanging knee 33
Main deck pillars 30
Main deck stringer plate 30
Main deck tie plate 30
Main engine 167
Main footrope 91
Main framing 45
Main gaff 92
Main gaff topsail 92, 102, 103
Main gauge board 158
Main gear 157
Main jeer 91
Main lift 90, 91
Main lower mast 72, 73
Main lower topgallant brace 107, 108
Man lower topgallant countline 108
Main lower topgallant clewline 108
Main lower topgallant sail 100, 101
Main lower topgallant sheet 108
Main lower topgallant yard 72, 73
Main lower topsail 100, 101, 102, 251
Main lower topsail brace 108
Main lower topsail buntline 108
Main lower topsail clewline 108
Main lower topsail sheet 108
Main lower topsail yard 72, 73
Main peak 116
Main peak halliard 116
Main piece 42
Main pole 176
Main rail 27, 33, 41, 109
Main rail cap 30
Main rigging 90, 91
Main royal 100, 101, 102
Main royal brace 108
Main royal buntline 108
Main royal clewline 108
Main royal mast 72, 73
Main royal pole 72, 73
Main royal sheet 108
Main royal stay 80
Main royal staysail 100, 101, 102, 119
Main royal staysail downhaul 119
Main royal staysail halliard 119
Main royal staysail sheet 119
Main royal yard 72, 73
Main shaft 46
Main sheer strake 30
Main shrouds 90
Main spencer 102
Main staysail 92, 103
Main tack 108
Main throat halliard 115
Main topgallant mast 72, 73, 92

Main topgallant sail 102
Main topgallant stay 80, 92
Main topgallant staysail 100, 101, 102, 119
Main topgallant staysail downhaul 119
Main topgallant staysail halliard 119
Main topgallant staysail sheet 119
Main topmast 72, 73, 92
Main topmast crosstree 72, 73
Main topmast stay 80, 92
Main topmast staysail 100, 101, 102, 103, 119
Main topmast staysail downhaul 119
Main topmast staysail halliard 119
Main topmast staysail sheet 119
Main topping lift 116
Main topsail 90, 102
Main topsail brigantine 130, 131
Main topsail schooner 130, 131
Main topsail sheet 91
Main truss 91
Main trysail 103
Main upper topgallant brace 107, 108
Main upper topgallant buntline 108
Main upper topgallant downhaul 108
Main upper topgallant sail 100, 101
Main upper topgallant sheet 108
Main upper topgallant yard 72, 73
Main upper topsail 100, 101, 102
Main upper topsail brace 108
Main upper topsail buntline 108
Main upper topsail downhaul 108
Main upper topsail sheet 108
Main upper topsail yard 72, 73
Main vang 92
Mainmast 20, 21, 74, 75, 76, 77, 80, 90, 91, 92, 249, 251
Mainmast head 91
Mainsail 90, 92, 100, 101, 102, 103, 113, 120, 198, 244, 245, 248, 251
Mainsail haul 249
Mainsheet 92, 108, 116
Mainstay 80, 90, 91, 92, 115
Maintop 72, 73, 90, 91

Mainyard 72, 73, 75, 77, 90, 91, 248, 249, 250, 251
Mainyard footrope 90
Mainyard stirrups 90
Makapuu Point (lighthouse) 240
Making iron 34, 35
Mallet 34, 35, 125
Mallorca (lighthouse) 240, 241
Maneuvering 138, 252, 253
Maneuvering stand deck crane 93
Maneuvering positions, engine room 167
Manger board 32
Manhole 107, 156
Manhole door 152
Manifold 167
Manzanillo Point (lighthouse) 240
Marine creatures 180, 181
Marine-lavatory 191
Mark buoy 176, 178
Markab (Egyptian) 129
Marline hitched lacing 115
Marlinespike 125
Marryat's code 139
Martingale 86, 88, 89
Martingale backrope 88, 89
Martingale boom 86
Martingale guy (Martingale stay) 86, 88, 89
Martinique (lighthouse) 240
Mast 72, 73, 74, 75, 78, 79, 80, 83, 90, 93, 114, 115, 199
Mast and spars 75
Mast and top 78
Mast band 93
Mast batten 115
Mast beam 29
Mast boom 191
Mast calipers 79
Mast carling 29
Mast coat 75, 77, 107
Master starting air valve wheel, diesel engine 166
Master station, Decca system 236
Masthead 75, 77, 91, 122, 135
Masthead aerial 197
Masthead fitting 197
Masthead light 65, 93
Masthead pendant 122
Mast hole 29
Mast hoops 117
Mast partner 26, 29
Mast, rotating 197
Mast step 32, 40, 78
Material 19
Mate's room 22, 23, 60
Mats 261
Matson Nav. Co. 137
Maul 34, 35
Mauretania 261

271

Mauritius (lighthouse) 241
Mayflower 50
Mazatlán (lighthouse) 240
Measure vessel, anti-roll tank 48
Mechanical firing mechanism 213
Mechanical mine 213
Mechanical one boat sweep 214
Mechanical screw steering gear 46
Medical assistance (signal flag) 138
Medicine chest 259
Medieval tops 78
Mediterranean 128, 129, 188
Mediterranean region 18
Mel Point (lighthouse) 240
Merchant flags 134, 135
Mercantile Navy List, The 138
Mercur 256
Merlin/Rocket class 192
Mesa de Roldan (lighthouse) 240, 241
Messageries Maritimes, Cie de 137
Messenger 56
Messenger wheel 46
Messroom 22, 23, 60
Mess table 60
Meta-Jan 50
Metal boat 67
Metal rivet 18
MGB 2009 159
Micrometer screw 233
Middle buntline 104
Middle-line plane 22, 23
Middle martingale stay 88, 89
Middle mast 74
Middle staysail 103
Middle watch 59
Midsection 18
Midship bend 28
Midship section 26, 27, 31
Milazzo (lighthouse) 240, 241
Mills release apparatus 66
Mine 213, 214
Mine casing 213
Mine Head (lighthouse) 240, 241
Mine horn 213
Minesweeper 214, 220, 221
Minesweeper turbine 157
Minesweeping 214
Minette 193
Missile 212, 220, 221
Missile launching platform 212
Missile tail fin 21
Mississippi River steamboat 161
Miter wheel 46
Mitsui-TBS 256
Mizzen 72, 73, 76, 77, 92, 102, 103, 120

Mizzen bonnet 120
Mizzen boom 92
Mizzen boom topping lift 92
Mizzen course 100, 101
Mizzen gaff 92
Mizzen gaff topsail 92, 102, 103
Mizzen lower mast 72, 73
Mizzen lower topgallant brace 108
Mizzen lower topgallant buntline 108
Mizzen lower topgallant clewline 108
Mizzen lower topgallant sail 100, 101
Mizzen lower topgallant sheet 108
Mizzen lower topgallant yard 72, 73
Mizzen lower topsail 100, 101, 102
Mizzen lower topsail brace 108
Mizzen lower topsail buntline 108
Mizzen lower topsail clewline 108
Mizzen lower topsail sheet 108
Mizzen lower topsail yard 72, 73
Mizzen peak 116
Mizzen peak halliard 116
Mizzen pole 72, 73
Mizzen royal 100, 101, 102
Mizzen royal brace 108
Mizzen royal buntline 108
Mizzen royal clewline 108
Mizzen royal mast 72, 73
Mizzen royal sheet 108
Mizzen royal staysail 100, 101, 102, 119
Mizzen royal staysail downhaul 119
Mizzen royal staysail halliard 119
Mizzen royal staysail sheet 119
Mizzen royal yard 72, 73
Mizzen sheet 92, 116
Mizzen spencer 102
Mizzen stay 92
Mizzen staysail 92, 103, 251
Mizzen throat 116
Mizzen throat halliard 116
Mizzen top 72, 73
Mizzen topgallant mast 72, 73
Mizzen topgallant sail 102
Mizzen topgallant sheet 107
Mizzen topgallant staysail 100, 101, 102, 119
Mizzen topgallant staysail downhaul 119

Mizzen topgallant staysail halliard 119
Mizzen topgallant staysail sheet 119
Mizzen topmast 72, 73, 92
Mizzen topmast crosstree 72, 73
Mizzen topmast stay 91, 92
Mizzen topmast staysail 100, 101, 102, 103, 119
Mizzen topmast staysail halliard 119
Mizzen topmast staysail downhaul 119
Mizzen topmast staysail sheet 119
Mizzen topping lift 116
Mizzen upper topgallant brace 108
Mizzen upper topgallant buntline 108
Mizzen upper topgallant downhaul 108
Mizzen upper topgallant sail 100, 101
Mizzen upper topgallant sheet 108
Mizzen upper topgallant yard 72, 73
Mizzen upper topsail 100, 102
Mizzen upper topsail brace 108
Mizzen upper topsail buntline 108
Mizzen upper topsail downhaul 108
Mizzen upper topsail sheet 108
Mizzen upper topsail yard 72, 73
Mizzen vang 92
Mizzenmast 20, 21, 40, 41, 46, 60, 74, 75, 77, 80, 92, 108
Moderator (nuclear fission) 159
Molokai (lighthouse) 240
Monitor 218
Montevideo (lighthouse) 240
Moonsail 76, 77
Moonsail mast 75, 77
Moonsail yard 75, 77
Moored mine 213
Moore-McCormack Lines, Inc. 49
Mooring 254
Mooring bollard 33
Mooring cable (rope) 213
Mooring cable drum 213
Mooring line 141
Mooring winch 58
Mooring watch 59
Morse lamp 65
Morse code 65
Mortar 206
Moth (yacht) 192
Motor 57, 191, 200, 201, 231
Motorboat details 201
Motorboat types 200

Motor coaster 163
Motor control lever 257
Motor cruiser 200
Motor fishing boat 174, 178
Motor generator 237
Motor ship 162, 167
Motor ship engine 167
Motor tanker 163
Motor torpedo boat 220
Motor trawler 173, 174, 179
Motsuta Misaki (lighthouse) 241
Mount Carmel (lighthouse) 241
Mousing (halliard) 109
Mud drum 156
Muleta 128
Mull of Galloway (lighthouse) 240, 241
Multi-purpose gun 217
Mushroom anchor 55
Musket ball bag 207
Muzzle 207, 209
Muzzle-loading gun 60
Muzzle swell 206
Mizzen upper topgallant sail 100, 101
Myggenaes (lighthouse) 240, 241
Möller, A.P. 49

N

N (signal flag) 138
Nao (Spanish ship) 126
Natchez 161
Natividad Island (lighthouse) 240
Navigating bridge 167
Navigation 226, 236
Navigational instruments 226
Navigation centre 257
Navigation table, adjustable 191
Nederland, N.V. Stoomvaart Maatschappij 49
Nederlandsch-Amerikaansche Stoomvaart Maatschappij 49
Needle 125
Nelson, Horatio, Viscount 218
Nemi, Lake 54
Net 176, 177, 178, 215
Net end 178
Net tail 177
Netherlands (flag) 134
Neutron 159
New Orleans 19
New Orleans cotton trade 19
New Year's Islands 240
New York pilot schooner 133
New York Yacht Club 197
New Zealand (flag) 134
Nippers 56
Nippon Yusen Kaisha 137
Nissho Maru 165
Noise suppressor 197
Norddeutscher Lloyd 137
Nordr 230

Norfolk wherry 128
Norman ship 126
Northern builders 18
Northern Europe 18
North Pole 231
North Sea ketch 173
Norway 134
Norwegian American Line 137
Norwegian fishing boat 173
Norwegian jacht 128
Norwegian motor fishing boat 174
Norwegian sealer 175
Nose fuse 209, 212
Nozzle 257
Nozzle propeller 158
Nozzle, turbine 157
Nozzle block turbine 157
Nozzle control valve turbine 157
Nuclear fuel elements 159
Nuclear power 159
Nuclear-powered cargo vessel 165
Nuclear-powered cruiser 220, 221
Nuclear-powered submarine 220, 221
Nuclear ship plant 159
Nugget Point (lighthouse) 241
Numeral pennants 138
N.V. Koninklijke Paketvaart Maatschappij 49

O

O (signal flag) 138
Oahu (lighthouse) 240
Oar 42, 148, 149
Ocean-going tug 256
Octant 233
Octopus 180
Odin 161
Oertz rudder 43
Officer's quarters 40, 60, 154, 210, 211
Oil drilling ship 256
Oil burner 157
Oil-cooled working piston 167
Oil cooler 167
Oil cooling channel 166
Oil cup 151
Oil lamp 231
Oil pan drain 166
Oil pump 167
Oil tank 163, 167
Oil tank ship 19
Oil tanker hatch cover 63
OK-dinghy 193
Okino-Shima (lighthouse) 241
Olinda Point (lighthouse) 240
Olsen & Co., Fred 49
Olympic Games 187, 194
One-design yachts 186, 187, 192
On the wind 246, 248, 249

Open shelter-decked vessel 53
Operating panel 235
Operating room 210, 211
Order of flags 137
Ore-carrying vessel 162
Ore tanker 163
Oriana 163
Organ-pipe whistle 59
Orlop deck beam 32, 40
Osaka Shosen Kaisha 49
Oscar II, Sweden 189
Oscillating engine 153
Oscillator, echo-sounder 227
Oseberg ship 54
Oslo-dinghy 193
Östergötland 220
Otter board 179
Otter trawl 179
Ottring (Norwegian motor fishing boat) 174
Ouessant 240, 241
Outboard motor 201
Outboard fiberglass boat 200
Outboard racer 200
Outer bobstay 80, 86
Outer buntline 104
Outer crossjack buntline 107
Outer jib 88, 89, 100, 101, 102, 103, 115, 119
Outer jib boom guy 88, 89
Outer jib downhaul 88, 89, 119
Outer jib halliard 115, 119
Outer jib sheet 88, 89, 119
Outer jib stay 80, 88, 89, 115
Outer jib tack 88, 89
Outer lower studding sail halliard 110
Outer martingale stay 88, 89
Outrigged four-oared rowboat 149
Outrigger 93
Outrigged canoe 128
Outside plank 29
Outside strake 30, 38, 39
Overflow oil tank 257
Overhand knot 142
Overhead beam engine 153
Overhead cooling-water pipe 166, 167
Over-speed governor 166
Overtaking light 65
Owens, Samuel 160
Oyster 181
"Oyster" mine 213

P

P (signal flag) 138
Pacific Steam Nav. Co. 137
Packet 124

Packing ring, steam piston 155
Paddles 148, 150
Paddle shaft 150
Paddle steamer 161
Paddle wheel 19, 149, 150
Paddle wheel engine 151
Paduakan (Celebes) 129
Painted ports 51
Pair mast 93
Pakistan, East, boat 128
Palm, sail-maker's 125
Palm and needle whipping 142
Pan, oil 166
Panama 134
Pan head rivet 38
Panel lighting 47
Pantry 257
Parabolic antenna 217
Parachute container, magnetic mine 213
Paraffin oil 65, 239
Paraffin oil lamp 231
Parapola (lighthouse) 241
Paravane holder 210, 211
Pargo Point (lighthouse) 240, 241
Parrel 82, 83, 112, 191
Parrel cheek block 112
Partners 29
Passage opening 31
Passenger liner 19, 165
Passenger service 19
Passenger ship 163, 164
Passenger vessel's engine room 167
Patches 114
Patent link, chain cable 55
Patent log 229
Patent reefing topsail 92
Patent self-reefing topsails 112
Patent steam windlass 57
Pawl 33, 56, 57, 201
Pawl bitt 33, 56
Pawl rim 56, 57
Pawling 213
Pawling mechanism 213
Pay off from the wind 244
Pay out 109
Paying-off 245, 248, 249
Pea, anchor 54
Peabody Museum 74
Peak 114, 115, 116
Peak cringle 114
Peak halliard 115, 116, 117
Peak halliard block 115
Peak patch 114
Peak shot 207
Peak tank 45
Pedestal of shaft bearing 44
Peephole, furnace 157
Pelorus 231
Pendant 55, 66, 122
Pendulum 48
Pennant 135, 136, 138

Pensacola (lighthouse) 240
Percussion fuse 212
Periples 242
Permanent magnet 231
Permanent magnetism 213
Perpendicular 24
Peruvian raft 148
P & O Steam and Nav. Co. 137
P 4 137
Pharos 238
Pier 247
Pig 260
Pillar 27, 30, 31, 44, 45
Pilot 138, 242
Pilot bridge 47, 210, 211
Pilot cutter 133
Pilot room 210, 211
Pilot schooner 188
Pilot staysail schooner 255
Pilot turret 210, 211
Pilot vessels 65, 133, 255
Pin 58, 63, 107, 124, 167
Pincer 34, 35
Pinion 46, 47, 157, 201
Pinion shaft 57
Pinion shaft cogwheel 58
Pinney's Patent self-reefing gear 92, 112
Pinnace 50, 51, 127
Pinrail 33, 41, 88, 89, 109
Pintle 42, 43, 44, 45
Pintle strap 42, 43
Pipe laying vessel 256
Pirate dinghy 193
Piragua 128
Pistol, torpedo 215
Piston 47, 150, 155, 156, 167
Piston cooling oil telescopic pipe 167
Piston pin 167
Piston rod 58, 62, 150, 154, 155, 156, 167
Piston rod crosshead 46, 154, 155
Piston rod oil cooling pipe 166
Piston rod stuffing box 156, 166, 167
Piston steam engine 155
Piston valve 156
Pitometer log 229
Pitot tube 229
Plaice 181
Planes 22, 23, 24
Plank butt 28
Planking 20, 21, 27, 28, 29, 57
Planksheer 27
Plank strake 28
Plan Position Indicator 236, 237
Plastic boat 200
Plate 20, 21, 27, 31, 37, 38, 39, 45, 124, 152
Plate floor 151

Platform 166, 167, 212
Plating 24, 30, 31, 36, 37, 45, 63, 151, 154
Plimsoll mark 52
Plot, chartwork surveying 243
Plummer, block 45
Plummet 213
Plywood boat 200
Plywood cruiser 193
Point Sur (lighthouse) 240
Polar Star 257
Polaris missile 220, 221
Pole 72, 73, 107, 176
Pole compass 92, 231
Polyprion Americanum, fish 180, 181
Ponta Quicombo (lighthouse) 240, 241
Poop 25, 44, 53
Poop bulkhead 44
Poop deck 25, 45
Poop deck beam 40
Poop lantern 64
Port 31, 33, 51, 167, 246, 248, 249
Port, altering course to 138
Port Cortez (lighthouse) 240
Port helm 247
Port Moresby (lighthouse) 241
Port Noumea (lighthouse) 240, 241
Port side 81
Port side light 65
Port tack 121, 246, 248, 249
Portable rudder section 44
Portugal, flag 134
Portuguese barkentine 173
Portuguese muleta 128, 129
Portuguese sardine steam drifter 174
Portulanes, (chartwork) 242
Position 234, 242
Position line 234
Post 20, 21, 40, 41, 42, 44, 45
Potosi 116
Powder horn 207
Powder keg 207
Powder magazine 210, 211
Powder measure 207
Powder room 40
Powder temperature 217
Power-driven pilot vessel 65
Power output shaft 159
Power output shaft coupling flange 159
Power stroke 167
P.P.I. 217, 237
Prawn 181
Predictor 217
Pre-fabricated sections 37
Preservation of food 260

Pressure mine 213
Pressure tube, distance speed logs 229
Preventer bolt 27
Preventer forestay 86
Preventer gauge 93
Preventer sheet 118
Preventer stay 93
Preussen 76, 77
Primary coolant 159
Primer 209, 213, 215, 216
Priming wire 207
Primitive craft 18
Prince Oscar 88, 89
Prince Royal 64
Prism 239
Projectile 212
Promenade deck 167
Propellant charge 209
Propeller 43, 45, 151, 155, 158, 199, 201, 210, 211, 215, 247
Propeller aperture 45
Propeller blade 44, 155
Propeller boss 44
Propeller cap 44
Propeller hub 155
Propeller motors 257
Propeller post 155
Propeller shaft 44, 155, 157, 166, 167, 201, 215
Propeller shaft coupling flange 166
Propeller shaft tunnel 53
Propeller thrust bearing 166, 167
Propulsion turbine 159
Protected cruiser 218, 219
Protecting hood (binnacle) 231
Protective deck 210, 211
Provisions 60, 260
Proximity fuse 212
Pulling lifeboat 67
Pulo Pisang (lighthouse) 241
Pump 47, 62, 107, 150, 154, 166, 167, 257
Pump arm 62
Pump axle 107
Pump brake 62
Pump bucket 62
Pump casing 62
Pump crank 107
Pump cylinder 62
Pump lever 154, 155
Pump link 154, 155
Pump shaft drive tail 62
Pump well 107
Punta de Campos (lighthouse) 240
Purchase (tackle) 123
Purchase rim 56
Purchase rod 56
Purse line 177
Purse seine 177
Purse seine netter 177
Pusher mast 74
Put about 117
Pyroscape 160

Q

Q (signal flag) 138
Quadrant 44, 66
Quadrantal correctors 231
Quadrant davit 66
Quadruple steam engine 156
Quadruple tackle 123
Quarters 210, 211, 246
Quarter block 82, 83
Quarter galleries 19, 40
Quartermaster 46
Quarter pole 176
Quay 247
Queen Charlotte Islands 240
Queen's Cup 188
Quoin 207

R

R (signal flag) 138
Rabbet 29
Racing 186, 189, 194, 200
Racked turn, mooring 254
Radar 201, 217, 237
Radar antenna 217
Radar reflector 239
Radiation, lead shield against 159
Radiator 217
Radio antenna 210, 211
Radio deviation 235
Radio direction finder 210, 211, 235
Radio navigation 236
Radio office 210, 211
Radio station 235
Radio unit 197
Raffee 102
Raft 148
Rägener system 111
Rail 20, 21, 27, 32, 33, 41, 88, 89, 107, 109
Raised quarter-deck vessel 53
Rålamb, Å.C. 149, 209, 254
Rammer 207, 212
Ramming 18
Range of target (Radar) 239
Range finder 210, 211, 217
Range light 65
Range receiver 217
Ras-al-Bir (lighthouse) 241
Ras Air (lighthouse) 214
Ratline 83, 84
Rattan ring 176
Rave hook 34, 35
Ray 180
Ray's bream 180
Reactor 159
Ready about 249
Ready to wear ship 248
Reamer 207
Rear header, boiler 156
Receiver 47, 217, 227

Recoil brake 209, 212
Recording unit 227
Rectangular boiler 152
Rectifier 257
Red ensign 135
Red snapper 180
Reduction gearbox 159
Reduction gearing 159, 210, 211, 257
Reduction pinion 157
Reed boat 128
Reef 113, 115, 120, 121
Reef band 113, 114, 120, 121
Reef cringle 114, 115
Reef earing 90
Reef knot 120, 121, 142
Reef points 114, 120, 121
Reef sail 120
Reef tackle 90
Reefing gear 191
Reefing halliard 112
Reel 34, 35, 46, 228
Reeming iron 34, 35
Reflector 217, 227, 239
Register (log) 229
Register class, 8 ft. 192
Release apparatus, Mills gear 67
Releasing gear, anchor 55
Releasing handle, Mills gear 66
Relief valve 157
Relievers cable 57
Repeater, gyrocompass 47, 231
Repeater transmitter 231
Replenishing tank, steering engine 47
Republic of South Africa (flag) 134
Rescue and survival capsule 67
Resistance experiments 19
Revenue cutter (Danish) 128
Reverse frame 29, 30, 36, 38
Reverse pawl 201
Reverse pinion 201
Reversed triple tackle 123
Reversed winding tackle 123
Reversing lever 58, 151
Reversing link 58
Reversing wheel 154, 155
Revolving topsail yard 112
Ribeirinha Point (lighthouse) 240, 241
Riders 26
Rider plate 38
Riding light 64
Rig 32, 76, 77, 113, 130, 131
Rigel 220
Rigging 78, 80, 81, 83, 84, 87, 90, 91, 92, 93, 108, 110, 124

273

Rigging and derrick arrangement 93
Rigging screw 85
Rigging seizing 85
Rigging work 125
Right-handed screw 252
Right-hand propeller 247
Rigid side lifeboat 69
Rim 33, 57, 104, 150
Ring 63, 123, 166
Ringbolt 206
Ripping iron 34, 35
Rising floor 19
Riverboat 18, 160
Rivet 18, 38
Rivet shank 38
Riveted frame 39
Riveted iron ship 30
Riveted joint 19
Riveted section 39
Riveted steel ship 38
Robands 105
Roca Partida (lighthouse) 240
Rocker arm (pump) 62
Rocket 216
Rocket class 192
Rocket launcher 216
Rod 46, 47, 58, 62, 167
Rodmeter 229
Roller 63, 112, 167
Roller lead 112
Roller reefing gear 191
Rolling hitch 142
Rolling spar 112
Rolls Royce Marine Proteus 159
Roman anchor 54
Roman merchant ship 42
Roman ship 18
Roman trader 126
Rope 140, 143
Rope guard 44
Rope welding 79
Roping needle 125
R.O.R.C. Rule 188
Rotating band 209
Rotating davit 66
Rotating mast 197
Rotator, patent log 229
Rotor case, gyrocompass 231
Rotor, gas-turbine 159
Rotterdamsche Lloyd 137
Rough-tree rail 20, 21
Round of ammunition 212
Roundhouse 41
Rounding a buoy 195
Round seizing 85
Round ship 18
Rowing 149
Rowlock 67
Royal 76, 77, 100, 101
Royal backstay 80, 81
Royal brace 108
Royal British Navy 139
Royal buntline 107, 108
Royal clewline 108
Royal halliard 72, 73
Royal lift 107
Royal Mail Steam Packet Co. 137

Royal mast 72, 73, 75, 77, 80, 107
Royal pole 72, 73
Royal sheet 108
Royal stay 80, 87, 88, 89
Royal staysail 100, 101, 102, 119
Royal yacht 48, 189
Royal Yacht Club of Gothenburg 186, 187
Royal Yacht Squadron 197
Royal yard 72, 73, 75, 77, 107
Royal yard footrope 107
Rubber fender 196
Rudder 18, 20, 21, 40, 41, 42, 43, 45, 46, 47, 199, 210, 211, 214, 215, 252, 253
Rudder angle 47
Rudder arm 44
Rudder arrangement 42
Rudder blade 42, 43
Rudder brace 42
Rudder frame 43
Rudder head 43
Rudder order indicator 47
Rudder plate 43
Rudder position indicator 47
Rudder post 44, 45
Rudder quadrant 44
Rudder rope 42
Rudder stock 43, 44, 45, 46
Rudder stock stuffing box 44
Rudder stock trunk 45
Rule (carpenter's tool) 34, 35
Rules of yacht racing 195
Runciman, Lord 189
Runner 106, 123
Running on the wind 244
Running before the wind 246
Running dead 246
Running free 246
Running gear 106, 119
Running gear of staysails 119
Running rigging 108
Running rigging of the square sails four-masted bark 108
"Running survey" 243
Running wire rope 141
Russian royal yacht 48

S

S (signal flag) 138
Saddle 167
Safety device 213, 216
Safety propeller 215
Safety valves 150, 152, 154, 156
Safety water ski flag 201
Sail 62, 90, 244, 247, 249

Sail, types of 99
Sails, four-masted bark 100, 101
Sail aft 248
Sail details 121
Sail locker 22, 23, 60, 199
Sail-maker's palm 125
Sail-making 125
Sail needle 125
Sail plan 198
Sailing 244, 246
Sailing ships 126
Sailing trawler 174
Sailing whaler 175
Sailing yacht 192
Sailor's hobbies 261
Sailor's outfit 258
St. Andrew, Cross of 135
St. Augustine (lighthouse) 240
St. Bees (lighthouse) 240, 241
St. Croix (lighthouse) 240
St. George, Cross of 135
St. Lucia (lighthouse) 240
St. Patrick, Cross of 135
Salén Lines 49
Salmon 180
Salt water summer loadline 52
Salt water summer timber loadline 52
Salt water tropical loadline 52
Salt water winter loadline 52
Salt water winter timber loadline 52
Samson post 25
Sandakan (lighthouse) 240, 241
Sandy Cape (lighthouse) 241
San Francisco (lighthouse) 240
San Miguel (lighthouse) 240, 241
Santa Elena Point (lighthouse) 240
Sao Thome (lighthouse) 241
Sapienza (lighthouse) 240, 241
Sappho 188
Sardine 181
Sardine drifter 174
Sauna, icebreaker 257
Savannah (paddle steamer) 160
Savannah (nuclear cargo vessel) 165
Saw 34, 35
Scalloped frame 39
Scanner 237
Scarf 41
Scarfed joint 19
Scavenging air compression chamber 167
Scavenging air delivery valve 167
Scavenging air double-acting pump 166

Scavenging air pump 167
Scavenging air pump connecting arms 166
Scavenging air receiver 166, 167
Scavenging port 166, 167
Schooner 50, 74, 75, 92, 103, 116, 129, 131, 132, 133, 173, 188, 189, 255
Scotch boiler 152
Scow schooner 129
Scindia Steam Navigation Co., Ltd. 49
Scraper 34, 35
Screw 34, 35, 43, 247, 252
Screw aperture 43
Screw effect 252
Screw propeller 19
Screw spindle 46
Screw steering gear 46
Screwbrake nut 57
Screweye bolt 123
Scroll 19
Scroll wheel 46
Sculling 149
Scurvy 260
Sea bed 227
Sea cabin 257
Sea cat 180
Seal 180
Sealer 175
Sea-link 256
Seam 38
Seaman's chest 258
Seaman's cabin 60
Searchlight 65, 210, 211
Sea-to-sea missile 217
Seatrain lines 49
Sea water inlet 257
Second reef band 114
Second reinforce 206
Second Substitute (signal flag) 137
Second tube bank 156
Section building 37
Securing clamp 201
Securing pendant 66
Section of ship's side 207
Seebeck 256
Seekreuzer, 6.5 KR 193
Seguin Island (lighthouse) 240
Seine net 177
Seine purse 177
Seiner 174, 177
Seizing 84, 85, 115, 124
Seizing wire 84
Selandia 162
Self-reefing topsail 112
Self-righting lifeboat 67
Selvagee 84
Semaphore 138
Semi-submerged ship 19
Sennit 261
Sensor 47
Serrated wire 214
Serutu Island (lighthouse) 241
Serving mallet 125
Set of sails 245
Set screw 46
7 (signal flag) 137

Seven-masted fore-and-aft schooner 74, 132, 133
Sewage treatment tank 257
Sewall, Arthur 136
Sextant 233
Shackle 55, 105, 115, 123, 176, 258
Shaft 44, 45, 47, 57, 58, 148, 149, 155, 157, 201, 215
Shaft alley 45
Shaft bearing 44
Shaft line 43
Shaft packing 157
Shaft stuffing box 45
Shaft tunnel 44, 53, 167
Shamrock IV 188
Shangani River (lighthouse) 241
Shank 38, 54
Shark 180
Shark hook 176
Shark's tail 88, 89
Shashi To (lighthouse) 241
Sheathing 214
Sheave (strop) 124
Sheave hole 106
Sheepshank 142
Sheer plan 24
Sheer pole 85
Sheer strake 20, 21, 27, 30, 154
Sheet 83, 87, 88, 89, 90, 91, 92, 104, 105, 106, 107, 108, 110, 113, 115, 116, 117, 118, 119, 122, 191, 247, 248
Sheet band 115
Sheet bend 142
Sheet block 122, 123, 124
Sheet of chain (lower topsail) 110
Sheet patch 114
Sheet tackle 113
Sheet winch 191
Shell 24, 124, 209, 212, 242
Shell longitudinal 45
Shell magazine 210, 211
Shell of boiler 152
Shell of mine 213
Shell plating 24
Shelter deck 25, 45, 167
Shelter-decked ship 25
Shelter-decked vessel 53
Shetland Islands (lighthouse) 240, 241
Shield 157, 212, 216
Shielding (radiation) 159
Shipbuilding 18
Ship plans 19
Ship plant 159
Ships of the line 19
Shoe 20, 21, 33, 41
Short bridle 121
Shortfoot 188
Shot gauge 207
Shot grommet 207

Shot locker 32, 40
Shroud, setting up a 84
Shrouds 80, 81, 83, 84, 85, 86, 88, 89, 90, 91, 93, 110, 118, 124, 196
Sicilian barkentine 129
Sicilian coaster 129
Sick bay 210, 211
Side bitt 57
Side carvings 19
Side coal bunker 154
Side hook 122
Side intercostal keelson 27, 30
Side keelson 27, 30
Side lever engine 153
Side longitudinal 31
Side planking 20, 21
Side plating 30, 154
Side plating of bridge 154
Side shell 31
Side stringer 37
Side-wheeler steamer 161
Sidelight 65
Sight glass 157
Sight vane 234
Signal bridge 210, 211
Signal flags 137, 138, 139
Signal stay 93
Silencer 167
Silencer room 257
Single block 122, 123
Single plate keelson 38
Single-riveted end lap 38
Single-stage centrifugal pump 62
Single tackle 123
Single topsails 76, 77
Single whip 123
Sinker 172, 176, 227
Sister hooks 123
6 (signal flag) 137
Six-masted barkentine 74, 130, 131
Six-masted fore-and-aft schooner 74, 132, 133
6-meter yacht 192
Skiff 177
Skin 18, 26
Skylight 167
Skysail 76, 77
Skysail mast 75, 77
Skysail yard 75, 77
Skärgårdskryssare 30 sq.m. 193
Slack rope switch 93
Slave station 236
Sledge hammer 34, 35
Sleeve 155
Slewing motor 93
Slide valve 155
Slide valve box 58
Slide valve casing 155
Slide valve casing door 155
Slide valve rod 62, 155
Slide valve box 62
Sliding parrel 82
Sling, mainyard 90
Slippery hitch 142
Sloop 75, 103, 128, 133

Slotted wave-guide scanner 237
Sludge hole door 152
Sludge tank 257
Smack 176
Small boat handling 247
Smoke box 150, 152, 154
Smoke box door 152, 154
Smoke-screen maker 210, 211
Smooth planking 18
Snap head 38
Snap head rivet 38
Snapper, red 180
Snatch block 122, 214
Snells 176, 178
Snipe 192
Snood 178
Snorkel 220, 221
Snow 76, 77, 90, 127, 130, 131
Snow mast 75, 77
Socket 141
Sole 180
Soleil Royal, Le 50
Solenoid-acoustic sweep 214
Sole piece 44
Soling 191
Sonar 216
Sonar lobe 216
Sound 227, 243
Sound pressure 213
Sound transmission 227
Sounding 201
Sounding machine 266, 227
Sounding tube 266, 227
Sounding tube 227
South Africa, Republic of (flag) 134
South Foreland (lighthouse) 240, 241
South Korea (flag) 134
South builders 18
Southern Cross 135
Spain 134
Spanish caravel 126
Spanish fishing boat 173
Spanish nao 126
Spanish steam tunny boat 175
Spanker 72, 73, 100, 101, 102, 103, 114, 116, 248, 249
Spanker boom 72, 73
Spanker gaff 72, 73
Spanker mast 74, 75, 77
Spar 72, 73, 112
Spar-decked vessel 53
Spark arrester 167
Spark plug 201
Spars of a four-masted bark 72, 73
Spear 75, 172
Speed 19, 217, 228, 231
Speedometer 229
Speed trial 138
Spencer 102
Sperrholzjollenkreuzer, 7 m. 193

Spider hoop 107
Spike 125
Spike bowsprit 72, 73
Spill the wind 249
Spindle 46, 167
Spindle guide 151
Spinnaker 190, 244
Spiral lacing 115
Splice 143
Splicing fid 125
Spokane 164
Sport fisherman 200
Sprat 181
Spreader 83, 191
Spreader lift 83
Spring 253, 254
Spring stay 91
Spritsail 87, 99
Spritsail brace 87
Spritsail clewline 87
Spritsail lift 87
Spritsail sheet 87
Spritsail topmast 87
Spritsail topmast backstay 87
Spritsail topsail 87
Spritsail topsail brace 87
Spritsail topsail clewline 87
Spritsail topsail lift 87
Spritsail topsail sheet 87
Spritsail topsail yard 87
Spritsail yard 87
Spur 30
Spur wheel 46
Squadron 137
Squall 245
Square foresail 102, 103
Square gaff topsail 117
Square in the mainyard 248
Square knot 105, 142
Square rig 18, 81, 104, 244, 248, 249
Square-rigged mast 107
Square-rigged topmast 75, 77
Square-rigged vessel 245
Square sail 99, 107, 108, 111, 113
Square stern 18
Square weld 39
Stability treatise 19
Stabilizer 48, 49, 217
Stabilizer-tank system 48
Stack 210, 211
Staff 92
Staghorn bollard 66
Stanchion 27, 29, 30, 31, 37, 44, 45, 63
Standards 46
Standard hoisting wire 141
Standard knee 33, 56
Standard vessel 162, 163
Standing gaff 114
Standing rigging 80
Standing rigging wire rope 141
Star 192
Starboard 52, 137, 246, 248, 249
Starboard, altering course to 138

Starboard side 81
Starboard side light 65
Starboard tack 246, 248, 249
Stars and Stripes, the 135
Starter bevel gear 159
Starter bevel gear unit 159
Starting air valve 167
Starting valve 154
Starting valve pipe 154
Starting wire 201
Staten Island (lighthouse) 240
Static orifice 229
Stay 58, 80, 81, 83, 86, 87, 88, 89, 90, 91, 92, 93, 115, 118
Staysail 87, 88, 89, 92, 100, 101, 102, 103, 107, 115, 118, 119, 198, 245
Staysail boom 118
Staysail downhaul 107
Staysail hank 118
Staysail rig 99
Staysail schooner 103, 132, 133, 255
Staysail sheet 118, 119, 245
Staysail tack 86, 88, 89
Stealers 28
Steamboat, inland waters 19
Steam-collecting baffle 156
Steam cylinder 62
Steam drifter 174
Steam drum 156, 157
Steam engine 155, 215
Steam engines, types of older 153
Steam exhaust pipe 58
Steaming light 65
Steam inlet 62, 151, 157
Steam line to intermediate re-heater 156
Steam line from turbo-compressor 156
Steam outlet 156, 157
Steam pipe 58, 150, 152, 155
Steam pipe flange 57
Steam port 155
Steam propulsion 19
Steam-sealed packing 157
Steam space 152, 156
Steam-steering wheel 46
Steam supply 157
Steam trawler 65, 173, 179
Steam tunny boat 175
Steam turbine 157, 159
Steam-valve wheel 151
Steam winch 58
Steam windlass 57
Steamer, about 1890 92
Steamer, rigging of older 92
Steamers 44, 160, 161
Steel 19

Steel hatch cover 63
Steel-section 39
Steel wire 141
Steel wire rope 141
Steeple engine 153
Steering arrangement 46
Steering chain 47
Steering compass 60
Steering control 47
Steering engine 47
Steering gear 46, 47, 257
Steering oar 18, 42
Steering room 210, 211
Steering rudder 215
Steering screw 43
Steering wheel 46, 47
Stella Polaris 189
Stem 18, 20, 21, 29, 32, 33, 36, 37, 210, 211
Stem knee 33
Stem piece 29
Stemson 32, 33
Stern 18, 20, 21, 40, 41, 45, 50, 66, 195, 235
Stern bearing 44, 45
Stern chock 214
Stern knee 40, 41
Stern light 19
Stern, old iron steamer 44
Stern ornament 42
Sternpost 18, 20, 21, 24, 40, 41, 42, 43, 44, 45
Stern rope 254
Stern rudder 18
Stern tube 45, 155
Stern tube bushing 155
Stern tube flange 155
Stern tube nut 45, 155
Sternway 252
Stern window 19
Stevns Klint (lighthouse) 240, 241
Stewart, John & Co. 136
Stiffener 31, 36, 37, 44, 45
Stirrups 90, 106, 121
Stock 42, 43, 44, 45, 46, 54, 206
Stockton, Robert F. 160
Stone sinker 172
Stone weight 179
Stop hatch 63
Stopper, cathead 55
Stoppering a rope 254
Storeroom 36, 40, 167, 210, 211
Stores 60
Storm staysail 198
Storm trysail 198
Stowage 199
Stowage space 191
Straight-edge 19
Strake 20, 21, 27, 30, 31, 38, 39
Strand 140, 141, 143
Strap 38, 42, 43, 44, 84, 122, 123, 156, 261
Strap-brake 58
Strap-brake, pedal 58
Strap-brake tightening screw 58

Strapping 19
Stray, S.O. & Co. 136
Strengthening beam 37
Stringer 30, 37, 38
Stroke 149, 167
Strongback (opening hatch lever) 63
Strop 120, 124
Structural frame 19
Structural keel 18
Strut 201
Stud 55
Studding sail 87, 111
Studding sail boom 87, 110, 111
Studding sail halliard 110
Studding sail sheet 100
Studding sail tack 110
Studding sail yard 110
Stuffing box 44, 45, 46, 154, 155, 156, 166, 167
Stuffing-box bulkhead 155
Stuffing-box gland 155
S-twist 140
Submarine 216, 218, 219, 220, 221
Submarine torpedo 215
Submerged ship 19
Substitute (signal flag) 137, 138, 139
Suction duct 167
Suction flange 62
Suction valve 167
Suction valve box 62
Sudr 230
Suluan Island (lighthouse) 241
Sumburgh Head (lighthouse) 240, 241
Sunbeam II 189
Sun deck 167
Sunfish 193
Sun valve (lamp) 239
Superheater tube 157
Super tanker 164
Surveyance antenna 217
Surveyance motor 217
Surveyance radar 217
Surveying 243
Surveying vessel 243
Sustainer motor 212
Svea, Stockholms Rederi AB 49
Swallow 192
Swallow Tail Line 136
Swash plate 37, 45
Sweden (flag) 135
Swedish American Line 137
Swedish bark 127
Swedish East Indiaman 127
Swedish fishing boat 173
Swedish krayer 127
Swedish motor torpedo boat 220, 221
Swedish-Norwegian Union 135
Swedish Orient Line 49
Swedish sailing pilot cutter 133
Swedish snow 127
Swedish west coast trawler 174

Sweep 214
Sweep wire 214
Swept mine 214
Swinging boom 88, 89, 215
Switchboard 167
Swivel 55, 93
Swivel becket 123
Swivel hook 122
Swivel jaw 123
Swivel screw eye bolt 123
Swordfish 221
Symington, William 150
Symmetrical catamaran 196

T

T (signal flag) 138
Table Island (lighthouse) 241
Tabling 106, 114
Tack 86, 87, 88, 89, 104, 108, 110, 113, 114, 117, 118, 121, 191, 195, 246, 248, 249
Tack cringle 114, 118, 191
Tack patch 114
Tacking 249
Tackle 91, 106, 107, 123, 124, 207
Taffrail log 229
Tahiti 128
Tail torpedo 215
Tail fin missile 212
Tail rod, engine 151, 154, 155
Tail shaft 45
Tank 36, 44, 57, 107, 167, 215
Tanker 161, 163, 164
Tanker lifeboat 67
Tank ship 19
Tank top 44, 45, 151, 167
Tank top longitudinal 45
Tank top plating 36, 151
Tapered rivet 38
Taperina Point (lighthouse) 241
Target 217, 237
Target speed vector 217
Tarpaulin 63
Tartan 128
Tasman Island (lighthouse) 241
Tassel work 258
T-bar 39, 82
T-connection 39
Telegraph 158
Telegraph reply wheel 166
Telemotor pressure gauge 47
Telemotor system 47
Telescope 217, 233
Telescope arm 166
Tempest 191
Temporary wire rope eye 141

Tenerife (lighthouse) 240, 241
Tenon 86
Tent raft 67
Tent pole 26
Texas 219
Thames River barge 129
Theory of sailing 244
Thimble 85, 105, 122, 141
Third Substitute (signal flag) 138
Thompson, George & Co. 136
3 (signal flag) 138
Three-by-four tackle 123
Three-cornered mainsail 113
Three Island vessel 53
Three-letter signals 139
Three-masted bark 41, 74, 76, 77, 80
Three-masted barkentine 74
Three-masted fore-and-aft schooner 74, 75, 189
Three-masted full-rigged ship 74, 76, 77
Three-masted ship 76, 77
Three-masted staysail schooner 103, 132, 133
Three-masted topsail schooner 92, 130, 131
Three-masted wooden ship 33
Throat 114, 115
Throat cringle 114
Throat halliard 116, 117
Throat-seizing 124
Throttle 58, 154, 155
Throttle valve 58, 155, 157
Throttle-valve spindle 155
Thrust 190
Thrust bearing 157, 167
Thwart 67
Tide 250
Tie 82, 83, 106, 107, 112, 124
Tie gin block 106
Tie plate 27
Tie rod 58
Tightening screw, strapbrake 58
Tiller 40, 42, 43, 46, 47, 199, 201
Tiller chain 46
Tiller wire rope 141
Tilting rope, rudder 42
Timber 28, 29, 32, 52
Timber hitch 142
Timber loadlines 52
Titicaca, Lake 128
Toggle 84, 191
Toi Misaki (lighthouse) 241
Tompion (gun) 207
Tonnage opening 25, 53
Tool bag 261
Tools 18, 34, 35, 125

Toothed quadrant 66
Toothwheel 57
Top 72, 73, 78, 79, 81, 83, 104, 107, 110, 113
Top platform 167
Topgallant 72, 73, 83, 107
Topgallant backstay 80, 81, 83
Topgallant bowline 87
Topgallant brace 92, 107, 108
Topgallant bulwark 29, 21, 41
Topgallant bulwark stanchion 27
Topgallant buntline 106, 107, 108
Topgallant cap 78
Topgallant clew 106
Topgallant clewline 83, 106, 107, 108
Topgallant crosstree 78, 79, 83
Topgallant futtock shroud 83
Topgallant halliard 72, 73
Topgallant leech 106
Topgallant lift 107
Topgallant mast 72, 73, 75, 77, 78, 80, 83, 92, 107
Topgallant rail 27, 33
Topgallant rigging 81
Topgallant sail 92, 100, 101, 102, 103, 106, 110, 121
Topgallant sheet 83, 106, 107, 110, 112
Topgallant shroud 81, 83
Topgallant stay 80, 87, 88, 89, 92
Topgallant staysail 100, 101, 102, 119
Topgallant staysail downhaul 107
Topgallant studding sail 110
Topgallant studding sail sheet 110
Topgallant studding sail tack 110
Topgallant tie 83
Topgallant truss 83
Topgallant yard 72, 73, 83, 92, 107
Topgallant yard footrope 107
Topgallant yard for single topgallant sail 75, 77
Topmast 72, 73, 78, 80, 82, 83, 92, 93, 106, 107, 110, 112, 115, 251
Topmast backstay 80, 83
Topmast, built in one with lower mast 83
Topmast cap 78, 83
Topmast cap backstay 80, 81, 83
Topmast crosstree 72, 73, 78, 79, 106, 110

Topmast crutch 112
Topmast futtock rigging 81
Topmast head 83
Topmast rigging 80, 81, 110
Topmast shroud 80, 81, 83, 90, 91, 93, 110
Topmast stay 80, 83, 87, 88, 89, 92, 93
Topmast staysail 88, 89, 92, 100, 101, 103, 107, 119
Topmast staysail downhaul 107
Topmast staysail tack 88, 89
Topmast studding sail boom 110
Topmast studding sail halliard 110
Topmast studding sail yard 110
Topper block 93
Topper rigging 93
Topping lift 92, 93, 116
Topping lift block 93
Topping motor 93
Topping rope 93
Topping winch 93
Topsail 72, 73, 87, 90, 92, 100, 101, 102, 103, 106, 110, 112, 117, 121, 122, 250
Topsail bowline 87
Topsail bowline bridle 90
Topsail brace 83, 90, 92, 107, 110
Topsail buntline 107, 108
Topsail clewline 83, 90, 107, 110
Topsail downhaul 83, 107
Topsail halliard 72, 73, 83, 109, 112, 124
Topsail halliards falls 107
Topsail halliard lead block 106
Topsail halliard spanner 106, 107
Topsail halliard tackle 106, 107
Topsail halliard, tie 107
Topsail halliard winch 109
Topsail lift 107, 110
Topsail parrel 83, 106
Topsail sheet 83, 90, 91, 107, 110, 113, 122
Topsail sheet bitt 32
Topsail sheet block 124
Topsail schooner 75, 92, 130, 131, 189
Topsail tie 106
Topsail yard 72, 73, 83, 92, 106, 107, 110, 112
Topsail yardarm 112
Topsail yard downhaul 106
Topsail yard for single topsail 75, 77

Topsail yard lift 106, 112
Topsail yard parrel 112
Topside planking 27
Topside strake 30
Top timber 26, 27
Torch (lamp) 176
Tor Line 49
Tornado-catamaran 191
Torpedo 215
Torpedo boat 218, 219
Torpedo net 215
Torre de Herculum (lighthouse) 238
Touch hole 206
Tour d'Ordre (lighthouse) 238
Tower, control 210, 211
Towing line 214
Towing tank 19
Towing warp 179
Towing winch 257
Track 75, 77, 245, 253
Tracking radar 217
Trackway (davits) 66
Trader 126
Trafik AB Grängesberg 49
T-rail 191
Train and car ferry 165
Training gear 212, 216
Training motor 209, 216
Training ship 133, 189
Train tackle (gun) 207
Transatlantic, Rederi AB 49
Transducer 216
Transistorized radio direction finder 196
Transit mark 242
Transmitter 227
Transom stern 66
Transverse deck beam 45
Transverse deck web 45
Transverse frame lines 22, 23
Transverse girder 93
Transverse section through engine room 167
Transverse web 31
Traveling crane 167
Trawl 179
Trawler 65, 173, 174, 179
Trawling 176
Treble-riveted butt strap 38
Tree nail 28
Trestletree 78, 79, 91, 115
Triangular course 194
Triangular sail 113
Trim 104, 247, 248
Trimming helm 197
Tripping bracket 31
Triple block 122, 123
Triple-expansion engine 151, 154
Triple fiddle block 122
Triple sheave block 93
Triple tackle 123
Trireme 18

Triton 193
Trotman's anchor 55
Truck 78, 79
True motion radar 22, 37
Trundles 191
T.R. unit 237
Trunk rudder stock 45
Trunk engine 153
Trunk of pump 62
Trunk vessel 53
Trunnel 28
Trunnion 206, 207
Trunnion keeper 206
Truss 83, 91
Truss tackle 91
Trysail 92, 102, 198
Trysail brails 90
Trysail gaff 90
Tryside mast 90
T-slide 191
Tub parrel 82
Tube bank 156
Tube nut 45
Tube plate 152
Tubes 45, 82, 152, 157, 216
Tucking 143
Tug 65, 255
Tumlaren (yacht) 192
Tuna clipper 175
Tunnel 44, 53, 167
Tunnel cock 155
Tunny 180
Tunny boat 175
Tunny yawl 175
Turbine 157, 210, 211
Turbine gland 157
Turbine shaft 157
Turbine passenger vessel 164
Turbocharged engine 166
Turbocharger by-pass pipe 166
Turbot 181
Turkey 134
Turkisk caique 128
Turk's head 261
Turn (rope) 105, 254
Turnbuckle 85, 196
Turning fid 125
Turning gear 151, 156, 166, 167
Turning rim 93
Turning wheel 166
Turntable platform 217
Turntable (pump) 62
Turret 209, 210, 211
Turret-deck steamer 53, 161
TV-monitor 217
Tween deck 27, 36, 44, 53
Tween deck beam 33, 41
Tween deck ceiling 27, 33
12 ft. class (yacht) 192
12-meter yacht 192
12 sq.m. class (yacht) 192
Twin gun 209
Twin-gun turret 210, 211
Twin mounting 209

Twin-screw ship 156, 1558
Twin spanner 112
Twist rope 140
2 (signal flag) 138
Two-letter signal 139
Two-masted fore-and-aft schooner 74, 132, 133
Two-masted staysail schooner 132, 133
Two-stroke engine 166
Two-topsail schooner 102, 131
Tyfon 167

U

U (signal flag) 138
Udsire (lighthouse) 240, 241
Underwater form 19
Unequal angle bar 39
Union Castle Mail S.S. Co., Ltd. 49
Union flag, Great Britain 135
Union Jack, Great Britain 135
United Fruit Co. 137
United States Lines 137
United States of America (flag) 135
United States Yacht Ensign 197
Up helm 247, 248
Upper deadeye 84
Upper deck 27, 31, 37
Upper deck beam 27, 30, 32, 40, 154
Upper deck clamp 27
Upper deck pillar 30
Upper deck planking 27
Upper deck stanchion 27
Upper deck waterway 27
Upper platform 167
Upper sail 245
Upper sheer strake 30
Upper spanker 100, 101, 116
Upper spanker gaff 72, 73
Upper tie plate 27
Upper topgallant brace 108
Upper topgallant buntline 108
Upper topgallant downhaul 108
Upper topgallant halliard 72, 73
Upper topgallant sail 100, 101, 103
Upper topgallant sheet 108
Upper topgallant yard 72, 73, 75, 77
Upper topsail 100, 101, 103, 110
Upper topsail brace 106, 107, 108, 110
Upper topsail brace fall 106
Upper topsail brace pendant 106

276

Upper topsail brace runner 106
Upper topsail buntline 108
Upper topsail clewline 110
Upper topsail downhaul 108
Upper topsail halliard 72, 73
Upper topsail lift 110
Upper topsail parrel 83, 106
Upper topsail sheet 83, 107, 108, 110
Upper topsail tie 106
Upper topsail yard 72, 73, 75, 77, 83, 106, 107, 110, 251
Upper topsail yardarm horse 107
Upper topsail yard footrope 107
Uptake 152, 154, 151, 157
Uranium 159
Utnordr 230
Utsudr 230
U-weld 39

V

V (signal flag) 138
Vacuum pump 151
Valve 48, 58, 151, 157, 166, 167, 215, 239
Valve casing 46, 57, 154
Valve drag links 166
Valve lever 167
Valve rod 46
Valve rod guide 155
Valve spindle 154, 156, 167
Valve spindle guide 151
Valve yoke 167
Vanderbilt, Fred W 189
Vane 197
Vänern, Lake of, barge 129
Vang 92
Vanguard 220
Vardöy (lighthouse) 240, 241
Vasaorden 188
Vedette 189
Vega, cruising sailing-boat 192
Velocera 129
Velocity stage 157
Venezuela (flag) 134
Vent auger 207
Vent bit 207
Ventilating fan 167
Ventilating fan suction duct 167
Ventilation duct 167
Ventilator 92
Vertical beam 37
Vertical bulkhead stiffener 36
Vertical cargo winch 58
Vertical donkey boiler 152
Vertical frame 45
Vertical keel 37, 38
Vertical planes 22, 23
Vertical plate 38
Vertical section 24
Vertical steering engine 46
Vestr 230
Victoria and Albert 189
Victoria, Lake 128
Victory 59, 218, 219
Viking Age 234
Viking anchor, Oseberg ship 54
Viking Line 49
Viking ship 18, 26, 47, 121, 126
Virginia-built 19
Visibility 240, 241
Voiliers Nantais, Soc. Anon. des 136
Voith-Schneider propeller 158
Voltage regulator 237
V-shaped bottom 19
V-weld 39

W

W (signal flag) 138
Wale 20, 21, 27
Walking passage 167
Wall header 157
Wall knot 84, 120
Wangi Wangi (lighthouse) 241
Wardroom 40, 210, 211
Warhead 21, 215
Warp 179
Warping head 56, 57, 58
Warping head coupling handle 58
Warrant officers' accommodation 210, 211
Warship 148, 218, 219, 220, 221
"Wart" (rudder) 42
Wärtsilä air bubbling system 257
Wasa 51, 61
Watches 59
Water ballast 154
Water charging valve 216
Water-cooled cylinder cover 167
Water-cooling jacket 166
Water course 30
Water drum (turbine) 157
Water level 152, 156
Water lines 19, 22, 23, 24, 28, 48
Water outlet pipe 155, 166, 167
Water pipe 155, 166, 167
Water pump 107
Water tank 67, 191, 215, 227
Water tube 152
Water-tube boiler 152, 156
Watertight bulkhed 45
Water wall (turbine) 157
Waterway, upper deck 27
Watt, James 160
Wave guide 217, 237
Waveline 51
Wear (sailing maneuver) 248
Weather adjustment 47
Weather leech 121
Weatherly 192
Weather side 117
Web 31, 45
Web beam 37
Wedge 63, 206
Weight shaft 154, 155
Weigh shaft arm 154, 155
Weight (fishing line) 179
Weight and swivel deck crane 93
Weir, Andrew & Co. 136
Weld 39
Welded cargo ship 37
Welding 19
Well-decked vessel 53
West Benito Island (lighthouse) 240
Westerly Longbow 192
Westfal-Larsen & Co., AS 49
West Germany (flag) 134
Whale, Greenland 180
Whale factory ship 175
Whaleback 44
Whaler 175
Whaling harpoon 176
Wheel 40, 46, 47, 157, 248, 249
Wheel box 46
Wheel grating 46
Wheel stand 46
Whelp 56, 57
Whelp chock 57
Wherry (Norfolk) 128
Whipping 141
Whipstaff 46
Whisker (frigate) 86
Whisker boom 88, 89
Whisker fitting 88
Whisker lift 86
Whistle 59, 239
Whippings 142
Whitby (lighthouse) 240, 241
White Star Line 136
Whiting 181
Wick, lamp 64, 239
Wigram, Money & Sons 136
Wildcats 57
Wilhelmsen, Wilhelm 137
Willis, Johan & Son 136
Winch 58, 66, 83, 93, 109, 196, 214
Winch drum 58
Wind abaft the beam 246
Wind abeam 244, 246
Wind ahead 252
Wind astern 252
Wind direction 217, 245
Wind helm 197
Winding tackle 123
Windlass 33, 56, 57, 60, 88, 89, 196, 210, 211
Windlass barrel 33, 56, 57
Windlass drum 57
Windmill pump 62
Wind speed 217
Windward 194, 245, 247
Wing stowage 199
Winter North Atlantic loadline 52
Winter North Atlantic timber loadline 52
Wire 85, 115, 141
Wire drum 213, 227
Wire-end socket 141
Wire jackstay 115
Wire rope 143
Wire rope bulldog grip 141
Wire rope eye 141
Wire stay 118
Wire sweep 214
Witch of Stockholm, The 160
Wood float 228
Wood pussy (yacht) 193
Wood sheathing 214
Wood toggle 191
Wooden bed (gun) 206
Wooden block 124
Wooden boat 67, 200
Wooden cleat 82
Wooden hatch board 63
Wooden hoop (fishing) 179
Wooden sailing ship 20, 21, 22, 23, 26, 27, 29
Wooden yard 82
Woolding 79
Working piston 167
Working piston with rings 166
Worm gear 57, 109
Worm-gear house 58
Wrasse 180
Wrist pin (paddle wheel) 140

X

X (signal flag) 138
X-weld 39

Y

Y (signal flag) 138
Yacht 48, 128, 129, 192, 193
Yacht Club of France 187, 197
Yacht fittings 196, 197
Yachts, large 189
Yacht racing 194, 195
Yacht Racing Union 186, 187
Yard 72, 73, 82, 83, 90, 91, 92, 105, 107, 110, 113, 121, 245, 250
Yardarm 104, 105, 106, 124
Yardarm band 105, 106
Yardam hoop 112
Yardam horse 106, 107
Yawing influence 247
Yawl 75, 175, 188, 192
Yoke 82, 167
Y W Cadet (sailing yacht) 192

Z

Z (signal flag) 138
Z-bar 39
Zim Israel Navigation Co., Ltd. 49
Z-twist 140

LIST OF SOURCES

AB. Allhems Förlag
SVENSKA FLOTTANS HISTORIA. Malmö 1942—1945.
Ashley, Clifford W.
THE ASHLEY BOOK OF KNOTS. New York 1944.
Babcock & Wilcox
MARINE STEAM. New York 1928.
Bartlews
YOUR NEW BOAT. London 1947.
Beck, Stuart E.
THE SHIP — HOW SHE WORKS. Southampton 1955.
Bergström, C. A.
FARTYGSMASKINER. Stockholm 1934.
Bernung, Holm, Petersson, Tegnér
SJÖMANSKAP. Göteborg 1959.
Blomgren, Axel S.
SJÖMANSKAP. Göteborg 1948.
AB. Bofors
BOFORS. Göteborg 1958.
Bonwick, George J.
SEAMANSHIP HANDBOOK. Liverpool 1952.
Branch, W. J. V. och Brook-Williams, E.
A SHORT HISTORY OF NAVIGATION. Annapolis 1942.
Burmeister & Wain
THE SHIPYARDS OF BURMEISTER & WAIN LTD. Köpenhamn 1929.
Chapman af, F. H.
ARCHITECTURA NAVALIS MERCATORIA. Stockholm 1768.
Classon, Edward och Franzén, Anders
WASA — FYND OCH BÄRGNING. Stockholm 1959.
Collinder, Per
FRÅN NOAKS DUVA TILL GYROKOMPASSEN. Stockholm 1943.
Crouch, H. F.
NUCLEAR SHIP PROPULSION. Cambridge 1960.
Dana, R. H.
TWO YEARS BEFORE THE MAST. London 1875.
Dodman, Frank E.
THE OBSERVER'S BOOK OF SHIPS. London 1961.
Dugan, James
THE GREAT IRON SHIP. London 1953.
Engström, Ivar A.
LÄROBOK I SKEPPSBYGGERI. Stockholm 1924.
Evans, I. O.
THE OBSERVER'S BOOK OF FLAGS. London 1959.
Forshell, Hans
MINAN I SJÖKRIGET. Stockholm 1959.
Föreningen Sveriges Sjöfartsmuseum i Stockholm
ÅRSBOK 1943. Lund 1944.
Försvarets Kommandoexpedition
ÖRLOGSBOKEN, SJÖMANSINSTRUKTION FÖR FLOTTAN. Stockholm 1961.
GKSS
PROGRAM FÖR MARSTRANDSREGATTAN. Göteborg 1962.
AB. Götaverken
PUBLICATION NO. 389. Stockholm 1951.
Handels og Søfartsmuseet på Kronborg
ÅRBOG 1960.
Hansen, G.
LAEREBOG I SKIBSBYGNING OG SKIBSKONSTRUKTION. Köpenhamn 1909.
Hardy, A. C.
HAVSFISKE I HELA VÄRLDEN. Malmö 1947.
MODERN MARINE ENGINEERING. VOL. II. London 1948.
THE BOOK OF THE SHIP. London 1948.
Hasslöf, Olof
SVENSKA VÄSTKUSTFISKARNA. Stockholm 1947.

Henschke, W.
SCHIFFBAUTECHNISCHES HANDBUCH, BAND IV. Berlin 1958.
Her Majesty's stationary office
MANUAL OF SEAMANSHIP. I, II and III. London 1951.
Hewson, J.
A HISTORY OF THE PRACTICE OF NAVIGATION. Glasgow 1951.
Hägg, Erik
UNDER TRETUNGAD FLAGGA. Stockholm 1941.
UNDER SEGEL. Stockholm 1943.
Imray, Laurie, Norie & Wilson Ltd.
LIGHTS AND TIDES OF THE WORLD. London 1961.
Kannik, Preben
FLAGGOR I FÄRG FRÅN HELA VÄRLDEN. Köpenhamn and Stockholm 1957.
Kerchove, René de
INTERNATIONAL MARITIME DICTIONARY. New York 1948.
Kierkegaard, N. C.
PRAKTISK SKEPPSBYGGNADSKONST. Göteborg 1864.
Kungl. Kommerskollegium, Sjöfartsbyrån
INTERNATIONELL SIGNALBOK. Stockholm 1931.
Laas, W.
DIE GROSSEN SEGELSCHIFFE (IHRE ENTWICKLUNG UND ZUKUNFT). Berlin 1908.
Lammeren, Van
RESISTAS PROPULSION AND STEERING OF SHIPS. Haarlem 1948.
Landström, Björn
SKEPPET. Weert 1961.
Laughlin Co.
CATALOGUE NO. 75. Portland 1912.
Lehmann, Johannes
BURMEISTER & WAIN GENNEM HUNDREDE AAR. Köpenhamn 1943.
Linder, Wilhelm
LÄROBOK I SJÖMANSKAP. Stockholm 1896.
Lindström, Claes
SJÖFARTENS HISTORIA. Stockholm 1951.
Lisle, B.
TANKER TECHNIQUE 1700—1936. London 1936.
Lubbock, Basil
THE CHINA CLIPPERS. Glasgow 1946.
THE WESTERN OCEAN PACKETS. Glasgow 1925.
THE LAST OF THE WINDJAMMERS. Glasgow 1927.
Lundmark, Efraim
REDERI SVEA. Stockholm 1951.
Magnus, Olaus
HISTORIA OM DE NORDISKA FOLKEN. Uppsala 1909—1951.
Marinstabens utbildningsavd.
ÖRLOGSFARTYG OCH MARINA VAPEN. Uppsala 1961.
Middendorf, F.
BEMASTUNG UND TAKELUNG DER SCHIFFE. Leipzig 1903.
Natur och Kultur
DET SVENSKA ATOMARBETET. Stockholm 1958.
Nilsson, N. G. and Åsbrink, G.
SVERIGES SJÖFART. Stockholm 1921.
Nordisk Familjeboks Förlag
NORDISK FAMILJEBOK. Stockholm 1904—1926.
Paasch, H.
FROM KEEL TO TRUCK. Antwerpen 1885.
MARINE ENCYKLOPEDIA. Antwerpen 1885.
Parker, H. and Bowen, F. C.
MAIL AND PASSENGER STEAMSHIPS OF THE 19TH CENTURY. London 1928.
Radcliffe, William
FISHING FROM THE EARLIEST TIMES. London 1921.

Rooij, G. de
PRACTICAL SHIPBUILDING A. Haarlem 1961.
Rålamb, Åke Classon
SKEPS BYGGERIJ ELLER ADELIG ÖFNINGS TIONDE TOM. Stockholm 1691 and Malmö 1943.
Röding, J.H.
ALLGEMEINES WÖRTERBUCH DER MARINE. Hamburg 1798.
Schiøtz, Eyvind
JEG ER SEJLER. Köpenhamn 1959.
Seaton, A. E.
THE MANUAL OF MARINE ENGINEERING. London 1904.
Smith, Edgar C.
A SHORT HISTORY OF NAVAL AND MARINE ENGINEERING. Cambridge 1938.
Sohlmans Förlag
SOHLMANS SJÖLEXIKON. Örebro 1935.
BOKEN OM HAVET. Stockholm 1950.
Strömberg, C. A.
INGENJÖRSHANDBOKEN, del II. Stockholm 1948.
Sullivan, Edw.
YACHTING. London 1894.
Svenska Lloyd
REDERIAKTIEBOLAGET SVENSKA LLOYD. Göteborg 1920.
Svensson, Sam
LÄROBOK I SJÖMANSKAP. Stockholm 1959.
SEGEL GENOM SEKLER. Amsterdam 1961.
Traung, Olof
UR SJÖFARTENS HÄVDER — EN VANDRING GENOM SJÖFARTSMUSEET. Göteborg 1933.
Tuxen, J. S.
SJØFARTEN OG SKIBSBYGNINGSKUNSTEN. Köpenhamn 1879.
Uggla, C. L.
AFHANDLING UTI SKEPPSBYGGERI TILL NAVIGATIONS-SKOLORNAS TJENST. Göteborg 1856.
Underhill, Harold A.
MASTING AND RIGGING THE CLIPPER SHIPS AND OCEAN CARRIER. Glasgow 1946.
SAILING SHIP RIGS AND RIGGING. Glasgow 1938.
Unger, Gunnar
ILLUSTRERAD SVENSK SJÖKRIGSHISTORIA. Stockholm 1909.
United States Naval Academy
NAVAL TURBINES. Annapolis 1955.
Weber, I. C.
FRA HJULSKIBENES DAGE. Köpenhamn 1919.
Webster, F. B.
SHIPBUILDING CYKLOPEDIA. New York 1920.
Wedge, Philip L.
FLAGS AND FUNNELS. Glasgow 1958.
Whitaker, H. E.
BRITISH AND INTERNATIONAL RACING YACHT CLASSES. London 1954.
Witt, G. C.
PRAKTISK OCH THEORETISK HANDLEDNING I SKEPPS-BYGGERI MED SÄRSKILD TILLÄMPNING PÅ HANDELSFARTYG. Stockholm 1863.
Åhlund, G. B.
HANDBOK I ARTILLERI FÖR FLOTTAN, SJÖARTILLERIETS GRUNDER. Stockholm 1951.

Periodicals
MARINE ENGINEER
NATIONAL GEOGRAPHIC MAGAZINE
SCHIFFBAU
VEREIN DEUTSCHE INGENIEURE
SVENSK SJÖFARTS TIDNING

COPYRIGHT AB NORDBOK.
PRINTED IN GREAT BRITAIN BY
HAZELL WATSON AND VINEY LTD, AYLESBURY.
1975